1995

The New Zealand Bed and Breakfast Book

Homes   Farms   Guest Houses

Compiled by J. and J. Thomas

MOONSHINE PRESS

Copyright ©1994. Janete and James Thomas

Published by Moonshine Press,
27 Marine Drive, Mahina Bay,
Eastbourne, New Zealand
Telephone 04-562-7667, Fax 04-562-7667

ISBN 0-9583262-3-1
ISSN 0114-2232

Drawings by Gerald Bull and Rema Naish.

Typesetting by The Eastbourne Herald

All information in this guidebook has been
supplied by the hosts. Information about the
homes listed is subject to change without notice.
Readers are asked to take this into account
when consulting this guide.

Cover Photo "Otamaire", Hunterville.

WIN

A WEEKS FREE B&B

FILL IN A COMMENT FORM AND YOU CAN BE IN THE DRAW FOR A WEEKS FREE B&B FOR TWO

★ At each B&B you will find a comment form and an addressed envelope. Simply fill in a comment form and return it to us, and you will be in the draw for **a weeks free B&B**.

★ Every comment form you send in will increase your chances of winning the **weeks free B&B**, so complete a form for each place you stay.

★ We suggest you save your comment forms in one envelope, and send them in together at the end of your trip.

★ If a B&B is temporarily out of comment forms you can complete one at the next home you stay.

★ Each person staying can complete a comment form - a couple can complete two separate forms.

★ Entries will be drawn on 21 December 1995 and the winner will be notified by mail immediately.

THE PRIZE:

★ The prizewinner will be given vouchers entitling them and a partner to stay 1 night and have breakfast at any 7 B&Bs they choose in *The New Zealand Bed and Breakfast Book*.

★ The stays can be any time between 1st March 1996 and 31 October 1996. They need not be consecutive.

TIPS
for easier travel

★ **Ensuite and private bathroom** are for your use exclusively, **Guests share** bathroom means you may be sharing with other guests, **Family share** bathroom means you will be sharing with the family.

★ In the tariff section of each listing **'continental' breakfast** consists of fruit, cereal, toast, tea/coffee; **'full'** breakfast is the same with an additional cooked course; **'special'** breakfast has something special.

★ Do not try to travel too far in one day. Take time to enjoy the company of your hosts and other locals.

★ **Telephone ahead** to enquire about a B&B. It is a nuisance for you if you arrive to find the accommodation has been taken. And besides hosts need a little time to prepare.

★ The most suitable **time to arrive is late afternoon,** and to leave is before 10 in the morning.

★ **If you would like dinner** please give your host sufficient notice to prepare.

★ If you are unsure of anything ask your hosts about it. They will give you a direct answer.

★ Our B&Bs are mostly private homes. **Most do not accept credit cards.**

★ If you have made your reservations from overseas, check that your dates are correct. You might cross the dateline to come to New Zealand.

★ **Please let your hosts know if you have to cancel.** They will have spent time preparing for you.

★ Make your Cook Strait Ferry reservation in advance.

★ **If you need to use a public phone,** use the first one you see. It may be hours before you see another.

★ **Carry a phone card.** Most public phones do not take coins. Phone cards can be bought from dairies, bookstores and petrol stations.

★ New Zealand road signs are getting better, but your best directions come from asking a local.

★ Most listings show hosts accept vouchers. The only vouchers accepted are New Zealand Bed & Breakfast Book vouchers.

The NZ Bed & Breakfast Book
SCHEDULE OF STANDARDS

GENERAL:
- Local tourism and transport information available to guests.
- Property appearance neat and tidy, internally and externally.
- Absolute cleanliness of the home in all areas used by the guests.
- Absolute cleanliness of kitchen, refrigerator and food storage areas.
- Roadside identification of property.
- Protective clothing and footwear available for farmstay guests.
- Hosts accept responsibility to comply with local body bylaws.
- Host will be present to welcome and farewell guests.

BEDROOMS:
- Each bedroom solely dedicated to guests with -
- bed heating
- heating
- light controlled from the bed
- wardrobe space with variety of hangers
- drawers
- good quality floor covering
- mirror
- power point
- waste paper basket
- drinking glasses
- night light or torch for guidance to w.c. if not adjacent to bedroom
- opaque blinds or curtains on all windows where appropriate
- good quality mattresses in sound condition on a sound base
- clean bedding appropriate to the climate, with extra available
- clean pillows with additional available

BATHROOM & TOILET FACILITIES:
- At least one bathroom adequately ventilated and equipped with -
  bath or shower
  wash handbasin and mirror
  wastebasket in bathroom
  extra toilet roll
  lock on bathroom and toilet doors
  electric razor point if bedrooms are without a suitable power point
- soap, towels, bathmat, facecloths, fresh for each new guest
- towels changed or dried daily for guests staying more than one night
- Sufficient toilet and bathroom facilities to serve family and guests adequately

New Zealand

Northland
Great Barrier Island
Auckland
Coromandel
Waikato, King Country
Bay of Plenty
Gisborne
Taranaki, Wanganui
Hawkes Bay
Manawatu
Wellington
Wairarapa
Nelson, Marlborough
Westland
Canterbury
Timaru, Oamaru District
Otago
Southland
Stewart Island

CONTENTS

INTRODUCTION

The popularity of B&B in New Zealand has doubled each year since we first published *The New Zealand Bed and Breakfast Book*. The reason for this amazing growth is quite simply that the hosts are such wonderful people. The hosts who are listed here are homeowners who want to share their love of the country with travellers. Each listing has been written by the host, and you will discover their warmth and personality is obvious in their writing. Ours is not simply an accommodation guide but an introduction to a uniquely New Zealand holiday experience.

Any holiday is remembered primarily by the people one meets. How many of us have loved a country simply because of one or two especially memorable individuals encountered there? Bed and Breakfast offers the traveller who wants to experience the feel of the real country and get to know the people to do just that. Bed and Breakfast in New Zealand means a warm welcome into someone's home. Most of the places listed are homes, with a sprinkling of private hotels and guesthouses. Remember that Bed and Breakfast hosts cannot offer hotel facilities. Therefore please telephone ahead to book your accommodation and give ample notice if you require dinner. Most of our B&Bs do not have credit card facilities.

GUARANTEE OF STANDARDS

Many B&Bs belong to national associations, which inspect the property, and guarantee the standard of facilities. *The NZ Association of Farm and Home Hosts*, *Home & Farmstay Auckland* and *Heritage Inns of NZ* represent private homeowners; the NZ B&B Hotels Federation, represents the more commercial B&Bs. Hosts that display a *KiwiHost* logo have taken part in a special workshop which trains them in communication, customer relations and visitor industry skills. The symbols are shown on each listing.

All B&Bs which are newly listed this year have been inspected to ensure that they conform to our required standard. We expect that all B&Bs in *The New Zealand Bed and Breakfast Book* will offer excellent hospitality. Please fill in a comment form for each place you stay at so that our very high standard can be maintained.

TARIFF

The prices listed will apply until the next edition is published in late 1995. Prices are in New Zealand dollars, and include Goods and Sevices Tax. There will be no extra costs to pay unless you request extra services. Some offer a reduction for children. Unless otherwise stated this applies to age 12 and under.

BREAKFAST

Breakfast is included in the tariff. Some homes offer a continental breakfast which includes fruit, cereal, toast and tea or coffee. Others offer a full breakfast indicated by (full) in the listing, which includes a cooked course as well. Some offer a special breakfast, indicated by (special) which includes some specialties of the house.

VOUCHERS

Most hosts have indicated in their listings that they will accept vouchers. The vouchers referred to are *The New Zealand Bed & Breakfast Book* vouchers which can be obtained from your travel agent. *Vouchers accepted* refers only to The Bed & Breakfast Book vouchers.

SELF-CONTAINED ACCOMMODATION

Many homes in towns and on farms can offer separate self-contained accommodation. In almost every case linen and food will be provided if required. The tariff will vary depending on your requirements, so check when booking.

CAMPERVANS

For those who get to know the country by camping or motor-home, Bed and Breakfast offers wonderful advantages. You will see in many listings the word 'campervans'. These homes have suitable facilities available such as laundry, bathroom, electricity and sometimes meals by arrangement. The charge, usually for up to four people, is modest and is shown in each listing.

FINDING YOUR WAY AROUND

A satisfying part of compiling *The New Zealand Bed and Breakfast Book* is that we have been able to change an irritating aspect of most New Zealand guide books. Usually towns are listed alphabetically so that we hop about the country from such places as Akaroa to Auckland to Blenheim for example. This is infuriating to a reasonably well-travelled native like myself, so I imagine the despair of a visitor unfamiliar with place names and local geography.

New Zealand is long and narrow. It makes more sense to me to travel southwards down the islands listing the homes as we come to them. We have divided New Zealand into geographical regions and have included a map of each region. We have simply listed the homes as they occur on our southward journey. In areas such as Southland where we travel across more than down, the route we have taken should be quite obvious.

Whether you are from overseas or a fellow New Zealander, please take the opportunity to stay with New Zealanders in their homes. Chat with your hosts. Enjoy their company. Each host will be your additional personal travel agent and guide. We wish you an enjoyable holiday and welcome comments from guests. Please write with compliments or suggestions to:

    The New Zealand Bed and Breakfast Book
    Moonshine Press
    PO Box 41-022
    Mahina Bay
    Eastbourne
    New Zealand

Happy travelling
James Thomas

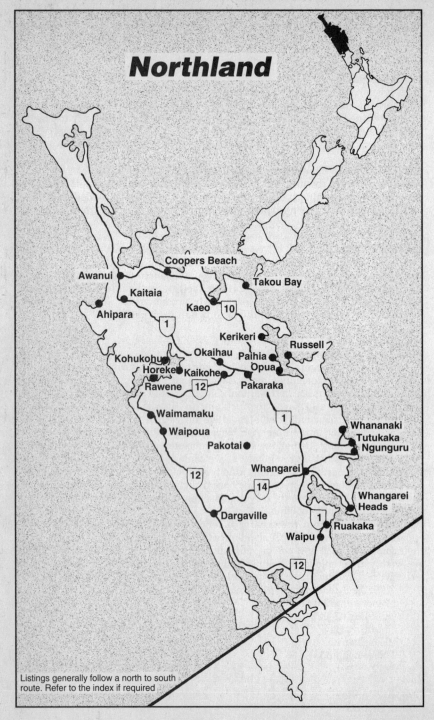

Northland

Awanui
Coopers Beach
Takou Bay
Kaitaia
Kaeo
10
Ahipara
1
Kerikeri
Kohukohu
Okaihau
Paihia
Russell
Horeke
Kaikohe
Opua
Rawene
12
Pakaraka
Waimamaku
Waipoua
1
Pakotai
Whananaki
Tutukaka
Ngunguru
Whangarei
12
14
Whangarei
Heads
Dargaville
1
Ruakaka
Waipu
12

Listings generally follow a north to south
route. Refer to the index if required

Ahipara - Kaitaia
Homestay
Address: Siesta Luxury Homestay, Tasman Heights Road,
P.O. Box 67, Ahipara
Name: Rolf and Hanna Stump
Telephone and Fax: (09) 409-4565
Beds: 2 Queen (2 bedrooms) Bathroom: 2 Ensuite
Tariff: B&B (special) Double $95, Single $70; Dinner $25 each, (Complimentary afternoon tea), Credit Cards. Vouchers accepted 1 May - 1 Nov. double only.
Nearest Town: Kaitaia 15 km

We are a family of four with two teenage girls, emigrated from Switzerland some 15 years ago to this beautiful country. As well as English we speak perfect German. Our home is especially designed and built with the comfort and privacy of our guests in mind. It is situated on a large hillside section, 50 m above sea level and 4 minute walk to safe swimming beach. You have a fantastic panoramic view, overlooking the famous Ninety Mile Beach, Ahipara Bay and rocky shore with sandhills to the left. The setting is very peaceful, framed by pine trees and the gentle rolling ocean beyond. The European-style house is solidly built to offer maximum quietness, faces north and receives all day sun.

Each of the large double guest rooms has natural timber ceilings, comfortable queen-size beds, colour TV, radio and writing desk, has its own bathroom, tea- and coffee-making facilities and sheltered balcony with uninterrupted sea views; even a sea view out of your bed.

Our house is most ideal for couples or anybody wanting to get away from it all and enjoy a clean environment with plenty of outdoor activities. As we will host no more than four people at any one time, we can provide you with the best of service in all aspects. Also we can offer you full board with a first class evening meal, served in our spacious family dining room.

Directions: *Take the road to the west coast from Kaitaia. Drive straight past Ahipara Primary School 1.2 km until you see the beach. Right opposite to the left you see the "Tasman Heights" sign. Follow the tar-sealed road right to the top, then follow the "Siesta" signs.*

New Zealand Association
FARM & HOME HOSTS

Awanui. Kaitaia
Farmstay
Address: Beach Road,
Awanui R.D. 1, Northland
Name: Tony & Helen Dunn
Telephone: (09) 406-7494 (Before 8:00 am or evngs)
Beds: 2 Double (2 bedrooms) Bathroom: 1 Guests share
Tariff: B&B (special) Double $80, Single $45, Children (under 10 yrs) 1/2 price,
Dinner $25, Campervans $20
Nearest Town: Awanui 9 kms, Kaitaia 16 km

*We have a comfortable, modern home, built for the sun and view, on a hill
overlooking the farm, the Aupouri Pine Forest and the Ninety Mile Beach.
"Ninety Mile Angoras" is a property of 40 hectares of rolling sand hill country,
presently carrying cattle, sheep and goats.
Ninety Mile Beach, noted for its fishing, is one minute drive away to the West,
while a feast of East Coast Beaches lie within thirty minutes easy drive. All have
beautiful golden sands and unpolluted waters.
Many local tours and trips are available.
This home is an excellent central point to fully explore the North of New Zealand.
Tour buses to the Cape pass the farm and will collect and deliver passengers from
the farm gate.*
Directions: *From Awanui, drive North approximately 6 kms. Turn left at signs
to The park Ninety Mile Beach. Our farm is on the right, approximately 3 km after
turn off, the last farm before the forestry and beach.*

Coopers Beach
Homestay
Address: 58 State Highway 10 Coopers Beach (1 hour drive north of Paihia)
Name: "Mac 'n' Mo's"
Telephone: (09) 406 0538
Beds: 1 Double, 2 Single (2 Bedrooms) Bathroom: 1 Guests share
Tariff: B&B (full) Double $50, Single $30, Children $15, Vouchers accepted
Nearest Town: Mangonui

*Our home at Coopers Beach has a sparkling view over all of Doubtless Bay. Enjoy
a continental breakfast on our sunny veranda and share our "slice of heaven",
cooked breakfast is extra. A private guests entrance is provided with secure off
street parking. Tours can be arranged to Cape Reinga, the Kauri Forest, the sand
dunes of Ninety Mile Beach, a glow worm grotto, kiwi house, salt water aquarium
or craft trail. Sunbathe, swim or walk on our unpolluted, uncrowded beaches.
Fish from the rocks, Mangonui Wharf or a boat, Coopers Beach is only a two
minute walk away. We have several fine restaurants handy and the best fish and
chip shop north of Auckland, we will cook dinner on request. The Northliner will
drop you at our gate or we can meet you at Kerikeri or Kaitaia airport.
We are sure that your stay at "Mac 'n' Mo's" will be a holiday highlight, just phone,
write or take a chance.*

One of the differences between staying at a hotel and a B&B
is that you don't hug the hotel staff when you leave.

Mangonui

Homestay, Farmstay
Address: "Abraham Lincoln's Bed & Breakfast" Hihi Road Mangonui
Name: Neville & Shirley Thomas
Telephone: (09) 406 0090
Beds: 1 Double, 1 Queen, 1 Single, (2 Bedrooms - upstairs)
Bathrooms: 1 Private (Guests have own toilet & bathroom & privacy of upstairs to themselves). 1 Family share
Tariff: B&B (full) Double $50, Single $30, Children half price, Dinner $20, Campervans $25 for 4 people.
Nearest Town: Mangonui - Kaitaia, Kerikeri 3/4 hour away

Enjoy a completely relaxing stay with amazing sea views at Neville and Shirley's home. We offer homestayers a chance to get to know our farm pets and enjoy the bird aviaries. Neville is born and bred in the North so can give a lot of stories and history about the area. Fishing is a major sport in the area and there are many boats to try your luck on!
Our home is just 2km off the main highway SH1 and very easy to find. We welcome children and have a cot for the babes. We are also only 5 mins from the Mangonui township.
If you are wanting a place to stay in a home where there is laughter and good home cooked meal please phone 09 406 0090.

Kaeo

Homestay
Address: Te Ngaere Beach, Wainui Bay Road, Kaeo
Name: John and Christine McBain
Telephone: (09) 405 0249
Beds: 2 Double, 2 Single (3 bedrooms) **Bathroom:** 1 Private, 1 Family share
Tariff: B&B (full) Double $65, Single $35, Children $15; Dinner $20, Vouchers accepted 1 April to 31 October
Nearest Town: About 35 kms north of Kerikeri

The drive to Te Ngaere is beautiful, with some of the most spectacular coastal scenery to be seen anywhere. Te Ngaere has a very safe and quiet beach suitable for swimming throughout most of the year (a little chilly in winter). There are miles of quiet coastline and secluded bays nearby. As Te Ngaere Beach is in the far north of New Zealand and is sheltered by hills, the climate is quite warm at all times of the year.
Accommodation - separate one/two bedroom flat with private bathroom or one bedroom upstairs overlooking the bay (share bath with hosts). Your hosts are well travelled and have enjoyed the company of guests from many countries. We are keen botanists and enjoy gardening.
Other attractions - yacht charters available, fishing and diving, sub-tropical rain forest one hour away by car.
Directions: *Travel north from Kerikeri on Highway 10 for approx 17 km to Matauri Bay Road (which is well signposted). Turn right onto Matauri Bay Road and follow the road signs to Te Ngaere Bay. We have Jack Russell terriers and a cat.*

Kaeo
Farmstay/Homestay
Address: Tepene, Matauri Bay Rd,
Box 104, Kaeo
Name: Ian & Lorelei Hayes
Telephone: (09) 405 0282
Beds: 4 Single (2 bedrooms)
Bathroom: 1 Family share
Tariff: B&B (Full) Double $65, Single $40, Dinner $20, Children half price.
Vouchers accepted.
Nearest Town: Kerikeri 35km south (30 mins)

We enjoy sharing the beauty of the area with our visitors. Ian's family have been around Kaeo since the 1830s, we have farmed here since 1962.

Our home is in an attractive native bush setting, with a tennis court and views to the Bay of Islands. The scenic family trust property has picturesque beaches, a large Kauri tree (5 mins walk), and tranquil walks to a beautiful waterfall. The whitest clay in the world is mined and processed here. We are within day trips to all Northland attractions.

We farm sheep, cattle, a few goats, and have a horse, two cats and breed Jack Russell terriers. Our interests include boating, gardening, tramping and music. Boating on the Whangaroa Harbour, diving to the Rainbow Warrior, Yacht charters, fishing can be arranged.

Directions: *Turn off SH 10 onto Matauri Bay Road, travel 13km, turn right to Tepene Tablelands. We are 2km up this road on the left, with our name on a brown wooden fence. We look forward to meeting you.*

Te Ngaere Bay, Kaeo
Self-contained Accommodation
Address: Te Ngaere Bay, RD 1, Kaeo
Name: Mrs June Sale
Telephone: (09) 405 0523
Mobile: 025 903 861
Beds: 2 Single (1 bedroom + 1 combined lounge-kitchen) **Bathroom:** 1 Ensuite
Tariff: Summer (Dec-Feb) $60 total per night - All other times $50 per night.

Credit cards: Visa,M/C,B/C. Vouchers accepted - Doubles only.
Nearest Town: Kerikeri, 35km south of Te Ngaere

Our home is situated on the beach at Te Ngaere Bay, a safe and sheltered bay on one of New Zealand's finest stretches of coastline, in the Far North near Matauri Bay. The drive out gives you spectacular views of the beautiful Cavalli Islands and many other secluded bays and islands along the coast.

There is much to do in the area: kauri forests to visit, sailing, fishing, big-game fishing, horse riding, coastal walks, swimming, snorkelling and diving are but a few activities, or visit the 'Rainbow Warrior' Memorial at Matauri Bay.

We personally run 'Snow Cloud', a skippered charter yacht from Whangaroa, doing day trips and longer. There are excellent licensed restaurants in the area. It is a good central base from which to explore the North, or, you might like to beachcomb or just sit on the beach.

Directions: *Please phone for bookings and details of how to find us. Bookings are essential.*

Kohu Kohu

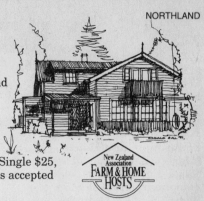

Farmstay
Address: Hawkins Road, Motukaraka,
Kohu Kohu, R.D. 1, Hokianga, Northland
Name: Catherine & John Bawden
Telephone: (09) 405-5534
Beds: 1 Double (1 bedroom) bunk beds
available for children
Bathroom: 1 Guests share
Tariff: B&B (continental) Double $50, Single $25,
Children 1/2 price, Dinner $15, Vouchers accepted
Nearest Town: Kohu Kohu - 8 kms

*Motukaraka is a peaceful rural retreat on the Northern side of the picturesque
Hokianga Harbour.*
*Our home is a former schoolhouse recently renovated using natural timber milled
on the farm and offering beautiful views of the harbour. We are a family of five
with three young children. I am formerly from Ireland, my husband John is a New
Zealander and we run a dairy farm.*
*The location is ideal for walking and tramping, close to the rugged West coast
beaches and historic settlements that were once the thriving hub of early New
Zealand.*
*Come and enjoy the hospitality, tranquillity and pace of life that is distinctly
Hokianga.*
Directions: *2.5 km West of the Northern vehicular ferry terminal, turn right into
Hawkins Road, we are 200 metres along the road on the right.*

Kohukohu (North Hokianga)

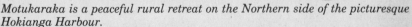

Guest House
Address: Cnr Maning &
Yarborough Sts, Kohukohu
Name: Maryellen Chandler
Telephone: (09) 4055 896
Beds: 1 Double, 4 Single (3 Bedrooms)
Bathroom: 1 Guests share, 1 Family share
Tariff: B&B (full) Double $65, Single $35, Children half
price, Dinner $20. Credit Cards: Visa, M/C. Vouchers accepted.
Nearest Town: Rawene

*You will stay in an historic colonial homestead in attractive grounds, set amongst
mature and exotic trees in the heart of New Zealand's first kauri milling port and
overlooking the waters of the Hokianga Harbour.*
*Enjoy wandering about our village with its quaint old houses, NZ's oldest stone
bridge, Masonic Lodge and Church. Learn something of the fascinating history of
early NZ settlement, while enjoying the tranquillity and timelessness of the
Hokianga.*
*You can explore the wild beauty of the west coast beaches, and are within an hours'
drive of all the Far Norths' main centres (including Bay of Islands) and many
attractions of interest.*
*I will prepare food from barbecue to vegetarian to suit your taste, and can offer
locally made beers and wines. You may choose to share my house or to enjoy your
own space within it.*
Directions: *Enter Kohukohu from the south by ferry from Rawene or from the
Maungamuka Bridge turnoff, for both north and southbound traffic.*

Kohukohu

Homestay, Guest House
Address: Rakautapu Rd. c/- PO Kohukohu Northland
Name: Harbour Views Guest House, Jacky & Bill
Telephone: (09) 4055 815
Beds: 3 Single (2 Bedrooms/main bedroom is twin)
Bathroom: 1 Private, 1 Family share
Tariff: B&B (full) Double $60, Single $30, Children half price, Dinner $15.
Vouchers accepted.
Nearest Town: Kohukohu

Harbour Views Guest House is situated in historic Kohukohu, on the north side of the Hokianga Harbour. Our fully and beautifully restored kauri home is set in two acres of gardens and trees and commands a spectacular view of the upper harbour. Our main guest room, opening out onto a private and sunny verandah, and with its own luxurious bathroom, is in a private wing of the house, but our guests are encouraged to feel part of the family and to use our living areas. Evening meals are prepared using home grown produce in season.

We have lived in this area for twenty years and are interested in and knowledgeable about its history and geography. Kohukohu, once the hub of Northland's kauri timber industry, is now a friendly and charming village. Apart from exploring the village, day trips to the rugged West Coast, Cape Reinga, Bay of Islands and Opononi are all possibilities. Laundry facilities available.

Okaihau, Bay of Islands

Farmstay
Address: Wiroa Road, R.D. 1, Okaihau
Name: Neville & Shennett Clotworthy
Telephone: (09) 401-9371
Beds: 4 Single (2 bedrooms) **Bathroom:** 1 Guests share
Tariff: B&B (full) Double $65, Single $35, Children 12 and under half price, Dinner $25, Vouchers accepted
Nearest Town: Kerikeri 11 kms, Okaihau 8 kms.

We have sheep, cattle and a sport-horse stud on our 280 acre farm. Explore our native bush complete with resident Kiwis. We have fantastic views of the Bay of Islands from our home which is sited 1,000 feet above sea level. Puketi Kauri Forest, historic Hokianga, Kerikeri, Kaikohe and Paihia are only minutes away. Okaihau Golf Club is only 1km away.

We are both descended from families that settled in Northland last century and our special interests are travel, farming, genealogy, Northland history and we are involved in Equestrian sports.

Guests have their own bathroom and toilet facilities.

Directions: *8 kms from State Highway 1. Take the Kerikeri Road, 500 metres South of Okaihau, and we are the 3rd house on the left, past the golf course. OR 9 kms from State Highway 10. Take Wiroa Road at the Kerikeri intersection and we are the first house on the right past the bridge.*

Okaihau
Homestay/Farmstay
Address: Vealbrook Farm, Waihau Valley, Okaihau RD 1, Northland
Name: Pre and Bob Sturge
Telephone: (09) 401 9622
Beds: 1 Double, 4 Single (3 bedrooms)
Bathroom: 1 Guests share, 1 Family share
Tariff: B&B (special) Double $55, Single $30, Dinner $20, Children $10. Vouchers accepted.
Nearest Town: Kaikohe

Our family homestead of four generations and over 100 years old is situated on State Highway 1, 7 kms north of Okaihau, Northland. It is close to Ngawha Hot Springs and St. Catherine Church. Our home was erected in 1883. It originally had a shingle roof. The furniture is in keeping with the house.

We are 50 minutes drive to Kaitaia, 20 minutes drive to Kerikeri airport. We are in the centre of Northland. The Bay of Islands on the east coast with Oponini and Rawene on the west coast. Our home is in a large well established garden and orchard. The house looks out onto the scenic Puketi State Forest where pig hunting and opossum hunting is done. Farm bike is available. Walks over the farm and through the bush is pleasant. We have a family game-room.

The standard of accommodation in *The New Zealand Bed and Breakfast Book*
ranges from homely to luxurious,
but you can always be sure of superior hospitality.

Waimate North, Kerikeri

Farmstay
Address: "Aspley House", Waimate North, Kerikeri R.D.3
Name: Frank & Joy Atkinson
Telephone: (09) 4059-509
Beds: 1 Double, 2 Single (2 bedrooms)
Bathroom: 1 Ensuite, 1 Private
Tariff: B&B (special) Double $100-110, Single $65, Children $30, Dinner $30, Vouchers accepted from February to November
Nearest Town: Kerikeri

"Aspley House" with its old-world charm offers a relaxing and comfortable stay and is ideally situated in picturesque rural surrounds of the Atkinson family farms.
Two large, well-appointed guestrooms open on to a wide verandah, with views of landscaped gardens, over-looking a small lake and beyond to rolling farmland where beef cattle graze.
Frank and Joy who are both descendants of pioneer families, and well versed in local history, have hosted guests from many countries over the past 13 years, and are themselves well travelled.
Family antiques contribute to the atmosphere of this stately, attractive, colonial-styled home.
The three-course gourmet evening meals feature home-grown fresh produce and New Zealand wines.
Summer-time guests can enjoy the inviting kidney-shaped pool.
"Aspley House", with its central location is an excellent base from which to explore the many tourist attractions of the Historic Bay of Islands and the far north.
We offer superior accommodation Pets: Jake, a Jack Russell and Mr.Cat
Directions: *West of SH 10 at Puketona Junction, 3kms up Te Ahuahu Road.*

Ask your hosts for local information.
They are your personal travel agent and guide.

Waimate North, Kaikohe
Homestay/Farmstay
Address: Twinpines Orchard,
Ohaeawai, R.D. 2, Kaikohe, Bay of Islands
Name: N.R. & J.M.F. Sharpe
Telephone: (09) 4059764
Beds: 1 Double, 1 with put-u-up or
Double (2 bedrooms) 4 berth caravan next to house.
Bathroom: 1 Private, 1 Family share
Tariff: B&B (special) Double $75, Single $40, Children under
12 half price, Dinner $20 - $25. Winter rates. Vouchers accepted.
Nearest Town: Kaikohe 12 mins, Kerikeri 15 mins, Paihia 20 - 25 mins.

This is a comfortable English looking country home set in beautiful, peaceful surroundings. We have 12 acres with many native and European trees, citrus, sub-tropical and other fruit, cattle, free-range hens, 2 dachshunds and 1 cat. For 'families' we have a well-found caravan next to house. We are widely travelled and have hosted people from different countries and really enjoy it. We speak French and some German and Italian. Historic Waimate North Mission House is close and we are an excellent centre for Kerikeri, the Hokianga and the Far North, good and empty golf courses and the Ngawha Hot Springs.
Directions: *1 km up SH 1 after Ohaeawai turn right onto Showground Road at RED B&B sign. House on left. From SH10 turn left at Puketona Junction onto Te Ahuahu Road then 3rd left about 8 k up to other end of Showground Road at RED B&B sign. House on right up hill past showground.*

Kerikeri
Homestay
Address: Matariki Orchard,
Pa Road, Kerikeri
Name: David & Alison Bridgman
Telephone: (09) 407-7577
Beds: 1 Double, 2 Single (2 bedrooms)
Bathroom: 1 Guests share
Tariff: B&B (full) Double $70, Single $40, Children $15, Dinner $25, Campervans $20, Credit cards accepted, Vouchers accepted
Nearest Town: Kerikeri (4 mins), Paihia (20 mins)

David and I would like to welcome you to our 4 bedroom brick home, set in the seclusion and privacy of a small mixed citrus and sub-tropical orchard, with a garden of colourful mature trees and swimming pool.
Our family of 4 have left home and we are now interested in meeting and entertaining people from all walks of life.
We are fortunate in having travelled extensively around New Zealand and overseas and look forward to sharing our knowledge and experiences with others. Kerikeri, the earliest settled area in New Zealand is widely known for its history, culture and many crafts and scenery. We are close to the famous Stone Store, Kemp House, golf and bridge clubs, and many scenic bush walks.
Local tours to Cape Reinga and cruises around the Bay of Islands can be arranged. We would love to provide a 3 course dinner of locally grown foods and wine, but if this is not required, there are many restaurants to choose from. Kerikeri supports an airport and a regular bus service. We are happy to meet you.
Directions: *Turn off Highway 10 into Kerikeri township - turn right into Cobham Road, which runs into Inlet Road and Pa Road is first on the left. We are the 2nd house on the right.*

19

Kerikeri
Farmstay
Address: "Kilernan",
State Highway 10, Kerikeri, RD2.
Name: Heather and Bruce Manson
Telephone: (09) 407 8582

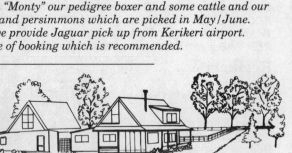

Beds: 1 Double (Queen), 2 single (2 bedrooms)
Bathroom: 2 ensuites
Tariff: B&B (full) Double $90, Single $50, Dinner $30, Not suitable for children.
Vouchers accepted 1 April to 31 October.
Nearest Town: Kerikeri 9 km, Airport 10km.

*"KILERNAN ORCHARD" offers superior accommodation only five minutes from
Kerikeri and an easy drive - 30 km to Paihia in the Bay of Islands.*
*Set in 45 acres well removed from the highway our brand new home has been
specially designed for guest accommodation. You have the choice of double or twin
room with your own ensuite for complete privacy.*
*Enjoy a full English style breakfast indoors or on our sunny spacious deck which
overlooks stream, pasture and native bush. For your evening meal we offer the best
of local fare including New Zealand wine and preceded by complimentary
sundowners.*
*We share our property with "Monty" our pedigree boxer and some cattle and our
orchard grows mandarins and persimmons which are picked in May/June.*
*If you are arriving by air we provide Jaguar pick up from Kerikeri airport.
Directions given at the time of booking which is recommended.*

Kerikeri
Homestay
Address: "Stoneybroke"
Edmonds Road, Kerikeri
Name: Vaughan and Gillian
Telephone: (09) 407 7371
Beds: 1 Double, 2 Single (2 bedrooms) **Bathroom:** 1 Guests share
Tariff: B&B(full) Double $60, Single $35, Dinner $20, Child $25, Vouchers accepted
Nearest Town: 12km east of Kerikeri

*Vaughan and Gillian welcome guests to their modern timbered home in its
tranquil rural setting, overlooking Kerikeri inlet.*
*From Kerikeri you are handy to many historical sites, coastal and rural walks, golf
courses, yacht and fishing charters, craft shops, galleries and restaurants.*
*Weary travellers and holiday makers may prefer to relax in our pleasant garden
and read from the extensive book collection, while sampling life on a typical NZ
small holding.*
*Full/continental breakfast is included; dinner is an optional extra. Homemade
bread, preserves and homegrown vegetables are served*
*Your hosts are experienced travellers and enjoy exchanging travel tales and
introducing visitors to the varied delights of the region.*
*Your accommodation consists of one doubleroom with inlet and garden views, one
twin bedded room and guests bathroom/toilet. Twin bedded "sleepout"
accommodation is also provided at reduced rates. We don't have any household
pets.Please telephone in advance. Smoking restricted to outdoors.*

Takou Bay, Kerikeri
Self-contained Accommodation
Address: Te Ra Road, Takou Bay
Name: Sandra Thornburgh
Telephone: (09) 407 7617
Beds: Upstairs flat: 1 Double, 2 Single (2 bedrooms) Bedsit flat: 1 Double
Bathrooms: 2 Private
Tariff: B&B (continental) 2-bed unit: Double $65, Single $40, Children $25, Bedsit: Double $50, Single $35, Weekly rates available. Vouchers accepted except between Dec 26 - Jan 20 + Easter.
Nearest Town: 20 kms north of Kerikeri off SH 10

Situated between the Bay of Islands and Matauri Bay, Takou Bay is one of Northland's best kept secrets. Twenty minutes north of Kerikeri off SH10, it is an ideal base to explore all the sights of the Far North right up to Cape Reinga. Or stay close to home and enjoy the quiet, unspoilt beauty of Takou Bay Surf Beach. My house sits a top the hill overlooking the sea, with panoramic views of the beach, river and Cavalli Islands which meet the rolling green hills of Northland. With my sister, I have a 50 acre life style farm carrying goats and horses. Americans by birth, we are Kiwis at heart and love the rural lifestyle.

Accommodation consists of two self-contained flats in my warm, two storey house. Both flats offer spectacular seaviews from every window and each have their own kitchen and private bathroom. The upstairs unit has two bedrooms and lounge while the downstairs is a double bedsit with cozy fireplace.

Breakfast is provided in the flats to be taken when desired. A selection of fresh seasonal vegetables from my garden is complimentary.
Directions: *Please phone or write.*

Kerikeri
Self-contained Accommodation
Address: 9 Mission Road, Kerikeri
Name: Studio Nine
Telephone: (09) 407 9075
Beds: 2 Single (1 bedroom)
Bathroom: 1 Ensuite
Tariff: B&B (special) Double $75, Single $50. Credit cards: Visa/MC. Vouchers accepted

Welcome to Studio Nine in the heart of historic Kerikeri. Studio Nine is a self-contained studio apartment which we have completely renovated and equipped with new refrigerator, television and tea and coffee making facilities. It has, of course, its own sparkling new ensuite bathroom. Studio Nine's setting too, is attractive with over an acre of garden, orchard and mature specimen trees. You'll find Studio Nine comfortable, quiet and conveniently located: just a stroll from the Stone Store, Kemp House, Rewa's Village and the Visitor Centre.

At Studio Nine you can choose from our range of special breakfasts. We take particular pride in our fresh fruit salads, orange muffins and omelettes.

We have secure, off-street parking but if you're not travelling by car, we'll be happy to pick you up from the bus depot or the airport.

We, your hosts Graeme and Valerie Josey, are long term residents of Kerikeri and ourselves experienced travellers. We welcome Visa and MasterCard.

Kerikeri
Self-contained Accommodation
Address: 'Wairawa', Waipapa
West Road, Waipapa, Kerikeri RD2;
Name: Judy Bell and Roger Larkin
Telephone: (09) 407 9888
Beds: 1 Double, 1 Single (1 bed-sitting room) **Bathroom:** 1 Ensuite
Tariff: B&B (full) Double $65, Single $40, Dinner $25pp, Vouchers accepted
Nearest Town: Kerikeri 10 mins

We live on a small, mostly organic kiwifruit and citrus orchard with a dog, cat and horse. Our adult children live away. Guest accommodation is separate, but adjacent to the main house. It consists of a large, sunny bedsitting-room overlooking lawn and trees, with its own private bathroom.
We are close to the historic and scenic Bay of Islands and also the coastal area to the north, including the Rainbow Warrior Memorial at Matauri Bay. We are a short distance to the Puketi Kauri Forest.
Kerikeri, our nearest town, is 10 minutes away and has a selection of 7 restaurants. As we both work off orchard at times, it is advisable to phone in advance. Waipapa West Road is left off State Highway 10, 2km north of Waipapa village. Our driveway is a further 1 1/2 km on the right, on the last bend in the no exit road. Name on letterbox.
Dinner possible by prior arrangement.

Kerikeri
Guest House
Address: The Pines,132 Kerikeri
Rd, Kerikeri Northlands
Name: Brian & Cindy
Telephone: (09) 407 6150
Beds: 1 Double, 4 Single (3 Bedrooms)
Bathroom: 1 Guests share, 1 Family share
Tariff: B&B (Special) Double $67.50, Single $40.00, Dinner $20, Campervans facilities available. Credit cards. Vouchers accepted
Nearest Town: Kerikeri

Situated just 500 metres from Kerikeri Shopping Centre our 2 storey home and detached dining room, offers plenty of windows to filter in the northern light by day and on open fire to warm you by night. We have a north facing balcony where you can relax in the sun. Or day trips can be organised to take you fishing or sailing around the nearby Cavalli and Bay of Islands. Take a trip up the beach to New Zealands most northerly Cape Reinga. Or nearby the historical Stone store by the river is just a stones throw away. Relax and take in nature with a stroll along some of the many bush walks available.
Your hosts are both non smokers with 1 pet and their home is freshly renovated. They will do their best to make your stay both comfortable and enjoyable.
So come and stay with us and enjoy some of the many things lovely Kerikeri has to offer.
Note: Building was not completed at the time of inspection, phone to confirm.

Kerikeri

Homestay, Bed & Breakfast
Address: "Jacaranda Lodge"
60 Cobham Road Keri Keri
Name: Lyn & Bernie Collings
Telephone: (09) 407 6280
Beds: 2 Single (1 Bedroom)
Bathroom: 1 Ensuite
Tariff: B&B (full) Double $65, Single $50, Children under 15yrs $20, Dinner $15pp with prior notice. Credit cards: Visa, M/C, B/C. Vouchers accepted.
Nearest Town: Keri Keri

A warm welcome awaits you at Jacaranda Lodge where you can relax , and let us spoil you a little, in our sunny home with lovely gardens and trees. Join us in our lounge, or have the privacy of your own comfortable room with ensuite, easy chairs, twin beds with electric blankets, TV, fridge and coffee / tea making facilities. We offer courtesy pick-up and delivery to Keri Keri bus depot or airport. Our reasonable tariff includes continental or cooked breakfast. We are situated just 5 minutes walk to Keri Keri township and excellent restaurants, and within easy walking distance you can enjoy the many attractions Keri Keri has to offer.
We have lived in many parts of New Zealand as well as Indonesia and enjoy sharing our home and experiences with fellow travellers. We enjoy meeting people and offering excellent hospitality, gardening, music, most sport and are both keen golfers. Smoking allowed in lounge only.
Visa, Mastercard and Bankcard welcome.
Pets: One friendly cat.
Directions: *Cobham Road is the 1st right turn after roundabout entering township.*

Kerikeri

Homestay - Orchard
Address: Koropewa Road, Waipapa, Kerikeri
Name: Kevan & Wendy Flannagan
Telephone: (09) 407 9629
Beds: 1 Double, 2 Single (3 Bedrooms) **Bathroom:** 1 Ensuite, 1 Guests share
Tariff: B&B (continental) Double $65, Single $35, Dinner $20, Vouchers accepted
Nearest Town: Kerikeri 8km, Airport 8km

Kevan & Wendy Flannagan, Max (black Labrador) and Midi (black cat) welcome you to our lifestyle / hobby orchard and flower growing venture and the total peace and quiet of the orchard we would like to call "Peace at last". We grow every fruit imaginable and you can sample our fruit and preserves with the continental style breakfast. Dinner by arrangement.
Kerikeri is central to all Bay of Islands attractions, commercial or rural. An itinerary can be arranged or you can just enjoy our surroundings.
We are happy to collect you from Kerikeri township or airport.
Our lifestyle is simple - sailing and orcharding, with meeting people a highlight. Accommodation: - A semi-detached unit (with ensuite & coffee making facilities) situated among the trees and birds and two single bedrooms with guest bathroom.
Directions: *Koropewa Road, off Pungaere Road which intersects SH10 7km north (towards Kaeo) from the Kerikeri turnoff and 500m through the village of Waipapa - follow B&B signs.*

Kerikeri
Homestay
Address: "Raemere Homestead" Cnr SH 10 &
Wiroa Road Keri Keri
Name: Dorothy & Bill Fletcher
Telephone: (09) 407 7787
Beds: 1 Double, 4 Single (3 Bedrooms)
Bathroom: 2 Guests share
Tariff: B&B (continental) Double $65, Single $45,
Children from 9yrs, Dinner $25
Nearest Town: Keri Keri

Lovely Raemere Homestead is situated just 3 mins from Keri Keri township and 20 mins from Paihia.
Nestled in one acre of trees, shrubs and gardens "Raemere" is a truly delightful place to stay in the Bay of Islands, exploring Historic places, playing golf, browsing through the many craft, ceramic and pottery shops or just sitting in the garden with a good book.
Bay of Island cruises, tours to Cape Reinga and the Far North can be arranged, with coach pick up at our gate.
Your hosts, Bill and Dorothy, have travelled extensively and have "homestayed" in the UK and France - most enjoyable experience which we now offer to visitors both International and Domestic.
The Bay of Islands Airport is just 2km down the road and we are happy to pick up guests upon request.
Dinner is an optional by prior arrangement.

Private bathroom is for your use exclusively,
Guests share means you may be sharing with other guests,
Family share means you will be sharing with the family.

Kerikeri
Bed & Breakfast
Address: "The Ferns"
4 Riverview Rd Kerikeri
Name: Jim & Penny
Telephone: (09) 407 7567
Beds: 2 Double, 2 Single (3 Bedrooms)
Bathroom: 1 Ensuite, 1 Guests share
Tariff: B&B (full) Double $80-90, Single $45, Vouchers accepted
Nearest Town: Kerikeri

Nestled in a quiet residential area of Kerikeri we offer a friendly Bed and Breakfast service. Our two storied modern accommodation offers spacious rooms, quality comfortable beds and off-street parking.
Guests can relax on spacious deck or in a comfortable fireside lounge.
Tea and coffee making facilities are available at all times. Enjoy a continental or cooked breakfast before exploring the far north with its many attractions and activities.
Directions: *Pass through Kerikeri township and follow the main road down to the Stone Store, continue along Landing Rd, we are the fourth street on the right. Our sign is clearly visible, or free pick up from public transport.*
Phone if possible, otherwise call in and we'll do our best to accommodate you

---

Kerikeri - Paihia
Bed & Breakfast
Address: "The Gables" cnr S.H. 10 and
Te Ahuahu Rd, Puketona, Kerikeri
Name: Margaret Dines
Telephone: (09) 407 7923
Beds: 2 Double, 1 Twin (3 bedrooms) **Bathroom:** 2 Guests share
Tariff: B&B (special) Double $70 - $90, Single $45 - $50, Dinner $25, off season rates apply, Vouchers accepted except between 25 December and 10 January
Nearest Town: Kerikeri 7 mins, Paihia 12mins

"The Gables" is an English style Country House, set in delightful rural surroundings and offering a comfortable and peaceful stay. We live in an area rich in early colonial history situated between Paihia and Kerikeri in the beautiful Bay of Islands.
We are English and have travelled extensively throughout the world, living in Australia for many years.
Enjoy a delicious breakfast of fresh local fruits, homemade muesli, breads, muffins, jams and marmalade.
Things of interest in the area include fishing, horseriding, golf, tramping and sailing. Tours can be arranged, and coaches to Cape Reinga pass the entrance to our property making this an ideal stopover for those wishing to take in the many attractions offered. Pets; two dogs, an Airedale (Emma) and a West Highland White terrier (Dougal). Non smokers preferred.
Prices apply to NZ Bed and Breakfast book holders only.

Waitangi
Homestay
Address: "Ngatamahine" 50A Tahuna Rd Paihia Bay of Islands
Name: Una Connon
Telephone: (09) 402 8021
Beds: 2 Single (1 Bedroom) **Bathroom:** 1 Family share
Tariff: B&B (continental) Double $60, Single $35, Dinner $25
Nearest Town: Paihia

"Ngatamahine" homestay is situated 2km from Paihia at Waitangi, the historic heart of NZ. The sun drenched Bay of Islands is the gateway to NZ history and the area around my home is full of sites of historical interest. You can take a short stroll to the Treaty House and grounds where 155 years ago the historic agreement was signed, from there you can also enjoy a gentle boardwalk through a spectacular mangrove forest to ancient Haruru Falls.
The magnificent Waitangi Golf Course is close at hand.
I am proud of my NZ heritage and welcome visitors from all over the world. I aim to make you stay as comfortable and enjoyable as possible.
"Ngatamahine" is a well lit, single storey house - no stairs to climb.
I enjoy cooking and will be happy to prepare a meal to suit your mood - with prior notice. I look forward to hearing from you.

Paihia
Homestay
Address: 31 Selwyn Road,
Paihia, Bay of Islands
Name: Bill and Bunny Lind
Telephone: (09) 402-7182
Beds: 3 Single (2 bedrooms)
Bathroom: 1 Guests share
Tariff: B&B (continental) $40 per person, Vouchers accepted

We are a retired couple now living on our own who enjoy meeting people from all walks of life. Our family are grown up and we now have just one daughter in Paihia who is a hostess on the cruise ships in our lovely bay.
We are a two minute walk from the beach and a five minute walk on the flat from all shops and restaurants. Departure points for all tours and cruises are within the five minute walk.
Our home is a modern 2-storey townhouse with spacious open plan living area and sea and bush outlook. We have one single bedroom downstairs and one twin room upstairs. The bathroom is upstairs on a guests shared basis, with one toilet downstairs and one upstairs.
We thank you for not smoking in the house.
Directions: *Turn left at Post Office, then first turn right which is Selwyn Road. We are the last house on right. Courtesy car available to meet buses.*

When you stay at B&Bs you are staying with genuine Kiwis

Paihia

Farmstay, Homestay
Address: "Wairoa" Overseas Visitor Farm Home Stays,
PO Box 36, Bayly Road, Waitangi, Paihia
Name: Dorothy Bayly
Telephone: (09) 4027-379
Beds: 1 Double, 2 Single (2 bedrooms) **Bathroom:** 1 Guests share
Tariff: B&B (continental, full on request) Double $80, Single $40,
Dinner $38, Children over 12 yrs only, $30. Vouchers accepted between June and
July at 15% only.
Nearest Town: Paihia 8 mins drive, Whangarei 1 1/4 hrs.

*My two storeyed farm home is built on the sea front set in gardens with tennis
court, overlooking historic Russell. Situated 5 minutes from the tourist town of
Paihia, through Waitangi Golf Course.*
Bedrooms have sea views. Electric blankets on beds.
Enjoyable farm walks, lots of bird life.
Private beach. Tennis raquet and balls provided.
*"Wairoa" Farm was bought by my father-in-law in 1929. This coastal farm plus
another undeveloped 1000 acre block purchased by us 30 years ago was developed
by my husband.*
*We farm Romney sheep and Angus-cross cattle, dairy beef bulls for the American
market.*
*My married daughter and husband and family live on the farm in the old
homestead built in 1838. My daughter trains and rides show jumping horses.*
3 course dinner by request also cooked breakfast by request.
TV, tea and coffee making facilities and laundry are available for guests.
*We will arrange deep-sea, line fishing, sailing trips and bus tours. If you wish to
dine at one of the fine restaurants in Paihia we will book for you.*
*Please pre-book to save disappointment. We can also meet the bus in Paihia for
a small charge. Looking forward to your stay.*

Paihia

Homestay/Self-contained Accom.
Address: 6 Moana Avenue,
Paihia, Bay of Islands
Name: Mrs Pat Beaufoy
Telephone: (09) 402 7201
Beds: 1 Double, 4 Single (2 bedrooms & 1 flat) **Bathroom:** 1 Ensuite, 1 Private,
1 Guests share
Tariff: B&B (continental) Double $75, Single $40, Vouchers accepted.

Two story modern home in central Paihia. Outstanding sea views, town and over to Russell. 5 minutes walk to all services, shops, wharf, and restaurants. Ideal for travellers using public transport. I am happy to meet the bus in Paihia. Comfortable furnished flat on lower floor. Lounge, TV, kitchen, frig, washing machine. Sea views.
I supply continental breakfast in flat to have at leisure. I enjoy meeting people from overseas and within New Zealand and would make you very welcome. I look forward to your stay.
Non smokers preferred. I haven't any pets.
Directions: *Turn left at Post Office into Williams Rd. Then first turn on the right into Selwyn Rd. Continue along to the Bounty corner. Turn left into Bayview Rd. Moana Ave is a few metres on the right. No.6 is on the left.*

Paihia

Homestay
Address: Puketona Road, Paihia, Bay of Islands
Name: Allwyn & Graeme Sutherland
Telephone: (09) 402-7041
Beds: 2 Double, 1 Single (3 bedrooms) **Bathrooms:** 1 Guests share
Tariff: B&B (full) Double $70 ,Single $35 ,Dinner $15. Vouchers accepted with continental breakfast only.

Our small holding (10 acres) is conveniently situated five miles from Paihia in the Bay-of-Islands and provides ready access to beaches, historical places, deep sea fishing, local tours and a number of golf courses including the picturesque Waitangi International.
We graze a few sheep and cattle and have 500 assorted fruit trees. Our homemade jams and preserves are served with meals.
Our comfortable Lockwood house is set in park like grounds with a large lawn and a variety of flowering trees and shrubs. A small lake readily seen from your verandah provides a refuge for wild ducks, shags and herons. The atmosphere is quiet and peaceful.
We have a wide variety of interests, are well travelled and enjoy the company of local and overseas guests. We do request that our guests be non-smokers.
Directions: *We can be found on the Paihia - Kerikeri road and the "Lily Pond Orchard" sign is at our gate.*

Paihia
Lodge
Address: 'The Totaras', 6 School Road, Paihia, Bay of Islands
Name: Frank & Christine Habicht
Telephone & Fax: (09) 402-8238
Beds: 1 King with ensuite. SC Studio: 1 Queen, 1 Single with ensuite.
Tariff: B&B (Special) Double $120, Single $100, Off Season Rate $95, Children $25, Dinner $20. Above rates apply to "NZ B&B Book" holders only. Credit Cards: Visa

For the sophisticated traveller , , ,luxury with charm. Enjoy Paihia's best location from a hill top residency and share our happiness.
In 1982 we moved with our two sons from Berlin to the beautiful Bay of Islands. Christine, my Austrian wife, has a degree in Hotel Management.
We are overlooking Paihia harbour, historic Waitangi and Russell and are nestled in old native Totara trees.
The 180 degree views from all rooms, terraces and pool area are simply stunning. Watch oceanliners and the game fish fleet right from your apartment.
We will spoil you with a healthy German breakfast in our conservatory or on one of the sundecks.
We are in the centre of township within walking minutes to beaches, tracks, wharf (15 minutes ferry ride to Russell), restaurants and shops.
My life is and has always been devoted to creative photography. My book "Young London" was published in the 'sixties
Recent guest comments: 'Paradise regained - our second visit'
'Relaxing, peaceful, stimulating'
'Far mor spectacular than expected
Try to book in advance! Courtesy car available.

Tell other travellers about your favourite B&Bs

Paihia

Homestay
Address: Puketona Lodge, Puketona Road,
P.O. Box 273, Paihia, Bay of Islands
Name: Heather & Maurice Pickup
Telephone & Fax: (09) 4028-152
Beds: 1 Double, 2 Single (2 bedrooms)
Bathroom: 1 Guests share
Tariff: B&B (Special) Double $70-$90, Single $45, Dinner $25, off season rates available. Campervans welcome.
Vouchers accepted except December 25 to January 7
Nearest Town: Paihia

Heather and Maurice are semi retired of English / NZ origin with family ties in USA.

Our luxurious modern home features native woods and is situated on 10 acres in quiet surroundings.

Our guest bedrooms are large and have access to outside verandahs. There is a separate bathroom and toilet for guests.

We have lovely rural views and are close to beaches golf course, bush walks, and horse trekking. We are just a few minutes drive from historic Waitangi.

We are happy to book tours and cruises.

Our friendly old dog is well behaved.

Breakfasts are special and feature home made bread, muffins, muesli and preserves and more!

We enjoy cooking and serve interesting meals on request, catering for vegetarians too, with fresh home grown produce.

We are situated on the main Paihia - Kerikeri Road 8km from Paihia beach.

We look forward to sharing our smoke free home with you. Prior booking recommended.

Guests share means you may be sharing the bathroom with other guests.

G.R.ZULL '93

Paihia
**Homestay+Self-contained Accommodation
+ Separate Cottage**
Address: 'The Cedars', 5 Sullivan's Road, Paihia, Bay of Islands
Name: The Cedar Suite, Jo and Peter Nisbet
Telephone: (09) 402 8516
Mobile: 025 969 281
Beds: 1 Queen with ensuite
Cottage: 2 Queen + 2 Single (bathroom private)
SC Studio: 1 Queen with ensuite
Tariff: B&B (special) Double $78, $88, $115, Dinner $20ea,
Children welcome (in cottage only).

We offer a homestay in the tradition of the best bed and breakfast, as well as an independent self-contained studio apartment. Breakfasts are continental and can be served in the room or with the family. Each suite has its own ensuite bathroom or shower.
Your hosts enjoy good music and good food, combined with a real interest in the garden, photography and interior design. Meals are a speciality of ours, and guests have remarked on our use of fresh produce from the bay, as gourmet food, creatively served. Our modern cedar home is set in beautiful native bush within easy walking distance of the bay, shops, and tour pick-up points. We are happy to collect guests from anywhere in Paihia.
Guests have off-street parking, decks, TV in rooms, quality appointments and particularly, comfortable beds. Laundry service available at small extra charge. 'Seaview Cottage' is an extension of 'The Cedar Suite' for larger groups with discerning tastes.

31

Haruru Falls, Paihia
Homestay, Self-contained Accommodation

Address: "Hacienda", 18 Goffe Drive, Haruru Falls, Paihia
Name: Chris and John
Telephone: (09) 402 7701 or 402 7849
Beds: 2 Double, 5 Single (2 bedrooms) and 1 two bedroom self contained apartment **Bathroom:** 3 Private
Tariff: B&B (full) Double $80-110, Single $65, Dinner (3 course) $28, Children $20, Off season rates. (Above rates apply to "NZ B&B Book holders" only.)
Nearest Town: Paihia 3km

Welcome to the "Hacienda". *Our large Spanish style home sits high on a hill-top capturing magnificent views of historic Russell, Haruru Falls, Waitangi River and the Bay.*
Guest areas while being part of the house, include separate entrances, private bathrooms, fridge, tea / coffee facilities and TV.
This offers a unique concept of homestay, as it allows the option of mingling and meeting, or being quite private.
Large guest lounge opens onto a garden setting overlooking the ocean and has conversation pit with open fire, pool-table and guest bar where the house brew may be sampled. We request there be no smoking indoors.
Breakfast of your choice - continental or cooked. Dinner with complimentary drink available on request or if you prefer there are a variety of restaurants in Paihia Centrally situated - 3km to safe swimming beach and Northland's famous tourist attractions.
We are able to arrange all local tours. Courtesy car provided from Paihia wharf/ bus terminal.
We delight in meeting people and extend an invitation to you to discover the Bay of Islands in your own personal way.
Directions: *Easily located. Please phone or write.*

G.R.BULL '93.

Paihia
Bed & Breakfast
Address: Te Haumi House,
12 Seaview Road, Paihia
Name: Enid & Ernie Walker
Telephone: (09) 402 8046
Beds: 1 Double, 2 Single (2 bedrooms) **Bathroom:** 1 guests share
Tariff: B&B (continental) Double $70, Single $35, Children
under 12 yrs half price. Vouchers accepted.

We have a well established home on the waterfront in Te Haumi Bay with fantastic seaviews of the inner harbour.
Location: 3 minutes north of the Opua turn off and 1 minute south of Paihia township and opposite the Beachcomber Motel.
Our interests since retiring, are gardening, floral art and involvement in the Masonic Lodge. We enjoy meeting people from all walks of life and are very proud to share our wonderful area with you and to make your stay as memorable as possible. Guest pick-up from Paihia is available.
P.S. Please no smoking inside, but outside is fine.

Paihia
Self-Contained Accommodation
Address: 49 Kings Road, Paihia, Bay of Islands
Name: Anne Corbett & Garth Craig
Telephone: (09) 402 7882
Beds: 1 Super King or 2 Single (1 Bedroom) **Bathroom:** 1 Ensuite
Tariff: B&B (continental) Double $70, Single $60. Credit cards. Vouchers accepted.

Our home is situated on a quiet elevated site in central Paihia.
Facing north we enjoy sun all day with lovely sea views across the Bay to Russell. Our new guest flat is fully self contained and private. A warm sunny, spacious area with a large sun drenched deck for guests to enjoy our garden and sea views. Native pigeons, tuis and rosellas are frequent visitors to our peaceful garden. We are within easy walking distance from all restaurants and shopping facilities and offer safe off street parking. For the past sixteen years we have owned and operated Paihia Dive Hire and Charter, entertaining visitors from all corners of the world. We have a wealth of local knowledge on the Bay of Islands area which we will gladly share with you in planning your holiday.
For bookings and directions please phone or write.

Opua, Paihia
Homestay
Address: Oromahoe Road,
Opua, Bay of Islands
Name: Pat & Don Jansen
Telephone: (09) 402 8099
Beds: 1 Double, 1 Twin, (2 bedrooms)
Bathroom: 1 Guests share
Tariff: B&B (continental or full) $35 per person. Vouchers accepted
Nearest Town: Paihia 5km

Our home is situated on a quiet peaceful site surrounded by native bush and enjoying magnificent sea views.
Sundeck and private entrance for guests.
The area features Waitangi Golf Course, one of NZ's most picturesque. Fishing, sailing, boat charter trips around the Bay are just some of the attractions. Others include bush and coastal walks, historic buildings, craft shops and gourmet restaurants.
Russell car ferry only 1km, Russell passenger ferry only 5km from our home.
Guests have complete privacy while at the same time a personal invitation to spend some time with us.
Our interests include sailing, Kauri woodwork, walking, travel, music, rose gardening and reading. With a good knowledge of our area we can help you plan your visit to make it as enjoyable as possible.
We enjoy meeting people and look forward to sharing our home and the beautiful area in which we live. Non smokers preferred.
Directions: *Please phone*

Opua, Paihia
Homestay/Self-contained Accommodation
Address: 7 Franklin St, Opua, Bay of Islands
Name: Margaret Sinclair
Telephone: (09) 402 8285
Beds: 1 Double, 2 Single (2 bedrooms)
Bathroom: 1 Family share. Self-cont. Accom: 1 Double, 2 Single separate toilet & shower.
Tariff: B&B (continental) Double $60, Single $35, Dinner $20pp. Self-cont. Accom: $100 per night. Vouchers accepted.
Nearest Town: Paihia

You are welcome to stay in my lovely home above the harbour at Opua.
Enjoy panoramic views of the water where there is much boating activity - there always seems to be something happening.
You are handy to all the tourist activities of this area and there is a large heated spa pool to relax in on your return from your day's outing. You may like to wander in my garden which is my big interest.
Downstairs there is a large 2 roomed self-contained unit with separate shower and toilet and the use of a large private deck with the same stunning views.
To find my home take the road to Paihia from Whangarei. Turn right where the sign indicates the Opua ferry - this is Franklin St. My house is the first visible house on your left. I can meet bus arrivals at Paihia.

Opua, Paihia
Bed & Breakfast
Address: Oromahoe Rd., Opua,
Name: Dennis Harrison &
Shiralee Beazley
Telephone: (09) 4027389
Beds: 1 Double, 4 Single (3 bedrooms) **Bathrooms:** 2 Guest
Tariff: B&B (Continental) $40 per person, (NZ B&B Book holders only), Children under 12 half price, off season rates. Vouchers accepted.
Nearest Town: Paihia 5km

Our large home in on top of a hill overlooking English Bay, with fantastic sea and bush views of the harbour and islands. The guests-lounge and each bedroom has its own water views. Two bathrooms one with spa-bath and shower.

Paihia township is 10 minutes by car, Opua wharf and store is about 2 minutes by car; where you can catch the car ferry to historic Russell, or board the vintage steam-train to Kawakawa and return. Local attractions include sailing, fishing, Maori Meeting House and canoe, glow-worm caves, geothermal hot pools for a spa, a bushwalk to giant Kauri trees, or take a stroll to the Opua yacht harbour (5 mins), or join the coastal walkway.

We are a family who love meeting people and our home in well signposted on the road to Paihia from Opua.

A small charge for guest pick-up from Paihia.

P.S. Please no smoking in our home, outside is fine.

Opua, Paihia
Homestay+Self-contained Accommodation
Address: 17 English Bay Rd
Opua Bay of Islands
Name: Frank & Vanessa Leadley
Telephone & Fax: (09) 402 7650
Beds: 1 Double, 2 Single (2 Bedrooms)
Bathroom: 1 Private, 1 Family share
Tariff: B&B (continental) Double $70,
Single $35, Vouchers accepted, Full breakfast on request
Nearest Town: Paihia

Our modern home is in a very tranquil setting with great sea and bush views. Only 6 minutes by car from Paihia and 2 minutes from the car ferry to Russell so you are well sited to take advantage of activities such as fishing, swimming, golf, bush and coastal walks, boating or just relaxing.

We are very proud of our country and district, have an excellent knowledge of both, and are keen to share it all with our guests. We both enjoy travel, music, boating (we have a gracious old kauri launch), and gardening. Frank is a keen Rotarian and Vanessa is a great cook.

One accommodation unit is also available as a fully self-contained flat (bedding, linen, TV etc) if you prefer to look after yourselves at $45 per night. No smoking inside, please.

Directions: *Phone or fax, or guest pick-up from Paihia. We love it here, so will you.*

Opua, Paihia

Homestay
Address: 10 Franklin St Opua Paihia
Name: Florence Morrison
Telephone: (09) 402 7488
Beds: 4 Single (2 Bedrooms)
Bathroom: 1 Family share (Separate toilet and shower)
Tariff: B&B (continental) Double $55, Single $30, Children $12, Dinner $20,
Vouchers accepted
Nearest Town: Paihia 5km

My home overlooks the Port of Opua from the front and the Kawakawa River, and busy boat yards to the back.
Franklin St leads to the Russell car ferry and my home is next to the school.
You are handy to all tourist attractions of the Bay - bush and coastal walks.
I have hosted Servas travellers for 13 years and really enjoyed, introducing them to this historic and beautiful part of the North.
I have lived in this locality most of my life, now retired, but find plenty to do, gardening, the local theatre group, Credit Union and simply enjoying the Bay and look forward to sharing it all with you.
Directions: *Whangarei-Paihia Rd turn right at Opua for the ferry. No 10 Franklin St will welcome you.*
Note: Building was not completed at time of inspection, phone to confirm.

Opua, Paihia

Homestay+Self-contained Accommodation
Address: "Waterview" 14 Franklin ST
Opua Bay of Islands Northland
Name: Val & Peter Sharp
Telephone: (09) 402 7595 or 402 8001
Fax: (09) 402 7595
Beds: 2 Queen, 4 Single (3 Bedrooms)
Bathroom: 2 Ensuite, 1 Private

Tariff: B&B (continental) Double $90, Single $60, SCA: Double $75, Single $50.
Credit cards: Visa/MC. Vouchers accepted 1 April to 30 September.
Nearest Town: Paihia

Our home on Franklin Street overlooks the closed export port of Opua where we have lived for the last 34 years. Opua is the first customs clearance port on New Zealand coast to 400 foreign cruising yachts a year.
It is also the base to many of the 130 charter craft and business that service the tourist and water related industries in the bay.
Local store - restaurant - takeaways - post office - vehicular ferry terminal to Russell are adjacent to the wharf where cruise-liners berth on occasions.
All this 2 minutes walk from your quality accommodation that give a choice. A self-contained basement unit sleeping 4 persons or our 2 studio units with TV, radio, refrigerator, coffee / tea making facilities with private balcony.
We will book or advise you of the many tours - walks and attractions.
Tourist coaches pick up - drop off at door.
Parking private. Our home is smoke free.
Directions: *Waterview sign at entrance. Phone or fax confirmation arrival.*

Tell other travellers about your favourite B&Bs

Russell

Homestay
Address: Wellington Street, Russell
Name: Kay Bosanquet
Telephone: (09) 403 7843
Beds: 2 Double, 1 Single, 1 twin (4 bedrooms)
Bathroom: 1 Private, 1 Guests share
Tariff: B&B (special) Double $77, Twin $77, Single $44, Vouchers accepted after Easter to end of November.

My home overlooks Russell Bay with magnificent water and bush views. Born and bred in Northland I take great pride in showing my guests NZ's first capital. I love every type of fishing and frequently escort my guests out game fishing. I am a national doll collector and I love the world coming to stay with me.

Meals are usually served on the terrace. Although I will serve all meals if requested I have found my guests like to explore and sample the different fish restaurants that abound in Russell.

We have several lovely walks handy, as well as golf, bowls, diving, cruises and yacht charters.

I belong to Russell RSA, bowling, gamefishing, yachting clubs, if my guests wish to meet our locals I take them to whichever club interests them.

All I ask of my guests is to completely relax and use my home as theirs.

Directions: *By car - take Opua car ferry to Russell and you will be met.*
By bus - choice of Northliner right to Russell or Intercity Services to Paihia, then ferry to Russell where you will be met.

There are some good tips for easier travel on page 4

Russell
Homestay
Address: Major Bridge Drive, Te Wahapu, Russell
Name: Eva and Denis Brown
Telephone: (09) 4037-431
Beds: 1 Double, 1 Single (1 Bedroom) **Bathroom:** 1 Private
Tariff: B&B (special) Double $65, Single $38, Child $20 Dinner $20, Vouchers accepted
Nearest Town: Russell, 7 km by car or 20 minutes rowing by our faering rowboat.

Our wooden house is near a quiet beach in a sheltered bay. We recommend walking shoes to our guests because parking is on the top of the hill and our house is by the water. A footpath leads down through a tunnel of native fern, kanuka and manuka.

We provide a rowboat free for fishing or crossing to Russell, the historic first capital of New Zealand.

Beach walks start at our door. Birdwatchers roost on our deck.

Other guests swim right off our beach or take a sailing trip to the islands.

Historic places, Maori pa sites or kauri trees, golf, diving, dolphin watching and kayaking are all nearby.

Eva cooks tasty dinners and caters for special diets. Breakfasts range from fresh fruit, muesli and yoghurt to wholemeal toast, bacon and eggs or pancakes to order. Please phone ahead as we have only one guest room. We can meet guests at the bus or ferry, or they may arrive by water taxi.

Russell

Homestay +
Self-Contained Accommodation
Address: Robertson Street, Russell
Postal: (PO Box 203)
Name: Dudley and Sharyn Smith
Telephone: (09) 403-7200 Fax (09) 403-7537
Beds: Self-Contained Villa, 1 Kingsize (1 bedroom) **Bathroom:** 1 Ensuite
Self-contained unit. Sleeps 4. **Bathroom:** 1 Ensuite
Tariff: B&B Self-Contained Villa: Double $110; Single $110 Homestay Unit:
Double $85, Single $85, Children welcome, Campervans welcome. Credit Cards.

Our property is centrally situated on an elevated section overlooking the historic town and harbour of Russell - a two minute walk from the wharf, shops and restaurants. We enjoy unsurpassed sea and bush views. The area is rich in the history of the country and famous for its warm climate, beautiful sandy beaches and excellent fishing and boating.
We have two choices of accommodation:
An attractively appointed, sunny and spacious de luxe self-contained Villa with its own private entrance, garden, sundeck and terrace. The Villa enjoys magnificent sea and village views, has a Super-King size bed and tasteful ensuite. Kitchen facilities, TV and BBQ. Breakfast available on request.
Our new modern home has a large basement flat with private ensuite facilities, refrigerator, TV, tea/coffee making. This unit can sleep up to four people, has excellent views and good parking. Breakfast is included in the tariff.

Russell

Homestay
Address: Titore Way, Russell, Bay of Islands
Name: Morrell & Diana Folley
Telephone: (09) 403-7658 **Fax:** (09) 403-7340
Beds: 1 Double, 2 Single (2 bedrooms) **Bathroom:** 1 Guests share
Tariff: B&B (full) Double $75, Single $40, Children under 12 1/2 price, Dinner $25

Overlooking the historic town of Russell with million dollar views of the Bay and Pacific, our home is set in a tranquil cul-de-sac with bush and beach walks starting from the property. There is a dinghy free for guests to use, and we also have available a 21ft cabin cruiser for light tackle fishing or picnics around the islands.
A couple of comments from our visitors' book "One hundred percent better than the Auckland hotel I paid a fortune for". Another summed up her feelings with "Making new friends in such a beautiful place is what I'd hoped my vacation would be".
Breakfast is cooked or continental, Dinner is three course and wine is served with the meal. (Seafood a speciality).
We are the proprietors of NZ Host Homes Ltd, and are therefore able to assist with ongoing accommodation and also have major credit-card facilities.

Would you like a weeks free B&B for two people?
Please complete and send us the comment form supplied by your host.

Russell

Farmstay, Self-contained Accommodation
Address: Wairoro Park, Aucks Road, PO Box 53, Okiato, Russell
Name: Yan and Beryl Boerop
Telephone: (09) 403-7255
Beds: 1 - 3 bedroom chalet, 3 - 2 bedroom chalets, 3 - 1 bedroom chalets
Bathroom: 7 Private
Tariff: B&B Double $80, Single $80, extra adult $12, Children $6, (Breakfast is not served, all ingredients are supplied as an optional extra). Credit Cards: Visa, M/C. Vouchers accepted 1 May to 1 October only.

Wairoro Park is a 160 acre (60 ha.) coastal estate in central Bay of Islands. Two thirds is native bush and on the remainder we breed pedigree Limousin cattle. We have built three A-frame holiday chalets, 1 large Lockwood and 3 small Klassic chalets. Each chalet is fully self-contained with private shower, bath, colour TV, fully equipped kitchen and large lounge with sundeck. Upstairs in the A-frame chalets there are two separate bedrooms, one with a king size double bed, the other with three singles. At the beach you will find a choice of boats including motor, sail and rowboat plus a kayak and surf sailer. Just behind the beach is a large lawn with garden furniture, a trampoline and a covered barbeque pagoda to cook your freshly caught fish.
We came to New Zealand some 20 odd years ago as refugees from the European rat race and we enjoy having the time and the opportunity to meet and get to know many different people.
Wij spreken Nederlands. Wir sprechen Deutsch.
PETS ARE WELCOME!!

Homes newly listed in this edition
of *The New Zealand B&B Book* have all been inspected.

Russell - Waipiro/Parekura Bay
Homestay
Address: P. O. Box 224, Russell
Name: Gasthaus Waipiro Bay
Telephone & Fax: (09) 4037095
Beds: 2 Double, 1 Single (2 bedrooms)
Bathroom: 1 Ensuite, 1 Private
Tariff: B&B (special) Double $125, Reduction for singles, Dinner $35, Credit cards accepted
Nearest Town: 19km east of Russell on the coastal scenic drive

Dream of a place, an artist's home high above a bay - so sweet the air, so clear the Pacific horizon. . . where land and sea are woven into a tapestry of such gentle majesty, with space and light so exquisite, it will take your breath away.
This is the world that has inspired resident artist Thomas Lauterbach to paint strong images of the land, the sea and the Maori people.
We offer our guests a warm and imaginative home and the company of people who are in harmony with their beautiful surroundings.
Comfortable bedrooms overlook the spectacular scene. . . enjoy a spacious private living room with open fire and works of art. . .
Verandahs lead to a wonderful garden where formal vistas combine with lush wilderness, rosebud and flaxbush, cabbage tree and cypress, bananas, palms, tuis. . .
Follow the path to the beach and roam the seashore or venture further with a kayak or sailing trip. Journey amongst the islands on a local boat - bring home your fish for the BBQ. Or shall we smoke it or bake it in banana leaves. . .
We love to cook. Superb gourmet meals with flavours from Italy to the South Pacific grace our table.
For a taste of heaven on earth - come along and let us spoil you a little.

Russell

Homestay
Address: "Treetops", 6 Pinetree Lane,
Te Wahapu Rd, Russell, Bay of Islands
Name: John & Vivienne Nathan
Telephone: (09) 403 7475 or (09) 402 7939
Beds: 1 King, 1 Double (2 bedrooms)
Bathroom: 1 Guests share
Tariff: B&B (full) Double $70, Single $45, Dinner $25(incl. wine), Credit cards.

Our home is situated at the end of Te Wahapu Peninsula, 2.5km from the Main Russell-Opua Road. We are surrounded by native bush, and Tuis and Fantails are our constant companions. Kiwis are often heard during the night.
Both upstairs bedrooms have beautiful sea views from your bed; one room has colour TV. The guest bathroom is also upstairs. Guests are welcome to sit in the spa pool and watch the sun set over Paihia across the bay.
A track through the bush leads down to the beach where you are welcome to use our dinghy for fishing or a pleasant row out to Torretorre Island for a picnic. Guest barbecue available.
Historic Russell is a mere ten minute drive and offers a unique charm.
Cooked or continental breakfasts are available and you are welcome to join us for dinner. Please phone in advance. Major credit cards accepted.

Russell

Homestay
Address: Titore Way (last house on right), Russell.
P O Box 148, Russell
Name: Michael and Robin Watson
Telephone: (09) 403 7458
Beds: 1 Double, 2 Single (2 bedrooms)
Bathrooms: 1 Guest share separate bathroom & toilet
Tariff: B&B (full) Double $90, Single $60.
Credit Cards: Visa & M/C.

Modern natural timber house with every comfort, magnificent bush and sea views, large sunny decks for outside lounging, eating and watching the passing parade of yachts and small craft, not to mention the occasional cruise liner..
Bush walks to the village (10 mins), adjacent "Flagstaff", and a private beach, begin at our property.
We are keen cruising yachties with our own 40 foot yacht. The use of a tennis court is available. Historic Russell has many tourist attractions as well as daily sea trips, fishing, diving, swimming with dolphins etc. available.
Predominantly bed and breakfast, dinner is supplied only by arrangement. There are excellent local restaurants open nightly to suit all tastes.

Russell
Homestay/Self-contained Accommodation
Address: "Inn-The-Pink" B&B,
1 Oneroa Road, Russell
Name: Mary and Kent MacLachlan
Telephone & Fax: (09) 403 7347
Beds: 1 Double, 4 Single (3 bedrooms)
Bathroom: 1 Ensuite, 1 Guests share
Tariff: B&B (special) Double B&B $80,
Double S.C unit $90, Single $60. Children welcome.
Nearest Town: Russell

Ten years ago we discovered Paradise! We fell in love with the Bay of Islands and found the most idyllic property in Russell.
Our house sits nestled on a hill, just minutes away from the waterfront and downtown Russell. Elevated over our lovely gardens, the self contained unit has its own bathroom, TV, fridge, mini kitchen and fold out double settee. Enjoy spectacular views over Russell from your own private deck. Our home also has two comfortable twin bedrooms with a shared bathroom.
Breakfasts are our specialities! Enjoy fresh orange juice, percolated coffee, our own homemade bread, muesli, yogurt and jams. We will even try to catch some fresh fish for you.
We've sailed, fished, explored and enjoyed the beautiful Bay of Islands and now we want to share it all with you!
Please phone ahead mornings or evenings as we are often out sailing or fishing in our boat. We are a non smoking household.

Te Wahapu Beach, Russell
Homestay or
Self-contained Accommodation
Address: C/- PO Box 73,
"Serendipity", Te Wahapu Beach, Russell
Name: John and Glen McGaughey
Telephone: (09) 403 7462
Beds: 1 Double, 2 Single (2 bedrooms) **Bathroom:** 1 Guests share
Tariff: B&B (continental or full) Double $80, Single $50, Dinner $20 per person, Children welcome only if both rooms are booked by one group.
Nearest Town: Russell 10 mins

We are proud of our Cape Cod style home on historic Te Wahapu beach, site of the first Army camp in NZ, the 58th Regiment (covered in beautiful native bush now). One of only 6 houses on the beach, we are half way between the ferry and Russell which is 10 minutes drive. Our two large bed sitters (which are easily converted into a luxurious flat for up to 5 people) have comfortable chairs, TV, and dining areas overlooking the sea. Being 90ft from the water makes fishing easy (fishing and sailing dinghies available).
Wake to lapping water and bird calls. Catch your own breakfast or dinner. We'll cook it; - or "do it yourself" in our guests' fully equipped kitchen. Breakfast in your own time.
Shellfish are abundant at our door. We have barbecue facilities, so, dine 'Alfresco' if desired. We're happy to organise you into the many wonderful tours available. Your comfort - privacy and enjoyment - is our satisfaction. Welcome to 'Serendipity'

John and Glen

Matauwhi Bay, Russell
Guest House
Address: 'Ounuwhao' Matauwhi Bay, Russell
Name: Allan & Marilyn Nicklin
Telephone: (09) 403 7310
Beds: 3 Queen, 2 Single (4 bedrooms, 3 with wash-stands in rooms)
Bathroom: 1 Ensuite, 1 Guests share (ie. 2 showers, 2 sep. toilets)
Tariff: B&B (special) Double $75, $90 with ensuite, Single $45, Children half price (if sharing with adults)
Nearest Town: Russell Village

'Ounuwhao' was built in 1894-1903 in Tangawahine, Dargaville. We shifted our homestead to Russell in 1991 and have spent some years in restoration. We are adjacent to picturesque Matauwhi Bay, where many yachts are moored, and alongside a large grassed reserve bounded by century-old Norfolk Pine trees. We are a stone's throw from the water's edge.

Our home has been restored, with B&B guests and visitors to our Devonshire tea gardens our first priority. Each room has its own character, with hand-made patchwork quilts, brass beds, old-fashioned wash-stand with hot and cold water, and fresh flowers to greet you on arrival.

The gardens and ballroom are a feature for visitors, with guests enjoying their own lounge with open-fire, tea and coffee making facilities.

We feature home-baked goodies for breakfast, served in our dining room, in your room, on the verandah or in the conservatory. There are several good restaurants in the village for dinner.

We know you will love Ounuwhao's 'old-worlde' charm and friendly hospitality. We look forward to sharing our home with you. Please write or telephone ahead. Ounuwhao is open for B&B guests from the August school holidays to the May school holidays inclusive. We are closed June and July. Our home is smokefree.

Some hosts are away from home during the day.

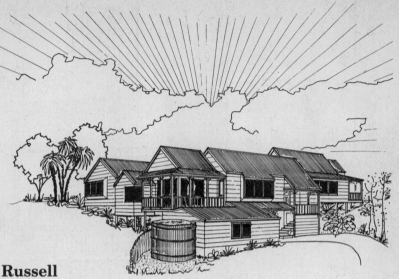

Russell

Homestay
Address: Top of Wellington Street, Russell
Name: Brampton House, Beverley and Raymond Whitehead
Telephone: (09) 403 7521 **Mobile:** 025 735 926
Beds: 1 Double, 3 Single (2 suites)
Bathrooms: 2 Ensuite
Tariff: B&B (special) Double $90 - $110, Single $70, Dinner by arrangement.
Credit cards: Visa, M/C.

Welcome to 'Brampton House'
Set in spacious grounds with private walkways, bounded by the Flagstaff Reserve and overlooking historic Russell with extensive sea views.
We offer our Luxury Guest Suites to visitors who seek the ultimate in comfort, quality and hospitality. Suite 1. (double bedroom, lounge, dining, sleeps 3). Suite 2. (large twin bedroom), each with Ensuite, toilet, private patio, T.V. Fridge, coffee & tea. Our wine is complimentary and room service provided on request.
Historic Russell and the Bay of Islands with its unique charm unfolds below and around you.
If your wish is to dine out, go sightseeing, shopping, sailing, fishing, diving, tramping, enjoy a sea cruise or simply relax in the peace and quiet of Brampton House the choice is yours.
At Brampton House we produce NZ style country wines and our cellar is now acclaimed by visitors from NZ and abroad. Guests are welcome to visit and sample.
We regret that our accommodation is unsuitable for young children and is smoke free.
Transport is provided to and from the Russell Wharf for arrivals and departures etc.

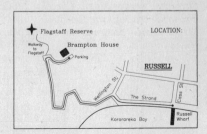

Russell
Homestay
Address: Brown Lodge, Ashby Street, Russell
Name: Roly & Joan Brown
Telephone: (09) 403 7693 **Fax:** (09) 403 7340
Beds: 1 Double (1 Bedroom) **Bathroom:** 1 Private
Tariff: B&B (full) Double $90, Single $90
Nearest Town: Russell

Unique position in Central Russell with beautiful sea views. Personal and friendly attention in one of the interesting new homes built in keeping with the historic nature of Russell. NZ timbers and old world charm of yesterday combine pleasing harmony with your hosts conscious of good living environment. We have airconditioning and heating for year round comfort. Smoke free home.
Deep sea and light tackle fishing, Island Cruising, Sailing or Diving can be arranged. Also Historic Places, Beaches, Bush walks, Restaurants and Ferry to Paihia and Waitangi are handy.
Our interests are Music, Porcelain dolls, Antiques and making of Kauri furniture. Fridge & tea making facility.
Directions - *please phone on arrival in Russell.*

One of the differences between staying at a hotel and a B&B
is that you don't hug the hotel staff when you leave.

Russell

Homestay
Address: Pomare Rd Russell
Name: Lesley Coleman
Telephone: (09) 403 7099
Beds: 1 Double, 1 Single (1 Bedroom)
Bathroom: 1 Private
Tariff: B&B (Special) Double $70, Single $45, Children half price, Dinner $20.
Vouchers accepted
Nearest Town: Russell

My home is in a cul-de-sac and the design inspired by Greece where I once lived. There are courtyards and a conservatory where you can breakfast or the deck looking out to Matauwhi Bay and Russell Boat Club. Start your day with fresh waffles with maple syrup fruit or a full traditional English breakfast. I'm a qualified chef who loves cooking for people in my own home.
My two children are students at Russell School - the oldest in NZ. They are comfortable mixing with people of different cultures.
The guest room is large with its own entrance and large bathroom featuring an antique bath set in a sun window.
Our combined interests include horses, music, gardening, travelling, art (I did the sketch) and our cat Mudge and dog Lily.
It's a ten minute amble to Russell central for kayaking, swimming, fishing, biking and hiking or just sitting round cafes.
Please phone.

Russell

Homestay
Address: "Hillcrest", Prospect St, Russell
Name: John & Eleanor Gibb
Telephone: (09) 4037 325 **Fax:** 4037 472
Beds: 1 Queen (1 Bedroom) **Bathroom:** 1 Private
Tariff: B&B (full) Double $90, Single $70

You will be 'halfway to heaven' when you come up the steep drive to our new home overlooking Russell and the bay. Our private guest wing enjoys spectacular views and is attractively appointed with comfort in mind. Your personal bathroom has a shower/spa bath, and a mini-kitchen is fully equipped with refrigerator and tea/coffee making facilities. Lounge chairs and a sunny deck invite relaxation and there is a private entrance with parking at the door.
Your hosts are lovers of good music, food and wine, and are busy developing a large garden. We have a sociable Siamese cat. We have a good knowledge of the many attractions Russell and the Bay of Islands has to offer. We'll look after you.

Russell

Historic Coastal Homestead

Address: Aucks Road, RD 1, Russell
Name: Orongo Homestead
Telephone: (09) 403 7527 **Fax:** (09) 403 7527
Beds: 3 double in 3 bedrooms (one dble converts to twin), 2 double in studio suite.
Bathroom: 2 Ensuite, 1 Private. 1 in self-contained studio.
Tariff: B&B ("champagne", a la carte, served til 1pm) - Oyster Bay Room (private facilities) $126 pp, Tui Room (ensuite) $136 pp, Consul's Suite (double ensuite, dressing room) $150 pp. Lakeside Retreat (ensuite, with facilities suitable for disabled) $300 dbl; additional persons $95 (children over 12 welcome, max occupancy 4). Candle-lit fine dining by prior arrangement $85 pp including premium NZ wine.
Credit cards accepted.
Nearest Town: Russell 5km

Known last century as "The First American Consulate", (Russell was the capital of New Zealand) our homestead, in 17 park-like acres opposite oyster beds, was built in 1860. It has been completely restored in consultation with the Historic Places Trust. The Consul's Suite and Oyster Bay room look across the Bay of Islands to Waitangi, New Zealand's most historic place, where Maori and the first Europeans made their treaty to share Aotearoa (New Zealand).

Other rooms have views across our natural spring-fed swimming lake and orchard to native bush, where easy walking tracks invite you into a private world of nature. The Retreat is a private studio with its own lake balcony, adjacent to our Finnish dry sauna and plunge pool.

Your hosts are Christopher Wharehinga Swannell, born of British and indigenous Maori races and Michael Hooper - the travel, food and wine writer and broadcaster. We look forward to sharing our quiet, pampering haven with its native kauri ceilings, large open fire, organically-grown herbs, cuisine featuring game and seafood and fine New Zealand wine. Massage available, with personal herbal skin creams prepared on request.

150 unspoilt islands invite your yachting and boating pleasure, with world-record game fishing, diving and watersports in a sub-tropical, unspoilt environment. Our homestead is smoke-free.

All rooms have robes, fluffy towels, hair-dryers, bed warmers and herbal niceties. Picnic hampers by prior arrangement (additional). Complimentary transfers to Kerikeri airport.

Russell - Okiato

Homestay+Self Contained Accommodation
Address: Aimeo Cottage, Okiato Point Road
RD 1 Russell
Name: Annie & Helmuth Hörmann
Telephone: (09) 4037 494
Beds: 2 Double, 1 Single (2 Bedrooms)
Bathroom: 2 Private
Tariff: B&B (special) Double $65, Single $57.50,
Children $15, Dinner $18, Vouchers accepted
Nearest Town: 9km eastw. to Russell

Aimeo Cottage " a quiet place to relax"
Your hosts Annie and Helmuth Hörmann sailed half way around the world to find this beautiful quiet place in the heart of the Bay of Islands. We would be happy to share this with you for a while.
We can communicate in English, French, German and some Spanish.
Aimeo Cottage is built on the hill of Okiato Point, a secluded peninsula overlooking the Bay. Only a stone throw from the site of the country's first Government House and just across the Bay, where the British and the Maori leaders signed the historic Treaty of Waitangi in 1840.
Your accommodation is a comfortable, private self-contained studio. We serve continental or cooked breakfast in our spacious living room or on your own porch. Dinner is available on request. Rates are very moderate.
In 10 minutes you are in New Zealand's first capital, Russell, the site of many historic buildings, and interesting museum and ait galleries.
There are bushwalks right from the door; we provide advice for sightseeing or local tours and you can use our bicycles for free.Golf course, tennis courts, bowling greens and beaches are close by.

Russell

Homestay
Address: 3 Russell Heights Rd Russell Bay of Islands
Name: Eldon & Gill Jackson
Telephone: (09) 403 7109
Beds: 1 Double (1 Bedroom) **Bathroom:** 1 Private
Tariff: B&B (full) Double $70, Single $60, No pets
Nearest Town: Russell

Our new home enjoys magnificent views over Russell toward Paihia and Waitangi, and is a 3 minute walk to glorious Long Beach.
We enjoy sharing our home, and garden, with guests and giving them a taste of the peace and tranquillity found here in Russell.
We are keen yachties and gardeners and our home has two resident felines (they are excluded from the guests' bedroom).
We provide complimentary tea and coffee anytime.
Enjoy the sounds of moreporks and hedgehogs at night and awake to the sound of tuis and fantails playing in the flame tree.
Friendly hospitality awaits you.
Directions: *Russell Heights Road is off Oneroa Road and our name is on the letterbox.*

Russell
Self-contained Accommodation
Address: PO Box 163 Te Wahapu Rd Russell
Name: Heino & Brigitte Sass
Telephone: (09) 403 7757
Beds: 1 Double plus 1 Bedsettee (1 Bedroom) **Bathroom:** 1 Ensuite
Tariff: B&B (continental) Double $75, Single $47.50, Vouchers accepted.

We welcome you to our new spacious one room cottage with kitchen facilities, comfortable and very cosy, in tranquil native bush setting with bay views and water access, near our home; Dinghy and fishing gear available; On private drive 200m off road. A snug hideaway - yet only 10 minutes away from the charming village Russell, which offers several good restaurants and shops. We share our 1 acre property with our friendly dog, cat and a bunch of chooks. Awake with the birds song and early sunrise and enjoy our own honey and free range eggs. Non smokers preferred. Please phone in advance.

Pakaraka, Bay of Islands
Farmstay
Address: "Highland Farm",
Pakaraka State Highway One,
R.D. 2, Kaikohe
Name: Bay of Islands Farmstay:
Ken & Glenis Mackintosh
Telephone & Fax: (09) 404 1040
Beds: 1 Double, 3 Single (2 bedrooms)
Bathrooms: 2 Ensuite
Tariff: B&B (special) Double $70, Single $40, Children half price, Cot/Highchair no charge. Dinner: 3 course $28, including Dinner drinks, Credit cards: Visa/MC/BC, Vouchers accepted
Nearest Town: Kawakawa, Paihia, Kerikeri, Kaikohe (very central)

Beautiful 51 acre property with historic stone walls, sheep, cattle, pigs.
Ken trains pups and dogs morning and evenings. You may enjoy watching and help shift the sheep and cattle, try your hand at shearing. Take farm walks and view the historic Pouerua Mountain, sit on or photograph with "Mr. Angus" our lovable pet steer. Our cats are named "Monkey" and "Governor Grey" you will understand why when you meet them.
Summertime: Swim in pool. A cosy home in winter. TV, video, pooltable, hairdrier. We book tours and horse rides. Skin-care beauty treatments by appointment. Inhome shopping: Environmentally safe products.
Only 15 minutes drive to Paihia, Kerikeri, Kaikohe. Golf, bowls, beaches, shopping, tours, Ngapha Springs, Kawakawa Vintage Train Rides. A good base, very central. only 1 hour to Whangarei or Kaitaia. Book early or take pot luck! Visa, Mastercard, Bankcard.
On SH 1., (10 minutes north Kawakawa) 1km south (Pakaraka Junction).
Welcome to the Bay of Islands! Enjoy your holiday. Be our guests!

Guests share means you may be sharing the bathroom
with other guests, especially at peak season.

Pakaraka, Bay of Islands

Homestay
Address: State Highway One Pakaraka,
RD 2 Kaikohe Bay of Islands
Name: Hugh & Roslyn Blomfield
Telephone: (09) 405 9815
Beds: 3 Single (2 Bedrooms/1 Twin, 1 Single)
Bathroom: 1 Guests share
Tariff: B&B (continental) Double $75, Single $40, Vouchers accepted
Nearest Town: Kerikeri 19km, Kaikohe 17km

We invite you to visit us at our 16 acre country retreat in the heart of the Bay of Islands. Twenty minutes to Kerikeri, Paihia, Kauri forest, three golf courses, thermal springs. 'Equestrian Centre' next door.
Pakaraka was established by early Christian Missionaries and is a delightful rural area characterised by drystone walls, old homesteads and picturesque Trinity Church.
Our large modern home features natural wood interior with indoor/outdoor living. It is set in spacious lawns with swimming pool and tennis court (racquets and balls available).
We cater for a maximum of three guests and have a separate guest lounge for privacy, but you're welcome to join us in the family room.
Our resident family comprises teenage son, cat, dog and our adorable native Kunekune pig.
Hugh is a part time tourist launch skipper and Roslyn a relief teacher. As well we have a native timber woodturning business and in spring we raise new born calves which join our sheep and pigs.
Despite our busy lifestyle we can usually find time to play tennis with our guests.

Rawene

Homestay
Address: "Hokingamai", P.O. Box 105, Gundry Street, Rawene
Name: David and Gillian McGrath
Telephone: (09) 405 7782
Beds: 1 Double, 2 Single (2 bedrooms) **Bathroom**: 1 Guests share
Tariff: B&B (continental) Double $55, Single $35, Children $20, Dinner $15, Vouchers accepted
Nearest Town: Kaikohe 35 mins

Rawene is NZ's third oldest settlement, and "Hokingamai" is situated on the shores of the Hokianga Harbour.
Enjoy the sunsets, peace and tranquillity.
There is only 5 mins walk to village, local pub, ferry, restaurant, library etc.
Your hosts have lived and travelled extensively in the South Pacific and Europe, and enjoy meeting people, being of service, and sharing the history of the Hokianga. Our home is sunny, warm and comfortable and it is our pleasure to make your stay enjoyable and memorable.
Laundry facilities available.
We are 1 hour from Bay of Islands and 3/4 hour from Waipoua forest.
Turn left at the Fire Station (Rawene) into Gundry Street (B & B sign on corner) drive down to waters edge.
Afternoon tea and supper included.
We have a friendly Labrador cross called Jenny.

Rawene

Homestay
Address: "Searell's" Nimmo Street, Rawene
(Postal: PO Box 100, Rawene 0452)
Name: Wally & Nellie Searell
Telephone: (09) 405 7835
Beds: 1 Double (1 Bedroom) **Bathroom:** 1 Private
Tariff: B&B (full) Double $60, Single $35, Dinner on request $20.
Vouchers accepted.
Nearest Town: Kaikohe 43 km east on Highway 12

We are retired couple who enjoy sharing our comfortable home and magnificent panoramic views of Hokianga Harbour and surrounding hills with all who visit. The sunsets are breathtaking. Our 10yr old dog is friendly and obedient.
Our 1 acre garden includes many native trees and tropical fruit trees. Fresh fruit can be picked almost every day.
Wally is an ex-navalman and active member of R.S.A. Our interests are many including gardening, wine making, photography and exploring New Zealand.
Rawene is on Highway 12, where the vehicular ferry crosses Hokianga Harbour then it's approx 1 hour to Kaitaia - Waipoua Kauri Forest is 3/4 hour south and Bay of Islands 1 hour east. Service station, hotel, restaurants, shops, boat hire, ferry and historic Clendon House only 1km.
Turn off main road, motor camp sign over hill veer left. At Nimmo St. turn left to top of hill, flat easy parking area, house on right, easy access.

Omapere

Bed & Breakfast
Address: Signal Station Road
Omapere Hokianga
Name: Alexa & Owen Whaley
Telephone: (09) 405 8641
Beds: 1 Double, 3 Single (2 Bedrooms)
Bathroom: Guests share W.C. with washbasin, 1 Family share
Tariff: B&B (full) Double $50, Single $25, Children 3-15 $12, Vouchers accepted
Nearest Town: 60km west of Kaikohe (SH 12), 20km north of Waipoua Forest

Our 6 year old home nestles into the hillside overlooking the historic Hokianga Harbour, its unique sandhills and bar-bound entrance, just a short drive up from Omapere village. So we have magnificent views all around which we feel everyone deserves to share.
We are recently retired with an adult family, enjoying our escape from city living, and busy planting trees, establishing gardens and keeping our 5 acres controlled with a handful of coloured sheep (for spinning) and milking-goats. Two friendly dogs and two cats keep us company.
We offer a restful stay for travellers - peaceful surroundings, comfortable sunny rooms with good beds, and fresh home-grown produce at breakfast. Restaurants are within easy walking distance, as are the ocean and harbour beaches and favourite look-out points; kauri forests, bushwalks, spectacular waterfalls a short drive away.
Directions: *Our name is on the gate and we are just 200m off SH 12, on the Waipoua Forest side of Omapere village.*

Waimamaku

Homestay
Address: Solitaire, SH12, Waimamaku, South Hokianga
Name: Betty and Lloyd White
Telephone: (09) 405-4891
Beds: 2 Double, 4 Single (4 bedrooms) **Bathroom:** 1 Guests share
Tariff: B&B (continental) Double $56.25, Single $35, Dinner by arrangement
$15 + GST, Children over 5 yrs, Campervans welcome. Vouchers accepted.
Nearest Town: Kaikohe 70 km

*Our home is a restored colonial style Kauri homestead situated in the Waimamaku
Valley, 6 km north of the Waipoua Kauri Forest, close to the Hokianga Harbour
and west coast beaches. We have an adult family all way from home and having
travelled ourselves we enjoy meeting people and sharing experiences while offering
a little piece of Kiwi hospitality.*
*Accommodation is two rooms with double beds and two rooms each with two single
beds. Guest showers (2) and toilets (2) facilities. We have 30 acres of farmland
bordered by two rivers which make a pleasant before or after dinner walk.*

Waipoua Forest

Self-contained Accommodation
Address: Waipoua Lodge, State Highway 12,
Waipoua, R.D. 6, Dargaville
Name: Raewyn & Tony Lancaster
Telephone: (09) 439-0422
Beds: 2 Double, 3 Single (1 room with double, and open plan with 1 double and
3 single) **Bathroom:** 1 Ensuite
Tariff: B&B (continental) Double $70, Single $70. All meals available in our fully
licensed restaurant, Credit cards accepted, Vouchers accepted May to October
inclusive
Nearest Town: 48km north of Dargaville on the edge of the Waipoua Forest

*Located on State Highway 12, half way between Dargaville and the beautiful
Hokianga Harbour, this lovely old homestead at the southern boundary of the
mighty Waipoua Forest has been tastefully converted into a licensed restaurant
and offers the ideal base for forest excursions. Your accommodation is a fully self
contained converted wool shed. You will have total privacy and enjoy views into
the heart of the Waipoua Forest. The master bedroom has a sheltered balcony
overlooking the landscaped grounds and our own native bush where guests can
stroll at their leisure.*
*A continental breakfast featuring home made bread is provided in your unit - a
cooked breakfast and all other meals are available in the restaurant.*
*Your hosts can help you enjoy all that the forest, nearby Kai Iwi Lakes and the
ocean beach have to offer, including fishing , night nature walks (with the chance
of seeing a kiwi), horse trekking, possum shooting or just relaxing.*
We look forward to your company.

Baylys Beach, Dargaville

Homestay+Self-contained Accommodation
Address: Baylys Beach Dargaville
Name: Ocean View Home Stay
Telephone: (09) 439 6256
Beds: 1 Double, 3 Single (2 Bedrooms) **Bathroom:** 1 Private, 1 Family share
Tariff: B&B (full) Double $60, Single $30, Dinner $15pp, Vouchers accepted May to October
Nearest Town: Dargaville

Jim and Ellie welcome you to share in their West Coast haven on the Kauri Coast at Baylys Beach.
Just 15 mins from Dargaville, it is ideally located to visit the picturesque unspoilt West Coast on your way to, or from the Waipoua Forest and the north.
Our home and detached unit is just 200m from the beach, with lovely sea views and sunsets from our living area and deck. The beach offers a host of activities fishing, gathering shellfish etc, Tua tua's are a well known delicacy from this region. The beaches are ideal for walking, horse rides can be arranged and there is a golf course nearby. You can choose your accommodation from either the detached unit with private bathroom or twin room with family share bathroom.
We provide a friendly comfortable non-smoking environment for you and outdoor smokers are welcome.
Please phone for directions.

Dargaville

Self-contained Accommodation
Address: Awakino Point Lodge, State Highway 14, Dargaville
Postal: P O Box 168, Dargaville
Name: June Birch
Telephone: (09) 439-7870
Beds: 2 Queen, 1 Double, 4 Single (3 suites) **Bathroom:** 3 Ensuite.
Guest Laundry available.
Tariff: B&B (special) Single $57, $15 each extra person per suite incl children, Credit cards accepted

This unique country lodge is situated in a peaceful rural setting on a five acre farmlet surrounded by attractive gardens, orchard and aviary.
It's just two minutes drive from the small township of Dargaville 1.5km along state highway 14.
The best features of the New Zealand Motel system and the Bed and Breakfast scheme have been amalgamated to create the best of both worlds. You will enjoy your own private self contained suite with private bathroom combined with friendly personal service and a good breakfast most of which is home produced.
Pottery, painting, gardening and making wine from various fruits are just a few of the hobbies persued, and after twelve years of hosting would say meeting people is yet another hobby.
There are plenty of good restaurants in Dargaville reasonably priced but should you wish to have dinner at the lodge please arrange in advance.
Credit cards will be accepted without question, but cash or travellers cheque would be much preferred.

Dargaville
Farmstay, Bed & Breakfast Inn
Address: "Kauri House Lodge",
Bowen Street, Dargaville
Name: June and Doug Blaxall
Telephone: (09) 439-8082
Beds: 1 King, 1 Double, 2 Single (3 bedrooms) **Bathroom:** 3 Ensuite
Tariff: B&B (continental) (full & special available extra) Double $125.00.

*Have you every wondered what it would be like to live in a stately home in the
country? Here is your chance! Kauri House was built early this century for a
millionaire and his large family. Only the best materials were used and we believe
the house represents a beautiful example of craftmanship of that era. All the rooms
are furnished in antiques with kauri (especially mottled kauri) being our special
interest.*
*We have been hosting for 20 years and enjoy sharing our home and lifestyle. Our
three guest rooms all have their own ensuites. We have a billiards room, library
and swimming pool. Also a 'run-off' for those with time to explore it. It's 100 acres
with 35 acres of native bush. Kauri House sits sedately on 8 acres of gardens and
trees overlooking the township of Dargaville, which is close to the Ocean Beach
that's 100 km long. Also Kai-iwi lakes, our summer playground and enroute to the
Far North via Waipoura Forest that personifies NZ
before man changed it.*
Booking is absolutely essential.

Always telephone ahead to enquire about a B&B. It is a nuisance for you if
you simply arrive to find someone already staying there.
And besides hosts need a little time to prepare.

Pakotai, Whangarei
Farmstay
Address: Mangakahia Road,
R.D. 2, Whangarei
Name: Joan & Bruce Alexander
Telephone: (09) 433 1784
Beds: 2 Single (1 bedroom)
Bathroom: 1 Guests share
Tariff: B&B (continental or full)
Double $55, Single $30, Dinner $20, Vouchers accepted
Nearest Town: Whangarei

We are midway between Whangarei and Kaikohe farming 600 acres and running dairy cows, sheep and cattle. Guests are welcome to observe or participate in seasonal farming activities.
Bruce is a keen hunter and outdoor sportsman when not actively farming or involved with establishing forestry.
We live in a spacious 40 year old homestead set in parklike gardens and offer comfortable accommodation with shared amenities. Dinner will be wholesome and generous with a variety of game meals served if desired.
Joan is a keen gardener, spinner and weaver.
Dargaville, Kai Iwi Lakes, the famous Trounson and Waipoua Kauri Forests and Bay of Islands are within comfortable driving distance.
Directions: *We are 45km north west of Whangarei on the Mangakahia Rd at Pakotai. Please phone for detailed instructions and reservations.*

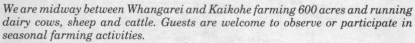

Whananaki North, Hikurangi
Homestay, Self-contained Accommodation
Address: Rockell's Rd, Whananaki, RD 1, Hikurangi
Name: Bev and Rex Scott
Telephone: (09) 433 8242
Beds: 2 Double, 4 Single (3 bedrooms)
Bathroom: 2 Private
Tariff: B&B (continental) Double $70, Single $40, Dinner $20. Vouchers accpeted.

We live on a delightful section of the scenic, sub-tropical Northland east coast and want to show it off.
We are 50km NE of Whangarei, 30km off State Highway 1. Easily accessible yet peaceful private and beautiful.
A sheltered bay is 100 metres from the front door of our new "Triboard" home, with many other beaches within easy reach, offering an excellent selection of recreational pleasures; swimming, snorkelling, surfing, fishing etc. There are scenic, bush and historic walks. Picnics and boat trips can be arranged. Dinghy available.
Guests have self-contained accommodation and meals can be shared with our family or served and eaten in the privacy of your own unit.
Our wish is that you make this your home away from home. Sample our library or play a game from our collection.
One flat is wheel-chair orientated and disabled guests are especially welcome. Please phone ahead so that we can endeavour to make your stay perfect.

Ngunguru, Whangarei

Homestay + Self-Contained Apartment
Address: "Riviera" 140A Ngunguru Road,
R.D. 3, Whangarei
Name: Jo La Krapes
Telephone & Fax: (09) 434 3916
Beds: 1 Double 4 Single (2 bedrooms) **Bathrooms:** 2 Private
Tariff: B&B (Full) Double $70-$80, Single $50, Dinner by arrangement, Not
suitable for children (Weekly rates available), Self catering if required. Credit
cards: Visa/MC, Vouchers accepted.
Nearest Town: Whangarei 25km on the Tutukaka Road

*Do as much or as little as you like in this quaint seaside resort of Ngunguru
situated 25 km / 15 miles from Whangarei. Take the Dinghy and gather
Cherrystone Clams and Pipi's (I will even make chowder for you) or just relax by
the water. Help yourself to tea and coffee. There is a 9 hole golf course and tennis
courts adjacent and an 18 hole golf course 20 minutes away. Ten minutes to
Tutukaka - deep sea anglers base and gateway to World renowned Poor Knights
Islands for Scuba diving.*
*Barbeque, refrigerator/freezer, ice and electric blankets available to guests.
Sourdough pancakes, speciality of the house. Guests are invited to join me for a
cocktail before dinner. Please make this your home away from home. Non smokers
preferred.*
Directions: *Take Tutukaka turn off at Whangarei. Advisable to phone or fax
first mornings or evenings - or leave a message on the answerphone as I may be
on the golf course.*

Ngunguru

Homestay
Address: "Glengarry" 45 Te Maika Road,
Ngunguru **Postal:** RD 3 Whangarei
Name: Bett & Noel Glengarry
Telephone: (09) 4343 646
Beds: 2 Single (1 Bedroom)
Bathroom: 1 Ensuite
Tariff: B&B (full) Double $55, Single $30, Vouchers accepted
Nearest Town: 25km east of Whangarei on Tutukaka Coast Road

*We invite you to visit with us in our cottage style home surrounded by half an acre
of tranquil gardens. Many birds visit our garden over the seasons and the fantails
love to tease our Siamese cat. You are welcome to enjoy our garden and use the
outdoor barbeque if you wish. We also keep hens which provide fresh farm eggs for
your breakfast which can be taken with us or served in your room.*
*There are several good restaurants on the coast or you can share a family meal with
us by prior arrangement.*
*We are keen Bridge players, always happy to spend an evening playing with fellow
enthusiasts.*
*Local attractions include fishing and scuba diving trips to the world renowned
Poor Knights Islands, big game fishing, beach walks, beautiful coastal drives and
a nine hole golf course.*
Directions: *From Whangarei follow Tutukaka Coast Road through Ngunguru
and turn right into Te Maika Road. Please phone ahead.*

57

Tutukaka

Homestay
Address: "Stormhaven" Oturu Bay Block Road
Tutukaka (c/- Ngunguru Post Office Northland)
Name: Jeannie & Gregor Casey
Telephone & Fax: (09) 434 3526
Beds: 2 Queen, 2 Single (2 Bedrooms) **Bathroom:** 1 Guests share
Tariff: B&B (full) Double $100, Single $50, Children half price, Dinner $25

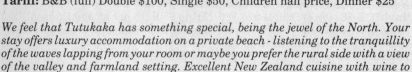

We feel that Tutukaka has something special, being the jewel of the North. Your stay offers luxury accommodation on a private beach - listening to the tranquillity of the waves lapping from your room or maybe you prefer the rural side with a view of the valley and farmland setting. Excellent New Zealand cuisine with wine to compliment.

Perfect peace with all the comforts, where you may choose to observe the comings and goings of all boating from the Tutukaka Harbour. Additionally a short walk around the beach will take you to the marina to observe the game fish being weighed in.

We can arrange charter boats to Poor Knights sightseeing, fishing, diving, whale watching (in season) and for the more adventurous the challenge of deep sea game fishing. Other recreation readily available are 9 hole golf course, tennis, swimming, kayaking and walks.

Your interests will be our interests. We will endeavour to make your stay an enjoyable experience as a home away from home right down to the family cat "Summer".

We prefer non-smokers.

"Stormhaven" is just 25 minutes from Whangarei on the Tutukaka Road, pass through Ngunguru township, wind up to first turn on right (approx 3km) into Block Rd, first entrance on left.

Tutukaka -Matapouri

Lodge - Located on Ocean
Address: 23km north-east of Whangarei
Name: The Lodge at Matapouri
Telephone: (09) 434 3543
Beds: 1 King, 1 Queen, 8 Single (6 Bedrooms) **Bathroom:** 2 Ensuite, 1 Guests share
Tariff: B&B (continental) Double/Single $130-175, Children welcome. Credit cards: Visa/MC/BC/Amex
Nearest Town: Tutukaka 2km south on Ngunguru Road

This luxurious newly remodelled lodge offers spectacular views from its coastal vantage point. Situated on 38 prime acres with picnicking and nature walks at your door. With the famous Poor Knights Islands in its front yard. You are in the heart of some of the most spectacular property in New Zealand. Scuba and snorkeling at the Poor Knights Islands was rated by the National Geographic Magazine as one of the top five locations in the world. Two kilometres south is the Tutukaka Yacht Club that offers deep sea fishing that is world renown.
Matapouri is just two kilometres north offering a beautiful horseshoe shaped sand beach. "Matapouri" means "A secret hiding place'.
We will be happy to be your home base and help you organize your activities. Such activities may include sailing, kayaking, horse back riding as well as many others. Swimming, snorkeling and fishing are available from the property. It is possible to see dolphin and whales from our spa on our viewing deck.
We believe you will have a memorable and relaxing stay.

Whangarei

Farmstay
Address: 59 Pukenui Road, Whangarei
Name: Patricia and Owen Flower
Telephone: (09) 438-8080
Beds: 1 Double, 2 Single (2 bedrooms)
Bathroom: Guests share
Tariff: B&B (continental, full) Double $60, Single $35, Children 1/2 price, Dinner $15. Vouchers accepted.

Our comfortable home is situated on a secluded twelve acre block with panoramic views of the town, countryside, native bush and coast. We have a variety of farm animals and our own orchard. We are five minutes by car from the town centre and within walking distance to such tourist attractions as the "Kiwi House" and Whangarei Heritage Museum and park. We are within a half hour drive to some of Northland's most beautiful beaches where you can enjoy swimming, fishing and surfing.
There are two guestrooms available and you have your own bathroom and toilet facilities. Cooked and continental breakfasts are available and you are welcome to join us for dinner.
Directions: *Transport can be provided to and from bus/plane at no charge.*

Whangarei

Homestay
Address: Tamaterau Bay,
Whangarei Heads Road, Whangarei
Name: Roy & Rae Atkin
Telephone: (09) 436 2265
Beds: 1 Double, 2 Single (2 bedrooms)
Bathroom: 1 Family share
Tariff: B&B (full) Double $50, Single $25, Children
5-12 yrs 1/2 price, Dinner $20. Vouchers accepted
Nearest Town: Whangarei

Your hosts now retired, originated from Somerset, England (1963). Family of 6 have all flown the nest. We try to create a friendly relaxed and comfortable atmosphere. We genuinely love meeting people having entertained visitors from England, America, Canada, Australia, South Africa, Germany, Switzerland, Israel and Japan over the last few years.
Our home is on the Northern side of Whangarei harbour, with the water at the bottom of our garden and lovely views from our deck. We are in a country area which includes bush-walks and a domain with tennis courts, changing sheds and a safe swimming beach. An 18 hole golf course is within walking distance from our house, again with wonderful views to be enjoyed while you play, and a friendly club to relax in after. A small boat is available for fishing and canoes for young ones. We prefer non-smokers.

Whangarei

Homestay
Address: 'The Rocks', 49 Ngahere
Drive Maunu, Whangarei
Name: Lynne and Alan
Telephone: (09) 438 5595
Beds: 1Queen, 2 Single, (2 bedrooms)
Bathroom: 1 Private, 1 Family share
Tariff: B&B (special) $50 per person, Children under 12yrs half price, Dinner $25, Credit cards accepted, Vouchers accepted

Enjoy the best of both worlds - sharing the comforts of a private home plus the pleasures of being a special guest. Our homestay offers warm and friendly hospitality in a quiet setting only minutes from town. We have a modern comfortable home set amongst exciting limestone outcrops. There are large decks offering great views or access to grotto like gardens. Here you can relax alongside the sights and sounds of the native wood pigeon, tuis and kingfishers. We live in an elevated attractive suburb with tree lined streets and beautiful gardens. We are close to an excellent golf course, museum, Heritage Park and Kiwi House. Join the 'Hole in the Rock Gang' namely Lynne, Alan and Blackie the cat and let us spoil you a little. It is our pleasure to make your stay easy and relaxed and if you are weary from your travels our spa set amongst rocks can sooth your tensions away. Breakfasts include all home made yoghurt, muesli, muffins, bread and jam. Fresh fruit and juice and a different treat each day. Beautiful three-course evening meals include local foods and wine.
1/2 hour to Tutukaka for superb deep-sea diving and game fishing.
3/4 hour to Bay of Islands.
Alan is a professional photographer with a residential studio. Our courtesy car will take you to airport or bus.Your privacy is respected.

Whangarei
Luxury Homestay
Address: Bukit Landing,
Manganese Point Road,
Manganese Point, Whangarei
(P.O. Box 351, Whangarei)
Name: Nelson & Jean Williams
Telephone: (09) 436 2304
Beds: 2 Double, 2 Single (3 bedrooms)
Bathroom: 2 Guests share
Tariff: B&B (full) Double $100, Single $50, Dinner $30, Schoolage children half price. Vouchers accepted from 1 May to 31 Aug only.

According to our many guests, Bukit Landing sums up all the best in a New Zealand vacation for those who wish to sidestep overcrowded resorts and cities. The waves lapping the doorstep, the lush green native bush, the peace and tranquillity are the Hallmarks of this beautiful coastal lodge which additionally provides the very best of New Zealand food and fine wine.

For recreation, fishing, swimming, golf, tennis and bush walks are all readily available. A four metre boat with sails or outboard motor is available for escorted fishing or just sightseeing.

The personal attention of your hosts Jean and Nelson will ensure you get exactly the vacation you wish.

Guests are accommodated in a choice of three pleasantly appointed bedrooms, each with a view and private facilities, on the upper storey of the lodge and have full use of the spacious lounge and deck.

For reservations and directions please phone.

Whangarei
Homestay
Address: Parakiore Road, R.D. 6, Whangarei
Name: Jack & Linda Lees
Telephone: (09) 4352610
Beds: 1 Double, 2 Single (2 bedrooms) **Bathroom:** 1 Guests share
Tariff: B&B (continental) Double $60, Single $40, Children $15, Dinner $15 each, Campervans $15, 2 people, Vouchers accepted
Nearest Town: Whangarei 2km from Kamo on north side of Whangarei

We live one kilometre north of Whangarei City boundary and one km off State Highway No 1. Our six acre property is in a rural setting bounding the Northland golf club. Two acres of native bush forms a backdrop to our large home and our two acre garden is a popular attraction for gardening clubs and interested people to visit. We grow most of the flowers Linda uses in her floristry work. I have been involved in horticulture all my life and now in retirement I have a small orchard and garden which supplies us with fresh fruit and vegetables most of the year. Having spent most of our lives in Northland, we can suggest places of interest to visit, which can be covered in an easy day trip from our central location. We enjoy entertaining and would like you to come and stay with us. Tea and coffee facilities are available at any time plus courtesy car if required.

Whangarei
Homestay Farmlet
Address: Horseshoe Bay,
Matapouri, RD 3, Whangarei
Name: Anne and Bill Ringer
Telephone: (09) 434 3678
Beds: 2 Single (1 bedroom)
Bathroom: 1 Ensuite

HORSESHOE BAY

Tariff: B&B (full) Double $60, Single $35, Dinner $20, Vouchers accepted.
Nearest Town: Whangarei

Our home overlooks the sea in our private bay and beach. Adjacent is a 35 acre reserve of native bush.
We organically grow most of our fruit and vegetables and have free range hens, a cow and home killed meat. We also provide vegetarian dishes on request.
Guests who wish to learn something of New Zealands bird life, native trees, shells etc can be helped by our reference library and by us as we are keen environmentalists. Guests can swim and snorkel safely in our sheltered bay, fish from our dinghy, or gather more than 50 varieties of shells. Some of New Zealands loveliest coastline and beaches are here to enjoy.
We would like to make your stay comfortable and make you feel at home. Our camper van is sometimes for hire at reasonable rates. We can meet a plane or bus at Whangarei.
Directions: *Take the Ngunguru Tutukaka Matapouri Road. We are 35km from Whangarei and 200 metres before Matapouri. It could help if you phone.*

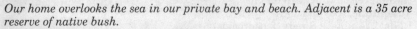

Whangarei
Farmstay+Self-contained
Accommodation
Address: Kaikohe Rd Maungatapere
Name: Ballater Lodge
Telephone: (09) 4346 514 or 4382 135
Fax: (09) 4300 278

Beds: Lodge: 1 King + Futon sofa (1 Bedroom) **Bathroom:** 1 Ensuite House: 1 Double, 2 Single (3 Bedrooms) **Bathroom:** 1 Private
Tariff: B&B (continental) Dble $80-$90, Sgle $45-$80, Dinner $25. Vouchers accepted.
Nearest Town: Whangarei

FOR SOMETHING DIFFERENT: Join us in our modern home with a self-contained lodge set against a backdrop of native bush on an 18 acre Avocado property just 10 minutes (12km) west of Whangarei in the tranquil Maungatapere countryside. Enjoy our pool and tennis court in the summer. Spa and open fire in the winter. Golf course only 5 mins away. We invite you to stroll through the Avocados & native bush, relax in your private lounge with TV, CD player and a wide selection of books & music. The lodge has an excellent well equipped kitchen. The fridge and cupboards are stocked with food for guests to cater for themselves. Join us for dinner if you wish. We love to serve innovative, fresh New Zealand food and good New Zealand wines. Continental or cooked breakfast with fresh fruit, home made muesli, muffins and bread is included. Ballater Lodge has easy access to ... The Bay of Islands, Waipoua Forest, Tutukaka Deep Sea Fishing, Poor Knights Diving and the beaches of historic, scenic Northland. Whangarei offers golf, horseriding, fishing, sailing, craft galleries, museums, bush and coastal walks.Non Smoking **Directions:** *Please phone.*

Taiharuru, Whangarei Heads
Farmstay, Self-contained cottage
Address: Taiharuru Road, RD 1, Onerahi, Northland
Name: Bob and Sue Stevenson
Telephone and Fax: (09) 436 5618
Mobile: 025 943 739
Beds: 2-4 Double, 2 Single (2 bedrooms + Lounge)
Bathroom: 2 Ensuite
Tariff: B&B (full) Single $65, Dinner $25, Lunch $15. Campervans $30
Nearest Town: Whangarei 27km (Onerahi 20km)

Guests have a new and completely self contained cottage next to our house. The views over the Pacific Ocean are incredibly beautiful.
"Harambee" is a coastal farm with 151 hectares of rolling grassland and native bush. We run mostly beef cows and calves with some sheep and goats.
Our private beach with its crystal clear water and rocky headlands is ideal for all sea activities.
Tariff includes: use of our private tennis court, loan of racquets, use of table tennis and pool table. Use of outside spa pool. Loan of dinghy, goggling gear and fishing rods. Guided walks, 4 wheel drive rides round farm hills. Three horses for experienced riders. Rabbit, possum or goat shooting. Golf, diving and deep sea fishing can be arranged.
Bob has been in business, Sue a midwife. We both play bridge.
2 small dogs and 1 cat.
Please phone at least the day before for reservations and instructions. Own transport recommended. Private airstrip. Self-catering option available.

The standard of accommodation in *The New Zealand Bed and Breakfast Book*
ranges from homely to luxurious,
but you can always be sure of superior hospitality.

Whangarei Heads
Homestay/Self Contained Accommodation
Address: Manaia Gardens,
R.D. 4, Whangarei
Name: Audrey & Colin Arnold
Telephone: (09) 434-0797
Beds: 1 Double, 2 Single (2 bedrooms) **Bathroom:** 2 Private
Self-contained cabin: 1 Double, 1 Single (1 bedroom)
Tariff: B&B (special) Double $45, Single $25, Children 5-12 yrs $12, Dinner by arrangement, Cabin; Double $35, extra person $5, Credit cards accepted, Vouchers accepted
Nearest Town: Whangarei

We live beside the sea among old pohutukawa trees in a bush setting. We have a small farm and a large garden, cattle, free range hens, a cat and a sheep. Several beautiful walks, deep sea or harbour fishing, safe swimming, old roses, and artist's gallery are all nearby. Golf 20 minutes.
We know how important a friendly welcome and comfortable beds are to travellers. We offer bed and breakfast and a self-contained cabin.
Bed and Breakfast: Pohutukawa is a two room cabin with one double bed and two single beds, bathroom, TV, radio, tea making facilities. Breakfast features homemade bread, fresh fruit, and our own eggs.
Self-contained cabin: Rata is a quaint old Kiwi bach with one double bedroom and a single bed in the living room, bathroom, sink, gas cooker, fridge, TV, linen supplied. Both cabins have sea views and are in our garden. You can be as private or as sociable as you wish. Laundry and barbecue available.
Directions: *Take the Whangarei Heads Road. We are 31 kms from the Whangarei Yacht Basin bridge and 1.7 km past Taurikura store. Ours are the only buildings in the bay. Look for the rock wall in front.*

Whangarei South
Farmstay
Address: Hewlett Rd, RD 1 Whangarei
Name: Jill and John Hewlett
Telephone: (09) 432 2817
Beds: 1 Double, 2 Single (2 bedrooms)
Bathroom: 1 Private
Tariff: B&B (full) Double $70, Single $40, Dinner $25, Vouchers accepted

Our 600 acre coastal sheep and cattle farm is 20 minutes south of Whangarei. The farm is almost completely surrounded by a marine wildlife habitat which is home to thousands of migratory wading birds.
We offer comfortable farm house accommodation and guests have a choice of two bedrooms with a private bathroom. Both bedrooms lead on to a deck with extensive and spectacular views of the farm, sea and at night the twinkling lights of Whangarei city on the far shore.
You may wish to explore the three miles of coastline, go fishing, watch a sheep being shorn, wander the park like surrounds of the 5th generation family farm with its interesting limestone rock formations, or just sit and delight in the wide open, unpopulated space.
We enjoy entertaining people with good food, wine and conversation.
This is an ideal half way stop between Auckland and the Bay of Islands.
Directions: *Please phone for reservations and directions.*

Ruakaka
Farmstay/Self-contained Accommodation
Address: Doctor's Hill Road, Ruakaka.
Postal: Dr's Hill Rd., RD 2 Waipu
Name: Vince & Joyce Roberts
Telephone: (09) 432 7842 **Mobile:** 025 981 065
Beds: 1 Double, 1 Single (1 bedroom) **Bathroom:** 1 Private
Tariff: B&B (full) Double $60, Single $35, Dinner $15, Children $10. Credit cards. Vouchers accepted.
Nearest town: 2 ks Sth Ruakaka, apprx 35kms Sth Whangarei

Magnificent views, peace and quiet greet you at our home.
Your accommodation is a bedsitter with its own bathroom, kitchenette and fridge, a ranchslider leads onto deck with views of the entrance to Bream Bay, Mt Mania and surrounding Islands.
Free bush and scenic drive over our 150 acre dry stock farm can be arranged. Our wetland area is home to the rare brown bitten. Beautiful beaches, squash courts, golf course, racetrack where Vince trains our racehorses and good restaurants are a short drive from our home.
Reserve time to see the FREE refinery Video and model at Marsden Pt, Claphams Clock in Whangarei and the Matakohe Kauri Museum an hours drive west.
As Ex dairy farmers with a grown family of four children, we have enjoyed doing B&B for the past four years, other interests include gardening and travel.
As we spend a lot of time outdoors, we suggest you phone in the evening for bookings, however passing callers are welcome.

Waipu Cove
Farmstay + Self-Contained Accommodation
Address: Cove Road, Waipu Cove
Name: Andre and Robin La Bonte
Telephone & Fax: (09) 432 0645
Beds: 3 Double, 2 Single (3 bedrooms) **Bathroom:** 2 Private
Tariff: B&B (special) Double $65, Single $35, Dinner $15, Children under 12 yrs half price, Vouchers accepted
Nearest Town: 10 km south of Waipu on Cove Rd, 50 km south of Whangarei via SH 1

My wife and I are Americans who became residents of New Zealand in 1985. We built a modern home with separate guest accommodation on a 36 acre coastal "lifestyle" farmlet by the edge of the sea.
Sleep to the sound of the ocean in either the separate efficiency apartment with private kitchen and bathroom facilities, queen-size sleeper and queen-size bed or in the guest bedrooms, with double or two single beds and private bathroom. No smoking please.
We have expansive views of the Pacific Ocean and offshore islands. Fish or explore our 850 ft of shoreline with its limestone rock formations and tidepools or just sit and relax under the mature pohutukawa trees that grace the shoreline. A ten minute walk along the shore takes you to the beautiful white sand beach of Waipu Cove, a ten minute walk inland takes you into native bush, streams and a swimming hole fed by a small waterfall.
We have cattle grazing the pasture, dozens of water fowl on our 2.5 acre pond, marine fish in our salt water aquariums, wild birds that enjoy being hand fed, and two flea free cats. Glow worm caves, deep-sea fishing, scuba diving and golf are all available locally.
Directions: *Please phone. Bookings recommended.*

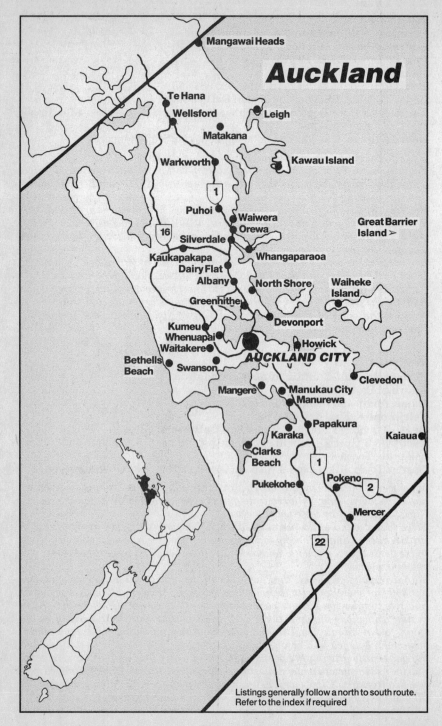

Auckland

Mangawai Heads

Te Hana
Wellsford
Leigh
Matakana
Warkworth
Kawau Island

Puhoi
Waiwera
Orewa
Great Barrier
Island ➢

Silverdale
Whangaparaoa
Kaukapakapa
Dairy Flat
Albany
North Shore
Waiheke
Island
Greenhithe
Devonport
Kumeu
Whenuapai
Howick
Waitakere
AUCKLAND CITY
Bethells
Beach
Swanson
Clevedon
Mangere
Manukau City
Manurewa
Papakura
Kaiaua
Karaka
Clarks
Beach
Pokeno
Pukekohe
Mercer

Listings generally follow a north to south route.
Refer to the index if required

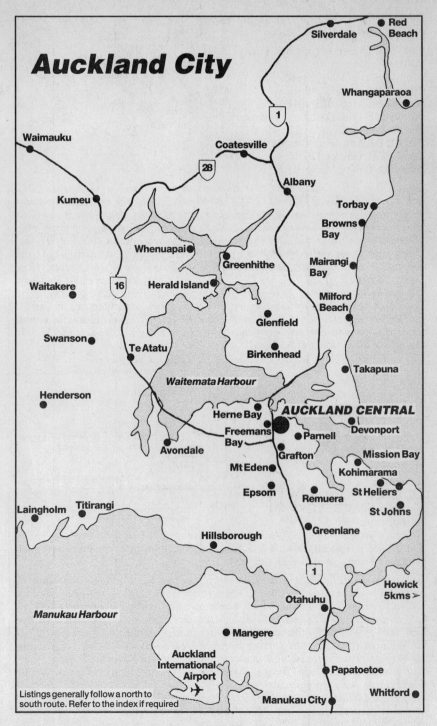

Auckland City

Silverdale

Red Beach

Whangaparaoa

1

Coatesville

28

Albany

Torbay

Browns Bay

Waimauku

Kumeu

Mairangi Bay

Whenuapai

Greenhithe

16

Herald Island

Milford Beach

Waitakere

Glenfield

Swanson

Te Atatu

Birkenhead

Waitemata Harbour

Takapuna

Henderson

Herne Bay

AUCKLAND CENTRAL

Devonport

Freemans Bay

Parnell

Avondale

Grafton

Mission Bay

Mt Eden

Kohimarama

Epsom

Remuera

St Heliers

Laingholm

Titirangi

St Johns

Hillsborough

Greenlane

1

Howick 5kms >

Manukau Harbour

Otahuhu

Mangere

Auckland International Airport ✈

Papatoetoe

Whitford

Manukau City

Listings generally follow a north to south route. Refer to the index if required

Mangawhai Heads
Self-contained Accommodation
Address: Moir Pt Rd,
Mangawhai RD 2, Kaiwaka
Name: Milestone Cottage
Telephone: (09) 431 4018
Beds: 2 Double, 1 Single (2 bedrooms)
Bathroom: 1 Ensuite, 1 Private
Tariff: B&B (special) Double $70-$95,
Single $50, Dinner $10-20
Nearest Town: Mangawhai

Situated on a tranquil East Coast Harbour midway between Auckland (1 1/2 hours) and the Bay of Islands (1 1/2 hours) reach us by the new sealed coastal scenic route. A private sandy beach provides the Easterly Boundary of our bush clad 5 acre property. Kayaks are available for exploring the estuary, neighbouring sand dunes, wildlife sanctuary and extensive ocean beaches. An 18 hole golf links, shops, restaurant and takeaways are a 5 minutes walk away. Attractions in close proximity include Pakiri Beach horseriding, Waipu glow-worm caves, Goat Island Marine Park, Matakohes Historic Museum and Marsden Point Refinery. Elevated with private decks overlooking an interesting and exotic garden, our 2 units each have their own bathrooms, TVs and kitchens. Breakfast is a fresh fruit platter using a variety of local and imported fruit (including avocados and tamarillos from the trees outside), toast, cereal and juice. We also provide dinners the nights the restaurant is closed

---

Leigh
Homestay
Address: 10 Ferndale Avenue,
Leigh, North Auckland
Name: Joan & Ken Helliwell
Telephone: (09) 422-6099
Beds: 1 Double,4 Single (3 bedrooms) **Bathroom:** 1 Guests share
Tariff: B&B (special) Double $55, Single $35, Dinner $20, Vouchers accepted
Nearest Town: Warkworth (23 km)

Leigh is a seaside fishing village 70-80 minutes drive North of Auckland, situated on the cliffs above the Leigh Cove. It offers facilities for boating, including a ramp and anchorage within the small harbour. The village community has an interdenominational church, a hotel, general store, "take-away" food store, garage and dairy. Within 5 minutes car travel are sandy swimming beaches, excellent underwater diving, a good surfing beach, tidal flats as well as deep water and rocky shore coastline, coastal and country walks, and the Marine Reserve.
Our home is in the village. We are retired school teachers living in the family home with a large, well laid out garden.
We have travelled overseas extensively, enjoying other people's hospitality, and would be glad to offer a warm "Kiwi" welcome to our guests.

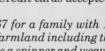

Te Hana, Wellsford
Historic Farmhouse
Address: "The Retreat", Te Hana, RD5, Wellsford
Name: Tony and Colleen Moore
Telephone: (09) 423-8547
Beds: 1 Double, 2 Single (2 bedrooms) **Bathroom:** 1 Guests share
Tariff: B&B (full) Double $55, Single $30 Dinner $20, Credit cards accepted

"The Retreat" is an historic kauri homestead built in 1867 for a family with 12 children. The house is set back from the road overlooking farmland including the eight acres where we graze black and white sheep. Colleen is a spinner and weaver and produces goods from the wool which are sold from the house.

Guests have a choice of twin or double bedrooms and use of their own bathroom.

Creating a garden to compliment the house is an ongoing source of enjoyment. It includes a large herb garden, croquet lawn and a walk through perennial borders to the summer-house.

We have travelled extensively overseas and in New Zealand and are keen to promote our scenic and historic places _ especially local ones.

Directions: *"The Retreat" is on the left 6km north of Wellsford on State Highway 1 and 13 km south of Kaiwaka. You will see the weaving sign by our entrance.*

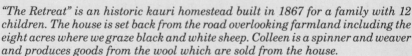

Continental breakfast consist of fruit, toast, tea/coffee,
Full breakfast is the same with a cooked course,
Special breakfast has something special.

Warkworth
Homestay/Self-contained Accommodation
Address: Homewood Cottage, 17 View Rd., Warkworth
Name: Ina & Trevor Shaw
Telephone: (09) 425 8667
Beds: 1 Double, 2 Single (2 bedrooms) **Bathroom:** 2 Ensuite
Tariff: B&B (continental) Double $55, Single $35, Dinner by arrangement.
Vouchers accepted Double room only.
Nearest Town: Warkworth - Auckland city 67km - SH1

*One hour from Auckland, one hour 20 minutes from the airport makes our home
a good starting off place for the North of NZ or a quiet place to pack before leaving
the country. Day trips abound from here.*
*Built for guests, our home has lovely views of Warkworth and the countryside.
Both double and downstairs twin rooms are cosy bedsitters. Each has an ensuite
shower and toilet, TV, guest entrance, tea making facilities, electric blankets and
own patio. The laundry, a small fridge and gas barbeque are available. The
double room has a kitchen unit with crockery but no cooking facilities. Two roller
beds are available. You can choose to be as private as you wish or also enjoy the
warmth of our home. First rate shops, restaurants, takeaways are close.*
*The substantial continental breakfast is a selection for you to choose from and
includes local fruits and preserves from our garden.*
*At home we are keen gardeners and enjoy tramping the many local walkways and
delightful beaches. Ina's art work is printed for Save the Children and Trevor is
an author and retired Herald journalist. We are keen to give quality hospitality
in our friendly home.*
Directions: *Turn left off SH1 at Hill St; top of Hill St is View Rd.*

Warkworth

Farmstay
Address: Blue Hayes, Martins Bay Rd,
13 km east Warkworth
Name: Rod and Rosalie Miller
Telephone: (09) 425-5612
Beds: 4 Single (2 bedroom)
Bathroom: 1 Family share, 1 Ensuite
Tariff: B&B (full) Double $55, Single $35,
Children 1/2 price, Dinner $20, Credit cards accepted, Vouchers accepted

We live on a 314 acre coastal farm overlooking Kawau Bay, Mahurangi Heads and river in the Hauraki Gulf, approximately 80 km north of Auckland. We farm sheep, poultry, deer and cattle. You are welcome to participate in daily farming activities including hand feeding deer. We live in a private setting with plenty of open space, close to good safe beaches and seaside shopping centre, 13 km from Warkworth on sealed road.
Our family home is 45 years old, comfortable, warm and relaxed with open fireplace, woodstove and beautiful views. Farm walks and natural bush reserves on property with tracks to view N.Z. flora.
Rod is a commercial pilot and flying instructor. Scenic flights both local and Hauraki Gulf available. Local area attractions include craft centres, Goat Island Marine Reserve and historic Kawau Island.
3 course dinner available. Family cat sleeps outside.
Directions: *Please phone.*

Matakana, Warkworth

Homestay
Address: Amberleigh Lodge,
Matakana Valley Road, R.D. 5, Warkworth
Name: Chris & Liz Tofield
Telephone: (09) 422-7059
Fax: (09) 422-7707
Beds: 2 Double, 4 Single (4 Bedrooms) **Bathrooms**: 3 Ensuite, 1 Private
Tariff: B&B (special) Double $99, Single $65, Daily rate $125 pp excluding lunch.
Credit Cards: Visa & M/C. Vouchers accepted Monday to Thursday year round.
Nearest Town: Warkworth 9km only 1 hour from Auckland

Amberleigh, an original farmhouse; the ideal halfway house between the Airport and Bay of Islands, nestles amongst rolling hills and native bush on the edge of Matakana in secluded landscaped gardens and paddocks - far from the madding crowd yet only an hour from the centre of Auckland. Relax to the sound of Tui's, Thrush's and Kookaburras or just watch the native birds flying about while you play with our 6 dogs which are part of our family or practice your croquet. Cocktails are served in the panelled sitting room or on the verandah before dinner which is taken in a gracious old world dining room with complimentary wines to suit the Cordon Bleu cooking. Take your breakfast on the spacious verandah overlooking the lawns and the native bush or be pampered with breakfast in bed. Explore the beautiful Tawhararuni Peninsula or take a trip to historic Kawau Island, laze on empty sandy beaches, play golf or tennis, visit the craft workshops or take a scenic drive. Picnic lunches by request. Remember our house is your home while you are with us.
Directions: *Please ask when booking.*

Warkworth

Homestay & B&B
Address: Mahurangi Lodge,
416 Mahurangi East Road,
Snells Beach, Warkworth
Name: Alison & Rodney Woodcock
Telephone: (09) 425-5465
Beds: 2 Double, 1 Twin, 1 Family - sleeps 5-6, (4 bedrooms)
Bathrooms: 1 Guests share, 1 Family share
Tariff: B&B (special) Double $60, Single $35, Family $20, Children $15, Dinner $15 (winter rate reductions). Credit Cards. Vouchers accepted.
Nearest Town: Warkworth 9km, just over 1km to Mahurangi Shopping Centre.

We are only 1 hour from downtown Auckland (1 1/2 from Airport) on the Mahurangi Peninsula overlooking Kawau Bay and the Mahurangi River. A spacious colonial style farmhouse on 30 acres offering farmstyle hospitality, meals in a relaxed friendly atmosphere, with a farm cat and native birds. Your needs are our top priority and we are able to offer special discounts with some local tour operators and will happily make your bookings free of charge.

We offer panoramic seaviews from large, clean, comfortable, upstairs bedrooms. Have a welcome 'cuppa' on arrival, feel at home with us and perhaps we can help you with your local sightseeing of the many attractions within a 10-15 minute drive or further North. Fishing and diving trips can be arranged and enjoy eating your fresh catch whenever possible.

There are several restaurants nearby and in Warkworth, or maybe enjoy local oysters from nearby Oyster farms and farm fresh venison.

Recommended by Jane King in 'N.Z. Handbook'. We look forward to meeting you.

Warkworth - Sandspit

Homestay
Address: "Belvedere Homestay",
38 Kanuka Rd, RD 2, Warkworth
Name: Margaret and Ron Everett
Telephone: (09) 425 7201
Beds: 1 Double, 2 Single (2 bedrooms)
Bathroom: 2 Private
Tariff: B&B (full) Double $60, Single $40, Dinner $25,
Childrens prices on request, Vouchers accepted
Nearest Town: Warkworth

Set in 11 acres, and overlooking the Spit where the ferries leave for Kawau Island with a 360 degree view from countryside to Kawau and Little Barrier Island.

We have farm animals, cows, calves, plus native bush with birds such as swallows, fantails, rosellas, hawks, pheasants. For your relaxing and pleasure, fishing from beach or boat, golf, tennis and town within 5km.

Two bedrooms (twin or double) each with own bathrooms. Games room, bar, pool table, darts and a relaxing separate spa pool conservatory with exercise gym plus outside decks with sunken garden and barbecue area. $60.00 double, $40.00 single both include continental breakfast with full breakfast on request. Three course dinner with wine available at $25.00 per person. Childrens prices for tariff on request.

Warkworth has many attractions and well worth visiting and we look forward to making your stay a memorable one.

Warkworth
- Algies Bay
Homestay
Address: 'Ceri', 56 Mera Road, Algies Bay, Warkworth
Name: Ngaire Miller
Telephone: (09) 425 5603
Beds: 4 Single (2 Twin bedrooms)
Bathroom: 1 Guests share
Tariff: B&B (full) Double $60, Single $35, Dinner $15, Children $20, Packed lunch by arrangement, Vegetarian meals on request, Vouchers accepted
Nearest Town: 10km from Warkworth, 1 hour drive from Auckland.

A warm welcome awaits you to share my new spacious and well appointed home in delightful garden surroundings. It offers panoramic sea views of Kawau Bay. From here you can explore many bays, parks and historical sites including Mansion House on Kawau Island.
Visits to a farm and native bush reserve can be arranged. You can walk to a safe and clear swimming beach in two minutes, or use the ramp for boating in the bay. Come and unwind in this quiet, relaxing and smokefree environment.
Ngaire is a registered nurse practitioner and offers therapeutic massages. I have 2 happy cats.
Telephone or call at Information Centre, Warkworth.

Warkworth
Country Homestay
Address: 10 The Bullock Track, Mahurangi West, RD3, Warkworth
Name: Valerie and David Napier
Telephone: (09) 422 0590 after 5pm
Fax: (09) 422 0766
Beds: 1 Double, 2 Single (2 bedrooms)
Bathroom: 1 Private, 1 Family share
Tariff: B&B (full) Double $75, Single $45, Dinner $20, Children $25
Nearest Town: Warkworth

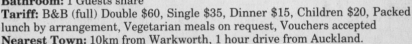

"Number 10" is situated in the Mahurangi Regional Park area overlooking the Upper Mahurangi Harbour.
We are approximately 50 minutes north of Auckland on the coast.
We have rural surroundings and the homestead of 3000 square feet is set in a one acre garden. The house is large and comfortable and contains a billiard room. We are close to Warkworth township, 'Puhoi' Village and 4km from Sullivans Bay which is a picturesque and safe swimming beach with interesting walks. The area has much of sightseeing interests including Sheepworld, satelite tracking station, kauri forests, the Sandspit which is the departure point for gulf cruises and Kawau Island.
We are situated 4kms from Highway 1 and will pick up from Warkworth or Auckland for an additional fee.
We only accommodate one set of guests at a time.

73

Warkworth
Homestay/Farmstay
Address: Hamiltons Road, Warkworth
Name: Mystery Heights
Telephone: (09) 425 7649 or 025 730 183
Beds: 2 Double, 1 Single (2 bedrooms)
Bathroom: 1 Family share
Tariff: B&B (special) Double $65,
Single $35, Dinner $20, Children $20, Campervans $25,
Nearest Town: Warkworth 4km - 3km to Mahurangi Shopping Complex.

I live on a 60 acre farm overlooking Kawau Bay and the Mahurangi River, 74km from Auckland. I offer you a relaxed secluded atmosphere and New Zealand farmstyle hospitality and cooking. An ex-Hospitality Industry worker, I will enjoy looking after your requirements. Warkworth's many activities, crafts and cultural areas are at your fingertips and you are surrounded by native and kauri bush and birdlife. During your stay I can take you fishing or point you towards Warkworth's best attractions, including sandy beaches or perhaps a picnic on an Island reserve near Kawau. My house is your home and you are very welcome to stay as long or short as you desire.
Directions: *Please phone.*
Note: Building was not completed at the time of inspection, phone to confirm.

Warkworth
Farmstay
Address: "Ryme Intrinseca"
Perry Road RD3 Warkworth
Name: Elizabeth & Cam Mitchell
Telephone: (09) 425 9448
Beds: 1 Queen, 3 Single (2 Bedrooms/1 Queen +1 Single - 1 room, 2 Singles - 1 room) **Bathroom:** 1 Guests share
Tariff: B&B (full) Double $75, Single $40, Children half price, Dinner $25, Vouchers accepted
Nearest Town: Warkworth

New Zealand Association
FARM & HOME HOSTS

Our 110 acre beef and sheep farm is ideally situated for travellers on their way to the Bay of Islands as it is an easy hours drive from Auckland, just 1km off SH 1 and 6km south of the attractive rural town of Warkworth.
Our spacious cedar and kauri home is set in a secluded valley overlooking 50 acres of native bush and surrounded by gardens and a croquet lawn.
We offer comfortable farm house accommodation and the upstairs bedrooms with their extensive farm views open into a guest sittingroom with TV, and tea / coffee making facilities.
Evening meals, if requested, feature home-grown produce and NZ wines.
Local sightseeing attractions include historic Kawau Island, the Mahurangi Harbour, Regional Parks and many lovely beaches.
Our interests include gardening, reading, sailing and caring for our farm and animals including our Jack Russell terrier. We are widely travelled within NZ and overseas and warmly welcome visitors to our home.

Kawau Island

Self-contained Accommodation
Address: Kawau Island Cottages for Couples,
Vivian Bay, Kawau Island
Postal: Private Bag 923, Warkworth
Name: Penelope & Ken McCormack
Telephone: (09) 422-8835
Beds: 3 Double, 2 Single (3 bedrooms)
Bathrooms: 3 ensuites **Tariff:** B&B (Continental)
Double $160 per couple - Includes all meals.
Nearest Town: Warkworth

Vivian Bay, Kawau Island is only a 45 minute ferry ride from Sandspit, 10 km from Warkworth. With a safe, sandy beach at the front entrance, our guests enjoy swimming, snorkeling, fishing (dinghies are free), beachcombing - some even relax and do absolutely nothing. For the more energetic, there are easy bush walks (we provide hamper lunches if desired) during which you are likely to see more wallabies than people. Visits to historic Mansion House and fishing trips can be arranged. Two modern chalets plus a flat, each accommodating only two guests, have en-suite bathrooms, sun decks, TV, refrigerators etc, for your comfort and convenience.
Our interests include gardening, music, ham radio and the comfort of our guests. We have two friendly Shetland collies, six cats and an almost-tame wallaby.

Vivian Bay, Kawau Island

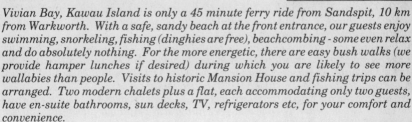

Superior Accommodation
Address: P.B. 940 Warkworth
Name: St Clair Lodge
Telephone & Fax: (09) 422 8850
Beds: 6 Double, 4 Single (7 Bedrooms)
Bathroom: 7 Ensuite
Tariff: B&B (continental) Double $200-240
(Tariff for 24hr stay - All meals inclusive - per couple), Vouchers accepted
Nearest Town: Warkworth

St Clair Lodge has been in the Barney family since 1953, offering deluxe homestay accommodation to guests who seek an idyllic setting where your front lawn is a white sandy beach and the only access is by water.
Guests who come to this newly built St Clair Lodge are transported by the Ferryboat Co which leaves Sandspit (70km north of Auckland) 3 times daily. After 40 minutes you can disembark, walk to the end of the pier and enter the Lodge. The large, modern lounge/dining room, complete with open fire, TV, piano, overlooks the beach and harbour. All meals are provided and served here (price included in tariff). Tea and coffee making facilities also available.
The privacy of the guests is catered for by the design of each bedroom unit complete with its own ensuite. These suites run off the main home, connected by decks surround a garden courtyard.
Activities may range from TV or scene gazing (binoculars provided) to early morning fishing, snorkelling, bush walking or rock climbing. Sometime during your stay, Piers will transport you in his launch to Mansion House, where you can view the splendour of the former Governor's (Sir George Grey) residence and stroll the magnificent gardens. Picnics are also available to take to adjacent bays either of foot or by launch. You may also see Wallabies, Penguins and experience the Glow-worms of the sea. St Clair Lodge is the place of choice if you truly wish for Rest and Relaxation. Personalized hospitality and excellent NZ food (maybe the fish you've caught that morning) are guaranteed.

No Smoking logo

Puhoi
Farmstay
Address: "Our Farm-Park", Puhoi, Auckland
Name: Peter and Nichola Rodgers
Telephone: (09) 422 0626
Beds: 1 Double, 2 Single (2 bedrooms) **Bathroom:** 1 Guest s share
Tariff: Dinner & B&B (farmhouse) Single $50, Double $100. All meals - first day $65 (Double $115), then per day $50 ($90), 10 days $450 ($800). Children $20 per day. Vouchers accepted.
Nearest Town: Waiera Hot Pools 8km, Orewa 15km, Warkworth 15km

Our 110 acre property is called "Our Farm-Park" - so you can say "our" as, high in the hills, you share with us the beautiful panoramic views, fresh air and clean water, quietness; just 4.5km of unsealed road off the main highway, 45 minutes north of Auckland's Harbour Bridge.

Our animals are farmed with kindness and peacefulness. No-one smokes here, we have no dogs, and farm successfully without chemicals. Our poultry runs free, we shear touchable sheep, and spin their wool. Our horses are totally safe; you could have your first ride ever, ride to the store, ride under stars....

We eat tasty meals (vegetarian if you wish) with our own meat killed without stress by our mobile butcher. No-one ever goes hungry. We milk our own cows (you can too), make butter, yoghurt and cheeses.

Our visitors stop off on their NZ tour with dinner timed to their arrival; or stay two nights sleeping late; some stay longer to learn about organic farming (venue Soil & Health Field Day, 1994); some to learn conversational English.

Building "The Manor" where you stay may cause some small inconveniences; if this could bother you, please say.

Peter E Rodgers T.T.C., Dip. T., B.Soc. Sci. (Psych)

Waiwera
Guest House
Address: Weranui Road, Waiwera
Name: Lissadell Lodge
Telephone: (09) 426 3089
Beds: 1 Double, 2 Twin (3 bedrooms)
Bathroom: 1 Ensuite, 1 Guests share
Tariff: B&B (full) Double $60, Single $35, Dinner $20 (3 course), Children half price, Vouchers accepted
Nearest Town: Orewa 12km

Lissadell Lodge, on a small organic orchard, surrounded by an abundant cottage garden, is situated in a peaceful river valley 6km away from sandy beaches and the Waiwera Hot Pools. The Hibiscus Coast is a picturesque part of New Zealand with many regional parks and a magnificent shore line.

We are Germans and have lived in Auckland for the last 10 years. When our children left home we decided on an alternative lifestyle away from the hustle and bustle of the city. Lissadell offered us all we ever wanted. We would like to share it with you.

The Guesthouse is separate from our own accommodation. It is a spacious 3 bedroom house with a large comfortable lounge. Board games and a library are provided for your entertainment. We also offer mountain bikes and kayaks for hire, horse trekking is only 5 minutes away. We will assist your visit to New Zealand and introduce you to unique attractions throughout the region.

Home-cooked dinner on request. Vegetarians welcome.

Courtesy car for meeting bus travellers in Silverdale or Waiwera (take The Yellow Bus no 893, 894, 895 or 89) from Downtown Auckland.

Red Beach, Orewa

Homestay
Address: 54 Walton Street,
Red Beach, Orewa
Name: Helen Bassett
Telephone: (09) 426-6963
Beds: 2 Double, (2 bedrooms)
Bathroom: 2 Private
Tariff: (full) B&B Double $50, Single $30; Dinner $15. Vouchers accepted
Nearest Town: Orewa

This is a pleasant place 2km from State Highway 1 and 100 metres from a good beach which we enjoy very much.
We have had many guests here, on their way or returning from the North, or simply to enjoy what this area has to offer. The pleasant town of Orewa 5km, Waiwere Thermal Pools 10km, the Whangaparaoa Peninsula with its many bays, and Auckland 30km.
A warm welcome is assured, comfortable beds and a breakfast to suit your taste. There is a resident cat.

Silverdale

Farmstay +
Self-Contained Accommodation
Address: Angel Valley, 42 Manuel Road, RD 2,
Silverdale 1462 **Name**: Ute Engel
Telephone: (09) 426-6175
Beds: 2 Double, 2 Single (3 bedroom)
Bathroom: 1 Guests share
Tariff: B&B (special) Double $60, Single $35,
Children half price; Dinner $20 (wine extra).
Self-contained, semi-detached flat Double $85,
Single $60, 1 Ensuite, Credit cards accepted. Vouchers accepted.
Nearest Town: Orewa 6 km, 40 km north of Auckland

The Wyatt Home

If you wish to experience the peace and tranquility of New Zealand country living, then my home is for you. It is situated in rolling farmland country, 2 km off Highway 1. My wooden home is cosy and modern and I pride myself in providing an atmosphere of friendliness and warmth. The self-contained flat is luxurious and spacious. On the 4 acres surrounding the house I raise a variety of animals, including sheep, and calves.
I was born in Germany and have lived in many European countries and Australia. I love biodynamic gardening, swimming and walking as well as cooking. I provide tasty vegetarian and meat dishes and delicious desserts. I do massages and offer colour analysis.
It is my pleasure to provide details of local attractions - beaches, boating, fishing, bushwalks, horse-riding, golfing and hot pools.
Whether you are touring New Zealand on holiday or seeking a quiet and harmonious retreat from daily life, I welcome you into my home.
Directions: *Opposite BP station on Silverdale Hill turn into Wainui Rd, 2nd Rd on right, 3rd letterbox on right. 1.6km off Highway 1. Phone early morning or late afternoon.*

Silverdale, Auckland

Farmstay
Address: "Mt Pleasant", Pine Valley
Road, Silverdale, Auckland
Name: Bob & Molly Crawford
Telephone: (09) 426 4280
Beds: 1 Double, 2 Single (3 bedrooms)
Bathroom: 1 Guests share
Tariff: B&B (full) Double $60, Single $30, Dinner $20, Children half price,
Campervans welcome, Vouchers accepted

Kia Ora!
Bob and I and our 8 year old son Robert would love to share our 320 acre dairy farm and family home with you. 'Mt Pleasant' homestead is a 90 year old building of unusual design which exudes the peace and charm of yester-year. Built from timber milled from our 120 acres of native bush and lovingly restored to its former glory, the homestead is an idyllic spot in which to relax.
Perhaps in and around the house, out in the garden which we all enjoy or sunbathing around the pool, where ever you are I'm sure you'll feel quite at home. Bob enjoys his wood turning, local and general history, and shares my love and appreciation for antique furniture with which the house is furnished. I also enjoy gardening, tennis, tramping (any outdoor activity) and love cooking honest to goodness farmstyle meals (Dinner bookings in advance please).
All nationalities are welcome including children.
30 mins north of Auckland - please phone for directions.

Whangaparaoa

Homestay/Bed & Breakfast
Name: Doreen & Ray
Telephone & Fax: (09) 424 5467
Beds: 2 Double, 1 Single (3 bedrooms)
Bathroom: 2 Ensuite, 1 Guest share
Tariff: B&B (full) Double $65 & $80, Single $35, Dinner $20,
Children under 12 half price, Credit cards accepted, Vouchers accepted
Nearest Town: Whangaparaoa Town centre

We provide luxury accommodation in our 3,500sq ft home, which is situated on over a 1/4 acre of attractive gardens. We have unrestricted views, with total privacy. Overlooking beaches, river estuaries, and overall views of the Hauraki Gulf and Rangitoto Island.
Large games room with table tennis, slate pool table, darts and a gym.
Nearest beach by car 45 seconds.
We enjoy meeting so many interesting people, and having travelled ourselves, we know how important it is to be able to come here and feel one can totally relax. We are British ex-pats who just love New Zealand. We have live here for 26 + years. We believe in healthy fresh foods, most veges from our own garden, organically grown. Everything is home baked, including fresh baked bread each day. We definitely have that 'touch of country'. You can be sure of a warm friendly welcome, and will be made to feel at home. Laundry facilities available, we are smoke free. Also privately escorted sightseeing tours, and a wide range of activities.

Whangaparaoa Peninsula
Self-contained Accommodation
Address: Te Maru, 36 The Crescent, Tindalls Bay, Whangaparaoa
Name: Joan & Peter Macpherson
Telephone: (09) 424-5407
Beds: 1 Double, 2 Single (2 bedrooms)
Bathrooms: 2 Private
Tariff: B&B (continental) Double $70, Single $40 (discount for longer stays), Vouchers accepted
Nearest Town: Whangaparaoa 3km and Orewa 10km West

Our home (Te Maru: the place of shelter) has a quiet bush setting on a pohutukawa fringed beach. We are New Zealanders, who have lived and travelled abroad and enjoy meeting people.

Your private guest facilities also have own entrance, dining area, kitchenette, lounge with TV, and bathroom with washing machine.

Guests find Te Maru a good base as nearby are more beaches, parklands, golf, tennis, bowls, Gulf Harbour (marina and ferry), Pacific Plaza, and several restaurants while thermal pools, wine trails, historic places and other attractions are not far away.

Telephone bookings necessary; No smoking indoors thankyou.

Directions: *One hour drive from Airport, 50km from city. Take Highway One North through Silverdale (40km), turn right onto Whangaparaoa Road for 10km to the roundabout at Manly Village. Continue east on Whangaparaoa Road, taking Tindall's Bay Road on your left. The Crescent is first (& second) on your left.*

Whangaparaoa Peninsula
Homestay

Address: 39 Cedar Tce, Stanmore Bay, Whangaparaoa
Name: Alan and Maureen Fullerton
Telephone: (09) 424 3133
Beds: 1 Twin, 1 Single (2 bedrooms)
Bathroom: 1 Guests share
Tariff: B&B (continental) Double $60, Single $35, Dinner $18, Vouchers accepted
Nearest Town: Orewa

We are recently retired dairy farmers whose family is now independent. Our home is on 10 acres of land on which we run beef stock and horses. Having guests to stay is one of our great pleasures and we like our guests to feel 'at home' with us. We have 1 twin and 1 single bedrooms, and 1 guest bathroom.

There is a large outdoor swimming pool, spa and games room with table tennis and darts for those wanting activity, and for those wanting a quiet restful stay, our home has a tranquil setting..

Whangaparaoa has many lovely beaches, bush and beach walks, golf course, modern leisure centre and shopping centre with most banks, only minutes away. Non smokers preferred.

Our home is 30 minutes drive north of Auckland Harbour Bridge and 5km from the Whangaparaoa turn off.

Please phone for reservation and directions.

Dairy Flat
Homestay
Address: Heather Lodge,
State Hwy 1, RD4, Dairy Flat, Auckland
Name: Kathleen Bradley
Telephone: (09) 426 4839
Beds: 2 Double, 2 Single (2 bedrooms)
Bathrooms: 1 guests share
Tariff: B&B (full) Double $65, Single $40, Dinner $20,
Children according to age, Credit cards, Vouchers accepted
Nearest Town: Orewa

Our home is set on 13 acres with rural outlook, small pool.
*My husband breeds horses (Trotters and Pacers). We both enjoy meeting people,
talking and listening, golf, travel (NZ and overseas), dining out, and the horse
races.*
*The rooms have tea/coffee making facilities and own balconies. We have two
lounges (TV or not TV). Inside is a no smoking area. Heather Lodge is set back from
State Highway 1 down a tree lined drive.*
*We are 33 kms north of Auckland. 7kms south of Orewa, a lovely seaside town, 10
minutes from "The Bays", Browns Bay, Mairangi Bay, etc. 15 minutes drive north
is Wenderholme Reserve and Waiwera Hot Pools. 20 minutes drive to black sands
of West Coast, numerous vineyards and Gannet Colony at Murawai. 50 minutes
drive from Auckland Airport.*
Directions: *From South: State Highway 1. 33 kms north of Auckland. 13 kms
from Albany. From North: State Highway 1. 7 kms south of Orewa. Well signed.
Heather Lodge.*

Kaukapakapa
**Farmstay + Self-contained
Accommodation**
Address: Kereru Lodge, Arone
Farm, Makarau Valley Road,
 RD 3, Kaukapakapa
Name: Betty Headford
Telephone: (09) 420 5223
Beds: 3 Double, 2 Single (3 bedrooms)
Bathroom: 1 Ensuite, 1 Family share,
1 Guests share

Kereru Lodge

Self-contained cottage: price on application
Tariff: B&B (full) Double $60, Single $35, Dinner $20, Children half price,
Campervans $20, Vouchers accepted
Nearest Town: Kaukapakapa 14km

*Kereru Lodge is a modern 2 storey home, set in a large developing garden, 45 mins
north of Auckland. On our 55 acre farm we run cattle and over the last few years
have planted hundreds of trees. We have over 10 acres of native bush, at our gate
the Makarau River and a few kms down the road the Kaipara Harbour with its
fishing and the wintering grounds of many migrating birds.*
*Come to completely relax and enjoy a quiet retreat or if you hanker for a bit of
excitement you will find within 20 mins a golf course, tennis courts, bowling clubs,
interesting walks, hot pools, fishing trips, parachuting and a flying school.*
*We have many and varied interests and love having a house full of people. We are
available by prior arrangement to pick you up from Auckland Airport for a
reasonable rate. We are non smokers.*

"Skovholm"

Waimauku

Country Home
Address: Hinau Road,
Waimauku, Auckland
Name: 'Skovholm'
Telephone: (09) 411 8326
Beds: 3 Double, 2 Single (5 bedrooms)
Bathrooms: 2 Ensuite, 1 Private,
1 Guests share
Tariff: B&B (special) Double $100, Single $65,
Credit cards accepted, Vouchers accepted
Nearest Town: Auckland

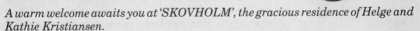

A warm welcome awaits you at 'SKOVHOLM', the gracious residence of Helge and Kathie Kristiansen.
At 'SKOVHOLM' guests are treated as respected friends.
Our 90 year old home is set in over 10 acres of lovingly tended gardens and native bush - a haven of peace and tranquillity - only 30 minutes north west of central Auckland. Bedrooms are well appointed, ensuite or with private bathrooms.
Nearby attractions include sampling local wines, visiting the gannet colony at nearby Muriwai Beach, hot thermal pools, or simply relaxing and enjoying the delights of our garden, bush and bird life.
It has been our privilege to share our home with people from many countries and we look forward to sharing it with you.
Directions: *Take SH16 (Motorway/Highway) past Kumeu and Huapai. Turn left into Fosters Road (3rd left past Huapai), then 5th left into Hinau Road. 'SKOVHOLM' is 2nd drive on right - advance reservations are advised. Our brochure is available on request.*

Huapai

Homestay
Address: "Foremost Fruits" 45
Trigg Rd Huapai Auckland
Name: Jim & Andrea Hawkless
Telephone: (09) 412 8862
Beds: 1 Double, 3 Single (2 Bedrooms)
Bathroom: 1 Guests share
Tariff: B&B (special) Double $60, Single $35, Children half price, Dinner $20.
Campervans welcome.
Nearest Town: Huapai/Kumeu 2km, Auckland City 30 mins

"Foremost Fruits" is situated in the heart of New Zealand's wine producing area on a small orchard growing apples, peaches, pears and plums, but specialising in hot house table grapes. Guests will be warmly welcomed by hosts with extensive overseas bed & breakfast experience. Our aim is to provide travellers with comfortable home from home accommodation consisting of 2 large bedrooms with separate guest bathroom. Breakfast is of choice. Foremost Fruits is within easy drive of several restaurants with fares ranging from A La Carte to take-aways. We are pleased to provide details of local attractions including golf course, wineries, riding school, beaches etc. Non smokers preferred.
Directions: *From Auckland take the Northwestern Motorway to end. Turn towards Helensville Highway 16 through Kumeu and Huapai, over railway line turn left on Trigg Rd before 100k sign. Foremost Fruits 500 metres on left.*

Coatesville - Albany
Farmstay
Address: 455 Coatesville/Riverhead
Highway RD3 Albany Auckland
Name: Chris & David Hempleman
Telephone: (09) 415 9009
Beds: 2 Double, 3 Single, Cot available (4 Bedrooms)
Bathroom: 2 Guests share
Tariff: B&B (full) Double $80, Single $50, Children Neg.,
Dinner $25, Vouchers accepted Mon to Thurs for March to October
Nearest Town: Albany 7km

*We are only 20 minutes from Auckland City. Relax in secluded tranquillity in a
park like rural setting, on our 18 acre farmlet running cattle and sheep.*
*Our large Tudor home opens into lovely cottage gardens native bush and stream,
offering the best of hospitality and a friendly relaxed atmosphere.*
*Our guest areas are spacious and well appointed consisting of queen and twins
bedrooms, guest bathrooms and delightful sitting room with colour television and
coffee / tea making facilities.*
Evening meals are available by arrangement.
- Barbeques a speciality -
*Coatesville is the centre of a horticultural area with many orchards, wineries,
restaurants, horsehire and golf courses close by. Both east and west coast beaches
are only 15 minutes drive away.*
Directions: *From Auckland city travel north on Highway 1 through Albany -
turn left into Coatesville / Riverhead Highway. Transfers are available.*
Further details please phone or write.

Kumeu
Farmstay
Address: Nor-West Greenlands,
Riverhead Road, RD2, Kumeu
Name: Kerry and Kay Hamilton
Telephone & Fax: (09) 412-8167
Beds: 1 Double, 2 Single (2 bedrooms)
Bathroom: 2 private

Tariff: B&B (Full) Double $110, Single $65, Dinner $25; Not suitable for
children, Credit cards accepted, Vouchers accepted
Nearest Town: Kumeu 3 1/2 km, Auckland city 26 km south.

*Our 20 acre farmlet 20 minutes from Auckland City is situated in a quiet peaceful
valley with native bush, pond and stream. We grow flowers commercially and sell
fresh & dried flowers from a shop on the property. Breeding sheep and cattle is a
hobby and the household is home to two cats and a dog.*
*A separate guest lounge with TV and tea / coffee making facilities opens out on to
a lovely garden which has a swimming pool and barbecue. You are welcome to join
us for a barbecue in summer.*
Dinner, Lunch and transfers are available.
*Kumeu is the centre of a horticultural area with many orchards, wineries,
restaurants and golf courses.*
Both east and west coast beaches are only 20 km away.
Directions: *From Auckland city travel via the North Western Motorway to State
Highway 16, 5 km north, right into Coatsville / Riverhead Highway and Riverhead
Rd is the second on the left.*

Bethells Beach, West Auckland
Self -contained Accommodation

Address: "Turehu Cottage" & "Te Koinga Cottage"
P O Box 95057, Swanson, Auckland.
(Bethells Beach, Waitakere Ranges, West Auckland)
Name: Trude Bethell & John Paice
Telephone & Fax: (09) 810 9581 Auckland

"Turehu Cottage"
Beds: 1 Double (in living room area). Separate caravan for up to two children
Bathroom: 1 Private. Great shower (separate room), includes the toilet.
Tariff: Self contained cottage: $65 per week day or $80 per weekend day or public holiday, $5 extra per child. Breakfast $8pp, Dinner $20pp. Meals by prior arrangement.
Check in 11.30 am, Check out 10 am (depending on prior bookings)
"Te Koinga Cottage"
Beds: 2 Double, 3 Single = 1 double divan in the main room + 2 bedrooms,
Bathroom: 1 bath and 1 shower - separate toilet
Tariff: Self contained cottage: 1 person $100/day, 2 people $130/day, More than 2 people $165/day, Breakfast $10 per person. Dinner $25 per person. Meals by prior arrangement.
Check in 1.30 pm, Check out 10 am (depending on prior bookings)
Nearest Town: Swanson 20 minutes, Downtown Auckland 40 minutes

"Turehu Cottage" - A cottage with spectacular views over a west coast surf beach. *A magic place for relaxing and doing nothing in the privacy of your own abode.*
Maybe surf casting, horse riding, surfing, summer swimming, tramping or just a walk along the beach across grand black sandhills to a remote lake.
The cottage has cream walls and white trim, cork floor, and matching chintz curtains, table cloth and bedspread, double bed, dining table and kitchen in one room. The bathroom is adjacent with the best shower in town! All amenities and linen provided. Just bring your favorite foods and champagne! Lavender and herb garden with your odd lettuce. Your own picnic table and bench under a Pohutukawa tree with sea views, breathtaking.

"Te Koinga Cottage" - *Long sweeping sunset views. A 35 sq metre deck lends nature to you, from two bi folding French doors. Pohutakawa surrounds and sounds of surf. Expansive barbeque areas.*
At 80 sq metres this cottage has terracotta floors (bedrooms carpeted). Separate toilet. Rag rolled and tongue and groove walls. Radio and record player (BYO records). Television, dishwasher, microwave, oven and fridge / freezer. All amenities and linen provided, just bring your own favourite foods and wines.
Champagne Weekend. For four people the cost is $550 (weekend) and you are treated to three bottles of champagne. Special decorations (Please let us know each persons favourite colour). A continental breakfast is provided on Sunday morning at a specified time. A few special goodies are there for your surprise.
Our main house in on the hill above. John and I are happy to give you ideas of what to do; eg. Waitakere Ranges walks are only fifteen minutes drive away. The Cascades and golf course are only ten minutes drive away. Surfing, swimming (lake or sea), surf casting, horse trekking (booked in advance). Volleyball on the front lawn. You are also welcome to use our telephone, fax or clothes washing facilities. For further information give John or Trude a telephone call. John's hobby this year is forging damask knives and my hobby is watercolour painting. We have two happy pets - a cat and a dog.
Parking available at each cottage.

Waitakere Ranges

Farm/Self-contained Accommodation
Address: Greenmead Farm, 115 Bethells Road,
Waitakere (R.D. 1, Henderson, Auckland)
Name: Averil & Jonathan Bateman
Telephone: (09) 810-9363, **Fax:** (09) 810-9122
Beds: 4 Single (2 bedrooms) **Bathroom:** 1 Private
Tariff: (Breakfast full $7.50 pp) Self-contained cottage (accommodation only)
Double $60 + $10 for each extra guest; Dinner $20.
Nearest Town: Henderson 16km, Auckland city 30km

Our property is situated in a rural valley in the Waitakere Ranges, only 30 minutes drive NW of Auckland City. We grow globe artichokes commercially and breed Simmental cattle. Gardens and orchard surround the homestead and guest cottage including an extensive organic vegetable garden and a herb garden featuring culinary and medicinal plants. Swings for children.
We handmilk a house cow, have two working dogs, some hens but no cats.
Visitors have sole use of the cottage which is fully self contained and has a well equipped kitchen / dining room, parlour (Tv), a bathroom and two bedrooms each with two single beds (linen provided).
Usually guests prefer to cater for themselves but breakfast or dinner can be provided by prior arrangement.
Longer stays welcomed.
A network of walking tracks through spectacular scenery link bush, beach and lake. Wine can be sampled at vineyards in Henderson or Kumeu. The cottage offers comfort and privacy in a tranquil setting close to Auckland city.
Directions: *Please phone.*

Always telephone ahead to enquire about a B&B. It is a nuisance for you if
you simply arrive to find someone already staying there.
And besides hosts need a little time to prepare.

Waitakere

Homestay
Address: 84 The Terrace, Herald Island,
Waitakere City, Auckland
Name: Harbourview Homestay
Telephone: (09) 416 7553
Beds: 1 Double, 2 Single (2 bedrooms)
Bathroom: 1 Private
Tariff: B&B (full) Double $65, Single $35, Dinner from $10 incl wine, Children under 12 yrs half price, Vouchers accepted
Nearest Town: Glenfield 15kms Henderson 20kms Auckland city 26kms

Your hosts Bev & Les have a two story home, and can offer you superb accommodation, right on waters edge, with 2 bedrooms, lounge, bathroom and tea and coffee making facilities. Each bedroom, 1 double and 1 twin, has its own sundeck overlooking the upper reaches of the Waitamata Harbour.
Within 20 mins radius, wine tasting, horse riding, golf course, bush walks, cinema and vintage care museum.
We also have a boat for excellent fishing or a leisurely cruise. Bev serves a hearty home cooked dinner if required, or you may wish to go to one of our local restaurants nearby. Rooms serviced daily and laundry facilities are available. Lunch if required also.
Directions: *Take North-Western (Helensville) Motorway to end. Turn right at traffic lights into Hobsonville Road. 2nd on left Brigham Creek Road.(Liquor store on corner) 1st on right Kauri Road. Continue along until Kingsway Road on right (Herald Island sign). 1st road on left over causeway The Terrace.*

Swanson

Redwood Homestay
Address: 26 Knox Road, Swanson, Auckland 6
Name: Colleen & Gary Sherwood
Telephone: (09) 833 7007 (hm), (09) 579 4189 (wk)
Beds: 1 Double, 2 Single (2 bedrooms)
Bathroom: 1 Guests share
Tariff: B&B (special) Double $55, Single $35,
Children half price, Dinner $20. Vouchers accepted.
Nearest Town: Henderson 6kms N.

This is a large comfortable home situated on half an acre of attractive garden and fruit trees of many varieties. A feature of the house are views from all rooms, of Redwood Park Golf Course, and surrounding bush. A wide variety of native birds live in the garden where plants have been grown as a food source for them. A conservatory with spa pool runs the length of the house and is used for growing orchids, and palms and other exotic plants.
A paved area is used for BBQs or relaxing in the privacy of an enclosed garden. Guest accommodation is spacious with tea making facilities available. Non-smokers preferred. Golf is on the doorstep as No.1 green adjoins the drive. Green fee players are welcome on this course.
Hosts: interests are fishing, dining out, theatre, golf, rugby, good wines. There are a wide variety of restaurants in the area. Tourist features of the area are: Scenic drive at the base of Waitakeres, ARA bush walks, West Auckland vineyards, western beaches. 10 minutes to Auckland on NW Highway.
Directions: *from NW motorway turn off at Lincoln Road - follow through to sign - at traffic lights - Swanson - continue down Universal Drive, turn right at traffic island into Swanson Road to the township. Knox Rd is on your right past Railway Station. Signs show Redwood Park. No. 26 is last house in the street on the left.*

Swanson
Self-contained Accommodation/Farmstay
Address: 148 Christian Road,
Swanson, Auckland 8
Name: Mac & Val McMillan
Telephone: (09) 833-9872
Beds: 2 Double (1 bed & bed-settee), (1 bedroom)
Bathroom: 1 Ensuite
Tariff: B&B (special) Double $60, Single $40, Dinner $20, Campervans $20, Vouchers accepted
Nearest Town: Henderson (7 km), Auckland (25 km)

We offer a motel type unit situated on a 10 acre farmlet with a large landscaped garden. A swimming pool is alongside the unit.
We are successful breeders of dairy goats and kune-kune pigs, keep poultry and have three cats, a German Shepherd dog and a rainbow lorikeet.
Our property has magnificent rural views of which the Waitakere Ranges are a feature and is only 400 metres from the Waitakere Centennial Park with its famous walking tracks, kauri trees, native bush and birds. Thirty minute drive to West Coast beaches and Muriwai gannet colony and 45 minutes to Parakai Hot Springs. Only 45 minutes from Auckland Airport.
Henderson is well equipped with shops and has a variety of restaurants and is well-known for its vineyards and orchards. The farmlet is within a 30 minute drive of approximately 20 vineyards.
Our interests include sport, classical music, gardening, animals, travel.
Directions: *Please telephone.*

Torbay
Homestay
Address: 23 Auld Street, Torbay,
North Shore, Auckland
Name: Colleen and Maurie Gray
Telephone: (09) 473-9558
Beds: 1 Double, 2 Single (2 bedrooms)
Bathroom: 1 Ensuite, 1 Guest share
Tariff: B&B (special) Double $75, Single $50,
Dinner $25; Campervans $35 for 2 (includes breakfast and guest bathroom)
Nearest Town: Browns Bay

Our spacious modern home is designed with guests' comfort in mind. We enjoy sharing the beautiful sea views, luxurious living and rambling garden. We have created a restful atmosphere and plenty of outdoor living area for the warmer days. A grand-piano graces the large lounge and we have a huge open-fireplace. We enjoy the outdoors, swimming, sailing, barbecues and are located within a few minutes walk of a beautiful beach. Torbay offers safe swimming, cliff-top walks, a choice of restaurants. Easy bus-ride to Auckland city.
I enjoy preparing attractive, wholesome meals so you're welcome to dine with us. We have two Persian cats who will love to meet you too!
A smoke-free home.
Directions: *Turn right as you leave the Northern motorway at East Coast Bays exit. Turn left into East Coast Road. Proceed to Browns Bay turnoff and turn right. Pass Browns Bay, travel along Beach Road, past picturesque Waiake Beach. Turn right at Torbay Service Station and you're in Auld Street.*

Mairangi Bay

Homestay
Address: 12 Marigold Place,
Mairangi Bay, Auckland 10
Name: Anthony & Julie Lewis
Telephone: (09) 479 6392
Beds: 2 Double (2 bedrooms) **Bathroom:** 1 Ensuite, 1 Private
Tariff: B&B (full) Double $70, Single $35,
Dinner $20, Children half price, Vouchers accepted
Nearest Town: Takapuna 9kms

We are an English couple who enjoy sharing our home and spending time with travellers to Auckland. Our home has a lovely view to the ocean and Rangitoto Island. We have two guest bedrooms both equipped with Queensize beds and tea and coffee making facilities. There is a comfortable guest lounge complete with Sky TV and stereo should you require privacy.
The beach and local shops are an easy ten to fifteen minute stroll away. There are restaurants and a number of pleasant cafes - but we would be very happy for you to share dinner with us. Please request when booking.
You can be sure of a special welcome and if you would like a personal tour of our locality we can introduce you to the many local beaches and cliff top walks that Auckland's North Shore has to offer.
House rule - No smoking indoors.
2 car garage available.
Directions: *Please phone. Airport collection if required (fuel cost only).*

Milford Beach

Homestay
Address: 4B Frater Avenue Milford Beach Auckland
Name: Margaret & George
Telephone: (09) 486 3551
Beds: Twin (1 bedroom) **Bathroom:** 1 Private
Tariff: B&B (special) Double $60, Single $35, Dinner by arrangement
Nearest Town: Takapuna 2km, Auckland 10km

Margaret and George have a friendly, informal private home, a quiet short stay environment. Centrally situated, it is only 10km from Downtown Auckland, about 30 minutes from Auckland International Airport and has nearby access to the main Motorway system. It is only two minutes walk to a beautiful beach or to shops and restaurants.
Guests can be picked up and delivered to the Airport or other terminal points, by arrangement. Local tours sightseeing, picnics and special meals can be provided. Guests arriving by car should phone for directions.
Margaret and George are a hospitable couple, much travelled and enjoy exchanging "traveller's tales" with congenial friends. Their domestic facilities are yours to use; their objective to make your Auckland stay a memorable one.
This is a smoke-free zone.

Takapuna

Homestay
Address: 89 Stanaway St,
Auckland 9
Name: Pat & John Heerdegen
Telephone & Fax: (09) 419 0731
Beds: 1 Double **Bathroom:** 1 Ensuite
Tariff: B&B (full) Double $60 Single $30, Dinner $20, Credit Cards accepted:
Visa & M/C.   Vouchers accepted

Planning a vacation in New Zealand.
Enjoy the hospitality of New Zealanders (in their homes). You will be met on your arrival at Auckland International Airport partake of a tour of our city as you travel to our two storey residence on the North Shore, with panoramic views of Rangitoto (illustration) Auckland Harbour and City in close proxmity to golf courses, beaches and shops. Quality accommodation, dinner, breakfast, plus transport to your next departing point, rental car, airplane, coach or train. Single $95, Double $90 pp.
Pat and John are seniors, have visited Australia, Canada, United States and Europe. Interests golf, boating, computers, square dancing or relaxing with guests.
You may plan an extra day in Auckland sightseeing or participating in a leisure activity of your choice. Advice on ongoing vacation, transport, accommodation, where to go and what to do if requested. Excellent references. Non smoking inside residence.

Takapuna

Homestay
Address: 9B Elderwood Lane, Takapuna
Name: Jim and Val Laidlaw
Telephone: (09) 489 5420
Beds: 3 Single (2 bedrooms)
Bathroom: 1 Ensuite, 1 Family share
Tariff: B&B (continental) Double $60, Single $35, Dinner $15, Vouchers accepted
Nearest Town: Takapuna and Devonport 10 mins, Auckland City 15 mins

Our house is in a very peaceful and central location with good parking, and for those downstairs in the twin room the use of a large living space with TV and outside patio. Tea and coffee and laundry facilities are available.
We have travelled extensively both at home and overseas and offer warm comfortable accommodation with a homely atmosphere. All our family including pets have left home so you can be assured of a quiet time with all the attention from us that you ask for.
Our area abounds in restaurants and food halls and we are close to bus routes. We will happily help with any travel arrangements. We request that guests do not smoke in our home. Please phone for directions.

Tell other travellers about your favourite B&Bs

Greenhithe

Rural Homestay
Address: 177 Upper Harbour Drive,
Greenhithe, Auckland
Name: Therese and Ned Jujnovich
Telephone: (09) 413 9270
Beds: 1 Double, 4 Single (3 bedrooms)
Bathroom: 2 Private (only family groups share).
Tariff: B&B (special) Double $70, Single $40; Dinner $25 (includes wine),
Children half price, Vouchers accepted
Nearest Town: Glenfield 5 km, Auckland city 15 km (about 15 minutes)

Our ranch-style home nestles above the upper harbour in 10 acres of pasture and Kauri and other native forest to the water's edge. The air is alive with bird song. Swimming pool in the summer months and warm wood fires in the winter. So peaceful and just 15 minutes from Auckland city.

You can do a spot of native birdwatching, swim or just relax in the tranquil surroundings. And you can take in the sights of Auckland city, the beaches and wineries.

Your hosts Ned and Therese Jujnovich have travelled extensively and they especially welcome overseas guests. Among our interests are our Angora goats, spinning, wine making, beach and bush walking.

Local sightseeing easily arranged. Greenhithe is a handy starting-off place to the Bay of Islands being just north of Auckland.

Directions: *From Auckland _ over the Harbour Bridge _ exit left at Tristram Avenue, right at Wairau Road, continue to Greenhithe intersection (Upper Harbour Drive) left turn then 2 km. 177 is at the end of right of way. Transport from city terminal available on request.*

Glenfield, Auckland

Homestay
Address: "Glenhaven",
17 Roberts Rd., Glenfield, Auckland
Name: Donald & Jean Wright
Telephone: (09) 444-3357
Beds: 4 Single (2 bedrooms) **Bathroom:** 1 Guests share
Tariff: B&B (full) Double $65, Single $35, Children half price.
Vouchers accepted.

Drive into 'Glenhaven', it's private, peaceful and for the travel weary, restful. A 24 hr rate available to rest up. Trees surround our comfortable smoke free home. By contrast we are a short bus ride from the city. No need to take the car!

Tea and coffee facilities in both guest rooms. Jean cooks generous breakfasts. Restaurant and Hotels nearby.

'Glenhaven' conveniently situated to SH1. Nearby a shopping mall and leisure centre, golf courses, driving ranges, 10 pin bowling, lovely beaches.

We are retired, enjoy our adult family and grandchildren. Interests include travelling, sport, gardening, outdoors, telling visitors about our lovely country.

Directions: *North bound - cross harbour bridge and take exit for Northcote - Birkenhead. Travel 2.5km, turn right at lights on major intersection. Travel 2.5km, Roberts Rd is on the left. South bound - travel on Northern Motorway towards city. Take Northcote - Birkenhead exit just before bridge. Then same directions as above.*

Bayswater, Auckland

Homestay
Address: 24 Lansdowne St
Bayswater Auckland 9
Name: Paul & Shona Barton
Telephone: (09) 445 8222
Beds: 1 Double, 2 Single (2 Bedrooms)
Bathroom: 1 Guests share
Tariff: B&B (continental) Double $50 Single
$25, Children under 13 half price, Dinner $15
Nearest Town: Takapuna

Situated on the pleasant North Shore midway between Takapuna and Devonport with Auckland city a 15 minute drive over the harbour bridge or a ferry ride from Devonport.

Our home is surrounded by shrubs and native trees with the sea lapping at the bottom of our driveway at high tide. Enjoy windsurfing, small boat sailing, rowing or stroll along the shell banks watching the sea birds.

Our interests are sailing in our Keeler, diving, tramping and in winter skiing and trout fishing. Our children have left home and we would enjoy sharing our comfortable home, our nautical environment and interests with you.

Directions: *From Harbour Bridge northern motorway - take Takapuna turn off into Esmonde Rd, turn right into Lake Rd and continue 2km to Belmont lights. Turn right into King Edward Ave 2km then right into Lansdowne St. Shuttle direct from airport or we can arrange pick up given prior notice.*

Devonport

Homestay
Address: "Cheltenham-By-The-Sea"
2 Grove Road, Devonport, Auckland
Name: Joyce and Harry Mossman
Telephone & Fax: (09) 445 9437

Beds: 1 Queen, 4 Single (3 bedrooms) **Bathroom:** 1 Private, 1 Guests share
Tariff: B&B (continental) Queen $70, Single $45; Children half price
Transport available by "Super" Shuttle Bus direct from airport

Adjacent to lovely Cheltenham Beach with safe swimming and pleasant walks in unique area. 45 mins from International Airport or 12 mins from downtown Auckland Ferry across Waitemata Harbour.

Large clean comfortable home in quiet area with spacious lawn, shade trees and secluded patio. Complimentary tea and coffee is provided. Several restaurants handy. An escort service by private car for business, sightseeing, pleasure and places of interest is available at reasonable rates. Two minutes walk to bus stops and shops. Short walk to golf course, bowling and croquet clubs, tennis and squash courts.

Our interests are people, travel, family, swimming, camping, fishing and gardening. We have a background of farming, navy and building.

There is no other marine suburb which offers so much in such a small picturesque area. We have enjoyed 12 years of home hosting, and a warm welcome is assured by your hosts.

Reservations are advisable to avoid disappointment.

Devonport

Homestay
Address: 'Devonport Villa/
Towers Bed & Breakfast',
46 Tainui Road, Devonport
Name: Yvonne Lambert and Philip Brown
Telephone: (09) 445 8397
Fax: (09) 445 9766
Beds: 4 Double (4 bedrooms)
Bathroom: 4 Ensuite
Tariff: B&B (special) Double $117.50-$160, Single $95 Credit cards: Visa/MC/Amex
Nearest Town: Devonport - 15 minutes by ferry or 20 minutes by car to Auckland City

'Devonport Villa' / 'Towers Bed & Breakfast' is located just two minutes walk from Cheltenham beach and only minutes from Devonport. Our home is an historic Victorian villa restored to the highest standard. We offer spacious, tastefully decorated rooms with handmade quilts and firm queen size beds. Each room has its own bathroom. Our Rangitoto Room with its large private bathroom, balcony and sea view is a favourite with honeymooners. Breakfast is very special - homemade muffins, fresh fruit salad with muesli, omelettes, Eggs Benedict, freshly squeezed juice and excellent coffee and teas. Devonport is a delightful seaside village just across from downtown Auckland. It offers an excellent variety of restaurants, shops and lovely beaches. We provide off-street parking and are close to McHughs Reception Lounge.
Directions: *From the Airport take the shuttle direct or the ferry from downtown Auckland. We can meet you at Devonport Wharf. If driving please phone. We are a non-smoking family.*

Devonport

Homestay
Address: "Morningstar" 25A
Queens Pde, Devonport, Auckland
Name: Ian & Rata Graham
Telephone: (09) 445 7123
Fax: (09) 445 9097
Beds: 2 Single (1 bedroom)
Bathroom: Private
Tariff: B&B (full) Double $75, Single $55, Dinner $25, Vouchers accepted

Haere Mai -
Welcome to "Morningstar", our home which enjoys peace, privacy, seclusion and sun. We are a four minute level walk from the downtown ferry , and the bustling, quaint, maritime Devonport village, with its shops, crafts, restaurants, cafes and bars. A courtesy car is available to / from the ferry to downtown Auckland.
Relax outdoors in our private garden courtyard, or by the fire in our comfortable home. If you want to "get up and go" we are happy to arrange garden, craft or sightseeing tours, sailing, theatre or restaurant bookings for you.
Enjoy breakfast, fresh fruit, muesli, cereals, yogurt and / or bacon, ham, sausages etc, plus a selection of teas or coffee. Traditional New Zealand dinner available on request.
We have travelled extensively in New Zealand and overseas, enjoy meeting people, good food, wine, a variety of music, theatre, gardening etc.
Directions: *Phone or Fax. We look forward to welcoming you to "Morningstar".*

Devonport

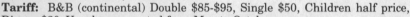

Homestay + Self -contained accommodation
Address: 14 Sinclair St, Devonport, Auckland 9
Name: Karin's Garden Villa
Telephone & Fax: (09) 445-8689
Beds: 2 Double, 4 Single (4 Bedrooms)
Bathrooms: 1 Ensuite, 1 Guests share
Tariff: B&B (continental) Double $85-$95, Single $50, Children half price, Dinner $20, Vouchers accepted from May to October
Nearest Town: Devonport 15 minutes drive or ferry from downtown Auckland.

Directions: *The Airport Super Shuttle brings you to our door.*
Northbound: After crossing Harbour Bridge, take Takapuna -Devonport turnoff; turn right at T-junction and follow Lake Road to end. Left into Albert Road, left into Vauxhall Road and first left is Sinclair Street.
Southbound: Leave motorway at Takapuna-Northcote exit, turn left then right at first lights. Go through Takapuna to follow Lake Road, as above.

Our charming restored Victorian villa shares large lawns with old fruit trees at the end of a quiet cul-de-sac. Your sunny comfortable room has separate private entry via French doors to verandah and garden.
5 mins' stroll to tree-lined Cheltenham Beach, golf, tennis, shops and bus. 3 mins' drive to the picturesque centre of Devonport Borough. Historic walkways to extinct volcanoes, lively panoramas of city and gulf. Cinema, museums, specialty shops, German bakery, bistros, international eateries, waterfront pubs with views of Auckland's skyline are just a few hundred metres from Downtown.
Delicious home cooking. Sunny breakfast room with bay windows. Guests are welcome to join the family barbecue and relax in the garden. Help yourself to tea and German-style coffee anytime and feel free to use the kitchen and laundry.
Karin comes from Hamburg, Tony is a native Kiwi who frequently visits Indonesia. With our 2 children Martina 15, and Stefan 11 we have travelled widely and enjoy meeting other travellers. Always happy to help you arrange island cruises, rental cars and tours.
"Bis bald - See ya soon - a bientot" - children welcome!

Devonport
Homestay/Self-contained garden room
Address: 'The Garden Room', 23 Cheltenham Road, Devonport, Auckland 9
Name: Perrine and Bryan Hall
Telephone: (09) 445 2472
Beds: 2 Double, (single rollaway bed available) (2 bedrooms)
Bathroom: 2 Ensuite
Tariff: B&B (special) Double $95, Single $75, Children $20. (NZ Winter rates available).
Nearest Town: Devonport 12 minutes by ferry from downtown Auckland or 20 minutes via Harbour Bridge. Super Shuttle minibus direct from airport to our doorstep.

We live in a large seaside villa, a few metres from Cheltenham Beach. Within our garden we have created a tranquil setting for guests. "The Garden Room" is a very special new self contained room with ensuite, set in the garden separate from the house. It has its own entrance and parking area, and is decorated with terra-cotta tiled floors, billowing calico curtains over large french doors opening into a garden of fragrant old roses.

Let us spoil you with a delicious breakfast brought to your room or set on the outside table in the courtyard - perhaps later a cappuccino.

A selection of teas, fresh coffee brewing facilities are available in your room. We are happy to do your laundry.

We offer also a guest room with ensuite in the house, where you may enjoy the ambience of a transitional villa with up to the minute decor and amenities.

Devonport is a unique seaside village with excellent restaurants, cafes and shops a pleasant 15 minute stroll away, although we are happy to drive you. Surrounding us are lovely beaches, parks, walks.

We have both travelled extensively and welcome you warmly to our house and garden.

Devonport
B&B Inn
Address: "The Peace & Plenty Inn", 6 Flagstaff Terrace, Devonport, Auckland
Name: Carol and Bruce Hyland
Telephone: (09) 445 2925
Fax: (09) 302 0389
Beds: 5 Double, 2 Single (5 bedrooms)
Bathroom: 1 Ensuite, 2 Guests share
Tariff: B&B (special) Double $110-$140, Single $85-$110, Children welcome,
Campervans welcome.   Credit cards: Visa/MC/Amex.
Nearest Town: Auckland; 15 mins by ferry or car

*The Peace & Plenty Inn is a romantic and luxurious Bed and Breakfast in an
unequalled location on the waterfront, in the very heart of Devonport. Within a
two minute stroll, there are thirty restaurants and cafes, art galleries, shopping,
a swimming beach and the frequent 10 minute ferry ride to central Auckland. Set
in a lush tropical garden, our inn features 5 charming guest rooms in a restored,
historic home, furnished to suit the most discerning traveller. Guest rooms feature
antique furniture, fireplaces, oriental carpets, fine art and the most comfortable
beds with fluffy duvets, plump pillows and always, fresh flowers everywhere.
Complimentary tea, coffee, sherry and port are served in an elegant, comfortable
private lounge. We pamper our guests with a breakfast that is a gourmet's delight,
using only the finest quality free range eggs, home made yoghurt and muesli,
double smoked bacon and freshly squeezed orange juice. Tantalize your taste buds
with Eggs Benedict, Smoked Salmon Scrambled Eggs, Omelets, Fritattas, and
French Baked Eggs; all served with freshly baked muffins, piping hot coffee and
a wide selection of teas. If you share our passion for sailing, join us for a cruise
on Auckland's fabulous harbour, on our classic wooden ketch (extra, by
arrangement).*

Devonport, Auckland
Bed & Breakfast
Address: "Villa Cambria " 71 Vauxhall Road, Devonport
Name: Noel Allen
Telephone: (09) 445 7899
Beds: 2 Queen, 1 Double, 1 Single (4 Bedrooms)
Bathroom: 2, Guests share
Tariff: B&B (continental) Double $85- $98, Single $60-$75, Dinner: By arrangement. Credit cards: Visa, M/C, B/C.
Nearest Town: Auckland 15 minutes by car or ferry

Villa Cambria is an historic Victorian Villa featuring Nineteenth Century architecture and ambience with amenities styled for today's living.
Come and experience warm hospitality, comfortable luxurious furnishings and delicious buffet breakfasts in a tranquil garden setting. Close by is Devonport, Auckland's unique seaside village offering gourmet restaurants, continental cafes and speciality shopping in an old-world atmosphere - charming and friendly. Enjoy the art studios, the museums, the antique shops or the lovely harbourside walks while Auckland City beckons just minutes away by ferry across the harbour. A short walk from the Villa Cambria you will find a full 18-hole golf course, delightful Cheltenham Beach and historic North Head.

Directions: *From Airport: Shuttle bus direct or to Downtown Ferry Terminal for Devonport Ferry. (Courtesy car pick-up from Ferry is available.) By Car: Take Lake Road south from Takapuna to the traffic roundabout at Mount Victoria. Turn left into Albert Road and continue onto Vauxhall Road. Turn left to Number 71.*

The standard of accommodation in *The New Zealand Bed and Breakfast Book* ranges from homely to luxurious, but you can always be sure of superior hospitality.

Devonport

Homestay (Opening January 1995)
Address: "Top of the Drive" 15c King Edward Parade Devonport Auckland
Name: Viv & Ray Huckle
Telephone: (09) 445 3362
Beds: 1 Queen, 1 Double, 2 Single (3 Bedrooms)
Bathroom: 2 Ensuite, 1 Private (toilet & vanity basin), 1 Family share
Tariff: B&B (special) Double $85-$100, Single $60, Children under 12 from $15.
Nearest Town: Auckland 15 mins by ferry or car

We consider ourselves to be very fortunate to live along Devonport's lovely waterfront, only a delightful 5 minute stroll to our local historic seaside centre with its shops, cinema, wide variety of restaurants and ferry service to Auckland city.

Devonport also offers the best views in Auckland from the top of Mount Victoria, lovely safe beaches, golf, walks, fishing, museums.

Our house is newly built, spacious and comfortable. We have 3 large guest bedrooms. The two double rooms have own ensuites. The single room has own private toilet and vanity basin plus sharing family bathroom. All have good quality furnishings and sea views.

Enjoy a leisurely special breakfast of your choice, with the best of homemade food, fresh fruit and juices, teas and coffees.

We have a smoke free home, with good off street parking and a friendly short haired Pointer, Frieda, who does not come into the house. Tea and coffee always available.

Directions: *From Airport take shuttle bus direct, or if driving follow directions to Devonport, past shops to waterfront turn left. Please phone ahead.*
Looking forward to meeting you!

Devonport

Homestay
Address: Argyll Cottage, 12 Garden Terrace, Devonport, Auckland 9
Name: Netta & Claude Smith
Telephone: (09) 445 1528
Beds: 2 Double, 1 Single (3 Bedrooms) **Bathroom:** 2 Family share
Tariff: B&B (special) Double $85, Single $50, Vouchers accepted May - September
Nearest Town: Devonport 200m, Auckland 10 minutes by ferry.

We would like to welcome you to Argyll Cottage, our pretty Edwardian home, situated in a pleasant quiet street, just off the waterfront in the marine village of Devonport, one of the earliest European settlements in New Zealand.
Situated only three minutes from the ferry which takes you to downtown Auckland; within easy reach of Devonport's excellent restaurants, boutiques and Galleries. Argyll Cottage offers old world ambiance along with modern comforts and a warm welcome.
Golf, museums, safe swimming and golden beaches, sailing and harbour cruising are all within easy reach.
We offer a variety of scrumptious breakfasts, cooked or continental style including home-made muesli, yoghurt, muffins and preserves. Coffee and tea are available at all times. We also offer our guests a smoke free environment.
Directions: *Garden Terrace is the third street from the Ferry Wharf going west*

Waiheke Island

Homestay/Guest House
Address: "Hauraki House", 50 Hauraki Rd, Sandy Bay, Waiheke Island
Name: Gladys Hurley
Telephone: (09) 3727598
Beds: 2 Double, 2 Single (3 bedrooms)
Bathroom: 2 Guests share
Tariff: B&B (special) Double $70, Single $40, Children $10-15, Dinner $25
Nearest Town: Auckland

Extracts from NZ Herald May 93:
Gladys runs a B & B on Waiheke Island. A perfect setting for those who don't want to drive - Arrive by ferry - be met by Gladys, taken to Hauraki House. Most people staying there were like us - just resting up - In the end what you remember is the well being of total indolence - In Gladys's case it's the memory of her cooking that remains.
Extracts from Pacific Way - Air NZ Sept 92:
Looking out over Sandy Bay and Peninsular Vineyard at the glassy blue waters of the Hauraki Gulf - Hauraki House is furnished with antiques and period furniture. Travellers seeking time out from city bustle can take refuge here.
The Waiheke Artworks are interesting or golf, bowls, kayaking, riding, fishing, winetours can be arranged.
Directions: *"Quickcat" catamaran from Ferry Buildings - Downtown Auckland. Buses meet ferries and stop outside or I provide a courtesy car.*

Waiheke Island

Homestay (2 self-cont. Dbl units planned for 1995)
Address: "Gulf Haven"
49 Great Barrier Road,
Enclosure Bay, Waiheke Island
Name: Alan Ramsbottom & Lois Baucke
Telephone: (09) 372 6629
Beds: 1 Double, 2 Single (2 bedrooms) **Bathroom:** 1 Guests share
Tariff: B&B (continental) Double $75, Twin $90, Single $50, Not suitable for children, Lunch & Dinner as requested, Vouchers accepted May to Sept. inclusive.
Nearest Town: Auckland

Waiheke Island is different. A unique lifestyle, superb scenery, yet only 35 minutes from downtown Auckland.
Our new home sits on a low ridge on over 2 acres of land running down to the sea. A garden path takes you to secluded rockpools and clear deep water for snorkelling. Warm and comfortable, the house and garden take advantage of the dramatic views of the Northern Coast of Waiheke Island, with Coromandel Peninsula and Great Barrier Island beyond.
We provide an excellent breakfast. There are good restaurants on the island. Tea or coffee is always available. Lois and I enjoy the outdoors and the Arts, and are non-smokers. We have a Burmese cat, Misty.
Explore the Island, (we have 2 bicycles), its beaches and hills, its acclaimed vineyards, its varied crafts or just relax. We can arrange golf, horseriding, kayaking etc.
We enjoy our island hideaway and its mild climate and welcome you to experience it with us.
Directions: *Shuttle bus from Auckland Airport, then passenger ferry from Ferry Buildings, Downtown Auckland, approx every 2 hours. Also vehicular ferry and plane service. We meet you from any, but please phone first.*

Oneroa, Waiheke Island
Homestay/Self-contained flatette
Address: 6 Karu Street, Oneroa, Waiheke Island
Name: Mrs Joan Beckingsale
Telephone: (09) 372 8152
Beds: 2 Single (1 bedroom) **Bathrooms:** 1Ensuite
Tariff: B&B (continental) Double $75 (Winter rate $65), Single $50 (Winter rate $40). Vouchers accepted from April to October
Nearest Town: Auckland, 35 mins

We have peace and tranquillity in a quiet cul-de-sac with views of farmland and sea, yet only a short walk to Oneroa Beach and the Village. I supply a generous continental breakfast and there are restaurants, cafes and take-aways in Oneroa which is the main shopping centre for Waiheke Island. The Post Office and banks are there and just up the road the Artworks, which is a centre for art exhibitions, pottery, leather work, craft shops and the Public Library.

Our accommodation is warm and sunny in winter, cool and comfortable in summer. It comprises a self-contained unit of twin bed-sitting room with electric blankets, colour TV and armchairs; a fully equipped dining-kitchenette and shower and toilet. A cot is available for a baby but not for children. I meet guests at both passenger and vehicular ferries.

Please telephone first if you are coming to stay.

Directions: *Quickcat Catamaran Ferry from the Ferry Building, Downtown Auckland. Subritzky Shipping Ltd for vehicles.*

Waiheke Island
Homestay, Self-contained Accommodation
Address: 40 Pacific Parade, Waiheke Island
Name: Patricia
Telephone: (09) 372-8181

Beds: 1 Double, 2 Single, (3 bedrooms) **Bathroom:** 1 Ensuite for double, 1 guest share. Self-contained flat sleeps 2, $55 per night, reduction for longer stays and during winter. Bach, 3 bedrooms sometimes available, $55 per night.
Tariff: B&B (continental) Double $65, Single $35, Dinner $20, Children half price, Vouchers accepted
Nearest Town: Auckland 35 minutes passenger ferry, 1 hour vehicular ferry

Anywhere on Waiheke seems close to the sea and to nature. It is a great place to just relax and be refreshed.

Our home is a former convent and we think a peaceful atmosphere is here. There are truely beautiful views from it. The area is quiet yet central.

The self-contained flat is on the sea-side of the house and opens on to a large deck, making outside dining and relaxing possible. The flat is well equipped, TV included.

Waiheke's popularity grows each year. There are cafes, restaurants, vineyards, artworks, tours. A shuttle bus or taxi will transport you from ferry to door. The house is smoke-free. The nearest beach os Little Oneroa. The island has a good variety of beaches and bays.

Previous guests have enjoyed the opportunity to unwind after or before further travelling. We are happy to reduce the rates for a longer stay or for one person. We find the Island a hard place to leave.

When you stay at B&Bs you are staying with "dinkum Kiwis"

99

Punga Lodge

Waiheke Island
Guest House
Address: 223 Ocean View Road,
Little Oneroa, Waiheke Island
Name: Waiheke Punga Lodge
Telephone: (09) 372-6675
Beds: 3 Double, 1 Twin (4 bedrooms)
Bathroom: 2 Guests share.
1 fully serviced Double bedroom with en-suite.
Tariff: B&B (continental) Serviced room with en-suite $120, Double $70, Single $55; Children over 12 years, Vouchers accepted
Nearest Town: Auckland

Only 35 mins by ferry from the hustle of Auckland, Punga Lodge on Waiheke Island is the perfect place to unwind. The informal relaxed atmosphere that is Punga Lodge gives the visitor a unique feeling of being treated as a friend rather than a tourist. The sunny rooms in Punga Lodge open onto sun decks overlooking the garden which is surrounded by native bush teeming with birdlife, yet Punga Lodge is only 150m from a safe sandy beach. The restaurants and shops of Oneroa are just a stroll away. Your hosts Derek and Catrina can arrange tours and other leisure pursuits, as well as recommend the best places for dining out. All guests are met from the ferry by the Punga Lodge courtesy car and returned to the ferry after their stay.
Directions: *'Quickcat' ferry from downtown Auckland. Bus or taxi, but please phone and we will be pleased to meet you from the ferry.*

Great Barrier Island
Farmstay+Guest House+Self-contained Accommodation
Address: "Orama" Karaka Bay Great Barrier Island
Telephone: (09) 429 0063 **Fax:** (09) 429 0155
Beds: 4 Double, 8 Twin, 2 Single (12 Bedrooms)
Bathroom: 4 Guests share
Tariff: B&B (continental) $25 per person, per night (Children half price), Price include Continental Breakfast, Other meals by arrangement
Nearest Town: Auckland

Orama offers the opportunity for a unique island holiday. Set on the shore of a secluded bay, surrounded by bush there are excellent opportunities for fishing, boating, swimming, tramping, or just relaxing. We are close to beautiful bush walks and other lovely surf beaches. Taxis and hire cars available. Guests have the use of a spacious lounge with sea views and a log fire in winter. Fully equipped kitchens allow you to cook your food as you like it and when you are hungry. Come by Fullers 'Jet Raider' to Port Fitzroy or Great Barrier Airlines to Okiwi and we will meet you. We have a library, trampolines, pool table, swimming pool, children's playground, and dinghies for your use. Our shop is well stocked with grocery items, gifts, and fishing gear. Our self-contained flats and cottage have beautiful sea views and some are situated right on the water edge. Orama is an ecumenical Christian Community offering both space and privacy in self-contained accommodation or the opportunity to share a meal with community families.

St Marys Bay, Auckland
Bed and Breakfast
Address: 14 Ring Terrace,
St Marys Bay, Auckland
Name: Rick & Sally Kerse
Telephone & Fax: (09) 3781-517
Beds: 2 Queen, 1 Double, Single rollaway, Cot available (3 bedrooms)
Bathroom: 1 Guests share
Tariff: B&B (full) Double $90, Single $70, Children under 12 half price

Our home is a large 1910 Victorian villa with delightful cottage gardens overflowing with roses as featured in April 94 edition of NZ Gardener magazine. We have city and harbour views from large decks.

Centrally located, 20 minute walk downtown, close shops, restaurants, markets, buses, harbour ferrys, and Westhaven Marina.

We offer a peaceful relaxing atmosphere with warm friendly hospitality.

Our home is divided in two so our guest accommodation is separate with its own entrance. Lounge area has access to our home so you may be private or join us. We have three large bedrooms decorated in an old world romantic charm. Fresh flowers, bathrobes and feathers duvets provided. Private guest bathroom, separate toilet.

Your lounge area overlooks the garden, has TV, video, small kitchenette, fridge, tea and coffee facilities. Tin of homemade baking usually available.

Breakfast is your choice - cooked or continental accompanied by homemade preserves, fresh fruit and cream, cereals and yoghurt, breads and pastries plus percolated coffee and variety of teas. We are happy to bring it to your room (with morning newspaper) or serve you on the sundeck or dining room.

So as to enjoy the local hospitality we suggest you sample some of the many wonderful restaurants and cafes we have within easy walking distance.

Directions: *Please phone.*

Freemans Bay, Auckland City
Guest House/Self-contained Accommodation
Address: 65 Wellington Street,
Freemans Bay, Auckland 1
Name: Freeman's Bed and Breakfast
Telephone: (09) 376-5046,
Fax: (09) 376-4052
Beds: 6 Double, 15 Single (11 bedrooms + 2 apartments)
Bathroom: 2 Ensuite, 3 Guests share
Tariff: B&B (special) Double $65, Single $43,
Self contained apartments: 2 persons $85,
3 persons $95, 4 persons $105, Credit cards accepted

Freeman's is a friendly bed and breakfast guest hotel located within a ten to fifteen minute walk of Auckland city, Victoria Park markets, Ponsonby and the harbour. "SUPERSHUTTLE" provides a 24-hour two-way service between the Airport and Freeman's.
Our guest lounge provides complimentary tea, coffee and chocolate making facilities. A fridge, telephone and television are available for our guests convenience. The lounge opens onto a secluded garden with a conservatory and barbecue. We also have laundry facilities.
Our healthy breakfast caters especially for the needs of our energetic travellers. Our coffee's the best in New Zealand, freshly ground every day.
Derek and Maureen provide a friendly, relaxed atmosphere for your stay in Auckland and New Zealand. Just ask about car rentals, tours, and all other travel requirements. Freemans the friendly guest house welcomes you to "your home away from home"

Auckland City
Guesthouse
Address: 62 Emily Place,
Auckland Central
Name: Aspen Lodge
Telephone : (09) 379 6698
Fax: (09) 377 7625
Beds: 6 Double, 26 Single (26 Bedrooms)
Bathrooms: 5 Guests share
Tariff: B&B (continental) Twin or Double $65,
Single $45, 1st Child under 12 free.

Aspen Lodge or "The Pink Palace" as people like to call it is in a prime location to access all of Auckland's exciting activities. Only 5 minutes walk to Queen Street, Ferries, Bus and Railway Stations, University, Art Gallery and Restaurants. So central and yet it's quiet! We have 24 hour tea and coffee facilities and a laundry is available for guests. Free baggage storage. Courtesy coach to pick up from rail and bus depots and other central city locations (please request this service in advance). We will gladly assist with booking sightseeing tours and arrange car and campervan hires at the best rates. If arriving from Auckland Airport take advantage of our special rate with "Supershuttle". We look forward to welcoming you to Auckland.

Herne Bay, Auckland

Tourist Lodge
Address: 75 Argyle Street, Herne Bay, Auckland
Name: Heathmaur Lodge
Telephone: (09) 376 3527
Beds: 9 Double, 12 Single (13 bedrooms)
Bathroom: 7 Ensuite, 5 Guests share
Tariff: B&B (full/weekends continental) Double $50, Single $35, (Additional $10 for ensuite facilities), Dinner $10, Children under 5 Free, Credit cards accepted, Vouchers accepted

'Heathmaur Lodge' is situated on the sunny northern slopes of Herne Bay. The 100 year old Lodge overlooks the Waitemata Harbour with Herne Bay beach being just two minutes walk. The quiet, tree-lined streets and the Victorian Villas give the locality an old world charm. The three storey Lodge is elegant and spacious. Seven rooms have ensuites, the rest have washhand basins and are close to communal facilities. Most rooms enjoy beautiful Harbour views. There is a very comfortable lounge with an open fire place, a pool room and a sunny reading room with tea and coffee making facilities. Off-street car parking. We as your hosts aim to create a relaxed and friendly family atmosphere in which you are made most welcome. We invite you to join our family in an evening meal to talk over the days events. Alternatively a 5 minute walk takes you to our fashionable restaurant district of Herne Bay. Guest Laundry available.

Parnell, Auckland City

Homestay
Address: 13 Birdwood Crescent, Parnell, Auckland City
Name: Lloyd & Jacqueline Walker
Telephone: (09) 377-3393
Beds: 1 Double, 1 Single (2 bedrooms) **Bathroom:** 1 Family share
Tariff: B&B (full) Double $60, Single $40. A surcharge of $15pp is added when guests arrive before 11am. Vouchers accepted May to November.

Take advantage of our inner city location! Our house is tucked away amid a mass of trees with Parnell on our doorstep: Parnell Village shops, the Rose Gardens, historic buildings including the lovely St Mary's Church, a dozen art galleries and about forty restaurants to choose from.
We're very close to the Domain Park, with its acres of open space surrounding the Auckland Museum, and along the road a few blocks is Newmarket's extensive shopping area.
We offer clean sunny bedrooms in an old house with mellow wood panelling, open fires in winter, an elevated balcony with wide views, and a secluded subtropical garden. The garden provides produce for guests' breakfast such as fresh fruit and honey from our hive.
We welcome you to our home.
The airport shuttle stops close by.
Directions: *Please phone. Note: longer stay, self-contained accommodation may be available on application.*

Parnell, Auckland City
Guest House, Small Hotel
Address: 36 St Stephens Avenue,
Parnell, Auckland 1
Name: Ascot Parnell
Telephone: (09) 309-9012
Fax: (09) 3093-729
Beds: 9 Double/Twin, 2 Single (11 bedrooms, all with phone, private facilities and heating)
Bathrooms: 10 Ensuite, 1 Private
Tariff: B&B Double/Twin $99-$108, Single $72-$76.50, Children $13.50. Cooked breakfast included, parking available, Credit cards accepted
Nearest Town: Auckland city centre - 2 km

The ASCOT PARNELL - an elegant mansion in a subtropical garden - "is one of Auckland's most pleasant and atmospheric lodgings." (FROMMERS GUIDE NZ).

All 11 non-smoker guestrooms have bathrooms, telephones, heating and electric blankets.

The intimacy of the ASCOT PARNELL makes it possible for the guests to enjoy a friendly service and personal attention. A delightful breakfast is served in a dining room which shows the beauty of this lovely home. Throughout the day free tea, coffee and juice are served in the lounge. The airport shuttle stops in front of the house. We will help you to book tours, find reasonable priced rental cars and recommend shops and restaurants. Although our house is a peaceful place to stay, it is nevertheless very close to the city centre (2km) and within walking distance to many tourist attractions such as PARNELL VILLAGE or Auckland Museum. We also speak German, French & Dutch.

We advise to book in advance. Your hosts: Bart & Therese

Some homes share the bathroom, others have bathrooms exclusively for guests – they are indicated in the listing.

Parnell, Auckland City
Guest House/Bed & Breakfast
Address: 14 Brighton Road,
Parnell, Auckland 1
Name: John & Judy Dufty
Telephone: (09) 3090-290 or 3090-291,
Fax: (09) 3735-754
Beds: 4 Double, 2 Twin, 2 Family (4 or 5), 4 Single **Bathrooms:** All ensuites
Tariff: B&B (Full) Double/Twin $95, Single $55, Extra $35 each. Includes cooked/continental breakfast .
Nearest Town: Auckland City centre 2km

Chalet Chevron is a large friendly house in historic Parnell. Many of our comfortable rooms have fabulous views of the harbour and Rangitoto Island. Each has ensuite facilities plus direct dial phones. The breakfast room faces north / east and provides a sunny place to relax, chat to others and enjoy the view.
Our cheerful staff are always pleased to help with tours, hire cars, sights to see and shopping suggestions as well as general information.
Picturesque Parnell Village, restaurants, the Museum and Domain, and the Ross Garden are a few of the attractions within walking distance.
All tour buses pickup from and deliver to the door. A warm welcome awaits you at Chalet Chevron.

Parnell, Auckland City
Bed & Breakfast
Address: 11 Judges Bay Rd, Parnell, Auckland
Name: "The Redwood" Dawn Feickert
Telephone & Fax: (09) 373 4903
Beds: 2 Queen, 1 Double, 1 Single (3 Bedrooms)
Bathroom: 2 Ensuite, 1 Family share
Tariff: B&B (special) Double $80, Single $50,
Children $25, Reduced winter rates. Vouchers accepted.
Nearest Town: Auckland city centre 2km

The Redwood Parnell is situated adjacent to the Dove-Myer Robinson Park which is renowned for its Rose Gardens. We are nestled in a peaceful bush like setting with a view across the Auckland Harbour to Devonport and conveniently located nearby many popular tourist attractions including Parnell Village, the Museum and Kelly Tarltons. A selection of Restaurants, Theatres and shopping centres are easily accessible and the city is with easy walking distance or just one stop on the bus route.
Facilities available to guests include: Tea / Coffee, Office Services, private telephone, electric blankets, television room, and tourist guides and information. The Airport bus stops closeby and door to door service can be arranged. We are happy to pick up from train or bus and arrange on going travel.
Having travelled extensively within New Zealand and overseas we aim to provide you with a home away from home making your stay with us a pleasant and memorable one.

Parnell, Auckland
Bed & Breakfast
Address: 11 Judges Bay Rd,
Parnell, Auckland
Name: "The Redwood" Dawn Feickert
Telephone & Fax: (09) 373 4903
Beds: 2 Queen, 1 Double, 1 Single
(3 Bedrooms)
Bathroom: 2 Ensuite, 1 Family share
Tariff: B&B (special) Double $80,
Single $50, Children $25, Reduced winter rates.
Vouchers accepted.
Nearest Town: Auckland city centre 2km

The Redwood Parnell is situated adjacent to the Dove-Myer Robinson Park which is renowned for its Rose Gardens. We are nestled in a peaceful bush like setting with a view across the Auckland Harbour to Devonport and conveniently located nearby many popular tourist attractions including Parnell Village, the Museum and Kelly Tarltons. A selection of Restaurants, Theatres and shopping centres are easily accessible and the city is with easy walking distance or just one stop on the bus route.
Facilities available to guests include: Tea / Coffee, Office Services, private telephone, electric blankets, television room, and tourist guides and information. The Airport bus stops closeby and door to door service can be arranged. We are happy to pick up from train or bus and arrange on going travel.
Having travelled extensively within New Zealand and overseas we aim to provide you with a home away from home making your stay with us a pleasant and memorable one.

Parnell, Auckland
Homestay
Address: 34 Awatea Rd Parnell Auckland
Name: Manning
Telephone: (09) 379 4100
Beds: 2 Double (2 Bedrooms) **Bathroom:** 1 Guests share
Tariff: B&B (continental) Double $82, Single $40, Dinner $20

Peaceful Parnell with seaviews with in walking distance of Parnell shops and restaurants.
Seaside walks via St Stephens Ave and overbridge to railway crossing and water front.
Separate games room for guests and upstairs reading room if required. Friendly relaxed hospitality. No smoking.
Your hosts are interested in people from overseas and New Zealand.
Directions available for trips to places of interest.
Comfortable warm beds and good food.
Dinner on request. Door to door shuttle bus.

Grafton, Auckland City

Homestay
Address: 17A Carlton Gore Road,
Grafton, Auckland 1
Name: George and Janette Welanyk
Telephone: (09) 3774-319
Beds: 1 Twin, 1 Single (2 bedrooms)
Bathroom: 1 Guests share
Tariff: B&B (full) Twin $65, Single $45.
Vouchers accepted.

*When visiting New Zealand we invite you to stay with my wife and I in our home
which is within walking distance of the city, shops, parks and other attractions.
We are situated in an inner city area of Auckland. Our house was built in 1925
and is large, comfortable and furnished with antique furniture.*
*The facilities for guests include a private sitting room with colour television and
video and guests bathroom. Breakfast is inclusive.*
Your hosts have travelled extensively overseas and welcome visitors.
Directions: *From the Airport take the door to door shuttle minibus. Please
telephone.*

Mt. Eden, Auckland City

Bed & Breakfast
Address: 811 Dominion Road,
Mt. Eden, Auckland 4
Name: David Fitchew & Bryan Condon
Telephone: (09) 620 4284. Fax: (09) 620 7283
Beds: 2 Double, 1 Twin (3 bedrooms, 2 guest bathrooms)
Tariff: B&B (Full) Double $55 Single $35 includes cooked breakfast,fresh
muffins daily. Tea & coffee always available

*Your hosts Bryan and David and their Irish Water Spaniels welcome you to their
turn of the century home. Our home reflects years of collecting and living overseas.
Centrally located on Dominion Road which is an extension of Queen Street city
centre. The bus stop at the door, only 10 minutes to city and 20 minutes to airport,
shuttle bus from airport. Easy walking to Balmoral shopping area (banks,
excellent restaurants, cinema).*
*We have operated a bed and breakfast on a farm in Digby County, Nova Scotia,
Canada. The nicest compliment we can receive is when Guests tell us, it's like
visiting friends when they stay with us. Our breakfast gives you a Beaut start to
your day...*
Directions: *from north-south motorway, Greenlane off ramp, continue on
Greenlane, to Dominion Road. Turn left and we are 7 blocks on your right to 811
(between Lambeth and Invermay and across from Landscape Road).*

107

Mt Eden, Auckland City
A Small Hotel
Address: 83 Valley Road, Mt. Eden
Name: Bavaria House
Telephone: (09) 638 9641
Fax: 6389-665
Beds: 7 Double, 4 Single (11 bedrooms)
Bathroom: 11 Ensuite
Tariff: B&B (full) Double $79 - $92, Single $49 - $62, Children $10; No pets! reduced winter rates. Credit cards. Vouchers accepted from 1 April 95 to 30 September 95.

Bavaria Guest House was originally an old villa which has been completely modernised and refurbished. It is situated in the heart of Mt Eden's residential area. Our establishment comprises double, twin, single and family rooms all with own bathroom and heating. Five rooms have queen size beds and balconies with sunny northerly aspect. All are friendly and tastefully decorated. During the day we serve free tea and coffee in the generously designed sunny guest lounge / breakfast area which opens out to a northfacing private sundeck. There is ample off-street parking available.
We are located only 3 km from the city centre and 15 minutes from the airport. The bus stop is nearby, so are restaurants, shops, banks, post office and famous Eden Park. A scenic walk leads up to magnificent Mt Eden, an extinct volcano. Your hosts Rudi and Ulrike from Germany are happy to assist you with your travel plans and endeavour to make your stay a pleasant experience.

Mt Eden, Auckland
Guest House/Small Hotel
Address: 22 Pentland Avenue,
Mt Eden, Auckland 3 (off Valley Rd)
Name: Pentlands Tourist Hotel
Telephone: (09) 638-7031
Beds: 7 Double, 14 Single (15 bedrooms)
Bathroom: 4 guests share, 5 toilets.

Tariff: B&B (continental) Double/Twin $59-$65, Single $39-$45, Triple $75-$80, Rates negotiable for long stays. Vouchers accepted.
Nearest Town: Centre of Auckland City 3km

Centrally located in a quiet street on the lower slopes of Mt Eden.
Pentlands is a spacious, well-maintained and tastefully decorated old house in pleasant grounds with elevated views, native trees, tennis court and barbeque area.
We have a large guest lounge with TV, stereo, pool table and an open fire. 24 hour complimentary tea and coffee is available. Pentlands offers ample off-street parking, laundry facilities, guest phone, luggage storage, poste restante. We are a short walk from buses, restaurants, cafes and village shops.
Your hosts are Gail and Keith who are pleased to assist you with information and travel arrangements.
Directions: *From airport: Free-phone at information desk for transport arrangements. From city terminals: Phone for free pick up. Driving from south: Exit at Symonds Street from motorway SH1, turn left continue left into Mt Eden Road, right turn into Valley Rd at Mt Eden Village. Third left into Pentland Avenue.*

Mt Eden, Auckland
Homestay/Guest House
Address: 33 Paice Ave Mt Eden Auckland Central
Name: "Beggar's Banquet" Bruce Balfour
Telephone: (09) 630 8308
Beds: 5 Double (5 Bedrooms)
Bathroom: 2 Guests share
Tariff: B&B (full) Double $89-99, Single $59-69.
Complimentary 3 course dinner, continental/cooked breakfast.
Nearest Town: Auckland

Being Canadian by birth and after travelling the world several times I have made NZ my home. With my experience of travel I've tried to reduce many of the problems I've encountered with hidden costs and endless forays looking for my home comforts. Therefore I provide a full service of dinner, breakfast, spa, laundry, TV, Sky and stereo. I encourage guests to feel free to help themselves at any time.

My home is a unique restored two storey villa filled with plants and shrubs providing an earthy ambience.

In addition to being only 7 minutes from downtown we are handy to the village shops including banks, post office, antique shops, restaurants, wine shop and cinema.

It is also convenient to some of Auckland's unique attractions; the zoo, MOTAT museum, and Eden park.

Give me a call and I will pick you up at any inner city terminal or ask for easy directions.

Tell other travellers about your favourite B&Bs

Epsom, Auckland City
Homestay
Address: 10 Ngaroma Road, Epsom, Auckland 3
Name: Janet and Jim Millar
Telephone: (09) 625 7336
Beds: 1 Queen, 1 Double, 2 Single (3 bedrooms)
Bathroom: 1 Ensuite, 2 Private
Tariff: B&B (full) Double $60, Single $40, Children $12;
Dinner 25, Vouchers accepted
Nearest Town: Auckland 5 km to City centre

Our 75 year-old home is on the lower slopes of One Tree Hill (Maungakiekie), and has walking access to its Domain, one of Auckland's loveliest parks with glorious views. We are 200 metres off the direct airport-downtown Auckland route in a quiet tree-lined street. Close by are several good restaurants and the bus stop to the City, a bank and postal facilities.

Our upstairs guest bedroom (Queensize bed) has its own en-suite. The downstairs area has a double bedroom and lounge with three single beds, enabling us to cater for families; its own bathroom facilities, plus laundry, refrigerator and crockery / cutlery. It takes 10 minutes by car to downtown.

We have three grown-up children no longer living at home, and six lively grandchildren. We enjoy meeting people and making them feel at home. We have travelled extensively ourselves, both overseas and in N.Z. and we enjoy exchanging experiences.

We prefer people to refrain from smoking indoors.

From the airport you can use door to door shuttle buses.

Directions: *Leaving motorway at Greenlane, travel west past Greenlane Hospital turning left into Manukau Road at the lights. Ours is the 4th street on the left (south) just past the V-junction lights with Pah Road. which our street runs off at Greenwoods Corner.*

Epsom, Auckland City
Homestay/Self-contained Accom.
Address: 82 St Andrews Road, Epsom, Auckland
Name: Kay and Bill Foley
Telephone: (09) 638-8628
Beds: 1 Double, 2 Single (1 bedroom)
Bathroom: 1 Private
Tariff: B&B (full) Double $60, Single $40, Children half price. Vouchers accepted.

Our 90-year-old villa is centrally located only 10 minutes drive from the city centre and the bus stops outside our gate. We recommend using the shuttle service from the airport to our door.

We are close to One Tree Hill, Alexandra Park & Ellerslie Racecourses, the Showground, the Auckland Museum and a variety of restaurants. A visit to a supermarket is provided if required.

Our self-contained guest flat consists of a bedroom with queen sized bed, bathroom with laundry facilities and a lounge with a kitchen corner, TV and two single divans. A second bedroom with queen sized bed and a bathroom are available. Extra beds and a cot are available for families.

Two of our three children are overseas and our dog and two cats are very much part of the family.

We have a house rule of no smoking inside.

Our pool, garden and comfortable family home are here for you to enjoy.

One of the differences between staying at a hotel and a B&B
is that you don't hug the hotel staff when you leave.

111

Epsom, Auckland

Homestay
Address: 2/7 Tahuri Rd Epsom
Auckland 3
Name: Kathy & Roger Hey
Telephone: (09) 520 0154
Beds: 1 Super King size, converts
to two singles, 2 other single (2 Bedrooms)
Bathroom: 2 Private
Tariff: B&B (continental) Double $70, Single $45, Children concessions,
Dinner $20 by prior arrangement, Vouchers accepted March to October
Nearest Town: 4km from central city

In 1993 we built this lovely spacious 4 bedroom house, with ideal features for homestay. All comforts, and bedrooms offer views of One Tree Hill, Mt St John and Mt Hobson. Epsom is a very quiet garden suburb, with parks, restaurants, showgrounds, hospitals, postal facilities, banks and shops around us, one minute from the motorway. The Airport is 15 minutes away on door to door shuttle bus service. Excellent bus service two minutes walk away.

We are extensive travellers, both in NZ and overseas, enjoy meeting people, swopping tales and helping guests feel at home. We will collect guests from the railway station, and can suggest a variety of Auckland attractions.

Laundry facilities, off-street parking, juice, tea and coffee always available. Family groups welcome. We ask no smoking indoors.

Directions: *Leave Motorway at Market Road, travel west, cross over Great South Road, first left into Dunkerron Ave., Tahuri Road is 2nd left, we're at the end of the cul-de-sac.*

Greenlane, Auckland City

Homestay
Address: 22 Maungakiekie Ave.,
Greenlane, Auckland 5
Name: Mrs M. Heisch
Telephone: (09) 524 4887
Beds: 1 Double, 1 Single (2 bedrooms)
Bathroom: 1 Ensuite, 1 Family share
Tariff: B&B (full) Double $60, Single $35,
Dinner $15, Children $15. Vouchers accepted.

Our 64 year old home is on the lower slopes of Auckland's lovely Cornwall Park, to which it has walking access immediately across the road. We are close to the Southern Motorway and within a few minutes of Auckland city centre, yet the area is pleasantly secluded while within easy reach of buses and some excellent restaurants.

The double guestroom has its own ensuite and off street parking on request.

We have a dog and a cat and a large restful garden. We request no smoking indoors. Full or continental breakfast as requested.

Directions: *Exit Motorway at Greenlane West and take the 1st turn to the left after the 2nd set of traffic lights into Maungakiekie Avenue.*

Avondale, Auckland

Kodesh Christian Community
Address: 31b, Cradock Street,
Avondale, West Auckland
Name: Kodesh Christian Community
Telephone: (09) 828 3298 **or** 828 5672
Beds: 1 Double, 1 Single, 1 Twin
(3 bedrooms) **Bathroom:** 2 Family share
Tariff: B&B (continental) Double $35,
Single $23, Dinner $8, Children $4.

Kodesh is an ecumenical Christian community hidden away on 3 acres in a quiet cul-de-sac in Avondale, West Auckland - 8 minutes by car from downtown and on good bus and train routes. Transport can be arranged. A moderate charge is made to cover cost.

The main ministry of the community is hospitality but many members are also actively involved in various churches and parishes around Auckland. The average number of residents is 25, including families and singles.

Our guest rooms are situated in a large modern home.

Meals are served in the communal dining room which normally caters for 10-15 people.

The atmosphere is casual and relaxed and guests can amalgamate into the life of the community as much or as little as they desire.

The type of accommodation available ranges from backpacker to full meals. Brochures available on request.

Enquiries to Sue or Gayle.

Remuera, Auckland City

Guest House
Address: Remuera House, 500 Remuera Road, Remuera, Auckland 5
Name: Ray King
Telephone: (09) 524 7794
Beds: 3 Double, 5 Twin, 2 Single (10 bedrooms) **Bathrooms:** Guests share
Tariff: B&B (full) Double/Twin $58, Single $39, includes GST, Credit cards accepted
Nearest Town: Auckland 6 km (10 mins by car, 15 mins by bus)

For connoisseurs of old-world character, Remuera House is worth a stay. Built in 1901, the last year of Queen Victoria's reign, the two-storey house is full of interesting memorabilia, the breakfast room being a feature with paintings, antiques etc.

The large foyer and lounge are panelled in native timbers. Remuera House offers quietness (no traffic noise), safe off-street parking, Guest TV lounge with free tea/ coffee making facilities. Walking distance to buses, shops, restaurants, take- aways, and an extinct volcano, within 2 km to many antique shops.

A full breakfast of cereals, bacon and eggs included in the price. Remuera house has been featured in newspapers, "Home & Building" and "Auckland Historical" magazines. As a member of the Auckland Historical Society and a local history author, the proprietor will be pleased to advise you on places of interest in and around Auckland and throughout New Zealand. Competitively priced hire car and bus tours arranged. Easy access by car to/from Airport and Motorway.

Directions: *Travellers with own transport driving from airports or on Motorways North or South of Auckland, turn off at Greenlane Road, and follow the signs to Remuera. Airport Shuttle Buses to/from house. On bus route from InterCity Bus and Railway Station.*

Remuera, Auckland City
Guest House
Address: 39 Market Road, Remuera, Auckland 5
Name: Aachen House - Jean and Don Goldschmidt
Telephone: (09) 520-2329
Fax: (09) 524-2898
Beds: 5 Double, 2 Single (7 bedrooms)
Bathroom: 3 Guests share
Tariff: B&B (full) Double $82, Single $58.50, Extra adults in the room $15.
Credit cards accepted, Vouchers accepted April to October incl
Nearest Town: 4 km from central city

Ours is a large Victorian house set in half an acre of garden. We overlook a large park and back on to Mt Hobson, one of Auckland's many extinct volcanos. We are close to the museum, showgrounds, hospitals and race tracks. The motorway off-ramp is nearby and there is an excellent bus service two minutes walk away. Our car will collect guests from the Railway Station while the shuttle buses have a door-to-door service from the airport. Off-street parking is available.

We have created a friendly, homely atmosphere in our large, beautiful home and people feel relaxed and comfortable. Our seven bedrooms comprise singles, doubles, triples and quads. Each room has a handbasin and there are three shared bathrooms.

Our one rule is NO SMOKING and this seems to please the overseas guests as well as New Zealanders.

Directions: *Take Market Road turnoff from the motorway, phone from the railway or bus stations, or come by minibus from the airport.*

Remuera, Auckland City
Homestay B&B
Address: 'Lakeside', 18 Darwin Lane, Remuera, Auckland 5
Name: Tony & Joanna Greenhough
Telephone & fax: (09) 524-6281
Beds: 1 Double, 2 Single (2 bedrooms)
Bathroom: 1 Guests share
Tariff: B&B (full) Double $70, Single $45, Children concession rates, Dinner $25, Vouchers accepted from May through to September
Nearest Town: Auckland City Centre 5km

Country living only 7 minutes from the city centre!
Come and enjoy staying in this unique location with its magnificent views. We have lived here for 29 years and offer you the opportunity to experience this quiet, peaceful, sunny home where all rooms overlook the waters of the Orakei Basin at the bottom of our garden.
In this tree filled evironment you are only minutes by car from the waterfront beaches and cafes, Parnell with its wide selection of restaurants and excellent shopping, the Museum, and many other visitor attractions. There is also a bus service to the city.
Our house is comfortable modern with a large private garden for you to enjoy. Guest accommodation is self-contained in one wing consisting of queen and twin bedrooms, spacious guest bathroom, and sitting room with colour television and coffee/tea making facility. There is plenty of off street parking.
We look forward to meeting you and know you will enjoy your stay.
Directions: *Door to door shuttle from the airport; by car take the Greenlane exit from the motorway.*

115

Remuera, Auckland City

Homestay
Address: 18 Waiatarua Rd,
Remuera, Auckland 5
Name: Judi and Roger Harwood
Telephone: (09) 524 6990
Beds: 1 Double, 2 Single (3 bedrooms),
Bathroom: 1 Guest share
Tariff: B&B (Special) Double $70, Single $45, Dinner $25, Children
half price, Credit cards accepted, Vouchers accepted March to October
Nearest Town: Auckland city centre 10km

*Our speciality is the gourmet dining we offer our guests. Jude is advanced Cordon
Bleu trained and loves preparing a feast. For $25 you can enjoy a real banquet with
good local wine. Breakfast is bountiful including a large individual platter of
fresh seasonal fruits. Add to this our rambling private spacious surroundings,
solar heated swimming pool, private deck, central heating and electric blankets
for winter, and the tons of care, comfort and attention we provide our guests - who
would want to leave!*
*The large double bedroom has french windows which open out into a sunny private
conservatory which is surrounded by peaceful greenery.*
We provide tea / coffee facilities and coloured TV is available.
*Our house is in Auckland's Eastern suburb of Remuera with the central city ten
minutes drive by car. We look forward to meeting you soon!!*
Directions: *Exit motorway Greenlane take Greenlane East to Remuera Road,
turn right at lights and sixth road on left.*

Remuera, Auckland

Homestay
Address: 3 Mt Hobson Lane
Remuera Auckland
Name: Graeme & Nan McKay
Telephone: (09) 524 5601
Fax: (09) 524 6660
Beds: 2 Single (1 Bedroom - an extra
single room is available on application)
Bathroom: 1 Private
Tariff: B&B (full) Double $65, Single $45 on application

*Situated on the slopes of Mt Hobson, our colonial style home is set in a private
sunny garden with a large swimming pool.*
*We are handily placed for the motorway, bus and rail routes to the city, and are
within easy walking distance of both the Newmarket and Remuera centres, which
provide apart from Auckland's most exciting shopping, a wide range of restaurants.
For Out of Town New Zealand families we are conveniently close to Dilworth,
Diocesan, Kings Prep and St Cuthberts schools.*
*Guests will have sole use of a pleasant sitting room with TV. An extra single room
is available on application.*
We, and our elderly Scots terrier 'Agnes' look forward to meeting you.

Remuera, Auckland City
Homestay
Address: 65 Lucerne Road,
Remuera, Auckland
Name: Sedgwick Kent Lodge
Telephone: (09) 524 5219
Fax: (09) 520 4825
Beds: 2 Double, 4 Single (4 bedrooms)
Bathroom: 1 Ensuite, 1 Guests share
Tariff: B&B (special) Double Ensuite $100, Double $70-$95, Single $50-$65,
Dinner from $25, Credit cards accepted, Vouchers accepted week days excluding
weekends from April through to end of September

*Enjoy luxury in the inner exclusive suburb of Remuera. A restored turn of the
century homestead featuring kauri, rimu, stained glass and antiques. Fabulous
outdoor living in courtyard. Barbecue and spa pool.*

*We enjoy guests and having travelled extensively ourselves know what the
traveller requires to make their stay enjoyable.*

*Comments from our visitors book. "Marvellous location - great meals", "Blueberry
pancakes with cream - a wonderful dream, thanks!", "We spent 2 months on
holidays but never had better lodging and breakfast", "Splendid accommodation
and company - NZ B&B at its best".*

*We offer delicious meals, comfortable beds with electric blankets, duvets and
damansk linens, tea making facilities and TV available. NZ wines are an interest
and we offer candlelit dinners and champagne breakfasts on request.*

Close to superb boutique shops, restaurants, theatres and golf course.

*Directions: Travel east along Remuera Road through Upland Road village
shopping centre then first left onto Lucerne Road. We look forward to meeting you.*

117

Mission Bay, Auckland

Homestay
Address: 10 Hawera Rd., Mission Bay
Name: Marvyn & Doug Smith
Telephone: (09) 5283-263

Beds: 1 Double, 1 Single (2 bedrooms) **Bathroom:** 1 Private
Tariff: B&B (continental) Double $69, Single $50, Dinner $25.
Vouchers accepted.
Nearest Town: Auckland City

Feel at home in our modern architecturally designed house. We have a wonderfully relaxing view of Rangitoto and the Waitemata Harbour. For summer use our swimming pool or winter our cosy fireplace are available for our guests to enjoy. We are situated within walking distance to shops, bus stops and only minutes by car from the beaches and restaurants of Mission Bay, Kohimarama and St Helier's. We can suggest a variety of Auckland based activities.

We have a farm on the coast at Waipu Cove (2 hours north of Auckland) which enables us to help you with accommodation there if you are planning to tour Northland.

Having travelled extensively both in NZ and overseas we understand and look forward to satisfying your needs. My interest in Ikebana and weaving has brought me into contact with many friends both in Japan and NZ.

As Auckland is often arrival or departure point for many visitors, we would like to welcome you to our home.

St Heliers, Auckland

Homestay & Self-contained Accommodation
Address: 51 Cliff Road, St Heliers, Auckland
Name: Jill & Digby Mathew
Telephone: (09) 575 4052
Beds: Homestay: 2 Single (1 bedroom) **Bathroom:** 1 Private
Self-contained Acc: 1 King (1 bedroom) **Bathroom:** 1Ensuite
Tariff: B&B (full) Double $85, Single $85, Self-contained Luxury Guest apartment $200. Vouchers accepted
Nearest Town: Auckland City 8km (5 miles)

Situated right on Achillies Point with panoramic close sea views over the whole city centre and many of the famous Islands of Hauraki Gulf, this private home offers not only conservatively priced Homestay accommodation for touring couples but also a most luxurious guest apartment which regularly attracts top executives from major multinational companies on assignment in New Zealand.

Poised immediately above the secluded beach of Ladies Bay and just four minutes walk to St Heliers village centre (reputed to be one of the most outstandingly beautiful marine suburbs in New Zealand) the property offers immediate access to most of the leading tourist spots of Auckland scattered along the world famous Waterfront Drive leading to Downtown just 8km (5 miles) away.

These attractions include Kelly Tarlton's Underwater World and Arctic Adventure (NZ's most popular tourist attractions), Mission Bay, the Savage Memorial at Bastion Point, Parnell Baths, the Rose Gardens at Judges Bay, Okahu Bay Marina and the Heliport at Mechanics Bay.

The Auckland Museum and the New Maritime Museum are just a little further (5 minutes drive) from the Heliport.

St Johns, Auckland City
Homestay/Self-contained Accommodation
Address: 150 St Johns Road, St Johns
Name: Diane and Murray Wilson
Telephone: (09) 521 4450
Beds: 4 Single (2 bedrooms) **Bathroom:** 2 Private
Tariff: B&B (full) Double $60, Single $35, Dinner $20,
Vouchers accepted.

We are a retired couple who have travelled extensively overseas staying in Bed and Breakfast accommodation so understand travellers needs. We enjoy meeting visitors and helping them discover our beautiful city.
Our comfortable two storied home has available for guests the lower floor with two twin bedrooms, two guest bathrooms, modern kitchen and lounge. Laundry facilities, separate entrance and off street parking. We are on a frequently served bus route. We are within 10 minutes drive from downtown Auckland restaurants, golf courses, beaches, bowling greens, race courses, hospitals, showgrounds and the motorway. There is also plenty of local shopping within walking distance.
You may have other meals in addition to breakfast by arrangement. No pets, and we have a house rule of no smoking indoors.
From the airport use the shuttle buses, for reasonable fares and a door to door service.
Our hobbies are golf, lawn bowls and Family History.
Please phone for directions.

St Johns Park, Auckland City
Homestay
Address: 47 Norman Lesser Drive St Johns Park Auckland
Name: Jean & Neville Taylor
Telephone: (09) 521 1827
Beds: 2 Single (1 Bedroom) **Bathroom:** 1 Private
Tariff: B&B (full) Double $65, Single $40, Dinner $20, Vouchers accepted
Nearest Town:

Relax with tea, coffee or cold drink in our conservatory, comfortable lounge or courtyard garden on arrival.
Our smoke free home is warm and comfortable in a quiet residential area with golf course view and off street parking.
Your bedroom has twin Queen Anne beds with electric blankets and cosy duvets. For extra warmth there are patchwork quilts. You have sole use of bathroom and toilet.
Feel free to ask for laundry and ironing facilities.
We are a retired couple who have travelled extensively in Europe, UK and New Zealand. Choosing to stay in B&B accommodation ourselves we understand your needs, and hope we can cater for them.
Join us for a relaxing pre-dinner drink and dinner; just let us know by 4pm, or we could direct you to any of Aucklands restaurants you choose.
We are 10 minutes by car to central city.
Directions: *Greenlane Exit (9) from Motorway. Shuttle Bus from Auckland Airport. Phone for directions.*

Our B&Bs are mostly private homes.
Most do not accept credit cards.

Ellerslie, Auckland

Homestay
Address: 'Taimihinga', 16 Malabar Drive Ellerslie, Auckland 5
Name: Marjorie Love
Telephone: (09) 579 7796
Beds: 1 Double, 2 Single (2 Bedrooms) **Bathroom:** 1 Ensuite, 1 Family share
Tariff: B&B (continental) Double $60, Single $40, Dinner $20, Vouchers accepted,
Full breakfast on request
Nearest Town: 8km to city centre (12mins on Motorway), 5 mins to Newmarket
or Remuera

*A special pleasure is sharing Auckland's particular attractions with travellers
from overseas and from other parts of New Zealand.*
*My modest but comfortable home is situated in Ellerslie in a quiet cul-de-sac with
a pleasant northerly outlook.*
*Ellerslie affords ready access to most places of interest around Auckland. Parks,
racing, sports, gymnasium, cinemas, hospitals, shopping centres and restaurants
are nearby.*
*Adult family - two daughters and a son - live away from home, but foreign students
are staying from time to time.*
Interests - people, the arts, travel, church (Anglican), gym, Probus.
*The twin room is downstairs, shares family bathroom and is at reduced rate ($55
double and $35 single).*
*Additional amenities by arrangement - dinner ($20pp), laundry, shared or private
meals - your choice. No smoking please.*
Directions: *Please phone or write.*

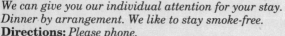

Titirangi, Auckland

Homestay
Address: 229 Golf Rd
Titirangi Auckland
Name: Brian & Waltraut Merrick
Telephone & Fax: (09) 817 4274
Beds: 1 Double (1 Bedroom)
Bathroom: 1 Family share
Tariff: B&B (special) Double $55, Single $30, Dinner $15-20, Vouchers accepted
Nearest Town: Auckland

*Situated on the foothills of the Waitakeres is our home with a 'View' from every
room: A gardenlike city with endless trees, stunning hills and water. We are 30
mins from the airport and 20 mins from downtown. You will find the rainforest
and the wild surf beaches not far. (30 mins for beaches like Piha.) Wonderful bush
walks with waterfalls, old kauri trees. On the northern slopes of the Waitakeres
grows good wine. You can sample it at several vineyards.*
*Brian is born in Auckland, Waltraut in Berlin. We met in New York, so we have
travelled a bit and understand the needs of the travellers. We speak both English
and German and learning Italian. In that order we also cook. The children have
flown the nest and only two cats are here to be pampered.*
We can give you our individual attention for your stay.
Dinner by arrangement. We like to stay smoke-free.
Directions: *Please phone.*

Hillsborough, Auckland
Homestay/Bed & Breakfast
Address: "Te Tapere", 8 Bluff Terrace,
Hillsborough, Auckland 4
Name: Jean & John Sandiford
Telephone: (09) 625-5848 **Fax:** (09) 529-1684
Beds: 1 Double, 1 Twin, (2 bedrooms) **Bathroom:** 2 Ensuite
Tariff: B&B (full) Double $70, Single $45. Credit Cards: Visa, M/C

Conveniently situated only 15 minutes from Auckland Airport or Down town, "Te Tapere" provides an ideal haven for the traveller. Nestled on the shores of the Manukau Harbour at Taylors Bay, our comfortable modern home offers guests a peaceful retreat in which to relax and enjoy the sparkling waters of the bay and an interesting variety of bird life.
Guests are accommodated in tastefully appointed double bedrooms each with ensuite bathrooms. All bedrooms have electric blankets, heating and colour television and one enjoys a private balcony overlooking the bay.
Complimentary tea / coffee, laundry facilities. No smoking indoors please.
John and I are second generation Kiwis who have travelled extensively both in New Zealand and overseas and have an intimate knowledge of our city and country. We can arrange reasonably priced, personalized tours in our luxury mini-coach to any destination in NZ.
We aim to provide warm, friendly kiwi hospitality and hope that guests will feel that they have a place to call home while visiting Auckland.
Directions: *Please phone. Meet & Greet service for Airport / Bus / Train available for small charge.*

We rely on your comments about our B&Bs.
Please send us a comment form from the back of the book.

Hillsborough, Auckland
Homestay/Self-contained Guest Wing
Address: 11 Saran Place Hillsborough Auckland
Name: David & Wendy Rhodes
Telephone: (09) 6257 051
Beds: 1 Double, 2 Single (1 Bedroom)
Bathroom: 1 Private
Tariff: B&B (continental) Double $70, Single $40, Children half price/under 5 free. Vouchers accepted
Nearest Town: Auckland City Centre

We offer a friendly welcome to the relaxing atmosphere of our home, situated 15 minutes from the airport and 20 minutes from Auckland City Centre.

Nestled amongst the trees on the waters edge, our picturesque stone house offers commanding views of the Manukau Harbour.

The self-contained guest wing, with separate entrance and parking, has breathtaking sea views. Facilities consist of a bedroom with double bed, bathroom, kitchen with microwave, fridge, tea / coffee. The lounge, opening to a patio, has a sofa bed, portable bed and TV.

Join us for homestyle continental breakfast including hot muffins, pancakes or we will deliver to your table. Within 10 minutes of banks, shopping complexes, restaurants, parks, golf course and swimming pools.

We have enjoyed B&B hospitality overseas with our two girls aged 7 and 17. Our elder daughter has studied Japanese and French for 5 years.

We are happy to cater for families, cot is available and a play area with swings. Baby sitting at reasonable rates. Please no smoking indoors.

Directions: *Door to door shuttle bus from airport. For detailed directions please telephone.*

Note: Building was not complete at time of inspection, phone to confirm.

Mangere Bridge, Auckland

Homestay
Address: 146 Coronation Rd Mangere Bridge
Name: Carol O'Connor & Brian Thomas
Telephone: (09) 636 6346
Beds: 1 Double, 2 Single (2 Bedrooms) **Bathroom:** 1 Guests share
Tariff: B&B (full) Double $60, Single $40, Children half price, Dinner $15, Vouchers accepted
Nearest Town: Auckland City 14km, Manukau City 14km

We invite you to share our home which is within 10 mins of Auckland Airport an ideal location for your arrival or departure of New Zealand. We enjoy meeting people from far and near and look forward to making your stay an enjoyable one. A full cooked breakfast is provided and we welcome you to join us for dinner by arrangement. We provide a courtesy car to and from airport, bus and rail depots. Off street parking is available for guests with own transport.
If you smoke we ask that you do so outdoors.
Although we have a cat we request no pets.
Inspection welcomed.
Directions: *Please phone.*

Mangere. Auckland

Homestay
Address: 288 Kirkbride Rd., Mangere, Auckland
Name: Ira & May Pepperell
Telephone: (09) 275 6777
Beds: 3 Single (2 bedrooms)
Bathroom: 1 Family share (guests have priority)
Tariff: B&B (continental) Double $60, Single $35, Dinner $15, Children half price, Vouchers accepted
Nearest Town: Papatoetoe

We are a retired active couple with a wide variety of interests including golf, aviation, t ravelling and meeting people.
Although our comfortable home is only five minutes from the airport we are not on the flight path so don't get any aircraft noise. We are ten minutes from 5 large shopping centres and Rainbow's End amusement park and walking distance to our local centre. Within walking distance to restaurants and take-away bars although an evening meal can be provided by arrangement.
Expo Pavilion (ex Brisbane) is three minutes away also Villa Maria Winery. Our golf course is situated near the airport, and green fee players are welcome.
A small charge is made for transport to/from airport at reasonable hour otherwise taxis available..
Vehicles may be left while you are away for $1 per day as we have off-street parking space. Beds have woollen underlays and electric blankets.
There is a sunny terrace and fenced swimming pool.

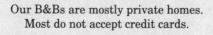

Our B&Bs are mostly private homes.
Most do not accept credit cards.

Otahuhu, Auckland City
Homestay
Address: 70 Mangere Road Otahuhu Auckland
Name: Gerard & Jerrine Fecteau
Telephone: (09) 276 9335
Beds: 1 Queen, 1 Double, 2 Single (3 Bedrooms)
Bathroom: 1 Guests share
Tariff: B&B (special) Double $55, Single $35, Children half price,
Dinner with wine $20, Vouchers accepted
Nearest Town: Auckland 10 mins

Gerard and Jerrine offer you Canuck-Kiwi hospitality in their comfortable home in the most central location in Auckland. Otahuhu is half way between central city and Papakura. The motorways and trains are just minutes away and the airport simply 10 minutes down the road. If you begin your Kiwi holiday and want to rest and organize yourselves then #70 is the place or if you want to rest before the long flights "home" - #70 is the rest stop and handy for the early morning flights.
We are also collectors of amazing things and have an interesting variety of many cactus, coins of the world, coloured depression glass tableware, native Canadian art, brass, glass birds and animals and more.
Relax in the hot tub in the gardens. In addition to breakfast you are invited to join us for lunch and dinner by arrangement.
Please phone or write for a car to pick you up at the airport or bus depot.

Papatoetoe, Auckland
Homestay
Address: 1/6 Pukeko Place Papatoetoe Auckland
Name: Noelene & Roy Davies
Telephone: (09) 278 0166
Beds: 3 Single (2 Bedrooms)
Bathroom: 1 Family share
Tariff: B&B (continental) Double $60, Single $35, Children $18, Dinner $15
Nearest Town: Papatoetoe (15 minutes walk)

We are a retired active couple with a variety of interests, including bowls, travelling and meeting people.
We offer you a warm welcome to our home. We live 15 mins from the International and Domestic Airport and 2 minutes off the North / South Motorway.
We are within walking distance to Papatoetoe, the Plaza, restaurants and takeaways. Manukau City Shopping Centre, Rainbows End and the Botanical Gardens are a handy distance. The Grange Golf Course is at the end of the street and green fee players are welcome.
A relaxed atmosphere is offered and each morning we serve a generous continental breakfast. You are invited to join us for dinner by arrangement.
A small charge is made for transport to / from the airport at a reasonable hour otherwise taxi or shuttlebus can be arranged.

Please let your hosts know if you have to cancel.
They will have spent time preparing for you.

Howick, Auckland

Homestay
Address: The Fishers, "Above the Beach",
141 Mellons Bay Road,
Howick, Auckland
Name: Max & Marjorie Fisher
Telephone: (09) 534 2245
Beds: 2 Double, 2 Single (4 bedrooms)
Bathroom: 1 Private (bath & handbasin)
+ 1 Sep shower & 1 sep toilet + 1 Dble has ensuite
Tariff: B&B (continental) Double $65, Single $40, Double with ensuite $70,
Dinner by arrangement, Credit cards: Visa accepted. Vouchers accepted.

We live 50 yards "Above the Beach" in a comfortable and roomy home with Kauri trees growing through our decks. Looking out to sea views as far as Waiheke Island and Rangitoto. Howick is on the east side of Auckland on the coast 20 kms from Auckland city and 13 kms from Manukau city. It is a quaint village with a historic Selwyn Church, the Howick colonial village, at least six restaurants, a village pub, and six beaches for swimming and boating within a 2 km radius.
The double bedrooms have feather duvets, electric blankets, and individual decks looking onto bush and sea.
We have an open fireplace, spa pool and a private courtyard and we enjoy outdoor living, weather permitting.
Our interests are travel, classic cars, genealogy, and walking along our beaches.
Directions: Shuttle bus to and from the airport. Please phone ahead for other directions. Non smokers, and no pets preferred.

Whitford

Farmstay
Address: Springhill,
Polo Lane, Whitford, Auckland
(Postal: R.D. Manurewa)
Name: Derek & Judy Stubbs
Telephone: (09) 5308674
Beds: 1 Double (1 bedroom) **Bathroom:** 1 Ensuite
Tariff: B&B (full) Double $70, Single $45, Dinner with wine $25 by arrangement, Children half price. Vouchers accepted.
Nearest Town: Auckland 30 km, Howick, 12 km

Springhill is a 16 hectare farm, situated in Whitford, an attractive rural area approximately 30km south east of Auckland, and 12km from Howick, a village suburb rich in early European settler history. The farm runs red deer and angora goats. Guests are welcome to observe or take part in farm activities where possible. Our family comprises six adult sons and daughters (only one still at home), two dogs, two cats, horses and assorted chickens. We have a large comfortable home which we enjoy sharing. We both enjoy travelling and Derek is a keen sailor.
Our guest accommodation is one detached bedroom with double bed, en-suite, TV and tea and coffee making facilities. The garden is spacious and barbeques are a speciality during summer. We are only ten minutes from local beaches, and two minutes from a beautiful golf course. We welcome guests to join us for dinner.
Directions: *Left off Whitford park Road just past golf course or please phone.*

Clevedon
Farmstay
Address: "Willowgrove",
Kawakawa Bay Road,
Clevedon, RD5, Papakura
Name: Brian and Eileen Wallace
Telephone: (09) 292-8456
Beds: 1 Double, 3 Single, (2 bedrooms)
Bathroom: 2 Ensuite
Tariff: B&B (full) Double $65, Single $35,
Children half price, Dinner $20. Vouchers accepted.
Nearest Town: Auckland 40 km, Papakura 22km, Howick 30km

Clevedon is a village in a rural area with craft shops, restaurants and all services. Eileen and I live and work on our property of about 11 acres.

We raise beef calves and also have sheep, goats, chickens and ducks. We produce our own vegetables.

The house is set in a delightful garden which has a very restful atmosphere. We enjoy the special atmosphere and peaceful surroundings and are pleased to share it with others.

We are close enough for visitors to take in any of the Auckland attractions, and golf courses, fishing and swimming beaches are within 15 minutes drive.

The main guest room is a large upstairs room with its own sitting area, toilet and shower. You may share our family room and lounge or relax in your room as you please. We also have a games room including a pool table.

Directions: *Please phone. If required we can collect from airport or public transport for a small charge.*

Clevedon

Farmstay + Self-Contained Accommodation
Address: 816 North Road, PO Box 72, Clevedon
Name: John and Annette Hodge
Telephone & Fax: (09) 292 8707
Beds: 1 Double, 2 Single (3 bedrooms)
Bathroom: 1 guests share
Tariff: B&B (full) Double $67.50, Single $40; Dinner $20; Children half price,
Campervans welcome.
Self-contained 2 bedroom unit, sleeps 5, one ensuite unit sleeps 3, tariff negotiable.
Longer stays welcome.
Credit cards accepted. Vouchers accepted.
Nearest Town: 40 km from Auckland, 23 km from Papakura

*Relax in a peaceful environment, 35 minutes from Auckland International Airport
in a rural community that has a wide range of farming activities.*

*Views from our comfortable home include the lower reaches of the Wairoa River
Valley from Clevedon, Waiheke and other small islands in the Hauraki Gulf to the
distant Coromandels.*

*We offer a range of guest accommodation, B&B with own bathroom, 2 self
contained motel style units, 1 sleeps 5 with full cooking facilities, 1 sleeps 3 with
tea and coffee.*

Meals, BBQ and games room are available.

*Activities that are available with hosts or nearby include fishing boat trips, sheep
shearing, bush, farm, beach walks, horse riding, dairy and orchard farm visits.*

We are available by prior arrangement to greet you at plane, train or coach.

Directions: *Clevedon is 14 km east of Papakura. Our home is on the left on North
Road, 9 km from Clevedon.*

The standard of accommodation in *The New Zealand Bed and Breakfast Book*
ranges from homely to luxurious,
but you can always be sure of superior hospitality.

Clevedon

Country Home Stay
Address: "Fairfield" Kawakawa Road,
Clevedon, RD 5 Papakura
Name: Christopher and Paddy Carl
Telephone: (09) 292 8852
Beds: 1 Queen, 1 Twin (2 bedrooms)
Bathroom: 1 Ensuite, 1 Guests share
Tariff: B&B (full) Double $90, Single $70, Dinner from $30 by arrangement,
Children half price, Vouchers accepted from March to October
Nearest Town: Clevedon 10 mins, Papakura 20 mins, Auckland 40 mins

Our Ranch Style house is on a hill, set in 14 acres with extensive rural views and a glimpse of the sea. Mangere airport and Auckland city are 40 minutes away, and there are many lovely beaches nearby leading to the pretty scenic route to the Coromandel.

We offer a new, self-contained bed-sitting room with ensuite and own private courtyard. The room has a television and coffee and tea making facilities. A twin bedroom with guest bathroom is also available. Local activities such as fishing, golf and horse riding can be arranged.

We are both well travelled; Paddy is now involved in the fashion industry and Chris retired after 35 years as a Naval Officer with the New Zealand Navy. We welcome you to join us in our comfortable spacious home.

Directions: *7kms from the roundabout at Clevedon down the Kawakawa Bay Road or please telephone.*

Always telephone ahead to enquire about a B&B. It is a nuisance for you if
you simply arrive to find someone already staying there.
And besides hosts need a little time to prepare.

Clevedon, Auckland
Maritime Marina Resort
Address: North Road, Clevedon
Postal Address: PO Box 152, Clevedon
Name: Elaine and Mark Balemi
Telephone: (09) 292-8572
Fax: (09) 292-8039
Mobile: (025) 951 889
Beds: 2 Double, 4 Single (4 bedrooms)
Bathroom: 1 Private, 1 Guests share
Tariff: B&B (full) Double $130, Single $100, Dinner $25.
Credit cards accepted. Vouchers accepted
Nearest Town: Papakura 12km, Auckland 30km

Clevedon Country Lodge is a unique combination of a stately country home, maritime resort and onsite relaxation.

The accommodation is a choice of a self-contained guest house capable of sleeping six persons and with full cooking facilities, or homestay in the 6000sq ft main house. Meals, BBQ, bar facilities, sauna, gymnasium, spa pool, billiard and table tennis tables are available to all guests.

Our own yacht and launch marina is the base for sailing or cruising on the Hauraki Gulf and for fishing charters (light or heavy game tackle).

The spacious grounds have a fresh water lake which is used for model yacht sailing, jet skiing and dinghy rides; a swimming pool and six hole golf course are under construction. All gear available for sporting and water relaxation.

We cater for horse riding and farm bike rides. Adjacent dairy and sheep farm visits, milking cows and sheep shearing.

Directions: *From Papakura 12km east to Clevedon, North Road 2.5km on RH side.*

Clevedon

Farmstay

Address: 'Birchwood House' RD 2 Papakura
Name: Ann & Mike Davies
Telephone: (09) 292 8729
Beds: 1 King, 1 Queen, 1 Double (3 Bedrooms)
Bathroom: 2 Ensuite, 1 Private
Tariff: B&B (full) Double $90-120, Dinner $35pp.
Nearest Town: Clevedon 5 mins, Auckland 25 mins

Ann and Mike take delight inviting guests to experience their hospitality on a South Auckland dairy farm.

Birchwood House is a fully restored kauri homestead originally built 1887, but with the comforts of the 1990's. We have 3 guest rooms decorated in old world charm. Fresh flowers and quality bed linen provided. Two rooms have ensuites and one private bathroom. Breakfast to suit - healthy or indulgent, or a little of both. Let us tantalize and spoil you with fine food and freshly brewed coffee. Guests are welcome to stroll through our large country garden, relax on the verandah, by the pool or wander over the farm. We are located on the outskirts of the Clevedon Village near restaurants, polo grounds, golf courses, shopping and beaches. Horseriding, fishing and a range of farm activities can be organised if you feel energetic. A great central location. Beach cottage available on the beautiful Coromandel Peninsular. We enjoy hosting guests from all over the world, and look forward to meeting you. Hospitality and tranquillity are assured. We are a non smoking family.

Complimentary airport transfers.

Directions: *Bookings advisable, please phone.*

"Birchwood"

Clarks Beach

Homestay
Address: 123 Torkar Road, Clarks Beach
Name: Ray & Elaine Golding
Telephone & Fax: (09) 232-1756
Beds: 4 Single (2 bedrooms) **Bathroom:** 1 Guests share
Tariff: B&B (full) Double $60, Single $30, Dinner $20, Children half price, Vouchers accepted
Nearest Town: Papakura, Pukekohe, Waiuku (equal distance)

We have a spacious home on the waters edge of the Manukau Harbour that overlooks the Auckland City and suburban lights.
Ray is a keen gardener and has a terraced garden down to the beach.
Clarks Beach offers a wide range of activities including fishing, yachting, bowls and an 18 hole golf course. Hire clubs and electric cars available. Visits to dairy farm and horticultural farms can be arranged and the vintage railway is only a short distance away.
You may share an evening meal with us and light lunch can be provided if required.
Transport to and from the airport available on request at a nominal rate and we can assist with further travel arrangements.
We are only 40 minutes from the Auckland Airport.
A good place to start and finish you holiday.
Directions: *20 mins south from the airport to Papakura then 20 mins west following the signpost.*

Pukekohe

Farmstay
Address: "Woodside", Ostrich Farm Road, RD1, Pukekohe
Name: Evelyn and Les Atkinson
Telephone: (09) 238-7864
Beds: 4 Single (2 bedrooms) **Bathroom:** 1 Guest share
Tariff: B&B (full) $60 Double, $35 Single, Children half price; Dinner $15 per person, Vouchers accepted
Nearest Town: Pukekohe 6 kms, Auckland 48 kms

Pukekohe is a thriving farm and vegetable growing area situated 48 km south of Auckland. Our 10 acre farm is mostly beef fattening with a few sheep, geese, cats (2), a dog called Buddy, ducks and hens. We are 5 mins away from an excellent golf course and 10 mins to the famous Glenbrook vintage railway. The wild west coast of NZ is a pleasant 20 mins drive. Auckland, our wonderful "City of Sails" is only a 40 mins drive, making it close enough for our visitors to view all of its magnificent attractions. Over the years, Les and I have been fortunate to enjoy travelling throughout NZ and overseas to the UK, Continent and Australia. We love meeting people and can offer warm Kiwi hospitality - we, also, enjoyed 'farm stays' on our trips abroad. Our guests are very welcome to dine with us, or in their own dining/lounge area.
Directions: *Southern motorway to Drury off-ramp - follow signs to Pukekohe-Waiuku (6 kms). Right turn at Golf Course - first left to Ostrich Road, then left into Ostrich Farm Rd. "Woodside" 2 km down road on right.*

Some hosts are away from home during the day.

Pokeno

Farmstay + Self-Contained Accom.
Address: Whangarata Road, RD4, Tuakau
Name: Pine Lodge
Telephone & fax: (09) 236 8797
Beds: Main homestead: 1 Double, 3 Single (3 bedrooms)
Bathroom: 1 Guests share.
 2 new self-contained chalets, 1 Double + 2 extra, 1 Twin + 2 extra.
Tariff: B&B (continental) Double $67.50, Single $50-$62, Chalets Double $78-75, Single $56.25. Dinner $20, Children half price, Campervans welcome. Credit cards.
Nearest Town: Tuakau 3km, Pukekohe 12km

Located 4km from Pokeno. Pine Lodge is a well maintained villa set amongst lovely gardens and 80 year old trees.

Two new self contained chalets with surrounding cottage gardens. Consisting of 5.8056ha beautiful rolling countryside.

A landscaped pond adds tranquillity, space to visitors and travellers. Pleasant walks within short distance.

Handy to Hot pools, beaches, golf course, zoo park, river boat trips. A NZ experience with quiet animals and friendly hostess.

Directions: *Travel State Highway 1 to Pokeno. Travel 5km up Whangarata Road which is next to BP garage. Pine Lodge is on the right just past Bridge, large sign by chalets. Hostess Maureen Blake.*

Some homes share the bathroom, others have bathrooms exclusively for
guests – they are indicated in the listing.

Kaiaua (Auckland Province)

Homestay
Address: "Corovista",
East Coast Road, Waharau, Kaiaua
Postal Address: Private Bag, Kaiaua
via Pokeno, Auckland
Name: Bob and Julia Bissett
Telephone: NZ (09) 232 2842 O/seas (9) 232 2842
Beds: 2 Double/Single (2 bedrooms)
Bathrooms: 1 Guests share
Tariff: B&B (full) Double $60, Single $35, Dinner (3 course) $20 Includes freshly caught fish in season and own home grown vegetables. Packed lunches by arrangement, Vouchers accepted
Nearest Town: Thames

Our home "COROVISTA", is so named because of its commanding and panoramic views of the Coromandel Ranges which rise above a foreground of the Hauraki Gulf and sparkling waters of the Firth of Thames.
Surrounded by a delightful garden, the home's elevated position with its full length deck has a special guest wing designed for the view. The added advantage of this locality, is its placement upon the recommended scenic route south of Auckland through Clevedon, and its near proximity to the Hunua Parklands, an internationally recognised bird sanctuary and thermal hot springs at Miranda, with fishing, tramping and picnicking also available.
We, your hosts, are widely travelled and offer warm hospitality to local and overseas guests. We retired within easy reach of the city, to a peaceful rural area, and our desire is to share it with those who travel this beautiful country.
We have a small terrier and cat who live outdoors.
Our interests are varied and include golf, arts, crafts, music and the pleasure of a comfortable smoke free home.
Directions: *Please phone.*

Mercer

Farmstay / Self-Contained Accommodation
Address: Koheroa Road, Mercer, Pokeno
Name: Alan and Dorothy McIntyre
Telephone: (09) 232-6837
Beds: 2 Double (2 bedrooms) **Bathroom:** 1 Private
Tariff: B&B (full) Double $65, Single $35, Children negotiable;
Dinner $20, Campervans welcome, Vouchers accepted
Nearest Town: Pukekohe 22 km, Auckland airport 40 minutes - Ideal for last night's stay in N.Z.

We live on a sheep and cattle farm with a modern brick home which has a self-contained unit attached. We have a large swimming pool and barbecue facilities. We are 3 km off the main Auckland_Hamilton highway. Our house site gives wide panoramic views of the countryside from Bombay to Thames. No pets or children. We are very happy to provide dinner. There are also numerous eating facilities in the area.
The farm provides ample opportunity for taking walks and viewing farm animals plus turkeys, pheasants, ducks and quail.
Directions: *Travel State Highway 1 to Mercer, cross railway lines, travel 3 km up Koheroa Road, house is on left right near road just past Kellyville Road junction. Name clearly visible.*

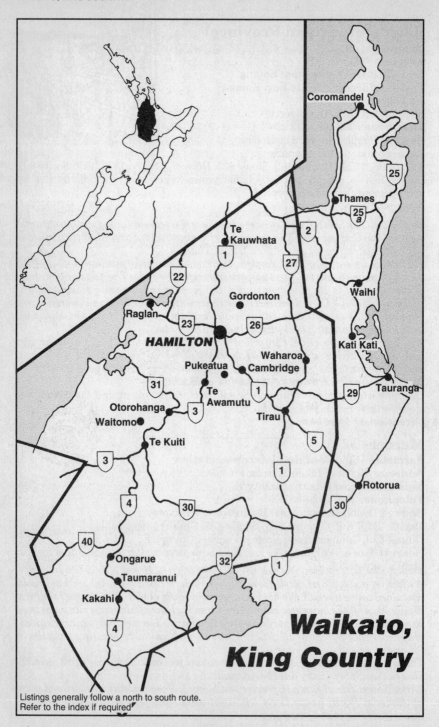

Waikato, King Country

Listings generally follow a north to south route.
Refer to the index if required

Te Kauwhata

Farmstay
Address: Te Wheoro Road, R.D. 2, Te Kauwhata
Name: Trixie & Rex Browning
Telephone: (07) 82-63016
Beds: 1 Double (Sleepout with ensuite), 3 Single (3 bedrooms)
Bathroom: 1 Guests share
Tariff: B&B (full) Double $50, Single $35, Dinner $15 (by arrangement), Children half price
Nearest Town: Huntly 13km, Thames 56km, Hamilton 60km, Auckland 70km

We have small farmlet very close to SH 1. We have a comfortable family home. You could have dinner with us or just bed and breakfast. Children are always welcome. Electric blankets available.
We are only 42km to Miranda hot pools and not far to Waingaro hot pools 56km to beaches and fishing. Just down the road is a lovely 18 hole golf course. We are interested in travel and enjoy meeting people from overseas and New Zealand in our friendly home.
We are handy to all areas.
Directions: *SH 1 going south. 2km past the Te Kauwhata turn off on the right. Coming north on SH1, we are 1km past the Rangiriri turn off on your left.*

Te Kowhai, Hamilton

Homestay+Farmstay
Address: Te Kowhai Ngaruawahia Road RD 8 Hamilton
Name: Bruce & Adrienne Lornie
Telephone: (07) 829 7932
Beds: 1 Double, 2 Single (2 Bedrooms) **Bathroom:** 1 Family share
Tariff: B&B (special) Double $35, Single $28, Children half price, Dinner $20, Campervans facilities available
Nearest Town: Hamilton City - or Ngaruawahia town

Our drystock farm is 40ac situated at Te Kowhai - which is NW of Hamilton and 2km from Te Kowhai township. We are 10 minutes from Te Rapa heated pool complex - half an hour to west coast (Raglan beach) surf and harbour, handy to bush walks, golf course, bike riding and tennis courts. Home: 3 B/R brick, lounge, family room, kitchen, sep. d/room, sep. shower, bath, W/C, laundry. Own swimming pool. Outside sleepout with own shower and W/C may suit campervan. We are both keen gardeners - especially roses and belong to Waikato and Heritage Rose Societies. Interested in all sports. Adrienne keen on cooking and loves to entertain.
Family: 2 grown up children and 3 grandchildren.
Directions: *From Hamilton - turn off at Te Rapa - take Te Kowai Road, go to Te Kowhai township - turn onto Ngaruawahia Road - go to 2km (we are on left). From S/H 1, go through Ngaruawahia township - turn right and take Raglan (S/H 23) travel approx 7km on Ngaruawahia Te Kowhai Road. We are opp. Crawford Road. "Rose haven" sign at gate.*

Gordonton, Hamilton
Homestay
Address: Grantham Lane, Gordonton Road, RD1, Hamilton
Name: Tim and Nan Thorrold
Telephone: (07) 855 6742 **Fax:** (07) 8461-635
Beds: 1 Double, 2 Single (2 bedrooms) **Bathroom:** 1 Family share
Tariff: B&B (full) Double $60, Single $35, Children half price, Dinner $20, Campervans $20. Vouchers accepted.
Nearest Town: 11 km N.E. of Hamilton P.O.

We have a lovely garden home with extensive rural views that we would love to share with you. Situated in the centre of the Waikato dairying district we are involved with farming and will be happy to arrange farm visits.
We are handy to golf courses.
Catch up on your washing if you wish – auto washing machine and drier available.
Directions: *Hamilton East–Taupiri bypass via Gordonton, 6 km from city boundary. 5 km from Gordonton*

Hamilton
Homestay
Address: 7 Delamare Road, Bryant Park, Hamilton
Name: Mrs Esther Kelly
Telephone: (07) 849-2070
Beds: 2 Single (1 bedroom) **Bathroom:** 1 Private
Tariff: B&B (continental) Double $60, Single $40, Dinner $20, Vouchers accepted
Nearest Town: Hamilton

I have travelled in many countries and would welcome tourists and would be happy to advise you on travel in New Zealand.
I live in the suburb of Bryant Park, close to the Waikato River with its tranquil river walks and I am within walking distance of St Andrews Golf Course.
Hamilton is a picturesque city with rose gardens, a new museum, Ruakura Animal Research Farm and an agricultural museum called "Farmworld". Hamilton is in the centre of the dairy industry.
My interests are cooking, gardening, tramping, boating, trout fishing, playing golf, art and also Mah Jong.
I look forward to offering you friendly hospitality.
Directions: *Approaching from Auckland. Leave main highway half way down Te Rapa Straight (4 lane highway entering Hamilton) by turning left at round intersection into Bryant Road. At end of Bryant Road turn left into Sandwich Road. Delamare Road is 2nd street on right.*

Hamilton

Farmstay
Address: "Farndale", RD10, Hamilton
Name: Sylvia and Rod Smith
Telephone and Fax: (07) 829 8511
Beds: 1 Double, 3 Single (3 bedrooms)
Bathroom: 1 Guests share
Tariff: B&B (full) Double $75, Single $40, Children under 10 half price; Dinner with NZ wine $25. Vouchers accepted.
Nearest Town: Hamilton 12km

Our home is roomy and comfortable with good views in every direction. We are situated in beautiful rolling countryside to the west of Hamilton.

Local attractions include tramping, horse riding, golf, beach at Raglan (half-hour drive), Waitomo caves (1 hour drive).

We farm deer and grow blueberries.Our interests include horticulture and animal farming, music, arts and crafts , flying and travel.

Helicopter scenic or photographic rides are available from the farm by arrangement, at competitive rates.

Laundry facilities available for guests. We have 1 dog and 1 cat.

Directions: *Please phone*

Please help us provide the best hospitality in the world.
Fill in a comment form for every place you stay.

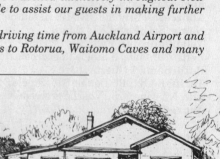

Hamilton

Self-Contained Accommodation
Address: 45 St Andrews Terrace, Hamilton
Name: Niel and Betty Andersen
Telephone & Fax: (07) 8493-258
Beds: 2 Single (1 bedroom) + folding bed or double settee
Bathroom: 1 Private
Tariff: B&B (continental, full if requested) Double $60, Single $50, $10 each extra person - reasonable weekly rates on request. $5 per person extra for full breakfast, Vouchers accepted

My husband and I are of retirement age and live in a quiet location of Hamilton. Our home overlooks the St. Andrews Golf Course and we are within close proximity of other courses.

We have a self-contained flat at the back of our home, which consists of one twin bedroom, bathroom, large lounge with billiard table, plus kitchenette and lounge area. The six foot settee opens up to sleep two, if required. We let this on a motel basis of clean towels each day, etc.

Our aim is to give travellers time to relax and do as they wish and it is with this in mind that we supply a Continental Breakfast in the flat to have at leisure.

Through business and pleasure we have travelled extensively throughout New Zealand and overseas, so have been able to assist our guests in making further travel plans.

Hamilton is only one and a half hours driving time from Auckland Airport and is centrally located for making day trips to Rotorua, Waitomo Caves and many other interesting places.

Hamilton

Homestay
Address: 530 Grey Street, Hamilton
Name: Norman and Frances Wills
Telephone: (07) 838-2120
Beds: 4 Single (3 Bedrooms) **Bathroom:** 1 Private, 1 Guest share
Tariff: B&B (full) Double $60, Single $35, Children under 10 half price, Dinner $20 by arrangement. Vouchers accepted.

Spacious nicely renovated family home away from traffic noise but only 3 minutes from CPO and central shopping. Easily accessible from all main highways. Secluded offstreet parking.

We have travelled overseas and are accustomed to entertaining visitors – American, Asian and European. We can assist with local and district sightseeing information or with planning your tour further afield. Comfort guaranteed.

Directions: *From South, Highway 1, watch for the second sign "Hamilton East, Grey Street" on right opposite Hamilton Gardens.*

From North, follow signs to City Centre then proceed to south end of main street, turn left on to Victoria Bridge.

From Highway 3, proceed straight down Bridge Street and across bridge. At top of Bridge Street (facing St. Mary's Church) turn left into Grey Street. No. 530 is less than 100m along, down driveway on right - tall trees at entrance.

138

Hamilton
Homestay
Address: 24 Pearson Ave, Claudelands, Hamilton
Name: Maureen & Graeme Matthews
Telephone: (07) 855-4269 or 025 747-758
Beds: 1 Double, 1 Single (2 bedrooms) **Bathroom:**1 private, 1 family share
Tariff: B&B (Full) Double $55, Single $35, Children 1/2 price, Dinner $18,
Campervans $20 (up to 4 persons). Vouchers accepted.
Nearest Town: Hamilton, 120 km south of Auckland.

We would like to welcome you to our home situated 2 seconds off the city by-pass on Route 5 & 7 through the city in the Five Crossroads area. Adjacent to the showgrounds and only 5 minutes from the inner city, it is a comfortable walk if you wish to shop. Ruakura, the world famous agricultural research station is just two blocks from our home, if farming is your interest.
Our home is a 'lived-in' comfortable home, warm in winter and cool in summer with an in-ground swimming pool for your use.
Our four children have left home and we enjoy spending time with guests from both NZ and overseas. We have hosted people from many parts of the world and for seven years Maureen taught conversational English to Japanese students. We have travelled extensively and therefore are able to help you plan your holiday. We look forward to having you in our home as part of our family.

Hamilton
Homestay
Address: 162 Beerescourt Rd, Hamilton
Name: John and Glenys Ebbett
Telephone: (07) 849 2005
Beds: 2 Single (1 twin bedroom) **Bathroom:** Private
Tariff: B&B (full) Double $60, Single $40, Dinner $20, Children half price,
Vouchers accepted

Having travelled extensively ourselves, we enjoy visitors to our home which was built in 1990 and commands a spectacular view of New Zealand's longest river. You are welcome to share travel anecdotes with us, or just enjoy the privacy of your own bedroom-bathroom-shower-ensuite facility.
Only minutes from town centre, river walks, swimming complex and St Andrews Golf Course.
Auckland International Airport is one and a half hours drive.
We treat home hosting as a way of reciprocating the pleasure we have had meeting people in other parts of the world. One request - non smokers please.
We don't have any animal pets, or young children.

Hamilton
Homestay
Address: 164 Clyde Street, Hamilton
Name: Val Wood
Telephone: (07) 856 0337 (has answerphone)
Beds: 1 Double, 2 Single (3 bedrooms) **Bathroom:** 1 Guests share
Tariff: B&B (continental) Double $60, Single $35,
Vouchers accepted.

Our home is five minutes drive from the centre of Hamilton and further along Clyde Street is the Waikato University. A bus stops outside.

Overseas we enjoyed staying in Bed and Breakfast accommodation and as our children now live overseas we enjoy having guests to stay. Our guest accommodation has television and tea making facilities and we endeavour to make you feel at home. We encourage people to stay in Hamilton while visiting the tourist areas of the Waikato and Rotorua and return each night to sleep in the same bed without the hassles of packing and unpacking. Hamilton is ideal for this type of holiday as it is within one and a half hours of most places of interest and has many delightful places to visit in the city itself.

Our home is a no smoking zone and we have off street parking. We look forward to having you visit us.

Hamilton
Homestay
Address: 1337 Victoria Street Beerescourt Hamilton
Name: Shirley Lugton
Telephone: (07) 838 0566
Beds: 2 Double, 1 Rollaway (2 Bedrooms) **Bathroom:** 1 Guests share
Tariff: B&B (continental) Double $70, Single $40, Vouchers accepted

Situated at the northern end of Hamilton's main street, come down the driveway and be surprised. So close to the city but so quiet and private. My home is sited on a large section which features cottage gardens, roses, camellia trees and an expansive lawn. Off-street parking is available.

The house is spacious and built for the sun. The garden lends itself to informal dining or you may prefer to join me inside. Continental breakfast offers fruit juice, a choice of cereals, fruit, yoghurt (porridge in winter), toast, croissants, spreads, percolated coffee and a variety of teas.

My home is five minute drive from the city centre and many restaurants. Alternatively I can provide an evening meal with NZ wine by prior arrangement. Laundry facilities are available.

I have a very friendly Cairn Terrier who is an integral member of the family. Wee Jock and I look forward to meeting you and extending our hospitality. Smoke free please.

Hamilton
Homestay+Cottage
Address: "Anlaby Manor" 91 Newells Road RD3 Hamilton
Name: Halina & Pryme Footner
Telephone: (07) 856 7264
Beds: 2 Queen, 2 Single (2 Bedrooms/1 Queen & 2 single beds in cottage, 1 Queen size in Homestead) **Bathroom:** 2 Ensuite
Tariff: B&B (special) Double $120.00, Single $80, Children $12, Dinner $30, Vouchers accepted
Nearest Town: Hamilton

Anlaby Manor is a beautiful replica of a Yorkshire stately home, nestling on 2.5 acres in an idyllic country setting, an original design by renowned architect, Sir Edwin Lutyen, its features are many and charming.
Surrounded by an English formal garden there is a swimming pool tennis court (racquets available) sauna and a billiard room. There are two 18 hole golf courses five minutes away. Guests feel relaxed strolling through this picturesque rambling cottage garden. Your hosts, Pryme and Halina, can offer you an elegant guest room with ensuite, as well as additional guest rooms in a cottage with a lounge, television, refrigerator, tea and coffee making facilities. We are only five minutes from the airport and 10 minutes from Hamilton. We prefer no smoking and this seems to please overseas guests and New Zealanders.
Complimentary pre-dinner drinks in our formal cosy lounge. We have an excellent cuisine using fresh garden produce and a fine selection of NZ wines. Please book in advance.
Farm tours by arrangement.
Personalized day tours by arrangement.

Hamilton
Homestay
Address: 11 Tamihana
Ave Hamilton
Name: Des & Marion Slaney
Telephone: (07) 855 3426
Beds: 1 Double, 1 Single (2 Bedrooms) **Bathroom:** 1 Guests share
Tariff: B&B (continental) Double $55, Single $30, Children half price, Dinner
$20, Vouchers accepted
Nearest Town: Hamilton

*Guest accommodation includes a double and single room in studio loft attached
to the house and overlooking the garden and patio. The double room has its own
small kitchen.*
*We welcome you to our home and friendly neighbourhood. Des is retired and very
interested in all sports and recreational activities. Marion is a teacher. We have
both travelled and enjoy meeting people.*
*We are in a quiet street within walking distance of the city centre and on a city bus
route. We are also close to the Waikato River with its lovely riverbank walks.*
*We are happy to help with sightseeing and recreational activities, eg golf, tennis,
lawn bowls etc. Transfers and pickups can be provided if required.*

Hamilton
Country B&B
Address: 'The Monastery', Newell Road, RD3, Hamilton
Name: Diana & Robert Scott
Telephone: (07) 856 9587
Beds: 2 Double 4 Single (4 Bedrooms) **Bathroom:** 2 Ensuite, 1 Guests share
Tariff: B&B (special) Double $112.50, Single $90, Dinner $22.50, **Nearest
Town:** Hamilton 5 minutes.

*This Historic Home built in 1907 as a private residence later became the
Passionist Monastery. Moved from Hamilton to its attractive ten acre rural*

142

setting on the edge of the Waikoto River, this grand old building containing stained glass windows, rimu carving, antiques and verandahs has been lovingly restored as a gracious family home.

Our four guest bedrooms have comfortable beds with electric blankets and quilts, heaters and attractive garden views. Two large lounges with open fireplaces, books and television provide a relaxing atmosphere. Breakfast is served in our formal dining room. Local restaurant information is available or dinner with New Zealand wine served by arrangment.

Enjoy our peaceful surroundings while strolling through our large developing garden or walk to the delightful little sandy beach nearby. Robert is a landscape designer, we enjoy gardening, antiques, equestrian pursuits and looking after our animals.

The Monastery is central to Hamilton city and gardens, the National Agricultural Fieldays and picturesque Cambridge. Waitomo Caves, Rotorua, Tauranga and Auckland are a leisurely one and a half hour drive.

Tea / coffee making and laundry facilities are available.

As a courtesy to others no smoking inside.

Please phone for bookings and directions.

Raglan

Farmstay + Self-Contained Accommodation
Address: "Matawha", RD2, Raglan
Name: Peter and Jenny Thomson
Telephone: (07) 825 6709 - Please ring
Beds: 1 Double & 2 Single or 3 Single (1 Bedroom) **Bathroom:** 1 Private
Tariff: B&B (special) Double $40, Single $20, Children half price, Dinner $15; Lunch $10, Campervans $20 (laundry and bathroom facilities available) Meals $15 per person. Vouchers accepted.
Nearest Town: Raglan 30 minutes, Hamilton 1 hour, Auckland 2 1/2 hours

We are a family of four with two boys aged 18 and 15 years. We are fortunate to farm right on the west coast with panoramic views of the Tasman Sea.

Our beach is very private with good fishing and hang gliding.

Our farm has been in the family for over 100 years and we take great pride in breeding top class Romney sheep, and stud and commercial Hereford cattle. We also do some riding and have a large flower garden. All vegetables and meat are supplied by a large vegetable garden and by the farm.

We have excellent scenic drives and bush walks plus of course our own beach. We enjoy having visitors from all over the world and they enjoy participating in all our farm activities.

Directions: *Take Hamilton—Raglan road (route 23) Travelling approx 30 minutes – through Te Uku, take the Kauroa and Te Mata Bridal Veil Falls (signposted) and turn left. Take the first turn to the right through Te Mata (Waimaori Road) and follow for approx 10 kms. Turn right at the first T junction into Matawha Road, following for 1 km to the second T junction (signposted "Matawha Rd No Exit, Tutu Rimu Rd, Ruapuke Beach Access, Te Mata 11 kms"). Our entrance is at this signpost, and clearly marked on letterbox and cattle-stop.*

Many homes have facilities for campervans. The ideal camping spot with electricity, bathroom, laundry and friendly hospitality.
Tell campervanners about this when you see them.

143

Cambridge
Bed & Breakfast
Address: "Park House",
70 Queen St, Cambridge
Name: Bill and Pat Hargreaves
Telephone: (07) 8276-368
Beds: 2 Double, 2 Single (3 bedrooms)
Bathrooms: 2 Ensuite, 1 Private.
Tariff: B&B (Special) Double $120, Single $100, Children welcome. Credit cards accepted.

Park House was built during the 1920s as a private inn, and is centrally situated overlooking the town square in Cambridge. Built in Georgian style, Park House is a large 2-storied mansion, now serving as a family home. Throughout the house patchworks and antiques combine with stained glass windows creating an elegant atmosphere. A separate guest wing consists of a large double room with ensuite, and a large twin room with adjacent bathroom. Electric blankets and woollen underlays are on the beds. Guests have a refrigerator and tea and coffee making facilities.

Breakfast is served in the family dining room. Local restaurant menus are available, all the restaurants being within walking distance of Park House.

Cambridge offers an excellent selection of antiques and quality handcraft shops. It is an hour's drive to Waitomo Glow Worm Grotto, a similar distance to Rotorua, the Coast, and a leisurely 2 hour drive to Auckland. Park House is an ideal base for touring.

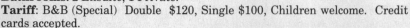

Cambridge
Homestay+Farmstay
Address: Postal Address: PO Box 523 Cambridge
Name: Ballinderry
Telephone: (07) 827 4275
Beds: 4 Single (2 Bedrooms) **Bathroom:** 1 Private, 1 Guests share
Tariff: B&B (full) Double $75, Single $50, Dinner $22pp, Vouchers accepted
Nearest Town: Cambridge

Jean and Bill live on a small farmlet midway Hamilton and Cambridge. We have a lovely colonial home with lots of French doors opening on to verandahs and decks so you can enjoy the sunshine, rural views and picturesque garden. From our place you have a choice of three golf courses within a 10 minutes drive, water skiing and boating on Lake Karapiro and a host of other recreational pursuits.

Cambridge is a lovely town noted for its magnificent trees, antique and craft shops and several first class restaurants.

We have interests in the commercial and sporting fields and race and train a couple of horses for ourselves.

We are situated 4km from Cambridge and 13km from Hamilton on State Highway One. Access to property is down Forrest Road No 31 on the left hand side.

Guests are welcome to join us for and evening meal.

Cambridge
Homestead
Address: Monavale Homestead, R.D. 3, Cambridge
Name: Graham Harbutt & Maureen Meijnen
Telephone: (07) 8273744, **Fax:** (07) 8273227
Beds: 2 Double, 2 Single (3 bedrooms)
Bathrooms: 1 ensuite, 1 guests share
Tariff: B&B Double $90pp, Single $110pp, ensuite $20 extra, Dinner by arrangement $50pp
Nearest Town: Cambridge

Monavale Homestead was rebuilt in 1910 and was designed by the American architect of Teddy's Roosevelt's home in Oyster Bay, Long Island for Charles Channing Buckland. The house has handsome proportions with spacious and elegant rooms, yet retains the atmosphere of a family home.

Three acres of English gardens and trees give in air of peace and quiet to the home, enabling guests to feel rested and restored. There is a pool to refresh yourselves in, and we suggest croquet and tennis for the more adventurous. Relaxing on the terrace in the early evening, we overlook undulating farmlands and beautiful trees and gardens. In the winter we have large open fires to enjoy while planning your next day's adventures.

Your hosts, Graham and Maureen, can offer you elegantly appointed rooms with a choice of a double with en suite, and a twin and a double sharing a bathroom. We personally prepare your meals and use our own organically grown produce where possible. Cambridge has a number of high quality cafes and licenced restaurants for guests to dine, and is five minutes away, For reasons of historic preservation and good health, there is no smoking in the homestead. Please book in advance.

Monavale Homestead is situated 5km along the main road south of Cambridge to Te Awamutu and is marked on most road maps on New Zealand.

Cambridge

Farmhouse
Address: "Birches",
Maungatautari Rd.,
Pukekura
Postal: PO Box 194,
Cambridge
Name: Sheri & Hugh Jellie
Telephone: (07) 827 6556
Beds: 1 Double, 2 Single (2 bedrooms)
Bathroom: 1 ensuite, 1 private
Tariff: B&B (special) Double $75, Single $45, Dinner $28 (GST inclusive)
Credit cards accepted, Vouchers accepted
Nearest Town: Cambridge 4km

*Our 1930s character farmhouse offers comfort from open fires in winter to tennis
and swimming pool in summer. The beautiful countryside surrounding our small
acreage and rambling cottage garden, is amongst leading horse studs.*
*Hugh, a veterinarian, specialises in animal breeding and we farm dairy heifers.
With Lake Karapiro only 2 minutes away we can offer waterskiing or a base for
rowing supporters. Picturesque Cambridge, "Town of Trees", with its many
antique shops and restaurants is only 5 minutes away and we are within an hour
of Waitomo, Rotorua and Mt Maunganui beach. We are both extensively travelled
and with our one daughter at home are keen water/snow skiers.*
*Guests have a choice of twin with guest bathroom and spabath, or a quaint garden
cottage, double with ensuite, both with tea making facilities. Dinner by arrangement
and we serve countrystyle breakfast in our sunny farmhouse kitchen.*
Please phone for directions.

Hora-Hora (Between Cambridge & Rotorua)

Farmstay
Address: 272 Orepunga Road
RD2 Cambridge
Name: N. Congdon
Telephone: (07) 827 2714
Beds: 5 Single (2 Bedrooms)
Bathroom: 1 Guests share, 1 Family share
Tariff: B&B (continental) Double $60, Single $35, Children over 12, Dinner $20, Vouchers accepted
Nearest Town: Cambridge 25km

We have a 107 acre, drystock farm overlooking the beautiful Waikato river valley, and our son-in-laws racing establishment. The race horses train on the hills in front of our house. Our house is a two storey, three bedroom, Cape Cod style house, built 1990, with a swimming pool which is solar-heated.

A thirteen foot, sailing boat with outboard engine is available for fishing and sailing on the lakes and river.

We have an air-conditioned de-luxe car, which is available with driver to meet guests at towns or airports and for guided tours of this lovely area. We must charge 50 cents NZ per kilometre for this service.

We have travelled extensively ourselves, and have hosted people from many parts of the world, all being delighted with their stay. A warm welcome waits for all our future visitors. Fresh garden vegetables are served, free range eggs are available, pony buggy rides and a stock horse is available for the experienced rider.

We do prefer people not to smoke.

Tirau

Farmstay
Address: Rotorua Road, R D 2, Tirau
Name: Lin and Joy Cathcart
Telephone: (07) 883 1471
Beds: 1 Double, 2 Single (2 bedrooms) **Bathroom:** 1 Ensuite, 1 Family share
Tariff: B&B (full) Double $58, Single $35, Dinner $15, Vouchers accepted
Nearest Town: Tirau

Our 250 cow dairy farm is an easy 2 1/2 hour drive south from Auckland International Airport. We welcome travellers to our attractive property over which you may wander at leisure, fish our two trout streams or Lin will give you a tour in his "ute".

The main guest room is large with ensuite, all beds have electric blankets, tea, coffee & herbal teas always available.

Our family are adult and away from home. We do have a cat. We enjoy golf, patchwork, gardening and travel.

By car we are 35 minutes from Rotorua and central to Taupo, Waitomo Caves, Tauranga, Hamilton.

Non-smokers preferred and sorry no children under 12 years.

Directions: *Follow SH1 south from Tirau 2 km. Then take SH5 left to Rotorua for 3 km, cross Waihou River Bridge, and 200 metres on left is our gate - name on mailbox.*

Te Awamutu
Farmstay
Address: "Tregamere",
2025 Ohaupo Road, Te Awamutu
Name: Ray and Betty Johnson
Telephone: (07) 871 8861
Beds: 1 Double, 2 Twin (3 bedrooms)
Bathroom: 1 Ensuite, 1 Guest share
Tariff: B&B (full) Double $80, Single $50, Dinner$20. Vouchers accepted.

*A two hour drive south of Auckland makes Te Awamutu a pleasant stop-over
before visiting the famed Waitomo caves. Our home is modern, warm and
comfortable set in approx two acres of garden, with a beautiful view west to Mt.
Pirongia and easy walks to ponds and bush area.*
*We are middle-aged plus _ retired _ then decided to go farming again on a 64 acre
dry stock farm on the verge of suburbia, and one minute from the Te Awamutu Post
Office.*
*Te Awamutu is the Rose Town of New Zealand with a superb rose garden and
beautiful park _ a pleasure to visit!*
Directions: *Very easy to find with a white stone entrance and black railing fence.
Situated on State Highway 3, the main road. On the right hand side coming from
Hamilton, or first farm on left after leaving Te Awamutu going north.*

Te Awamutu
Farmstay/Guest House
Address: Storey Road, Te Awamutu
Name: Mrs Regula Bleskie
Telephone: (07) 871-3301
Beds: 1 Double, 8 Single (5 bedrooms)
Bathrooms: 1 Ensuite, 1 Guests share
Tariff: B&B (full) Double $90, Single $50,
children $25, Dinner $20, Campervans welcome, Vouchers accepted
Nearest Town: Te Awamutu

*The 85 acre farm is situated in beautiful rolling countryside with cattle, horses,
pigs, poultry, sheep and pets. A spacious home with large living area, swimming
pool and tennis court (racquets available) in a well planned garden. It welcomes
you in winter with underfloor heating and a huge open firplace. Large guest
rooms, some with lofts, the bathroom being available for your exclusive use.*
You are welcome to have dinner with us, or if preferred, only bed & breakfast.
*Specials: horseriding available for beginners and experts. For children there is a
pony with a gig, long or short trips only $10.*
Directions: *From Te Awamutu, 100m after signpost Cambridge turn left into Te
Rahu Rd, follow 3 1/2 km - come into Woodstock Rd, follow 1 km - Storey Rd. 1st
driveway on your left.*

Te Awamutu

Farmstay
Address: "Leger Farm",
St Leger Road, R.D. 5, Te Awamutu
Name: Peter & Beverley Bryant
Telephone: (07) 871 6676
Beds: 1 Double, 3 Single (3 bedrooms)
Bathroom: 1 Ensuite, 1 Guests share
Tariff: B&B (full) Double $85, Single $50, Dinner $20
Nearest Town: Te Awamutu

Our property is part of the picturesque fertile Waikato Basin, with extensive views across various farming operations, to Pirongia and Kakepuka Mountains.
The panoramic views of the surrounding countryside is seen from every aspect of our new home, which is built of 'old' red brick and redwood timber.
We farm red deer and sheep on our property, which includes an attractive pond area.
NZ meals of lamb, venison and beef are our specialty.
We are only 3km from historic Te Awamutu which is renowned world wide for its beautiful rose garden. Te Awamutu has one of the largest dried milk dairy factories in the Southern Hemisphere.
30 minutes to Waitomo, 1 hour Rotorua, 30 minutes Hamilton, Te Awamutu is centrally situated. Handy to Arapuni Lake for trout fishing. Several 18 hole golf course are nearby, nearest 1km away.
Interests include music, gardening, tree planting, tramping, travel, antiques, Lions and B&PW Clubs.
Directions: *Please phone for reservations and directions.*

Te Awamutu

Homestay
Address: Budden Road, Pokuru
RD 5, Te Awamutu
Name: Marg and Dick Morton
Telephone: (07) 871 8814
Beds: 1 Double, 2 Single (2 bedrooms)
Bathroom: 2 Family share
Tariff: B&B (full) Double $60, Single $35, Dinner $15, Campervans welcome, Vouchers accepted
Nearest Town: Te Awamutu 8 mins

If you are looking for hospitality, peace and tranquillity then read on. We have a large home set on one acre commanding grand views of Mounts Pirongia and Kakepuku.
We are situated approximately eight minutes west of Te Awamutu, thirty minutes from Hamilton and the renowned Waitomo Caves are barely half an hour away.
We enjoy our garden, especially the roses, have a swimming pool and barbeque facilities for summer relaxation, also table tennis and a model railway. Golfers and tennis players are well catered for (equipment available for hire). An evening meal can be provided and campervans are welcomed. Our one request is no smoking in the house.
Directions: *Please phone.*

Pukeatua, Te Awamutu

Farmstay
Address: "Jandir Nubian Dairy Goat
Farm" 9 Tari Rd Pukeatua
Name: Heather Macferson
Telephone: (07) 872 4527
Beds: 1 Double, 2 Single (2 Bedrooms)
Bathroom: 1 Guests share
Tariff: B&B (full) Double $65, Single $40,
Children $20, Dinner $20, Vouchers accepted
Nearest Town: Te Awamutu, 27km

*Come and experience peace and tranquillity on Pukeatua's Nubian Dairy Goat
Farm, surrounded by restful views of mountain and bush. Enjoy the animals and
have a go at milking and feeding the friendly goats. Tennis court nearby and
racquets available or take a walk into the bush or through the adjacent Tautari
gardens.*
*Comfortable, cosy living, suitable for travellers seeking rest and relaxation. An
ideal stopover on the road between Waitomo Caves and Rotorua.*
*Heather is actively involved in the day to day running of the commercial dairy goat
farm, enjoys pets, country crafts, gardening and cooking.*
*There are two guest rooms, one with two single bed, the other a double bed.
Separate toilet and bathroom available for guests. New Zealand dishes are
speciality, featuring local and home grown produce, served with quality NZ wines.
You are assured of a warm and friendly welcome. We request non smoking in the
house.*
Directions: *Please phone.*

Otorohanga - Waitomo District

Homestay+ Self-contained Accom
Address: "Brake's B&B",
147 Main North Road, (SH3), Otorohanga
Name: Ernest & Ann Brake
Telephone: (07) 873-7734

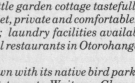

Beds: 2 Single (1 bedroom) **Bathroom:** 1 Family share.
Self-contained unit 1 Queensize, 1 single, plus rollaway bed, cot and high-chair
(1 bedroom) **Bathroom:** 1 Private
Tariff: B&B $58 Double; $39 Single; In self-contained unit $50 Double, $35
Single, $10 each extra, $5 cot. Breakfast optional and extra (continental $4, full
$7), Vouchers accepted.

*We are a retired farming couple with an adult family and have travelled overseas.
Our home is on the northern outskirts of Otorohanga and we enjoy extensive views
of the countryside from our elevated position.*
*The self-contained unit is a quaint little garden cottage tastefully furnished with
walls of natural timber panelling, quiet, private and comfortable. It has tea / coffee
making facilities, toaster, fridge, TV; laundry facilities available.*
*Evening meals are available at several restaurants in Otorohanga, while we invite
you to enjoy breakfast with us.*
*Otorohanga is an interesting rural town with its native bird park featuring a Kiwi
house and aviary. It is the nearest town to Waitomo Glow-worm Caves and
numerous bush walks, Waitomo Golf Course and the Waipa River, a good trout
fishing stream.*
Directions: *from Otorohanga town centre take the main road (SH3 north and
find us on the left approx 2 km from town.*

Otorohanga - Waitomo District

Country Homestay
Address: Main South Road,
R.D. 7, Otorohanga
Name: Michael & Riki Loughnan
Telephone & Fax: (07) 8738-620
Beds: 1 Double, 1 Twin (2 bedrooms)

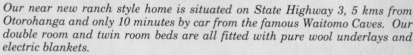

Bathroom: 1Guests share, 1 Family share
Tariff: B&B (full) Double $70, Single $50, Dinner with wine and pre dinner drink $25per person, Vouchers accepted April to September
Nearest Town: Otorohanga 5 kms

Our near new ranch style home is situated on State Highway 3, 5 kms from Otorohanga and only 10 minutes by car from the famous Waitomo Caves. Our double room and twin room beds are all fitted with pure wool underlays and electric blankets.

Other attractions in the area include: The Otorohanga Kiwi House, the Angora Rabbit farm, The Ruakuri Bush Walk, Marakopa Falls, the Natural Bridge walk and Black Water Rafting. For the golfing enthusiast we are only an eight iron from the third green of the Waitomo Golf Club (Championship Course) where visitors are always welcome.

We are an active semi-retired farming couple, enthusiastically developing a spacious garden enjoying life and sharing our activities with guests from either overseas or New Zealand. We are well travelled and are sure you will enjoy your stay with us in this most interesting part of New Zealand.

Otorohanga - Waitomo District

Self-contained Accommodation
Address: Crofthill, RD 3, Otorohanga
Name: Jim & Jennifer Beveridge
Telephone: (07) 873 8232
Beds: 4 Single (2 Bedrooms - each with 2 beds)
Bathroom: 1 Guests share
Tariff: B&B (full) Double $80, Single $45, Dinner $15.
Vouchers accepted
Nearest Town: Otorohanga

Our house, Crofthill, is set in a large rural section near Otorohanga. We have panoramic views from Mt Pirongia to Mt Ruapehu.

In 1993 we built a self-contained unit with 2 large twin bedrooms, shower, toilet, and sitting room with television. There are tea/coffee making facilities. It is connected to the house by a walkway.

We welcome your company, but recognise you may enjoy time to yourselves.

You are particularly welcome to join us at dinner (with a little notice).

Most weekdays, Jim goes to our farm in the heart of the King Country.

We are ideally situated for visiting the Kiwi House, Waitomo Caves and other areas of interest in the region.

Directions: *Turn on to S.H.31 at the Southern end of Otorohanga (by the BP Service Station). We are 6km from Otorohanga on the left hand side at the top of the first hill.*

Tell other travellers about your favourite B&Bs

Otorohanga
- Waitomo District

Homestay+Farmstay
Address: Main Road North RD4
Otorohanga
Name: Jean & Philip Newman
Telephone: (07) 873 1873
Beds: 1 Double, 4 Single (2 Bedrooms)
Bathroom: 1 Guests share
Tariff: B&B (special) Double $70, Single $45, Children under 12 half price,
Dinner $20, Campervans welcome. Vouchers accepted
Nearest Town: 10 mins from Otorohanga, 20 mins from Te Awamutu

Mt Heslington Angus Stud
*Guests are very welcome in our home and are treated as friends. Your comfort is
our aim. For those hot summer days our swimming pool is at your disposal, for
those wishing for mild competition our pool table is readily available.*
*Our home is conveniently situated on SH3 20 mins from Te Awamutu 10 mins
from Otorohanga and very easy to find.*
*Picturesque Waitomo Golf Club is only 20 mins away and continuing on to
Waitomo Caves.*
*We feel our situation lends itself to our Stud Angus cattle and our thoroughbred
racehorses winning both in Australia and New Zealand enjoy attention and
interests.*

Waitomo Caves
- Waitomo District

New Zealand Association FARM & HOME HOSTS

Farmstay
Address: Glenview Station, R.D. 8, Te Kuiti
Name: Cindy & Warren Clayton-Greene
Telephone: (07) 878-7705
Beds: 2 Double, 3 Single (3 bedrooms)
Bathroom: 1 Private, 1 Family share. Private lounge available
Tariff: B&B (full) Double $60, Single $40, Dinner $20, Special prices &
equipment for kids, Vouchers accepted
Nearest Town: Waitomo (5 km), Te Kuiti (23 km), Otorohanga (20km)

*You're invited to stay on a scenic New Zealand sheep and cattle station. A 2,200
acre station with 6000 sheep and 700 beef cattle and other farm animals. The farm
is run in the traditional way with horses and dogs. Enjoy the quiet and hospitality
of rural life in New Zealand. Relax amongst the beautiful native bush, trout
streams and unique limestone formations. Our guests enjoy hiking on the farm,
or taking a drive out to the trout streams.*
*We have a young family, so private lounge is available or enjoy the evening with
the family in the main lounge. We have a large attractive home set in beautiful
gardens. You'll find us nestled in the hills above the Waitomo Caves with
panoramic views.*
Directions: *5km from Waitomo Caves: carry on past the Waitomo Caves going
west towards Marakopa: we are on the tar seal road. Look on the right for the
"Glenview" sign and our name on the mail box. Please phone.*

152

Waitomo Caves
- Waitomo District

Self-contained Accommodation
Address: Waitomo Caves Village
Name: Andree & Peter Dalziel
Telephone: (07) 87 87641
Beds: 2 Double, 4 Single (4 bedrooms)
Bathroom: 4 Ensuite
Tariff: B&B (continental) Double $25-30pp, Single $35-40,
Nearest Town: Waitomo Caves

Our home is only 100 metres from the Museum of Caves information office in the centre of the village and a few hundred metres from the Glow Worm Caves.
Our four detached double and twin rooms with their individual ensuite toilet and shower facilities are of the highest standard.
With a variety of cave adventure trips - Black Water Rafting, Lost World, horse riding, excellent bush walks, a top golf course and a selection of the country's best gardens to visit, all within a short distance - we recommend that you allocate at least two days to spend with us. We will arrange your meals.
If you cannot reach us by phone, just arrive - you will find a place with warm and friendly hospitality.

Waitomo Caves
- Waitomo District

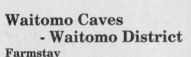

Farmstay
Address: R.D. 1, Te Kuiti,
Please phone
Name: Sue & Bill Kay
Telephone: (07) 878 8762, if no reply ring (07) 878 7702
Beds: 2 Double, 1 Single (3 bedrooms) Bathroom: 1 Guests
Tariff: B&B Double $70, Single $45, Dinner $25, Children
negotiable, Vouchers accepted from 1 April to 31 October
Nearest Town: Waitomo Caves Village 7km, Te Kuiti 15km

It would be a pleasure to have you to stay with us in our comfortable large family homestead set amongst extensive garden and mature English trees. Our garden is listed in the book "Gardens to Visit in New Zealand" and "New Zealand Town and Country Gardens". The native bush we look upon attracts beautiful native birds to our garden.
We live on a 2000 acre sheep and beef farm where you are invited to see various farming activities. In our garden we have a swimming pool and hard tennis court you are welcome to use.
From our house we have a wonderful view of the historic Tumutumu rock, and adjacent a Maori fortress and unique limestone formations.
Additionally to staying in the homestead we have garden accommodation.
Only six minutes down the road are the Black Water Rafting ventures, tourist caves, bush walks and walkways.
We have both travelled and enjoy the opportunity to meet overseas visitors and people from different parts of New Zealand.

Te Kuiti - Waitomo District

Homestay
Address: 5 Grey St, Te Kuiti
Name: Pauline Blackmore
Telephone: (07) 878 6686 after 4pm
Beds: 1 Queen, 2 Single (2 bedrooms)
Bathroom: 2 Private
Tariff: B&B (full) Double $50, Single $30, Children half price, Vouchers accepted

Our home is about 1 km from the township of Te Kuiti which is 80 km south of Hamilton. We are situated in a quiet street just off Highway 3.
Both bedrooms have private toilet facilities and all the beds are comfortable and have electric blankets. The atmosphere is relaxed and guests are welcome to use the comfortable lounge. We offer a wide choice for breakfast and a flexible timetable.
The Waitomo Caves Village is 18 km north west. Attractions in this area include White Water Rafting, Black Water Rafting and, for the very adventurous, the Lost World Experience. All this as well as the Waitomo Caves and the Caves Museum. One well-behaved cat resides with us.

Te Kuiti - Waitomo District

Homestay
Address: Gadsby Road, Te Kuiti
Name: Margaret & Graeme Churstain
Telephone: (07) 878 8191
Beds: 1 Double, 6 Single (4 bedrooms)
Bathroom: 1 Private, 1 Family share
Tariff: B&B (continental) Double $40, Single $20, Dinner (with prior notice) $10, Campervans $10 per person

Our B&B is on a farmlet on Gadsby Road, signposted on S.H.3 at the Northern end of Te Kuiti.
We have enjoyed accomodating visitors from all over the world and New Zealand for some years now, offering a relaxed and comfortable homestay.
To sit on the deck we guarantee rural views you would find hard to forget, with aerial topdressing and farming activity common scenes from all round views.
In one of New Zealand's best sheep and cattle producing areas and boasting the "Shearing Capital of the World" and a statue to match Te Kuiti and surrounding areas offer many leisure activities with the famous Waitomo Caves only minutes away.
Warm comfortable beds we can provide with family share bathroom or if you prefer, a seperate unit is available, ideal for families, campervans, and disabled. Laundry facilities are available at a small charge.
We are happy to collect you from bus or train in the town. Our dog and cat welcome yours.

Continental breakfast consist of fruit, toast, tea/coffee,
Full breakfast is the same with a cooked course,
Special breakfast has something special.

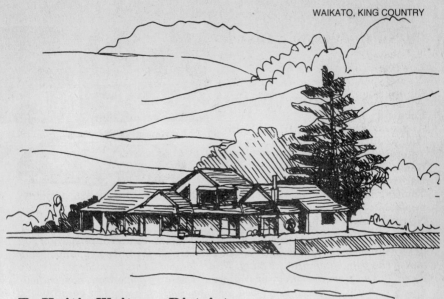

Te Kuiti - Waitomo District
Farmstay
Address: "Tapanui",
Oparure Road, R.D. 5, Te Kuiti
Name: Sue and Mark Perry
Telephone & Fax : (07) 877-8549

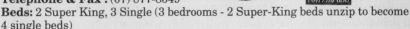

Beds: 2 Super King, 3 Single (3 bedrooms - 2 Super-King beds unzip to become 4 single beds)
Bathroom: 1 Ensuite, 1 Guests share
Tariff: B&B (full) Double $80, Single $55, Dinner $25, Not suitable for children, Vouchers accepted April, May, June and August
Nearest Town: Te Kuiti 21km, Otorohanga 32km, 17km from SH 3.

Our large beautifully appointed homestead provides warm hospitality that ensures every comfort, from feather duvets and electric blankets to heated towel rails, fly screens and central heating. Spacious bedrooms feature vistas of green rolling hills and spectacular outcrops of limestone. Here complete relaxation is the keynote. This is New Zealand at its best.

A separate guest wing consists of a Super King size bed and single bed with ensuite and patio.

Guests also have a choice of a twin or Super King size room with a bathroom.

Our sheep and cattle farm consists of 1400 acres carrying 3000 Romney sheep and 800 head of Angus cattle.

"Tapanui" is an impressive scenic drive from the Waitomo Caves on a sealed road. We are happy for our guests to take part in or be shown the activities on the farm and to meet our pet sheep and donkey.

We are an active farming couple, with interests in gardening, fishing and travel. We enjoy meeting people.

Directions: *Please phone for reservations and directions.*

Our B&Bs are mostly private homes.
Most do not accept credit cards.

Te Kuiti - Waitomo District

Farmstay
Address: 'Blackdown', RD1, Te Kuiti
Name: Jill and Derek Mason
Telephone & Fax: (07) 878 7622
Beds: 4 Single (2 bedrooms)
Bathroom: 1 Ensuite, 1 Family share
Tariff: B&B (continental) Double $70, Single $45, Dinner $25, Children negotiable, Vouchers accepted May to October
Nearest Town: Te Kuiti, 11 kms

Derek and Jill are happy to invite you to stay at "Blackdown". The property of 700 acres has been in the family for three generations with the daily occupation being that of sheep and beef cattle farming. We are located 7 kms from State Highway 3 and 12 kms from the village of Waitomo. The large homestead, now without family at home, has been developed for your comfort, heaters in guest rooms, electric blankets, tasteful decor, garden views from bedrooms and a croquet lawn for your enjoyment. The pleasant garden is surrounded by mature trees. Because of its elevation the property offers panoramic views of the King Country. You are invited to walk the farm for viewing. We like to travel and enjoy sharing the experiences of others.
Glow worm caves on the farm can be visited as an extra and are approached through a beautiful tree lined gorge. Time required for the personally escorted tour is 3 hours.
Directions: *Please phone / fax.*

Piopio - Waitomo District

Farmstay
Address: Aria Road, Piopio
Name: Maurice and Jennifer Kearns
Telephone: (07) 8777-801
Beds: 4 Single (2 bedrooms) **Bathroom**: 1 Private
Tariff: B&B (full) Double $65, Single $32.50, Children half price, Dinner $20, Lunch $5, Vouchers accepted
Nearest Town: Te Kuiti 30 km, Piopio 8 km

We welcome visitors to our modern home on a 163 acre sheep and cattle farm in the clean green King Country. 8 km from SH3 on a sealed road, it is an ideal stopover before or after visiting the Waitomo Caves area en route to Taranaki or the Central North Island region.
The 2 twin rooms have snug beds, feather duvets, electric blankets and heaters. All rooms have garden outlooks. No steps. We accept only one booking (1-4 persons) per night.
Gardening is our special interest and our home is nestled amongst natural limestone outcrops and mature trees, interspersed with perennial plantings. A pond and working waterwheel contribute to an atmosphere of peace and tranquillity. Enjoy too, a walk with us around our farm.
Directions: *travelling south on SH3, turn left at crossroads in centre of Piopio. Proceed for 8 km. We are first home on right after passing the Paekaka Road (which turns off to right). Name on mailbox.*

Pio Pio - Waitomo District

Farmstay
Address: Carmel Farm, Main Road, Box 93 Pio Pio
Name: Leo and Barbara Anselmi
Telephone & Fax: (07) 877 8130
Beds: 6 Single or 2 King-size & 2 single (3 bedrooms)
Bathroom: 1 bathroom per bedroom; Ensuite family unit
Tariff: B&B (full) Double $80 Single $45, Dinner $25 with
wine and pre-dinner drink. Vouchers accepted
Nearest Town: Te Kuiti and Otorohanga

Barbara and Leo Anselmi own and operate a 1040 acre sheep and cattle farm. The property is on the Main South Road 20km south of Te Kuiti and 3km north of the rural township of Pio Pio.

You will be welcomed into a 3000 square feet home set in picturesque gardens and will be treated to delicious home cooked meals and the warmth of our friendship. Whether the excitement of mustering mobs of cattle and sheep, just relaxing as you drive around the rolling hills on the 4 wheeled farm bike, basking in the pool or wandering through the gardens interest you, no matter what your age you will experience unforgettable memories of breathtaking scenery, a clean green environment and warm friendship.

We have many farm pets who all love the attention of our guest including horses to be ridden and donkeys to be fed.

As well as farming activities we look over a beautiful 18 hole golf course which welcomes visitors. The property is just minutes from White Water Rafting and Canoeing activities, the beautiful Piopio Pioneering Museum, The Lost World Cavern and only 35km from the famous Waitomo Caves. We are only minutes away from breathtaking bush walks and 140km to Rotorua.

Directions: *On State Highway 3, 6km south of the junction of State Highway 4 to New Plymouth. We can arrange to pick you up from Otorohanga, Te Kuiti or Waitomo if required.*

Piopio - Waitomo District
Country Homestay

Address: "Bracken Ridge"
Aria Road Piopio
Name: Rob & Susan Hallam
Telephone: (07) 877 8384
Beds: 3 Single (2 Bedrooms)
Bathroom: 1 Private
Tariff: B&B (full) Double $60, Single $35, Children half price, Dinner $15, Campervans up to 4 people $25 meals extra, Vouchers accepted
Nearest Town: Te Kuiti 24km, Piopio 1km

We welcome guests to our large modern, family home which is situated on a 10 acre farmlet. Our elevated site provides panoramic views of the beautiful surrounding countryside. Self-contained private guest facilities are provided on a separate level including use of the laundry.

We look forward to your company for a relaxing, enjoyable stay and are happy to share our knowledge of local points of interest such as bush walks, white water rafting, scenic drives, trout fishing, golf or a stroll over the farm. Waitomo Caves is only 30 minutes away. Visits to sheep, dairy farms and local gardens can be arranged.

We ask guests not to smoke inside our home nor bring pets.

Our family has a variety of interests from music to boating and enjoys meeting people from different places.

Directions: *Travelling south on SH 3 turn left at centre of Piopio village and proceed 1 kilometre. Look for our name at gate on right. Please phone ahead.*

Taumarunui
Homestay

Address: "Hide-Away" P.O. Box 294,
Taumarunui (Postal), 3 Porou Street, Matapuna,
Taumarunui (Residential)
Name: Anna & Hugh Halliday
Telephone: (07) 895-5075
Beds: 1 Double, 2 Single (2 bedrooms) **Bathroom:** 1 guest
Tariff: B&B (Special) Double $60, Single $35, Dinner $18, Vegetarian but plenty of choice.
Nearest Town: Taumarunui

Our spacious 4 bedroom home is set in a quiet suburb, with an attractive garden and trees. We have off street parking and a separate bathroom and toilet for guests. Although our 3 sons were brought up in New Zealand and are now all grown up, we have lived overseas and visited many countries in Europe, Africa and Asia. We enjoy meeting overseas visitors.

All meals are vegetarian and nutritious. Naturopathic services are available from my clinic at home. Taumarunui is the gateway to the Tongariro and Whanganui National Parks, giving visitors a wide choice of outdoor pursuits such as tramping, canoeing, rafting, jet boating, and skiing (winter). Taumarunui has a top-rated golf course and a heated swimming pool.

Directions: *Brochures with map available from Taumarunui Information Centre (Railway Station). Phone or write for booking or further information and brochure.*

Ongarue, Taumarunui
Farmstay
Address: 'Foxley Station', RD Ongarue
Name: Tony & Kitrena Fullerton-Smith
Telephone: (07) 896 6104 **Fax:** (07) 8966919
Beds: 1 Double, 3 Single (3 bedrooms) **Bathroom:** 1 Private (only 1 party of guests taken at a time).
Tariff: B&B (continental, Full on request) Double $70, Single $30, Dinner from $20. Campervans welcome. Discount offered for 2 nights. Vouchers accepted. Nearest Town: 25km north of Taumarunui.

'Foxley Station' is a 3500 acre hill country farm situated in the heart of the King Country, running sheep, cattle and deer.
The 'Homestead' is set in a lovely country garden with tennis court and swimming pool. We like to encourage people to observe or participate in our farm life. Go walking through our Native Bush Reserve or just relax.
Enjoy home cooked meals with complimentary wine or for something special try our 'Game Menu'.
Why not stay for two nights and enjoy a day on the farm or some of our nearby attractions all within one hour of us: Lake Taupo, Wanganui River, Tongariro National Parks, Scenic Flights, Waitomo Caves, Ski Fields, Local Gardens and Golf Course.
We are in our early 40's. Our children are away at Boarding School.
Non-smokers preferred.
We invite you to experience our friendly and relaxed farm life and country living. Looking forward to entertaining you in our home.
Directions: *Please phone for reservations and directions.*

Taumarunui
Farmstay
Address: Waituhi RD4 Taumarunui
Name: Yvonne & Eric Walker
Telephone: (07) 896 6041
Beds: 1 Double, 2 Single (2 Bedrooms) **Bathroom:** 1 Family share
Tariff: B&B (full) Double $60, Single $35, Children half price, Dinner $15
Nearest Town: Taumarunui 25km east on SH 41

Our home is large and comfortable, with a spacious living area, overlooking garden and swimming pool. It is set in pleasant surroundings in a peaceful valley only 20 minutes from the rural township of Taumarunui.
Taumarunui offers Jetboat tours down the Wanganui River, canoeing and trout fishing, as well as a golf course with an excellent reputation which welcomes visitors.
Our farm is a 45 minute drive from Tongariro National Park where seasonal activities such as skiing and tramping are available.
For those keen on exploring a genuine NZ farm, we have 360 hectares, 60 of which are in native bush. We farm sheep, cattle, deer and have various other animals such as pigs, dogs, a cat and also horses suitable for riding.
Please phone for directions.

Kakahi, Taumarunui
Farmstay
Address: "Rawhide", Kakahi via Taumarunui
Name: Rex and Barbara Taylor
Telephone: (07) 895-4550
Beds: 4 Single (2 bedrooms)
Bathroom: 1 Family share
Tariff: B&B (full) Double $60, Single $35;
B&B, Lunch and Dinner – Double $110, Single $60; Dinner $15; Campervans $12
Nearest Town: Taumarunui 20 km

Be our guest in a modern home on 20 acres at Kakahi which is 20 km south of Taumarunui, one of the country's best, yet least-used vacation spots in New Zealand.
Our property is next to bush reserve and the Wanganui river. Good country-style cooking with 90% of the food being home produced on the property. Quarter Horse breeder, stud, western saddlery and leather craft workshop.
Attractions include trout fishing, tramping, swimming, glow worms, handy to jet boat tours, canoeing, top golf course. Three-quarter hour drive to ski fields. Large gun collection short drive away. Horse riding available.
Packed lunch available for day trips away. Special diets can be catered for. Extra charge for liquor or bring your own.

Homes newly listed in this edition
of *The New Zealand B&B Book* have all been inspected.

TIPS
for easier travel

★ **Ensuite and private bathroom** are for your use exclusively, **Guests share** bathroom means you may be sharing with other guests, **Family share** bathroom means you will be sharing with the family.

★ In the tariff section of each listing **'continental' breakfast** consists of fruit, cereal, toast, tea/coffee; **'full'** breakfast is the same with an additional cooked course; **'special'** breakfast has something special.

★ Do not try to travel too far in one day. Take time to enjoy the company of your hosts and other locals.

★ **Telephone ahead** to enquire about a B&B. It is a nuisance for you if you arrive to find the accommodation has been taken. And besides hosts need a little time to prepare.

★ The most suitable **time to arrive is late afternoon**, and to leave is before 10 in the morning.

★ **If you would like dinner** please give your host sufficient notice to prepare.

★ If you are unsure of anything ask your hosts about it. They will give you a direct answer.

★ Our B&Bs are mostly private homes. **Most do not accept credit cards.**

★ If you have made your reservations from overseas, check that your dates are correct. You might cross the dateline to come to New Zealand.

★ **Please let your hosts know if you have to cancel.** They will have spent time preparing for you.

★ Make your Cook Strait Ferry reservation in advance.

★ **If you need to use a public phone,** use the first one you see. It may be hours before you see another.

★ **Carry a phone card.** Most public phones do not take coins. Phone cards can be bought from dairies, bookstores and petrol stations.

★ New Zealand road signs are getting better, but your best directions come from asking a local.

★ Most listings show hosts accept vouchers. The only vouchers accepted are New Zealand Bed & Breakfast Book vouchers.

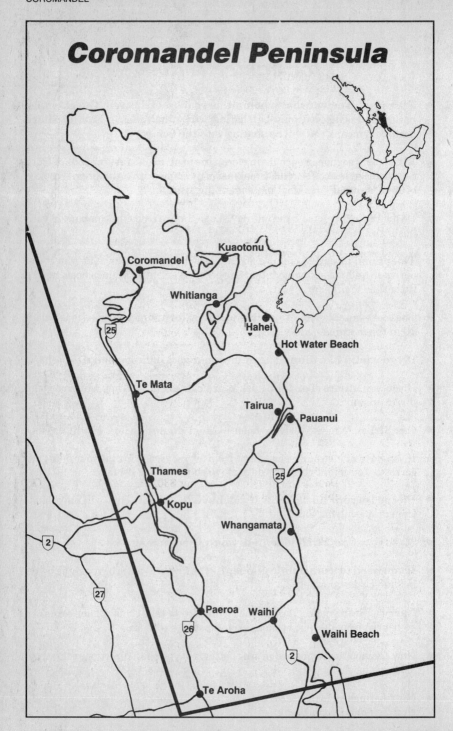

Thames

Homestay
Address: Please phone
Name: Glenys and Russell Rutherford
Telephone & Fax: (07) 868 7788
Beds: 1 Double, 2 Single (2 bedrooms)
Bathroom: 1 Private, 1 Family share
Tariff: B&B (special) Double $60, Single $35, Children 1/2 price; Dinner $20. Vouchers accepted.

We have a spacious and comfortable home with sweeping views of the Firth of Thames.
Our interests include gardening, golf, music and entertaining family and friends. The double room adjoins a private lounge with TV and reading material. A twin room upstairs opens onto a balcony, All beds have electric blankets. Self service tea and coffee provided.
Being an historic goldmining settlement, museums and gold prospectors diggings are of particular interest. Due to its natural beauty the Coromandel has attracted many potters and painters. Their galleries can be visited on a scenic day trip up the coast to Coromandel village, and continuing back through the popular beach resorts of Whitianga, Pauanui and Tairua. The rugged hills and native bush appeal to hikers and nature lovers.
Our intention is for you to enjoy some of these features and we welcome your visit. You may care to join us for dinner or simply enjoy a comfortable night's rest and a satisfying breakfast to set you off on your day's journey.

Kopu, Thames

Farmstay
+ Self-Contained Accommodation
Address: "Thorold", Kopu, RD1, Thames
Name: Helen and Tony Smith
Telephone: (07) 868 8480
Beds: 1 Queen, 2 Single (2 bedrooms) **Bathroom:** 1 Private
Tariff: B&B (full) Double $90, Single $60, Dinner $30, Children on request. Off season rates available. Vouchers accepted.
Nearest Town: Thames - 5 minutes

'Thorold' is set in a peaceful farm setting of 50 acres on the main highway 5 minutes from Thames and perfectly situated for visitors to the Coromandel Peninsula.
The guest wing is deluxe, private, spacious and beautifully appointed. Queen size bed and two single beds with bathroom adjoining. A small kitchen with fridge. Sitting room has comfortable chairs, T.V., billiard table. All rooms open out onto a large verandah and swimming pool.
Only one group of guests at any one time.
We have a beef farm at Coromandel and Tony has his own Livestock Company based at home and he is available to enjoy breakfast with guests in our dining room most mornings. You are welcome to have breakfast in your unit if preferred. Our interests are tramping, fishing, gardening, forestry and meeting people. Thames and the Coromandel Peninsula have so much to offer and we would be pleased to be part of your stay.
Directions: *Please phone.*

Te Mata Bay, Thames
Country Homestay
Address: 29 Eames Cres, Te Mata Bay,
Thames Coast, RD 5, Thames
Name: Charles & Helen Burgess
Telephone: (07) 868-4754
Beds: 1 Double, 2 Single (2 bedrooms)
Bathroom: 1 Guests share + shower room + separate toilet.
Tariff: B&B (special) Double $60, Single $30,
Dinner $15, Credit cards accepted, Vouchers accepted

Our home has panoramic views of the sparkling waters of the Firth of Thames from the wide balcony which surrounds the house. The sunsets are spectacular as are the views of the surrounding farmland and coromandel Ranges. We are 21 km, north from the Thames P.O along the most picturesque Thames Coast with the old Pohutukawa Trees (N.Z Christmas Tree) shading the beaches. A day out hunting or fishing with experienced members of our family is a possibility.
You are welcome to relax in our peaceful garden or enjoy a game of pool or play the paino is our spacious games room.
The guests' bedrooms are pleasantly furnished and have wonderful sea views. There is a seperate shower room and bathroom for guests use. Breakfast is special in our house, with hot bread, marmalade, muesli and yoghurt all homemade. Dinner is available on request, with fresh vegetables or salad with your evening meal. We are a NON SMOKING family.
Directions: *Please phone.*

Kopu, Thames
Farmstay
+ Self-contained Accom
Address: "Wharfedale Farmstay",
R.D. 1, Kopu Hikuai Highway, Thames
Name: Chris & Rosemary Burks
Telephone: (07) 868-8929
Beds: 1 Double, 2 Single (2 bedrooms)
Bathroom: 2 Private
Tariff: **B&B** (special) Double $90, Single $55, Dinner $30 pp
Nearest Town: Thames

Recently featured in Air NZ's "Pacific Way" and Japan's "My Country" magazines. We cordially invite you to share our idyllic lifestyle, set in 9 acres of paddocks and gardens surrounded by lovely native bush.
Meander across the lawn to the riverwalk picking, perhaps, some peaches or citrus fruits which abound and enjoy in total privacy natures swimming pools whilst Kingfisher and Rosella swoop overhead.
Our gardens reflect our interest in herbs, old roses and no dig cultivation, we enjoy wholefoods and organically grown produce. We have hardcourt tennis and barbeque area. Our goat herd allow us to share their lives, milk and fibre for spinning.
My husband practices medicine and our son is studying at Otago University.
The property is situated 1 hour from Auckland, 15 mins from Thames, close proximity to beautiful Coromandel beaches.
We offer a double room with double bed, electric blanket and private bathroom. Or a self-contained flat with twin beds. Cosy farmhouse kitchen with range in winter and cool shade in summer. We look forward to meeting you.
Directions: *Please phone for directions.*

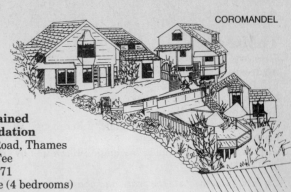

Thames
Homestay & Self-contained
Accommodation
Address: 304 Grafton Road, Thames
Name: Ferne & David Tee
Telephone: (07) 8689-971
Beds: 3 Double, 1 Single (4 bedrooms)
Bathroom: 4 Ensuite
Tariff: B&B (Free continental. Cooked breakfast $5 pp)) Double $85-95, Single $55, Dinner $20 by request. Credit Cards.

Grafton cottage is nestled in the foot hills of the Coromandel Peninsula, overlooking the historic town of Thames, with panoramic views over the Firth with it's picturesque sunsets.
Thames, considered the Gateway to the Peninsula, boasts extensive bush reserves covering the rugged mountainous range. To the East lie the world renowned beaches, while to the West, the calmer waters of the Firth.
Also of interest are the many activities catering for the art and craft, goldmining and kauri history enthusiast.
The cottage itself consists of dining room, two lounges, one double bedroom with ensuite available for guests, plus, adjoining the main house, are four chalets all doubles with ensuites, tea and coffee making facilities, two with cooking facilities.
As keen outdoor people, we offer personalised tours of the Coromandel and Central North Island (by prior arrangement).
Directions: *Turn right at Toyota factory (Bank St) follow to end, turn right into Parawai Road, 4th on left is Grafton Road.*

Thames
Homestay/Self-contained Accommodation
Address: 509 Upper Albert Street, Thames
Name: Ms Gail McIntosh
Telephone: (07) 868 8426
Beds: 2 Double, 2 Single (3 bedrooms) **Bathroom:** 1 Private, 1 Guests share
Tariff: B&B (continental) Double $60, Single $35, Dinner $15, Children half price, Campervans $30. Vouchers accepted.

My 2 storey home is situated on the hills overlooking Thames with sweeping views of the sea. Recently redecorated throughout with facilities to ensure a relaxing visit. Guests can enjoy a private breakfast on the balcony of the queen bedroom. The twin room has bush views and the bathroom is shared by guests (4 maximum). The self-contained flat on the ground level is spacious with its own cooking facilities. It is a non smoking household without pets.
My home is surrounded by 3/4 acre of native bush with abundant bird life. Campervans are welcome as there is ample parking and laundry facilities.
Thames township is 1km away so complimentary transport is available to transport depots.
Thames is the gateway to the beautiful Coromandel Peninsula, known for its bush walks and great beaches.
I have travelled extensively and know the hospitality to offer tourists. I take a keen interest in current events and world politics.

Thames

Homestay
Address: Brunton House
210 Parawai Rd Thames
Name: Albert & Yvonne Sturgess
Telephone: (07) 868 5160
Beds: 1 Queen, 1 Double, 1 Single (2 Bedrooms)
Bathroom: 1 Guests share
Tariff: B&B (full) Double $75, Single $40, Dinner by arrangement $20, Vouchers accepted

We invite you to share the grace and charm of our lovely Victorian home. Built in 1869 it is spacious but also homely, comfortable and smoke-free.
In summer excellent indoor outdoor living, BBQ area, tennis court and swimming pool make this a great place to relax.
In winter with fires and good heating, comfortable beds with electric blankets and fluffy quilts our home is cosy and warm.
Tea and biscuits are always available for you to help yourself.
In the evening enjoy the use of our billiard table, read and relax with a book from our comprehensive library, watch TV or sit and chat in the comfortable lounge.
Our interests include travel, steamtrains, embroidery, square dancing, reading, gardening.
Thames is the gateway to the Coromandel Peninsular for you to explore and enjoy the whole of the Coromandel.
Directions: *Opposite Toyota turn into Banks St, turn right into Parawai Rd. After Brunton Cres look for us on the left.*

Coromandel

Homestay
Address: 740, Kowhai Drive,
Te Kouma, Coromandel
Name: Hilary & Vic Matthews
Telephone: (07) 866 8046
Beds: 1 Double, 3 Single (1 b'room +
one sleepout) **Bathroom:** 1 Guests share
Tariff: B&B (continental) Double $60,
Single $35, Dinner $25, Children half price,
Vouchers accepted after Easter to November
Nearest Town: Coromandel 11km to the north, Thames 60km south, Auckland 2.5 hours by road.

Our modern pole house is situated 740 metres from a safe, sandy beach on the southern side of the Coromandel Harbour.
Vic is a professional furniture designer and maker. Our home is full of beautiful hand made furniture. Hilary weaves, spins and enjoys gardening. We travel widely and have many interests.
We feel that due to open stairs and balconies, the house is unsuitable for toddlers. We have a pet cat and are a smoke free home.
Coromandel area offers beaches, swimming, fishing, walking and a craft trail for the area.
Directions: *Travel north from Thames (SH 25) for about 60 minutes, down a steep hill to Coromandel Harbour, turn very sharply left into Te Kouma Road. Drive around the Harbour's edge, past a big boat ramp for about 3km. Turn left into, Kowhai Drive. Our house is 740 metres up the steep hill. There is a large wooden sign on the right giving our name.*

Coromandel
Guest House
Address: Tiki Road
State Highway 25 Coromandel
Name: Jacaranda
Telephone: (07) 866 8002
Beds: 2 Queen, 2 Double, 1 Single (4 Bedrooms)
Bathroom: 2 Guests share, 1 Family share
Tariff: B&B (continental) Double $60, Single $35, Dinner $18, Credit Cards.
Vouchers accepted
Nearest Town: 3km south of Coromandel township SH25

Tony and Michelle welcome you to Jacaranda. A beautiful modern 7 bedroom home in eloquent surroundings set on 6 acres of peaceful farmland just 3km south of Coromandel township on SH 25. Relax and enjoy our spacious lounge, comfy bedrooms, ample verandahs and farmlet atmosphere. The peninsula is a goldmine of activities. There are golf courses, beaches, fishing, bush walks, kauri groves, horse riding and a miniature railway. For the more adventurous there is a climb up Castle Rock for superb views, mountains bikes and more. We provide a free shuttle to town or to the nearby 309 road. (A restricted area for rental cars) Animal lovers will enjoy our 2 cats and dog.
The tariff includes continental breakfast. Full breakfasts and dinners available on request. Visa and MC accepted. Just 2 hours from Auckland.
Call us to avoid disappointment. Jacaranda Ph 07-866 8002.

Kuaotunu
Homestay
Address: Main Road, Kuaotunu,
Coromandel Peninsula
Name: John and Robin Twemlow
Telephone: (07) 8665-735
Beds: 2 Single (1 bedroom) **Bathroom:** 1 Private
Tariff: B&B (full) Double $50, Single $30, Dinner $15; Credit Cards. Vouchers accepted
Nearest Town: Whitianga 16 km on State Highway 25

We are a Christian family with one teenage daughter. Our house is across the road from the beach where we enjoy fishing, walking and spending time – in fact just plain relaxing. Rowboat, canoes and fishing gear for your use. This area offers bushwalks and exploring of old goldmines.
If you are looking for a stopover on your way round the Coromandel Peninsula, our home could well be the place you're looking for. We're a very relaxed household - no frills but food to fill. Vegetarian meals prepared on request.
We also have two single beds in the library for extra sleeping if needed. Cot also available. 1 friendly labrador X and 1 cat in family.
Directions: *Please phone collect.*

Kuaotunu

Homestay
Address: Grays Ave
Kuaotunu
Name: The Kaeppeli's
Telephone: (07) 866 2445
Beds: 2 Double, 1 Single (2 Bedrooms) **Bathroom:** 1 Guests share
Tariff: B&B (special) Double $70, Single $43, Children 6-12yrs half price, Dinner $20, Vouchers accepted
Nearest Town: 17km north of Whitianga on SH25

We are a Swiss/Kiwi family who have had restaurants in Switzerland for 14 years. We now enjoy sharing with our guests, the peace and tranquillity of Kuaotunu, in our newly built home, with its tremendous views out over the bay. Our 51/2 hectare property is approximately 300 metres from the beach. Evening meals by arrangement. Robert is an excellent Swiss Chef who takes pride in preparing our guests meals, using home produce, vegetarian meals are also no problem.
Meals can be enjoyed in the guests dining-room or in the garden enjoying the views. Children are welcome and can make acquaintance with our animals.
Kuaotunu has clean, safe, white sandy beaches, is also handy to many other beautiful spots and an ideal starting point for exploring other parts of Coromandel Peninsula or for bush walks, fishing, horse trekking, water-sports or just relaxing. Look forward to welcoming you at "The Kaeppeli's".
Note: Building was not completed at the time of inspection, phone to confirm.

Whitianga

Homestay
Address: The White House,
129 Albert St, Whitianga
Name: Delphine & David Carter
Telephone & Fax: (07) 866-5116
Beds: (Sealey Postupedics)1 Queen, 1 Twin (2 singles can be made into a King size bed), 1 Double + 2 Single (usually taken by families) (3 bedrooms)
Bathroom: 1 Ensuite, 1 Guests share
Tariff: B&B (full) Room with Ensuite Double $85, Single $50, Double $75, Single $45, Credit cards accepted, Vouchers accepted.

When only the best will do
We are recent arrivals to the Mercury Bay area, semi retired, attracted by the wonderful climate and the old fashioned small town friendliness. We are involved in the town through the Business Association, Masonic Lodge, The Lionesses and in our spare time play bridge and golf. In addition we are Picture Framers and provide a range of accounting services. Over the years we have travelled extensively and lived for a period of time in Barbados.
Ours is a new home, designed for visitors with an extensive garden, in which we grow flowers and our own vegetables and fruit. Our home overlooks the inner harbour, where swimming is available at high tide and on the beach less than 100 metres away are a large range of native and migratory seabirds.
We believe that Mercury Bay has something to offer to all visitors and we make a promise that all our visitors enjoy their stay in Whitianga.
We have a policy, due to complaints from guests that we do not list tariff from a certain figure. We will be happy to list your tariff as $75-$100 for example, but we like the full information to be available to guests.

Whitianga

Bed & Breakfast/Homestay
Address: "Cosy Cat Cottage",
41 South Highway, Whitianga
Name: Gordon and Janet Pearce
Telephone: (07) 8664-488
Beds: 1 Double, 1 Queen, 3 Single (3 bedrooms)
Bathroom: 1 Ensuite, 1 Private, 1 Guests share
Tariff: B&B (special) Double $70-$90, Single $45-$60,(off season discounts)
Dinner $20. Credit cards: Visa/MC
Nearest Town: 1 km south of Whitianga Post Office; Thames 93 km via SH25
and Tairua.

*Welcome to our picturesque two storied cottage, filled with feline memorabilia.
Relax with complimentary tea or coffee any time, served on the verandah, in the
garden or in the guest lounge which has a library, television and board games for
your use.*
*Enjoy a good night's rest in comfortable beds. Choose a variety of treats from our
breakfast menu - fresh fruit salad, homemade muesli and preserves, honey from
our own bees, and hot dishes prepared the way you like them. Special diets catered
for.*
*You will probably like to meet our three cats (playful Tonkinese kittens are
sometimes around before going to their new homes) or just be amused by the feline
ambience.*
*Whitianga enjoys a pleasant climate and relaxed way of life, with magnificent
scenery and safe sandy beaches. Our excellent restaurants and other amenities
make it an ideal base for your Coromandel Peninsula exploration.*
Friendly, helpful service is assured at Cosy Cat Cottage. See you soon!

Whitianga

Homestay
Address: "Anne's Haven"
119 Albert St., Whitianga
Name: Bob & Anne
Telephone: (07) 866-5550
Beds: 2 Double, 3 Single (3 bedrooms)
Bathroom: Family share
Tariff: B&B (full) Double $50, Single $25, Dinner $15, Children $15, Vouchers accepted

A warm welcome awaits you along with a cup of tea or coffee. Relax in our modern spacious home and enjoy the cottage country garden. After a good nights sleep in the comfortable beds you will enjoy breakfast which can be light and healthy with home preserves and muesli or the traditional bacon and eggs both can be followed by toast with homemade jams and marmalade served with tea or coffee. Dinner is available on request. There are 6 beautiful beaches within strolling distance and we are only 200 meters from the shopping centre. You may like a round of golf, scenic flight, fishing trip, coffee cruise or a bush walk to see NZ' gigantic Kauri trees which we can help you arrange. Whitianga Mercury Bay is the perfect location to unwind and relax or to make a base to explore the Coromandel Peninsular. Whether it be 1 day or 1 week, let us help you to make your stay a memorable one. Our courtesy car is available.

Whitianga

Homestay
Address: "Homestay 127",
127 Albert Street, Whitianga
Name: Meriana and Jurrie Bael
Telephone: (07) 866-5055
Beds: 1 Double, 2 Single (2 bedrooms)
Bathroom: 1 Guests share
Tariff: B&B (special) Double $60, Single $35, Dinner by arrangement, Vouchers accepted

Whitianga is a quiet fishing village with beautiful, safe beaches, breathtaking seaviews - there are plenty of activities including boating, fishing, swimming, walking, scenic drives, horse riding etc. There is also a magnificent golf course and bowling club.
Before we came to Whitianga we owned and operated a restaurant specializing in European and Asian cuisine.
We serve continental or cooked breakfast with hot muffins, fresh fruit (in season) tea, coffee, fruit juice, cereals.
Well appointed accommodation is self contained, laundry available.
No pets. No smoking inside please.
Access to river across the road, to town centre and beaches 5 mins walk.
Our comfortable home, although on the main road, is set back far enough to minimise traffic noise.
Just follow the long drive next to the yellow sign "Bed and Breakfast 127 Albert St". We love meeting people and are happy to share our home with them.

Whitianga
Homestay
Address: "Whitianga Bed
& Breakfast"
12 Cook Drive, Whitianga
Name: Pat and Bill Carse
Telephone: (07) 866 5547
Beds: 1 Double, 2 Single (2 bedrooms) **Bathroom:** 2 Family share
Tariff: B&B (full) Double $50, Single $35, Dinner $15 by prior arrangement,
School children $15, Pre-schoolers free. Credit cards. Vouchers accepted

*We are a semi-retired couple, with a grown family, and are originally from
Scotland.*
*Our comfortable modern home is away from busy main street traffic. Guests may
share the family lounge/TV room. Tea or coffee is available at any time. During
the colder months our home is warm throughout. Children are welcome. We have
bicycles for guests to use around town, free of charge. Free pick up from bus station
or airfield.*
*We offer a friendly homely atmosphere and a relaxed base from which to explore
the many unspoiled features of Mercury Bay. We are always ready to supply local
information to make your stay more interesting*
*Bill is a retired research chemist and now spends his time tending our large fruit
and vegetable garden, and wine-making. Pat is a legal secretary, and is a
volunteer ambulance officer.*

Whitianga
Bed & Breakfast
Address: Camellia Lodge
South Highway Rd 1
Whitianga
Name: John & Pat Lilley
Telephone & Fax: (07) 866 2253
Beds: 2 Double, 2 Single (4 Bedrooms) **Bathroom:** 1 Guests share
Tariff: B&B (full) Double $70, Single $45, Children under 12 half price, under
5 free, Dinner $20. Credit cards. Vouchers accepted
Nearest Town: Whitianga 4km south of Whitianga SH 25

*Kia ora. Welcome to our friendly home, surrounded by 73 camellia bushes. Our
home is nestled at the rear of a spacious parklike garden, which includes kauri,
rimu, totara trees, also we offer for your enjoyment the use of a spa, swimming pool
and lots of lovely gardens to relax in.*
*You may like to have a round of golf or a scenic flight. We would be glad to arrange
this for you. You would normally be woken up to the tune of the bellbirds singing
in the trees, then you settle into a hearty breakfast which will set you up for the day.
We are situated approx 4km south of Whitianga in a quiet rural area, but not to
far a bushwalk, swimming, fishing or any of the lovely attraction Whitianga has
to offer. We can assure you of a warm friendly welcome and a comfortable stay.*

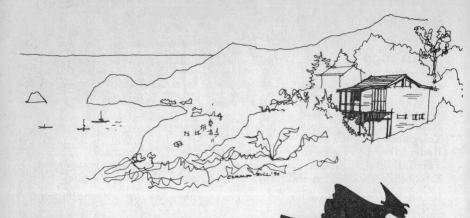

Hahei Beach, Whitianga

Homestay/ Bed & Breakfast
Address: "Spellbound", 77 Grange Road,
Hahei Beach, RD1, Whitianga
Name: Barbara and Alan Lucas
Telephone: (07) 866 3543
Beds: 2 Double, 2 Single, (3 bedrooms)
Bathroom: 2 Guests share
Tariff: B&B (Continental) Double $70, Single $40,
Children under 10 half price; Dinner $20,
Credit cards accepted, Vouchers accepted April to October
Nearest Town: Tairua 36 km, Whitianga 38 km

*Barbara and I live in a Lockwood home overlooking the sea with panoramic views
from the Alderman Islands to the Mercury Islands.*

*We are five minutes from Hahei Beach and are on the road to Cathedral Cove Te
Whanganui A Hei: Marine Reserve and its beaches, a must when visiting this area.
Hot water beach is just a short distance away where you can enjoy a warm soak
at any time of the year.*

*The area offers bush walks, surf beaches, fishing and spectacular views for
photography.*

*Our interests are meeting people and gardening. We enjoy our own vegetables and
can assure you of excellent meals, my wife is a first class cook, at least, I think so.*

*Please give us a telephone call when you wish to come and we can promise you a
most enjoyable, relaxed stay. We look forward to hearing from you.*

Directions: *Turn off at Whenuakite. Grange Road is on left by Hahei Store, We
are on left near top of hill. Street numbers not consecutive.*

Always telephone ahead to enquire about a B&B. It is a nuisance for you if
you simply arrive to find someone already staying there.
And besides hosts need a little time to prepare.

Hot Water Beach, Whitianga
Self-contained Accommodation
Address: Radar Road
Hot Water Beach RD1 Whitianga
Name: Auntie Dawns Place
Telephone: (07) 866 3707
Beds: 2 Double, 1 Single, Baby Crib available (2 Bedrooms)
Bathroom: 2 Private
Tariff: B&B (continental) Double $65, Single $35, Children $10, Dinner $20.
Vouchers accepted
Nearest Town: Whitianga 28km, Tairua 27km

Hot Water Beach is a beautiful surf beach. At low tide hot water bubbles up at a particular place on the beach and you can dig yourself a "hot-pool" to bathe in. At the other side of the bay, rocks and rock pools are ideal for surf-casting snorkelling etc.
Your hosts "Auntie Dawn" (and Joe) are past 50 and enjoy gardening and relaxing on 1.5 acres set amongst giant Pohutukawa trees. (And Joe likes making home-brew beer.)
We have a large new family home only 100 metres from the sea.
We provide comfortable bedrooms, private bathrooms, cooking and laundry facilities (meals on request). Children and pets welcome.
Tea and coffee, bread butter milk sugar jam and cereal are in the units and guests usually prepare their own breakfast at whatever time they wish.
Directions: *Turn right into Radar Road 200 metres before Hot Water Beach shop/Holiday Park, we are just around the corner. A phone call would be appreciated 07-8663707.*

Tairua
Bed & Breakfast
Address: Hornsea House
80 Main Rd North, Tairua, via Thames
Name: Doreen and Derek Cory-Wright
Telephone: (07) 864 8536
Beds: 4 Single (2 bedrooms) **Bathroom:** 1 Family share
Tariff: B&B (special) Double $60, Single $35,
Children under 4 free, 5 -12 half price, Vouchers accepted
Nearest Town: Thames 45km south, 45km north Whitianga

Ours is a farm homestead built of Kauri early this century by Derek's grandfather; it is situated in an acre of spacious old established grounds including an area of native bush. We frequently see and hear tuis and native wood pigeons. We have 2 family cats, Katie & Meerow.
Doreen is a spinner and weaver, weaving mostly floor rugs. We both spend much time in the garden keeping the lawns and gardens looking attractive.
Hornsea House is in a quiet secluded spot, with off-road parking, ten minutes walk from Tairua Village and beach. The Tairua Country Club is adjacent with golf, bowls and croquet.
Local legend has it, climb Paku and you will be back within seven years.
Come and enjoy our relaxed, friendly hospitality.

Tairua
Bed & Breakfast
Address: 33 Main Rd Sth Tairua
Name: Kotuku Lodge
Telephone: (07) 864 7040
Beds: 1 Queen, 4 Single (3 Bedrooms)
Bathroom: 2 Ensuite, 1 Private
Tariff: B&B (full) Double $70, Singl
Credit cards accepted. Vouchers accepted
Nearest Town: Thames 45km

Our modern home has large bedrooms with ensuites and their own balconies overlooking lovely Tairua Harbour and Paku Mountain.The guest TV lounge opens onto a paved patio surrounded by peaceful gardens and swimming pool. A very pleasant place to just sit and relax.
First class restaurants, reasonably priced, are only 3 or 4 minutes level walk away.
Hot Water Beach *and* ***Cathedral Cove*** *are within 20 minutes easy driving.*
Tairua is set among green trees - safe sandy beaches and is handy to some outstanding bush walks including a 40 minute stroll through a mining tunnel to old gold mine workings. A magical place.
Although we have been open only 12 months, we have been much heartened by tourists telling us that we are among the top Bed & Breakfast homes in New Zealand. Come to see us and find out why.

Pauanui Beach
Bed & Breakfast/Semi self contained
Tourist accommodation
Address: 7 Brodie Lane
(off Dunlop Drive), Pauanui Beach
Name: Pauanui Pacific Holidays:
Hosts Kevin & Kay Flooks

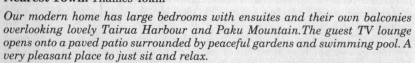

Telephone: (07) 864-8933 **Fax:** (07) 864-8253
Beds: 2 Double, 2 Single (4 bedrooms) **Bathroom:** 4 Ensuite
Tariff: B&B (full) Double $85-$99, Single $65-$99, Children same fee. Tariff from 1st May 1995 Double $95-$110, Single $75-$110. Credit cards accepted, Vouchers accepted
Nearest Town: Thames apprx 50 kms

Pauanui is on the east coast of the Coromandel Peninsula and one of the most magnificently planned resorts in this area with red chip roads to add to the landscape. Activities are catered for by 9 and 10 hole golf courses, 4 tennis complexes each with 4 courts, mini-putt, restaurants, bistro and internationally known Puka Park Lodge.
We are semi-retired dairy and pig farmers (which we still own) from Thames. We shifted to Pauanui in 1991 and built our accommodation complex on the waterfront. We have 4 units, each with ensuites, TV, fridge and tea / coffee facilities. Games room / lounge, cooking facilities, large BBQ area, sauna, spa and swimming pool. Included in tariff are bikes, canoes and windsurfers. We also cater for fishing trips and scenic tours.
Nearest town Thames 40 mins, Whitianga 1hr 15 mins, Tairua 20 mins (5 min by ferry). Auckland 2 hrs. Transport to and from airports arranged.

Pauanui Beach

Homestay

Address: "Penrhys House",
96 Pauanui Boulevard, Pauanui
Name: Ethel & Julian Evans
Telephone: (07) 864 7052 or 867 3290 (Farm)
Beds: 1 King or 2 Single (1 Bedroom) **Bathroom:** 1 Private
Tariff: B&B (special) Double $85, Single $50, Vouchers accepted Monday to Thursday, not Public Holidays
Nearest Town: 50km east of Thames on SH 25A

Warm and generous hospitality awaits guests at "Penrhys House" on the Coromandel East Coast. We spend most of the time here, returning to our farm, an hour drive away, in mid winter and early spring. Spend one night, or stay longer to relax and enjoy the magnificent natural beauty of the area.

Our modern three level house has commanding views of the Pacific Ocean, offshore islands and surrounding ranges. The ocean beach is 100 metres away. The property borders the Pauanui Airfield, so why not "Fly in" and be delivered to the back door?

Guest accommodation on the ground floor is private and well appointed, with tea and coffee making facilities, refrigerator, private shower and toilet, separate entry and off street parking. Breakfast is special and leisurely, served at a time to suit your holiday plans. There are several restaurants and food outlets nearby.

Please phone or write for reservations and directions.

Whangamata

Guest Lodge
Address: Brenton Lodge,
Cnr Brenton Place, SH 25, Whangamata.
P O Box 216, Whangamata
Name: Jan & Paul
Telephone & Fax: (07) 865 8400
Beds: 1 Double (1 Bedroom + sofa sleeper) **Bathroom:** 1 Ensuite
Tariff: B&B (Special) Double $150, Single $100, Dinner $30 by arrangement. Credit cards.
Nearest Town: Whangamata

We would like to welcome you to a very personal style of accommodation, with a separate guest lodge where you can enjoy privacy. Brenton Lodge is set in a semi rural setting with 1 acre of lovely gardens. Both the lodge and home have beautiful views over Whangamata and out to sea to Mayor Island. Only 1 1/2 kms to surf beach and town.

The separate upstairs guest house retains the look of the main house with french doors and it's own balcony, all overlook the garden and the lovely seaviews. The lodge is open plan with its own bathroom, tea-coffee making facilities, TV and video. Furnished to a high standard with a personal touch. A special breakfast can be enjoyed with us or brought to the lodge. An evening meal is available. You may wish to join us in a summer BBQ or if you have been fishing, have your catch of the day prepared for you. Fishing trips, picnic hampers, whatever your needs can be catered for. We like to serve fresh NZ fare.

Come and enjoy our hospitality in our character home with its peaceful tranquil setting.

Whangamata
Homestay
Address: Please phone
Name: Elsa and Snow's
Telephone: (07) 865 7018 **Fax:** (07) 865 7685
Beds: 4 Single (2 bedrooms) **Bathroom:** 1 Guests share
Tariff: B&B (continental) Double $50, Single $30, Dinner by arrangement $15 per person, Vouchers accepted

Elsa and Snow invite you to share their smoke free home.
With a 9 hole golf course at our back door, an 18 hole golf course 10 mins drive away plus surfing, fishing, diving and tramping, Whangamata has tremendous appeal. We hope all our guests enjoy their stay with us in friendly Whangamata.

Waihi
Homestay
Address: 41 Seddon Ave, Waihi
Name: Chez Nous
Telephone: (07) 863 7538
Beds: 1 Double, 2 Single, (2 bedrooms) **Bathroom:** 1 Guests share
Tariff: B&B (continental) Double $45, Single $35, Children $15, Dinner $15, Campervans welcome $15, Credit cards accepted, Vouchers accepted

Waihi is the Southern gateway to the beautiful Coromandel Peninsula and a mere 15 minute drive from the spectacular expanse of Waihi Beach. The latter is a favourite with surfers and is also very safe for bathing.
The Bay of Plenty resort of Mt Maunganui is a comfortable 50 minute drive to the South. Waihi is steeped in history, particularly with respect to goldmining. Tourists can tour a goldmine which is currently under production. Waihi is also a mecca for small craft industries. With a superb golf course, salt and freshwater fishing and challenging bush walks, it is an outdoor sportsperson's paradise.
Chez Nous is a large modern house situated within easy walking distance of Waihi's shops, restaurants and hotels. I am interested in travel and enjoy meeting people from New Zealand and overseas. I own 2 friendly cats. Guests have their own shower and toilet facilities.
Directions: *Seddon Ave runs parallel to the main road out of Waihi to Paeroa.*

Waihi
Homestay
Address: 22 Roycroft Street, Waihi
Name: Josie & Bob French   **Telephone:** (07) 863-7208
Beds: 4 Single (2 bedrooms) **Bathroom:** 1 Separate shower, 1 Family share
Tariff: B&B (continental) Double $40, Single $20, Children $10, Dinner $10, Vouchers accepted

Waihi is on the East coast and is the gateway to both the Coromandel Peninsula with all its beautiful beaches and native bush and the Bay of Plenty, the kiwifruit centre of New Zealand. Local attractions include a vintage railway running between Waihi and Waikino. Also New Zealand's largest gold mine is operating on the out-skirts of the town and the workings can be observed from a look-out. The Martha lode was discovered in 1878 and was worked as an underground mine until 1952. It was reopened in 1989 as an opencast mine. Our home has three bedrooms. The beds are new and have electric blankets. We have a large garden of 3/4 acre. Our interests are tramping and dancing. Non-smokers please.

Waihi
Country Homestay

Address: The French Provincial Country Homestay,
Golden Valley, Trig Road North, RD 1, Waihi
Name: Margaret and Johannes van Duyvenbooden
Telephone: (07) 863 7339
Beds: 1 Extra King, 1 Queen, 1 Double, 1 Twin (4 bedrooms)
Bathroom: 1 Luxurious Ensuite, 1 Luxury Private + spa
bath & shower, 1 Guests share, 1 Family share
Tariff: B&B (special) Large luxurious Honeymoon Suite $185 2nd nite special
price, Queen Luxury Private $145 2nd nite special price, Queen $95, Double $85,
Single $65-$75, Sleepout Single $45, Twin $65 with toilet & tub shower in house.
Breakfast tray in room. Not suitable for children.
Nearest Town: Waihi 5km, Auckland Airport 2 hrs, Ideal for last night's stay in NZ.

*We welcome you to The French Provincial Country Homestay, situated in a pretty
farming valley with nice grounds and swimming pool for your leisure. We offer
quality accommodation in our spacious charming home. The guest wing has three
pretty bedrooms, frilly duvets, electric blankets, heaters and fresh soft towels
daily. Nice guest bathroom, large spa, bath and shower.*
*For that special time away, (PLEASE BOOK IN ADVANCE) the luxurious
kingsize bedroom and ensuite, where the decor is soft in colour, lavish and
romantic, hidden away above a winding stairway, for privacy. Enjoy summer
evenings on your own private balcony with beautiful farmland and garden views.
In the morning you may wake to the gentle cooing of white doves. If you desire a
latish breakfast, it will be served in our olde worlde formal dining area or garden
room. Good restaurants, beautiful beaches (easy bushwalks, we will escort at
extra cost) winery and much more. One night in this beautiful area is not enough,
guests tell us so.*

Te Aroha
Farmstay

Address: 407 Rawhiti Road,
R.D. 2, Te Aroha
Name: Bev Shallue
Telephone: (07) 884 9585 **Mobile:** 025 748 230
Beds: 1 Double, 2 Single (2 bedrooms) **Bathroom:** 1 Guests share
Tariff: B&B (full) Double $65, Single $35, Dinner $20 each, Children half price,
Campervans welcome. Vouchers accepted.
Nearest Town: Te Aroha

*Over the past 12 years overseas guests have enjoyed warm, relaxed hospitality in
our modern spacious architect designed home set in landscaped gardens. Situated
on a large dairying enterprise this home is set to the sun for relaxation with
extensive views of farms and hills and has underfloor heating.*
*Complimentary wine served with 3 course dinner of lamb or beef, or chicken, or
venison with fresh vegs, plenty of iced mountain stream water and percolated
coffee. Breakfasts are generous with pure fruit juice, fruit and cereals, toast and
spreads, bacon and eggs.*
*Bev has travelled to the USA and Australia. Interests include cooking, gardening,
farming, knitting and floral art.*
*Two guest bedrooms - 1 double, 1 single. Guest shower. bath, bathroom and toilet.
A very central location, well situated to the many activities of the Coromandel and
Bay of Plenty. Just off SH 26 8kms Te Aroha, 14 kms Paeroa. 10 minutes by car
to Golf course, restaurants.*

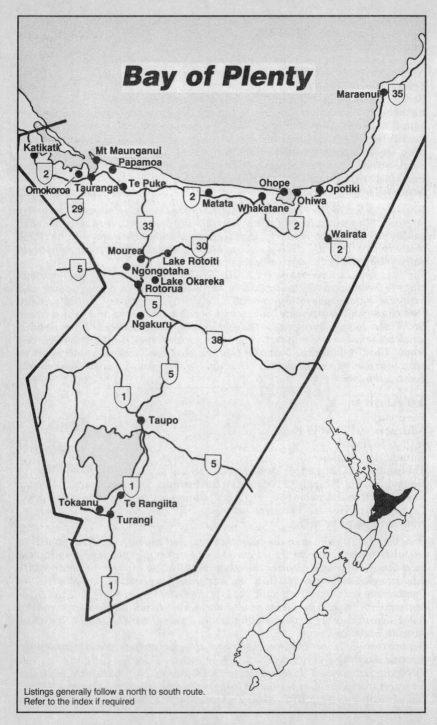

Bay of Plenty

Listings generally follow a north to south route.
Refer to the index if required

Katikati

Farmstay & Self-Contained Accommodation
Address: Jacaranda Cottage,
230 Thompson's Track, RD2, Katikati
Name: Lynlie and Rick Watson
Telephone: (07) 549 0616 after 4 pm
Beds: (House) 2 Single (1 bedroom)
Bathroom: 1 Family share
Tariff: B&B (full) Double $55, Single $35, Dinner $18, Campervans $20, Budget
accommodation $12, Children discounted, Cyclists /backpackers welcome.
Beds: (Self contained cottage) 1 Double, 1 Single (1 bedroom) plus divan in
lounge. **Bathroom:** 1 Ensuite
Tariff: Double $60, $20 each extra adult, weekly rate discounted. Vouchers
accepted.
Nearest Town: 30 km north of Tauranga, 8 km south of Katikati

Jacaranda Cottage, on a 5-acre farmlet, enjoys magnificent views in every direction - from sea to mountains, from rolling farmlands to native forests.
We offer you a taste of simple country life - friendly hospitality; plenty of wholesome farmhouse food; and clean, warm accommodation in either the main house or in our new fully-equipped hillside cottage. We do ask guests not to smoke inside.
Enjoy the variety of animals on our farmlet. You are welcome to join in with any of the farm activities that may be taking place during your visit. Horse rides generally available.
Jacaranda Cottage is situated amidst farms of deer, goats, sheep and dairy cattle, as well as kiwifruit, avocado, persimmon and other orchards. The area offers unspoilt beaches, hot pools, bird gardens, winery, good restaurants, doll collections, arts and crafts, a private museum, and more. In Katikati township a growing number of colourful murals show scenes from the area's past - well worth a look.
Experience the nearby native bush by tramping to the Twin Falls, old Eliza Mine or the Sentinel Kauri Tree. Or simply relax in the tranquil surroundings of Jacaranda Cottage!
Directions: *Thompson's Track is 6 km south of Katikati, on the Tauranga side of the Forta Leza Restaurant. Jacaranda Cottage is 2.4 km up Thompson's Track on the right.*

When you stay at B&Bs you are staying with "dinkum Kiwis"

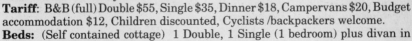

Katikati

Farmstay
Address: 'Craftlink', 426 Busby Rd, Katikati
Name: Lynn & Marsden Carrad
Telephone: (09) 549-0652
Beds: 4 Single (2 bedrooms)
Bathroom: 1 Guests share
Tariff: B&B (special) Double $65, Single $35, Dinner $20, Visa & M/C. Vouchers accepted

Our home on 120 acres of organic farmland nestles against the bush clad Kaimai Range and overlooks breathtaking views of the whole Tauranga Harbour.
The guest bedrooms have ranchsliders opening onto the patio and lawn, and many native birds can be seen in the nearby bush.
A craft centre catering for residential courses in all crafts is part of the complex and our flock of multicoloured sheep provides wool for many of these. A full time weaving and dyeing studio is incorporated here.
Relax, go for a bushwalk, wander up the rocky streams, or go sightseeing - we will attend to your comfort.
We offer home cooked meals using fresh Bay of Plenty produce.
Busby Rd is 1km north of Katikati, the 'Mural Town'.
We request no smoking in our home please.

Katikati

Farmstay/Self-contained Accommodation
Address: 325 Lunds Road
Name: Gordon & Kay Schroder
Telephone: (075) 490-218
Beds: 1 Double, 4 Single (2 bedrooms)
Bathroom: 1 Ensuite, 1 Family share
Tariff: B&B (full) Double $55, Single $30, Dinner $15, Children half price. Vouchers accepted.
Nearest Town: Katikati 6km, north of Tauranga

We welcome you to Pineview a cosy home. Do some bush walking or simply laze around the pool and enjoy the magnificent views of the Bay. Dine with our family or sample our two very good restaurants the Forta Leeza or Mortoms Estate Winery. Interesting places handy to visit include the Waihi Gold Mines, Bird Gardens or enjoy the town of Katikati with its beautifully painted murals.
Our interest include gardening, weaving and crafts, farm animals.
Directions: *Please phone.*

Always telephone ahead to enquire about a B&B. It is a nuisance for you if
you simply arrive to find someone already staying there.
And besides hosts need a little time to prepare.

Katikati

Self-contained Apartment
Address: Pahoia Road, R.D. 2, Tauranga
Name: Trevor & Thora Jones
Telephone: (07) 548 0661
Beds: 1 Double (1 bedroom) 1 convertible divan in lounge, 1 cot. Additional beds available in main house.
Bathroom: 1 Private
Tariff: B&B (continental) Double $60, Single $35, Children $15, (includes supply of continental breakfast foods for self-catering) Vouchers accepted
Nearest Town: Katikati 20km, Tauranga 23km

We have retired to this pleasant rural region of the Bay of Plenty, with a large home on a horticultural lifestyle property.
The modern, self-contained apartment is furnished with all amenities. For larger family groups, additional beds (and additional guests' bathroom) are available in the main house.
We look out northwards across the Tauranga Harbour (water's edge 200 metres away) and westward to the Kaimai Range.
A dinghy is available for guests' use, also games rooms for billiards, table tennis etc.
Attractions in the area include hot pools, beaches, walking and tramping opportunities in the Kaimai Range. We have special interests in tramping, the bush and mountains, and can negotiate guided tramping trips if desired.
For the less energetic, a peaceful place to relax and contemplate the scenery and listen to the birds.
Directions: *Out on Pahoia peninsula, 3km from State Highway 2. Please phone for bookings and directions.*

Katikati

Farmstay
Address: "Aberfeldy" 164 Lindemann Road, RD 1, Katikati
Name: Mary Ann and Rod Calver
Telephone: (07) 549 0363
Beds: 1 Double, 3 Single (2 bedrooms, also private lounge)
Bathroom: 1 Private, 1 Family share
Tariff: B&B (full) Double $70, Single $40, Dinner $20, Children $20, Vouchers accepted

Aberfeldy is on Lindemann Road off State Highway 2, north of Katikati, the unique murals town.
Your hosts have a sheep and cattle farm with a stoney bottomed stream, and 100 year old trees. They also operate a high producing kiwifruit orchard nearby. There are panoramic views of farmland, bushclad hills and the Tauranga Harbour.
Mary Ann and Rod have travelled extensively and love people, gardening, horseriding, tramping, music, reading and cooking.
Activities can include bush and farm walks, swimming and meeting the various tame animals.. A golf course is nearby and we are close to the ocean beach. There is fishing and boating when available.
Guests can be picked up from Katikati if required at no charge.
The accommodation is downstairs with own lounge and bathroom. . It is also sunny.

R. NBirch

Katikati
Country Homestay+Self-contained Accommodation
Address: "Hammond House", 195 Beach Road, Katikati
Name: Jan and John Nicoll
Telephone: (07) 549 1377
Fax: (07) 549 2217
Beds: 1 Double, 2 Single (2 bedrooms) **Bathroom:** 2 Private.
SC Cottage: 1 Double, 2 Single **Bathroom:** 1 Private
Tariff: B&B (full) Double $90, Single $50, Dinner by arrangement $25 pp, School children in cottage half price, Vouchers accepted
Nearest Town: Katikati 2 km

Hammond House is an elegant and spacious two storey Tudor style home set in 5 acres of trees, shrubs, cottage gardens and a small kiwifruit orchard. We offer guests a choice of accommodation a new two storey Tudor style cottage which has a double and two single beds, bathroom and kitchen, or in the main house which has one double and one twin bedded room, each with private bathroom. A leisurely breakfast is served in our sunny conservatory or cottage guests may wish to have breakfast brought to them.

Attractions within 15 minutes drive from our house are beautiful native bush walks, ocean beaches, golf, bird gardens, hot mineral springs, a winery and a selection of restaurants. Katikati (the town of murals) is on the main route between Rotorua and Coromandel and an excellent choice for a rural experience.

Your hosts who are semi retired will do everything possible to ensure your visit is memorable. Please phone or fax.

Tell other travellers about your favourite B&Bs

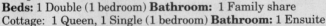

Omokoroa, Tauranga

Homestay
Address: "Walnut Cottage"
309 Station Rd,
Omokoroa, R.D. 2, Tauranga
Name: Ken & Betty Curreen
Telephone: (07) 548 0692
Beds: 1 Double (1 bedroom) **Bathroom:** 1 Family share
Cottage: 1 Queen, 1 Single (1 bedroom) **Bathroom:** 1 Ensuite
Tariff: B&B (full) Double $50, Single $25, Dinner $15, Children under 12 half price, Packed lunch $5 pp, Dinner $15 (3-course + pre-dinner drinks), Vouchers accepted
Nearest Town: 12 minutes north Tauranga on SH2

Walnut Cottage is situated on scenic Plummers Point Peninsular and we overlook beautiful Tauranga Harbour.
The furnished cottage has its own bathroom and tea / coffee making facilities. We are semi-retired couple who invite our guests to enjoy the tranquility our "little-corner-of-the-world" has to offer. Relaxing mineral hot pools are a 5 minute walk away and a 2 minute stroll takes you to the waters edge where you can enjoy the peace of the estuary or fish from the jetty with handlines which we provide. Other local leisure activities include horse-riding, golf, bowls, tramping, sketching. Wholesome meals include fresh eggs and vegetables from our garden. Try Kens "homebrew" or a sherry before dinner. Vegetarians are also catered for and we do packed lunches if required.
Our semi-rural retreat is a 12 minute drive from Tauranga city, popular for its shopping, fishing trips and sightseeing.
Directions: *Station Rd is opposite Whakamarama Service Station on SH2. We are 3km along Station Rd.*

Omokoroa, Tauranga

Homestay (Beach)
Address: 'Sunrise', 69 Harbour View Road, Omokoroa, Tauranga
Name: Harold and Beth Meekings
Telephone: (07) 548 0456
Beds: 1 Double, 2 Single (1 bedroom partitioned, suitable parents and children)
Bathroom: Ensuite
Tariff: B&B (continental) Double $50, Single $28, Dinner $15, Children half price, Vouchers accepted
Nearest Town: Tauranga

Welcome to our home "Sunrise" at Omokoroa Beach, which is 20kms or 15 minutes north of Tauranga. We offer you comfortable accommodation where you can relax and feel at home, overnight or longer. Omokoroa Beach is a pretty seaside town boasting safe swimming, fishing, bowls, golf and horse riding, as well as some lovely easy walks. Hot pools are just 2 minutes away. The children would love exploring the beach and park or catching "whoppers" from the jetty. A game of snooker in the games room makes a change from watching TV. A phone call prior to arrival would be appreciated, especially if dinner is required. Your hosts Beth and Harold are semi retired farmers who enjoy fishing, gardening, walking or just talking and looking at the lovely view. Our children have all flown the nest and we have no cats, dogs or canary.

Omokoroa, Tauranga

Homestay
Address: Kotuku Orchard, 377 Station Road,
Omokoroa, R.D. 2, Tauranga
Name: Ian & Joyce Smith
Telephone: (07) 548 1289
Beds: 1 Double, 1 Single (2 Bedrooms) **Bathroom:** 2 Private
Tariff: B&B (continental) Double $60, Single $35, Dinner $20 by arrangement.
Vouchers accepted
Nearest Town: 15 minutes North Tauranga on S.H. 2.

Kotuku Orchard is a beautiful location 17 km from Tauranga. We have magnificent harbour views and one can lie in bed and watch the sunrise on the sea directly opposite our home. The boat ramp and hot pools are within walking distance and local sporting activities include horse riding, golf and bowls.
Our small orchard consists of kiwifruit, citrus and avocados with attractive gardens.
We are a semi-retired farming couple who have travelled within New Zealand and overseas and will enjoy sharing our experiences with yours.
Our grown-up family are away from home but we do look after their animals - 2 dogs and 3 cats.
Guests will enjoy family meals and hospitality in a spacious modern home with every convenience (Dinner - available by arrangement).
Directions: Station Road is opposite Whakamarama Caltex Service Station on S.H. 2. We are 3.77 km along Station Road on the point of this peninsular.
Arrive as a visitor - Depart as a friend - We look forward to meeting you.

Te Puna, Tauranga

Homestay
Address: "Kohanui" 18 Elliot Way
RD6 Te Puna Tauranga
Name: Ursula Kassin & Judith Simpson
Telephone: (07) 552 5800
Beds: 1 Double, 1 Twin (2 Bedrooms)
Bathroom: 1 Guests share
Tariff: B&B (special) Double $80, Single $45, Dinner $25, Vouchers accepted
Nearest Town: Tauranga 15 mins

Your private and personal holiday choice in the Bay of Plenty. Share our home, nestled into a bushclad hillside with 180 degree sea, bush and farmland views. "Kohanui" is the ideal base for exploring the many natural gifts of the Bay of Plenty.
Stride out on bush walks, wander our sweeping beaches, soak in natural hot pools, delight in beautiful gardens, visit the thermal wonderland of Rotorua, tempt your taste buds at the wineries.
In the evening you may choose to join us for a meal fresh from our garden. For the vegetarian we take pride in considering your requirements.
We came to New Zealand 4 years ago from London. Ursula is originally from Austria, Judith is New Zealand born. Prior to leaving London we spent 2 years working on Menorca (Balearic Islands, Spain) welcoming, fun loving and ever adaptable, be our guests and let us pamper you.
Directions: *Please phone.*

Tauranga
Homestay
Address: 2A Tenth Avenue (at end of drive), Tauranga
Name: Gordon and Christine Ross
Telephone: (07) 578 4826
Beds: 2 Single (1 bedroom) **Bathroom:** 1 Private
Tariff: B&B (special) Double $55, Single $30,
Vouchers accepted.

"Welcome to Our World"
Our home is an attractive townhouse, easily located and within walking distance of town but we also have within two blocks numerous eating houses, banks and shops. We are a retired couple although I still do some caring work. A family of three all married.
Christine's interests include miniatures, porcelain doll making and lots of travel. Gordon enjoys his golf.
The guest room is large with every comfort and that includes tea making facilities and television. The views are great, with Memorial Park in immediate foreground, to inner harbour and hills beyond.
Breakfast of your choice. Off-street parking. Will meet public transport. We are at end of drive.

Tauranga
Homestay
Address: 38 Freyberg St.,
Cherrywood, Tauranga
Name: Trevor & Gloria Shepherd
Telephone: (07) 576-2791
Beds: 1 Double, 2 Single (2 bedrooms) **Bathroom:** 1 Guests share.
Tariff: B&B (continental) Double $50, Single $30. Vouchers accepted.

We are a retired couple, early seventies, have travelled extensively overseas and within New Zealand. We offer hospitality in a modern home, (built 1992) close to town, in a quiet location, five minutes walk from Cherrywood Shopping Centre - with restaurant and "take-away" facilities. Hot dinner available at nearby hotel at very reasonable price $12 - $15. Mt Maunganui beach just 9km away. We have no pets nor family at home.
Our special interests include Church, travel, nursing and organ music.
We offer two bedrooms - one with a double bed and one with 2 single beds. Guests bathroom. Continental breakfast. We can meet the plane $5, (train or bus $2.50).
Directions: *Travel along Chapel St to Ngatai Rd. Freyberg St turns off to the left. If travelling South via Highway 2, turn left at the first round-about onto Otumoetai Rd - then right into Cherrywood Drive, and right into Freyberg St. Come to Tauranga, where things don't cost the earth.*

Tauranga
Homestay
Address: 'Bolney Gate',
20 Esmeralda Street,
Welcome Bay, Tauranga
Name: Jack & Joyce Ingram
Telephone: (07) 544 3228
Beds: 1 Queen, 4 Singles, (2 bedrooms) **Bathroom:** 1 Family share
Tariff: B&B (continental - special $10 extra) Double $55, Single $30, Children
1/2 price, Dinner $20, Credit cards accepted, Vouchers accepted

Bolney Gate is an interesting, spacious, welcoming 4 level Mediterranean home set on a rise overlooking a lovely park dotted with a variety of mature trees. The park has activities for both old and young. Practice golf, jogging, jungle gyms, swings & slides, trolley riding, kite flying or just walking.

The view is varied from quiet residential homes set on the hills around the park to restful rural views. We have both indoor and outdoor living. An enclosed and secluded pool with an elevated wooden deck at one end as a leisure area for reading, writing, eating out or just sharing.

We live in the very heart of the Bay of Plenty and Welcome Bay is just a few minutes drive from downtown Tauranga and Mount Maunganui - 15 to 20 minutes from the horticultural centre of Te Puke or 40 minutes to the delightful small rural town of Katikati, known as the Mural town of New Zealand, offering Kiwi orchards, art in every form, rural and bush walks.

We have both travelled widely in N.Z. and many countries of the world and enjoy people from all walks of life. We have Sky TV.

Tauranga
Bed and Breakfast Inn
Address: 11 5th Avenue, Tauranga
Name: Taiparoro Guest House
Telephone: (07) 577 9607
Beds: 3 Double, 2 Twin, 1 Single (6 bedrooms)
Bathrooms: 6 Ensuite
Tariff: B&B (special) Double $100, Single $70, Credit cards accepted

Taiparoro House is an historic home built in 1882. Restored it combines historic beauty with modern comfort and retains the atmosphere of a family home.

We have six guest rooms - all have ensuite facilities, private telephone and heating. These rooms have been lovingly furnished with colonial furniture in keeping with the character of the house.

A delightful breakfast is served in a dining room / conservatory which overlooks the herb garden and native tree stand. Throughout the day, tea, coffee and fruit juice are available for self service.

The lovely cottage garden overlooks Tauranga harbour and displays many of the trees, bushes and flowers native to New Zealand. Taiparoro House is located in a very quiet area of town which is a 10 minute stroll to the city centre, excellent restaurants, and tourist attractions.

We look forward to sharing our home with you on your visit to Tauranga.

Tauranga
Homestay
Address: 181 Edgecumbe Rd, Tauranga
Name: Kath and Vic Leach
Telephone: (07) 578 5990
Beds: 2 Single (1 bedroom, plus bed sitter double)
Bathroom: 1 Family share
Tariff: B&B (full) Double $50, Single $30, Dinner $12.50, Campervans welcome.

We are a retired couple. We live in a modern 3 bedroom townhouse, with all amenities, close to Tauranga South Shopping centre, banks, post office, hospital, RSA and Historic Village.
Our interests are golf, bowls, croquet, Pakeke Lions, music, travel, church, RSA and we enjoy meeting people.
We have a bedsitting-room for privacy, reading or correspondence, small TV.
We have enjoyed travel overseas, as well as in New Zealand.
You are assured of a very warm welcome. If needed, you will be met at Airport, or Coach Terminal, or Railway Station.
Please phone previous evening after 5.30pm or before 8.30am in the morning or just write.
We look forward to meeting you.

Tauranga
Farmstay + Self Contained Accommodation
Address: 'Baumgarten Lodge',
322 Oropi Road, RD 3, Tauranga
Name: Henri and Colleen Limacher
Telephone & Fax: (07) 543 2799
Beds: 1 King, 1 Double, 2 Single (3 bedrooms/Electric blankets)
Bathroom: 1 Guests share. 1 Detached shower, toilets, laundry, changing facilities
Tariff: B&B (full) Double $60, Single $35, Dinner $20 per guest including aperitif and dinner wine. Vouchers accepted
Nearest Town: 9 minutes from Tauranga City Centre. Courtesy car to meet bus and air travellers.

Baumgarten Lodge, 2km off Highway 29, is a large spacious single storied home with indoor spa room situated on a 5 acre farmlet nestled amidst our avocado orchard, various fruit trees and gardens. We also graze a few calves and sheep, and have one outdoor dog.
Semi retired, our family live away from Tauranga so we always enjoy meeting visitors. Henri, Swiss born speaks German. The interesting walk and rustic fitness track which runs the entire perimeter of our property plus 9 pin bowling ally and outdoor swimming pool are features to be enjoyed by all. We can arrange various excursions to tourist attractions including therapeutic hot pools, deep sea fishing, white water rafting, deer hunting trips etc. Comfortable detached, self contained fully furnished accommodation sleeps 5 persons also available. Tariff on request. 4 minutes from local restaurants and RSA.
We request no smoking indoors.

Please let your hosts know if you have to cancel.
They will have spent time preparing for you.

Matua, Tauranga
Homestay
Address: 210 Levers Road,
Matua, Tauranga
Name: John & Heather Christiansen
Telephone: (07) 576 6835
Beds: 1 Queen, 2 Single (2 Bedrooms)
Bathroom: 1 Guests share
Tariff: B&B (special) Double $60, Single $35, Vouchers accepted

Our home is in the pleasant suburb of Matua, enhanced by a garden of New Zealand native trees, shrubs and ferns.

The guest wing is new. Please join us in our lounge, read our books and listen to our music. Our other interests include the performing arts, growing New Zealand native plants, collecting antiques and motorcycling.

Our friendly, middle-aged cat is "out of bounds" in the guest wing. Our home is smoke-free. Breakfast - see our special menu when you arrive. We can cater for people with food allergies.

We are close to harbour beaches and parks; seven minutes drive to Tauranga city centre and fifteen minutes to Mount Maunganui's ocean beach. We have a broad knowledge of the Bay of Plenty and its attractions.

A gift of home grown citrus fruit can be provided, in season, when you depart.

Best to call or phone before 9.00am or after 5.30pm. It will be our pleasure to welcome you.

Tauranga
Homestay
Address: Westridge Park
Name: Dave & Jenny Demler
Telephone: (07) 571 0016
Beds: 1 Double (1 Bedroom)
Bathroom: 1 Private
Tariff: B&B (continental) Double $60, Single $30, Dinner $20,
Vouchers accepted Mon to Thurs
Nearest Town: Tauranga

You are welcome to visit us in our cosy new home situated just a six minute drive away from the beautiful seaside city of Tauranga.

We live in a country sub-division and have wide sweeping views of the countryside around us.

We enjoy healthy food, invitingly presented, cooking being one of my interests, also gardening.

I'm happy to present vegetarian meals if they're required.

Dave is a sales representative and has a good knowledge of our surrounding area.

We have an elderly pet cat.

We would appreciate it if you didn't smoke in our home.

Please phone to make a booking. We look forward to meeting you.

Tauranga
Farmstay
Address: Ohauiti RD 3 Tauranga
Name: Bernie & Alison Rowe
Telephone: (07) 544 0966
Beds: 2 Double, 2 Single (3 Bedrooms)
Bathroom: 1 Private, 1 Guests share
Tariff: B&B (continental) Double $70,
Single $40, Children$20, Dinner $20, Vouchers accepted
Nearest Town: Tauranga

Welcome to Tauranga and home hospitality on our farm and horticulture property. We have a large spacious modern home situated on 212 acres within the city boundary only 10 mins from centre of town. The home is surrounded by beautiful trees, gardens, tennis court, swimming pool and spa. Tennis racquets available.
The property grows kiwifruit and orchids commercially for export. Property also runs a dry stock unit supporting owners large dairy farm.
Guests have their own bathroom. Two bedrooms have adjacent private lounge with TV, fridge, tea and coffee making facilities.
You are only minutes away from beautiful golf courses, beaches, diving, deep sea fishing and tramping.
Bernie and I enjoy entertaining and meeting new people and are happy for you to stay as long as you wish.
Please no smoking in our home, outside is fine.
Directions: *Please phone.*

Mt Maunganui
Homestay
Address: 26 Sunrise Ave,
Mount Maunganui
Name: Rita and Harry Figgest
Telephone: (07) 575 2427
Beds: 1 Double, 2 Single (2 bedroom)
Bathroom: 1 Private, 1 Family share
Tariff: B&B (full) Double $60, Single $35, Vouchers accepted

Harry has just retired and is early 60's and we are both originally from England. We have travelled extensively and enjoy meeting people from all over the world, and give our own warm hospitality and friendliness to our visitors to make them very welcome in our home.
We are both interested in outdoor and indoor bowls, and watching any sport and Harry enjoys sea fishing.
We are only a few minutes from Mount Maunganui and few kms from Tauranga. We have just moved to Mount Maunganui where we have a lovely modern colonial 3 bedroom house, parklike surroundings and short walk to beach and few minutes drive to Bayfair shops, Mount, golf, bowls, and fishing etc.
We enjoyed having Bed and Breakfast guests in Rotorua for some years and met many lovely and interesting people and decided to continue to do it at Mount Maunganui. Non smokers preferred.
Please ring first, we are in the Ocean Downs estate.

Mount Maunganui
Homestay
Address: 311 Oceanbeach Rd, Mount Maunganui
Name: Roger & Kay Farrell
Telephone: (07) 575 2136
Beds: 1 Double, 2 Single (2 bedroom) **Bathroom:** 1 Private
Tariff: B&B (full) Double $60, Single $40, Dinner $20
Nearest Town: Tauranga and Mount Maunganui

Our large modern home overlooks the oceanbeach where you can enjoy swimming, surfing and beach walks.
For guests there is a separate lounge with TV, fridge, tea making facilities. It opens onto a large sundeck with ocean views.
One bedroom with two single beds opens onto the deck. There is another bedroom with a Queensize bed.
There is a guests bathroom and separate shower and toilet.
Mount Maunganui is a popular seaside resort, is an ideal stopover point between Auckland, Rotorua and the Coromandel.
Hot salt water pools are five minutes away at the base of the 'Mount'.
Bayfair shopping centre (38 stores) only minutes away.
We are keen golfers and there are two courses only minutes away. We have been selling wines for the last twenty years and have travelled to vineyards of the world. We have a smoke free home.
Dinner arranged with prior notice. New Zealand wines.
Please phone first for booking and directions.

Mt Maunganui
Bed and Breakfast
Address: 463 Maunganui Rd,
Mt Maunganui
Name: Fitzgerald's Irish Inn
Hosts: Bill & Edna Fitzgerald
Telephone: (07) 575 4013
Beds: 4 Double (4 bedrooms)
Bathroom: 2 Guests share
Tariff: B&B (full) Double $70, Single $45.
Vouchers accepted.
Nearest Town: Tauranga

Cead Mile Failte

Are you looking for a relaxed, friendly atmosphere? The 'Fitzgerald Irish Inn' offers real hospitality at affordable prices, including new comfortable rooms, separate amenities and a fun billiard and games room with tea and coffee on tap for you to enjoy. Complimentary Irish coffee will help you sleep at night and a good hearty breakfast will get you going the next day. Our Irish Inn is situated close to the shops, harbour and ocean beaches, sports centre, golf course and have you experienced the famous salt water hot pools at the base of Mt Maunganui?
Our Irish Inn is a grand place to put the world on hold and tour the Bay of Plenty - plenty to see and do either by mini coach or independantly. Being garden lovers we also operate delightful garden, nursery and Art and Craft Trails.
We are warm and caring hosts ensuring every guest enjoys a memorable stay.
cead mile failte   (A hundred thousand welcomes)

Mount Maunganui

Homestay
Address: "Pacific Shores",
85c Ocean Beach Road, Mt Maunganui.
Name: Larraine & Bernie Cotter
Telephone: (07) 575-4879 (home)
or 575 0077 (bus), Mobile 025 944 549
Beds: 1 Queen, 2 Single + 2 rollaway available (2 bedrooms)
Bathroom: 2 Private
Tariff: B&B (full) Double $90, Single $50, Dinner $25 by prior
arrangement with wine, Children half price.
Vouchers accepted from March to October
Nearest Town: Mount Maunganui, Tauranga

Welcome to Mount Maunganui and our modern home with suberb seaviews.
Our double room has a queensized bed. The twin has its own bathroom upstairs.
Extra rollaway beds available. Electric blankets, seperate TV lounge with tea and
coffee making facilities. A full and varied continental breakfast with eggs (any
style) is included in this tariff.
We enjoy cooking and with prior advice would enjoy sharing a meal with you. The
wine is on us. The third member of our family is a Himalayan cat called Champas.
We are both in our 40's (non smokers) and have travelled extensively throughout
Europe, North America and Australia.
Close by are first class golf and bowling facilities, and 8km away hot water pools,
and a 45min walk around the mountain. Tennis court 100 metres.
An easy 2 1/2 hour scenic drive from Auckland, 1 hour from Rotorua.
Phone on arrival or leave a message on answerphone or call Bernie at office.
Look forward to having you stay.

Omanu Beach, Mt Maunganui

Homestay
Address: Please phone
Name: Judy and David Hawkins
Telephone: (07) 575 0677
Beds: 2 Single (1 bedroom) **Bathroom:** 1 Private
Tariff: B&B (continental) Double $55, Single $30, Dinner $15, Vouchers accepted
Nearest Town: Tauranga or Mt Maunganui

We are a retired farming couple who invite you to share our comfortable home just
60 seconds off one of the country's finest beaches. Quiet and relaxing you can enjoy
our sea view and watch the shipping coming and going to the Port of Tauranga,
or if more energetic there is plenty of good swimming, surfing and walking
available or even climb up "The Mount" for a 360 degree view of the Bay. Hot salt
water pools (great for tired limbs), the golf course and bowling greens are all just
a few minutes away as is the Bayfair Shopping Complex. A twin bedded room with
bathroom for guests is available and a home cooked dinner by prior arrangement.
An excellent place for visitors to stop and unwind for a day or two between
Auckland and Rotorua.
We enjoy meeting people and would like to share your travel experiences over
supper each evening. A smoke, pet and child free home. Please phone for directions.

Ask your hosts for local information.
They are your personal travel agent and guide.

Mt. Maunganui
Bed & Breakfast
Address: 360 Maunganui Road,
Mt. Maunganui
Name: Sail Inn
Telephone: (07) 574 0433
Beds: 1 Double, 2 Single (2 Bedrooms) 1 Cot available
Bathroom: 1 Guests share
Tariff: B&B (full) Double $65, Single $50, Vouchers accepted at all times
Nearest Town: Mt. Maunganui, Tauranga

Pam and Barry invite you to experience their hospitality in their clean, comfortable, and central accommodation.
Mt. Maunganui has so much to offer the traveller or holiday maker. There are beautiful beaches, walks, views, fishing, boat cruises and hot salt-water bathing. The shopping is excellent, or you may prefer to relax in the sun.
As the name implies, the Sail Inn has a distinctly nautical feeling. This reflects Barry's interest in the lore of the sea, especially the maritime past, and the area in general. We have a good knowledge of the region and its attractions.
We serve a full, wholesome breakfast in a sunny conservatory. Guests have their own lounge with tea and coffee making facilities at all times.
We really enjoy caring for our guests to make sure your stay is as enjoyable as possible.
We request no smoking indoors please.

Mount Maunganui
Homestay
Address: 28a Sunbrae Grove Mt Maunganui
Name: Barbara Marsh
Telephone: (07) 575 5592
Beds: 1 Double, 2 Single (2 Bedrooms) **Bathroom:** 1 Guests share
Tariff: B&B (full) Double $75, Single $40, Children half price, Dinner $20, Campervans $20, Vouchers accepted
Nearest Town: Mount Maunganui, Tauranga

Beachfront Paradise.
Come and stay with me, in very attractive surroundings, on the shores of beautiful Mount Maunganui.
Relax in the guests private, self contained lounge with TV, and enjoy stunning ocean views. There are two bedrooms, one double, one twin, and a separate guest bathroom, all new. Laundry facilities are available if required.
Your well travelled hostess shares her smoke free home with a very sociable Balinese cat.
You are invited to dinner - by prior arrangement please.
We are 10 minutes from the hot salt pools at the foot of the Mount itself, and the same distance from Tauranga.
The Bayfair Shopping Centre is only a few minutes away.
We welcome your enquiries and look forward to meeting you.
Please feel free to phone for directions.

Mt Maunganui

Homestay
Address: 204 Oceanbeach Road Mt Maunganui
Name: Jennie & Norm Reeve
Telephone: (07) 575 8948
Beds: 1 Queen, 3 Single (2 Bedrooms) **Bathroom:** 1 Ensuite, 1 Private
Tariff: B&B (full) Double $70, Single $40, Vouchers accepted
Nearest Town: Mt Maunganui and Tauranga

We invite you to stay in our spacious home overlooking the restful setting of the Mt Maunganui Golf Course and only one minute from surfing or sunning on the beach.
Our guests may choose double or twin bedrooms, each with own bathroom.
Walk through the garden gate on to the golf course (clubs available) or enjoy the hot salt pools nearby.
A walk to the top of the Mount is rewarded by outstanding panoramic views, and excellent shopping facilities are within walking distance.
We have travelled extensively and do enjoy listening to travel tales.
Our interests include travel, skiing, cycling, golf, gardening and walking.
Be sure of a warm welcome to our home.

Papamoa

Homestay
Address: 274 Dickson Road, Papamoa
Name: Joan & Jim Francis: Mark Beech Homestay
Telephone: (07) 542-0815
Beds: 1 Double, 2 Single (2 bedrooms) **Bathroom:** 1 Guests share
Tariff: B&B (full) Double $55, Single $30, Children half price; Dinner $18. Vouchers accepted
Nearest Town: Mount Maunganui or Te Puke 11 km each on SH 2

Yes we are the same Joan and Jim who hosted guests in Percy Road for five years! Although we do not have the lovely views now we are still only five minutes walk from a safe swimming beach. Retired and in our 60's with four children and grandchildren in England and New Zealand, friends in many countries, our interests are travel, gardening and social work. Our home is full of antiques, books, sunshine and we hope, is a home away from home for guests.
We offer electric blankets, cot and high chair, bath and shower, free laundry facilities, pre-dinner drinks and wine with dinner.
10-15 minutes drive to local tourist attractions - 45mins to Rotorua - we will meet public transport or take you sightseeing (for a small fee).
Directions: *About 2kms from SH2 (Rotorua - Tauranga) turning at the garden centre, signposted 'Papamoa Domain', Dickson Road is the fourth turn right (just after the Papamoa Family Tavern). Joan and I look forward to making you fell welcome and relaxed.*

Papamoa
Homestay
Address: 1228 Papamoa Beach Road, Papamoa, Bay of Plenty
Name: Max & Shirley Braun
Telephone: (07) 542-2076
Beds: 1 Double, 2 Single (2 bedrooms)
Bathroom: 1 Guests share, 1 Family share
Tariff: B&B (full) $60 Double, $35 Single, children $15,
Dinner $15m, Vouchers accepted
Nearest Town: Mount Maunganui or Te Puke

We have a large two storeyed home with a special guest wing consisting of 2 bedrooms, your own bathroom and toilet, and a large billiard room. (Max will delight in giving you a game if you wish).
We are a two minute walk across the road to a beautiful beach, 10 minute drive to the Mount or Te Puke, and a 40 minute drive to the thermal area of Rotorua. We can pick you up from the bus station at Te Puke, Mount Maunganui or Tauranga if you don't have your own transport.
Hooray for holidays. Have a good journey - we are waiting to welcome you into our home.

Papamoa
Homestay
Address: 8 Taylor Road, Papamoa
Name: Genyth Harwood
Telephone: (07) 5420-279
Beds: 1 Double, 2 Single (2 bedrooms)
Bathroom: 1 Ensuite,1 Guests Share, 1 Family share.
Tariff: B&B (full) Double $55, Single $35, children 1/2 price, under 5 free, Dinner $15 p.p, Vouchers accetped.
Nearest Town: Tauranga

Our beachfront home is situated about 50 metres from the waves of the Pacific Ocean, with beautiful views of Mayor & Motiti Islands.
Things to do include swimming, fishing, sunbathing, or beach walks plus, endless interesting excursions round the district.
We have a two storeyed home with guest accommodation on the lower level serviced by a shower, toilet and laundry facilities.
Continental or cooked breakfast is offered and a home cooked dinner if desired - we also enjoy a barbeque in the warmer weather.
Resorts such as Mt Maunganui and Rotorua with its thermal attractions are within easy reach.
Directions: *Turn off State Highway 2 (Tauranga to Rotorua) at "Wilsons Garden Centre", proceed about 2 kms to roundabout at Papamoa Domain, take right turn then about 4 kms to Motiti Road on left and left again into Taylor Road.*

Papamoa Beach

Farmstay
Address: "Bent Hills Farmstays"
Name: Malcolm and Trudie
Telephone & Fax: (07) 542 0972
Mobile: 025 982 354
Beds: 1 Double, 2 Single, (2 bedrooms)
Bathroom: 1 Ensuite, 1 Family share
Tariff: B&B (special) Double $100, Single $70, Dinner $25, Children under 12 half price/under 5 free, Cot available. Vouchers accepted April through October.
Nearest Town: 12km Tauranga/Mt Maunganui, 2.5km Papamoa Beach

Situated in a stunning spacious valley Bent Hills Farm is totally private with magnificent rural and coastal views.
Our home built house features a range of NZ timbers and unconventional ideas. With 700 sq.ft. of covered decks it is designed for outdoor living to take full advantage of a magical setting.
We are a down to earth coupe in our 30's with 2 children and a variety of friendly animals.
On farm we offer complimentary horse riding, target shooting, abseilling, mountain biking and grass skiing.
The farm is situated amongst ancient Maori Pa sites and from the top 360 degree views cover the whole BOP region.
We have extensive gardens featuring 80 varieties of fruits and nuts. Locally there is a bush waterfall, fabulous beach with beachfront bar and restaurant, hot pools and the city is only 10 mins. away.
We encourage our guests to feel at home and aim to provide the friendliest service available.

Papamoa

Farmstay
Address: RD 7, Te Puke
Name: Cecily and Graham Umbers
Telephone: (07) 542 2155
Beds: 1 Double, 2 Single (2 bedrooms)
Bathroom: 1 Guests share
Tariff: B&B (full) Double $65, Single $35, Dinner $20.
Credit cards: Visa, B/C & M/C. Vouchers accepted.
Nearest Town: Te Puke and Mt Maunganui

We have retired to the Bay of Plenty - a very aptly named area of New Zealand, where we have 20 acres near the sea, running beef cattle and citrus orchard. Our interests are a large garden, embroidery and all craft (hers), fishing and lawn bowls (his). Mt Maunganui is a few minutes drive and an easy climb with hot pools to soak in afterwards and a beautiful beach to walk on, fish from or swim. We enjoy a relaxed lifestyle and offer quiet informal surroundings with home comforts and a wish to make your stay a happy one. Non smokers preferred.
Directions: *Please phone.*

Private bathroom is for your use exclusively,
Guests share means you may be sharing with other guests,
Family share means you will be sharing with the family.

Paengaroa, Te Puke

Homestay
Address: "Hafod", 151 Wilson Road,
Paengaroa, Te Puke
Name: Maureen Oliver
Telephone: (07) 533 1086
Beds: 4 Single (2 bedrooms)
Bathrooms: 2 Ensuite

Tariff: B&B (continental) Double $60, Single $35, Dinner $18, Children half price, Campervans welcome, Vouchers accepted
Nearest Town: Te Puke 10km, Tauranga 25km.

Welcome to the HAFOD.
Two acres of garden, designed on a Welsh theme, compliments this lovely old country home, part of which are turn of the century.
Each bedroom has its own ensuite and the large lounge with piano, library, reading area are available for the use of guests as is the garden room for BBQ.
HAFOD, a Welsh name meaning, peace, retreat, is appropriate for this large rambling home and garden that is used extensively for weddings and open to the public.
Travel, tramping, gardening and local promotions are some of your hosts interests together with the family pets.
The Te Puke golf course is only 2 mins away, the beach 10. Rotorua and Whakatane 40 mins.
Pre dinner drinks can be served and your pets are welcome.
Directions: *Travelling south from Te Puke - Whakatane Highway 2, 1st right passed Te Puke Golf Club, 1st drive right.*

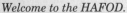

Te Puke

Farmstay+
Self-contained Accommodation
Address: 1384 No 3 Road, Te Puke
Name: Val & Ken Charlton
Telephone: (07) 573 5400/ 573 5402

FARAWAY FARM

Beds: 1 Double, 2 Single (2 Bedrooms) **Bathroom:** 1 Private
Tariff: B&B (special) Double $90, Single $50, Children half price, Dinner $25. Credit Cards. Vouchers accepted.
Nearest Town: 14km from Te Puke

We have the perfect retreat in the hills overlooking the Bay of Plenty and surrounded by huge tracts of native bush. Accommodation is in the luxurious rimu-panelled farmhouse, with an upstairs den giving views to White Island and over the property where wild deer are often seen. Guests have private facilities with spa bath. French doors in the bedrooms open to the garden. Beds are fitted with electric blankets. Additional bunks can be provided.
We serve local and home-grown produce and we would enjoy your company for dinner. Added attractions include horse treks, guided bushwalks, abseiling and general farming activities. We milk daily to feed the calves and shear our own sheep. Fishing trips and jet boating can be arranged, or you can just relax!
We also have a fully-equipped bush cabin sleeping nine.
Ken, Val and Emily (the labrador) would be pleased to look after you in true New Zealand style. Please phone for directions.

Te Puke

Homestay
Address: "Lindenhof"
58 Dunlop Rd Te Puke
Name: Henry & Sandra Sutter
Telephone: (07) 573 4592
Beds: 1 Double, 2 Single (2 Bedrooms)
Bathroom: 1 Ensuite, 1 Private
Tariff: B&B (full) Double $90, Single $50, Dinner $15. Credit cards accepted.
Nearest Town: Te Puke 2km

"Lindenhof" was built in the kiwifruit boom and is a replica of a mansion. Feature of house is stain glass windows, central stairway and chandelier. House is furnished with period furniture. It is set in semi rural area with landscaped gardens, tennis court and swimming pool. We also offer a spa pool and a full size billiard table. Also available are tours of our area fishing and hunting trips.
We are a multi lingual family. I speak English and Swiss, my husband speaks Swiss, French, German and English.
Hobbies: Doll making, spinning and vintage cars. No smoking in the house.
Directions: *On reaching Te Puke on S.H. 2 from Tauranga, Dunlop Rd is on your right by the Gas Centre, "Lindenhof" is at the end of Dunlop Rd. Phone if you need to be picked up.*

Matata

Farmhouse
Address: "Pohutukawa Lodge",
State Highway 2, R.D. Matata
Name: Edmund & Marilyn Turney
Telephone & Fax: (07) 32-22182
Freephone: 0800 10 20 60
Beds: 1 Double, 4 Single (3 bedrooms) **Bathroom:** 1 Ensuite, 1 Guests share
Tariff: B&B (full) Double with ensuite $80, Twin $70, Single $40, Dinner $20-25, Children half price. Campervans welcome. Kennels available. Vouchers accepted March - November.
Nearest Town: Whakatane 32km or 25 minutes drive

Our small holding is situated in a magic location overlooking the vast Pacific Ocean. Of English and NZ origin, we have many overseas guests, and take a pride in hosting and spoiling them. Our interests and activities are, people, gardening, tennis, windsurfing, motorcycling and patchwork.
We offer clean comfortable accommodation, with abundant, wholesome fresh food; home-grown meat, and fruit and vegetables all year round from the orchard and garden. Dinner is always preceded by complimentary "real ale", and NZ wine served with the meal. The garden is rambling, and surrounds our flood-lit tennis court and pool, and with the adjacent beach renowned for its excellent fishing, you can choose to be either very active, or just simply relax in this incredible setting. We would be happy to help organize tours to the many nearby, local attractions; an active volcano, being an almost compulsory visit, view it in action from our lounge; or visit our glow-worms at night.
Directions: *Situated on SH2 halfway between Te Puke and Whakatane. Look for Farmhouse Bed & Breakfast sign.*

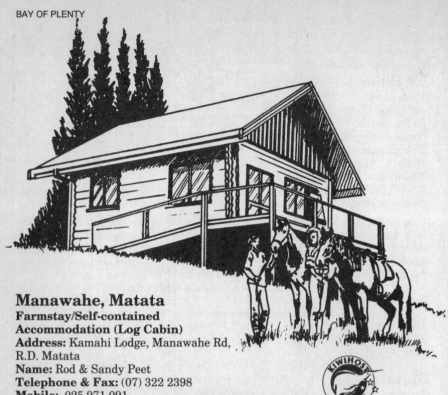

Manawahe, Matata
Farmstay/Self-contained
Accommodation (Log Cabin)
Address: Kamahi Lodge, Manawahe Rd,
R.D. Matata
Name: Rod & Sandy Peet
Telephone & Fax: (07) 322 2398
Mobile: 025 971 091
Beds: 2 Queen, 6 Single (1 bedroom + mezzanine)
Bathroom: 1 Private
Tariff: B&B (full) Queen $65, Single $40, Dinner $15, Children half price,
Campervans welcome, Credit cards accepted, Vouchers accepted
Nearest Town: Rotorua 35 minutes, Whakatane 30 minutes

Paradise is the Bay of Plenty. With so much to offer many guests stay a week.
*Gerhard from Germany stayed nine weeks! Rod and Kylie from Australia
said,* "Best part of our NZ holiday. Loved everything about the cabin, the views
and the moonlight horse ride with Jack Daniels"
Frank from Hawaii said "A terrific week riding, relaxing. Many thanks for
making this special place available."
*On the slopes of an ancient volcano we built Kamahi Lodge in 1991 for people like
you. Fantastic views over miles of native bush to the sea include Mayor Island, Mt
Maunganui and Coromandel Peninsula. Sited 800 metres from our home your
privacy is assured.*
*Genuine log cabin. Warm and cosy, totally self contained; Shower, toilet, cooker,
crockery, linen, BBQ, with breakfast in your fridge for your convenience. Dinner
may include venison, lamb, local seafood.*
*A young couple in our 30s we love meeting new people and thanks to B&B now have
friends around the world.*
We farm 250 acres; deer, sheep, cattle and pine forest.
*Things to do locally: rafting, jet boating, hot pools, sea and trout fishing, swim
with dolphins, visit White Island active volcano.*
Airport and bus transfers arranged.
Directions: *Please phone.*

Whakatane

Homestay on a Farm
Address: Thornton Road,
i.e. Whakatane - Tauranga Highway
Name: Jim and Kathleen Law
Telephone & Fax: (07) 308-7955
Beds: 1 Double, 2 Single (2 bedrooms)
Bathroom: 1 Guests share
Tariff: B&B (continental) Double $50, Single $30; Dinner $20; Campervans welcome. Credit Cards: Visa/BC. Vouchers accepted
Nearest Town: Whakatane 7 km west

Whakatane is off the beaten tourist track, yet it is the centre for a wide range of activities. The local golf course is nearby. We can arrange sight-seeing trips, including White Island. Ohope Beach is a short drive away. You may wish to relax in peaceful surroundings or watch the activities in our Red Barn craftshop which promotes over 270 local craftspeople.
We have lived on this farm for 44 years. Two 50/50 sharemilkers milk over 400 cows. We also grow citrus and feijoas and breed black and coloured and spotted sheep.
We have travelled extensively overseas and enjoy meeting people of all ages.
As "young oldies" we enjoy bowls, Lions Club, genealogy, organic gardening and ballroom dancing - not necessarily in that order.
The Kiwihost concept motivates us. A warm welcome awaits.
Directions: *State Highway 2 has moved. We haven't. We are on the Whakatane / Thornton Road.*

Thornton, Whakatane

view from "T" Tree Lodge

Farmstay
Address: Please phone for easy directions
Postal address: P O Box 295 Whakatane
Name: "T Tree Lodge"
Telephone: (07) 322 2295
Beds: 1 King, 1 Single, 1 Twin, (3 bedrooms)
Bathroom: 2 Guest share (1 with spa bath, 1 with shower)
Tariff: B&B (full) Double $80, Single $50, Children half price by arrangement, Dinner $25 if required. Other languages spoken: Dutch, French, German. Vouchers accepted
Nearest Town: Whakatane 17 km

We live adjacent to the main Tauranga - Whakatane Highway.
Our modern home is built of mostly native timbers, surrounded by Kanuka shrubs, pine forest and the gently rolling Pacific in front, with beautiful views of White Island, Whale Island and Rurima Islands.
The beach is 250 steps away.
A warm welcome awaits those who look for a complete rest in tranquil surroundings with only the sounds of the birds, the rustling of the trees and the pounding waves of the ever changing ocean.
This area is like a hidden gem. Attractions range from a visit to an active volcano, scenic flights, hot pools, bush walks, surfing, tramping to swimming with the dolphins.
We are happy to collect you from the airport or bus.
Our interests are wide and varied. We thank you for not smoking in our home.

Whakatane

Farmstay
Address: Paul Road,
RD2, Whakatane
Name: Jill and John Needham
Telephone: (07) 322 8399
Beds: 1 Double, 1 Single (2 bedrooms)
Bathroom: 1 Private, 1 Family Share
Tariff: B&B (continental) Double $60, Single $40, Dinner $20, Children half price, Campervans welcome $20, Vouchers accepted
Nearest Town: Whakatane

Our large modern spacious home sits high on a hill with wonderous views of the Rangitaiki Plains - guest accommodation is provided in a room with double bed or a twin room with your own bathroom and toilet. We have a pool room, exercise equipment and spa pool.
Our interests are travel, people, skiing, golfing, tramping, fishing, diving, boating. On our 32 HA farm we run 300 Red Deer with hens, pigs, sheep, 2 dogs and a burmese cat. The farm is rolling hill with two lovely lakes - Awakeri Hot Springs are 2km away and within 10 minutes we have great beaches, trout fishing, jet boating, sport fishing - we are 40 minutes from Rotorua.
Directions: *18 kms from Whakatane on State Highway 30. Please phone first for booking - during business hours phone Jill at office 07 3071122 or mobile 025 973716 or home 07 3228399.*

Whakatane

Farmstay
Address: Western Drain Rd,
RD 3, Whakatane
Name: Rakaunui
Telephone: (07) 304 9292
Beds: 1 Double, 2 Single (2 bedrooms)
Bathroom: Guests share
Tariff: B&B (full) Double $60, Single $40, Dinner $20,
Children half price, Campervans welcome. Vouchers accepted.
Nearest Town: 12km west of Whakatane

Kia Ora
We invite you to stay with us on our farm in the middle of the Rangataiki Plains where we graze dry stock and have a kiwifruit orchard. Our house is a comfortable renovated farmhouse, set in 1.5 acres of garden.
Guests have a choice of double or twin bedrooms and use of their own bathroom incorporating both shower and bath, also spa pool. All beds have electric blankets. Rooms have pleasant views of the garden with either doves, coloured sheep, guinea fowl and chickens to enjoy.
From our verandah White Island's steam can been seen pluming into the sky. The ocean is 2km to the north of us. Mt Tarawera is in the distance, with the magnificent Urewera hills waiting to be explored. All within easy visiting distance for walks and picnics.
We offer you a warm "Kiwi" welcome. Children under 13 half price.
Delicious continental or cooked breakfast. Garaging available.
Directions: *1.5km from SH2 between Edgecumbe and Awakeri. Please phone.*

Whale Island and *Volcanic White Island*
as seen from *The Rafters*

Ohope Beach
Homestay, Deluxe, self-contained, beachfront suites
Address: "The Rafters", 261A Pohutukawa Avenue, Ohope Beach
Name: Mavis & Patrick Rafter
Telephone: (07) 312-4856
Suites: "Bridge" - 1 King and 1 Single or 3 Single (2 rooms). "Lodge" - 1 Double; 2 Single (2 rooms). Each suite has panoramic sea views; total privacy; lounge, TV; ensuite; full cooking facilities, fridge, microwave; laundry; private entrance plus entry to hosts' home. Own sunken garden, BBQ, use of two beach bicycles.
Tariff: B&B (special) Double $80, Single $65, infants free by arrangement; each extra person $20 (limit 2). Haute cuisine five course dinner (including vegetarian), complimentary pre-dinner drinks, premium wines, $35 each. Three course dinner in suite, $25 each, five course $35 each.
Nearest Town: Whakatane 8 km, Rotorua 80 km, Tauranga 90km.

Safe swimming, surfing in front of your suite. Many interesting walks. Golfing, fishing, tennis, bowling, chartered club within minutes. Trips to White Island, deep-sea fishing, jet boat, diving arranged.
Trout-fishing conducted by experienced guide, gear, transport provided; cost: $30 hour per party.
Mavis, experienced cook, interests: nursing, bowls, art. Pat, interests: wines, golf, bowls , music, literature, History.
Courtesy car available. House trained dogs, cats, welcome. We look forward to your company.
Directions: *On reaching Ohope turn right, proceed 2 km to 261A (beachside). Illuminated house number on footpath.*

Tariffs are constant for this year. However some
may have had to change slightly. Always check.

Ohope Beach

Self-contained Accommodation
Address: 122A Harbour Rd, Ohope
Name: Ray & Audrey Butler
Telephone: (07) 3124441
Beds: 1 Double, 3 Single (2 bedrooms +
Sunporch) **Bathroom:** 1 Private
Tariff: B&B (full) Double $60, Single $45, Each extra person $15
Nearest Town: Whakatane

Our home is situated beside the magnificent harbour with unrestricted views.
Only walking distance to Ohope Beach.
Guests are accommodated in our self contained unit, (full cooking facilities).
Ray and Audrey enjoy outdoor bowls and gardening. Ray a keen, experienced
fisherman will enjoy taking you fishing, even smoking your fish for you.
Barbecue area and pool room available minutes from Chartered Club and
restaurant, golf course, bowling club, bush walks.
Cooked and continental breakfasts on request.
Directions: *On reaching Ohope turn right drive 3km turn left into Harbour Rd*
drive 1km. Sign on letter box turn into drive way then sharp left.
We both assure you a warm welcome.

Ohiwa Harbour

Homestay
Address: Vedders Road
Ohiwa Harbour RD2 Opotiki
Bay of Plenty
Name: Ngaire Kalilic
Telephone: (07) 315 4869
Beds: 2 Double (2 Bedrooms)
Bathroom: 1 Private
Tariff: B&B (continental) Double $70,
Single $40, Dinner by arrangement, Vouchers accepted
Nearest Town: Opotiki

A modern cottage, naturally heated by woodfire, situated on a hill overlooking the
beautiful Ohiwa Harbour and Pacific Ocean. Approximately 30 mins drive to
Whakatane and 10 mins to Opotiki.
Enjoy your stay in a peaceful, private, non-polluted environment, with seafood at
the bottom of the hill.
I offer warm, comfortable beds and an excellent continental breakfast with home-
made bread and preserves, cappuccino or percolated coffee, also tea and fruit juice.
Dinners and cut lunches available on request. Dinner - $20, Lunches - $8 per person.
Your hostess is well travelled both nationally and internationally and enjoys
discussion on many topics.
I choose to use separate self-contained accommodation for sleeping, so from bed-
time to breakfast-time guests have the main house to themselves, allowing
absolute privacy. Come stay with me and enjoy Ohiwa Harbour, A Jewel in our
magnificent Bay of Plenty.
Trips to volcanic White Island by boat or helicopter, and dolphin viewing
available at Whakatane.

Haurere Point, Opotiki

Farmstay +
Self-contained accommodation
Address: Corals B&B, Morice's Bay,
Highway 35, RD1, Opotiki
Name: Coral Parkinson
Telephone: (07) 315 8052
Beds: 1 Double, 4 Single (2 bedrooms)
Bathroom: 2 Private
Tariff: B&B (continental) Double $70-$80, Single $40, Dinner $25 Children $15, Campervans $20, Credit cards accepted, Vouchers accepted
Nearest Town: 18km to Opotiki

Signposted halfway between Opape and Torere on Highway 35, 18 km from Opotiki. We are a mature couple with two children, Nigel 11 and Soraya 7. Our small farm has chickens, ducks, cows and a pet goat called Tin Tin. We have a collection of memorabilia and a fleet of 1950 motor vehicles and are fortunate to live in the Eastern Bay of Plenty. Our rustic cottage illustrated ($80 a night double, each additional adult $20) has Queen size bed plus 2 singles on the upper story, a fold out double settee on the ground floor. Timbered interior with stained glass windows our cottage has views of bush and sea from decks on both levels. The 2 single bed unit ($70 per night) is part of our garage complex, opens out onto our country garden. Both have TV and full kitchens. Nearby is secluded Morices Bay, ramble over the rocks or laze on the sandy beach, safe swimming. Our beds are comfortable with woollen underlays and feather duvets. We would appreciate no smoking indoors.
Directions: *Call or write. Should you want dinner (wine included) prior notice is required.*

Opotiki

Homestay/Self-contained Accommodation
Address: Ohiwa Beach Road
(locally known as Bryans Beach)
Name: Denby B&B By The Sea
Telephone: (07) 315 4838
Beds: 1 Double, 2 Single (2 bedrooms)
Bathroom: 1 Private
Tariff: B&B (full) Double $55, Single $40, Dinner $15,
Children $7.50 up to age 10yrs
Nearest Town: 25 minutes and 35km from Whakatane.
10 minutes and 11km from Opotiki.

Denby's Bed and Breakfast By The Sea, fresh air, safe swimming beach, beautiful pohutakawas, fishing, long stretches of sand to walk on, relax on, and our own live volcano White Island, and seclusion if wanted. Also glorious sunsets. We have a lovely lifestyle and want to share it with you.
From Whakatane turn left before Waiotahi Bridge. From Gisborne turn right after Waiotahi Bridge into Ohiwa Beach Road.
The beach is commonly and locally known as Bryans Beach there is a signpost at our gate.
We are rock hounders, gardeners, military vehicle restoration buffs, Dick is ex-army engineer, Kath is a keen CWI member and both are good Kiwi Hosts.
We hope you enjoy your stay.
Please telephone before coming we would hate you to be disappointed.

If you love touring New Zealand B&B style...

...check out what is available in Australia

The Australian Bed & Breakfast Book is the perfect accommodation guide for those who want to see the real Australia.

For ordering details, turn to the back of this book

Waioweka Gorge, Opotiki

Luxury Farmstay
Address: Wairata, Waioweka Gorge, Opotiki
Name: Bob and Mary Redpath
Telephone: (07) 315 7761
Beds: 1 Double, 4 Single (2 bedrooms)
Bathroom: 1 Private
Tariff: B&B (full) Double $60, Single $35, Dinner $20,
Children $15, Campervans no power $15. Vouchers accepted.
Nearest Town: 50km south of Opotiki on State Highway 2.

Come and join us in the heart of the scenic Waioweka Gorge on our 1900 hectare hill country farm retreat. Our cattle, deer, sheep and goat farm is surrounded by 'native bush' with a host of activities for you to enjoy. There are numerous tracks to walk, streams to meander alongside, glow worms and a crystal clear river at your doorstep for trout fishing, eeling, swimming or kayaking and rafting. Mountain bike rides and hunting are available for the more adventurous and four wheel drive excursions. We serve hearty home baked meals, guests may dine with the family or in their own dining/lounge which serves as the second bedroom should a group require it. We have a pretty garden, guest accommodation is separate but adjoins the main house. We take only one party at a time. We have two older children and two younger children. We always welcome guests to our home and look forward to meeting you.
Directions: *Please phone.*

Opotiki

Self-contained Cottage
Address: Capeview Orchard
Tablelands Road Opotiki Bay of Plenty
Name: Capeview Cottage
Telephone: (07) 315 7877,
Toll Free: 0508-315 7877
Beds: 2 Double or 4 Single (2 Bedrooms)
Bathroom: 1 Private
Tariff: B&B (special) Double $150 per night,
Children $20, Dinner $35. Long term and off-season rates available.
Vouchers not accepted (unless prepared to use two vouchers per 1 night)
Nearest Town: Opotiki

Capeview Cottage
The cottage in the country you've always dreamed about with fabulous views of the East Cape Mountains and Sea. Surrounded by farmland, avocado and kiwifruit orchards. Our home is located 100 metres away, behind trees. We have two children, a dog and two cats.
This brand new purpose built two storey cottage features two upstairs bedrooms with super kingsize beds in each room, or four large singles. Downstairs is open plan living with a combined lounge and dining room, office area and telephone. A fully fitted kitchen including dishwasher and microwave. A bathroom with combined bath/shower, separate toilet and laundry room with washer/drier. Outside is the wooden hot-tub (spa) surrounded by private gardens and big lawn. This is the place if you want comfort, privacy, space and peace and quiet.
Directions: *Leave Opotiki on State Highway 35, heading towards Te Kaha. Within one kilometre of Opotiki is Gows Road - turn right and follow the Capeview Cottage signs.*

Westbrook, Rotorua

Homestay
Address: Please phone
Name: Venus and David Jones
Telephone: (07) 3479-194
Beds: 1 Double, 2 Single (2 bedrooms)
Bathroom: 1 Ensuite, 1 Family share
Tariff: B&B (continental) Double $60, Single $35, Children under 12 half price; Dinner $20 (with prior notice)
Nearest Town: Rotorua 4 km, 10 minutes by car

We live in a quiet cul-de-sac, down a right of way in a split-level home overlooking several parks and golf courses and sports venues. We are close to all tourist sights, and we enjoy visitors.

We are both retired with family all married. Our hobbies are the great outdoors, walking club, travel, arts and crafts. We love meeting people and have travelled overseas.

Breakfast grapefruit, cereal with fruit, toast, tea and coffee or cooked breakfast if requested.

I guess you would class our home as a comfortable quality abode with comfortable beds - electric pads. You have your own toilet, bathroom and shower.

We prefer non-smokers.

Rotorua

Farmstay
Address: Please phone
Name: Maureen and John Hunt
Telephone: (07) 348-1352
Beds: 1 Double, 2 Single (3 bedrooms)
Bathroom: 1 Guests share, 1 Family share
Tariff: B&B (full) Double $65, Single $40, Children half price
Nearest Town: Rotorua 4 km (10 minutes by car)

Guests will be warmly welcomed to our large, modern home on the city outskirts. Superb views of the lake, city, forest and surrounding countryside. Enjoy our garden and solar heated swimming pool.

We farm 150 acres running deer, beef and sheep. Scenic farm tours available.

Our adult family of five have now sought pastures new allowing us to offer an attractive suite of rooms consisting of one double bedroom, two single bedrooms and a small sunroom.

Underfloor heating, innersprung mattresses, plenty of room for cars, campervans and luggage storage. Non-smokers preferred.

Be sure and allow a few days stay so you have time to rest as well as enjoy the many nearby world renownedattractions.

We enjoy gardening, water-skiing, tramping and travelling and look forward to sharing our home and farm with you

Ngongotaha, Rotorua
Country House
Address: R.D. 2, Rotorua
Name: Roslyn & John Livingstone
Telephone: (07)357 2368
Beds: 3 Single (2 bedrooms)
Bathroom: 1 Guests share
Tariff: B&B (full) Double $60, Single $35. Vouchers accepted.
Nearest Town: Rotorua 9km

New Zealand Association
FARM & HOME HOSTS

"ROTORUA FULL OF SURPRISES"
Enjoy a rural home stay in a Spanish Mission style house on the outskirts of Rotorua (just off Highway 5, Rotorua - Auckland).
Sybaritic accommodation in guest wing consists of large bed - sitting room, and single bedroom, both centrally heated, plus luxurious guest bathroom. Each room has its own TV, radio, tea and coffee making facilities, electric blankets, ice water, cookies etc.
The residence which is on one level, has panoramic views of Lake Rotorua, Mount Ngongotaha, and the local countryside. Nearby is the famous Agrodome and Rainbow Springs, and in Rotorua itself the world renowned area of Whakarewarewa, the heart of Maori culture.
Please note that children are not hosted.
I request that guests do not smoke inside the house.

Ask your hosts for local information.
They are your personal travel agent and guide.

Ngongotaha, Rotorua

Farmstay + Self-Contained Accommodation
Address: Jackson Road,
Kaharoa (PO Box 22), Ngongotaha, Rotorua
Name: 'Deer Pine Lodge',
Hosts: John and Betty Insch
Telephone: (07) 332 3458
Beds: 4 Double, 12 Single (11 bedrooms)
Bathrooms: 4 Ensuite, 2 Private, 2 Guest share
Tariff: B&B (special) Double $80-$90, Single $45-$50, Children under 12yrs half
price, Dinner $25; Campervans $20 - 4 persons, Vouchers accepted
Nearest Town: Rotorua

*Welcome to Deer Pine Lodge. Enjoy the panoramic views of Lake Rotorua and
Mokoia Island. We farm 260 on a property surrounded with trees planted by the
New Zealand Forest Research as experimental shelter belts. The nearby city of
Rotorua is fast becoming New Zealands most popular tourist destination offering
all sorts of entertainment.*

*Our bed / breakfast units are private, own bathroom, TV, radio, fridge, microwave,
electric blankets all beds, coffee / tea making facilities, heaters.*

*Our two bedroom fully self contained units, designed by prominent Rotorua
architect Gerald Stock, each having private balcony, carport, sundeck, ensuite,
spacious lounge, kitchen, also laundry facilities, TV, radio, heater etc. New dining
room and kitchen just completed, holding NZ certificate in food hygiene ensuring
high standards of food preparation and serving. Guests are free to do the
conducted tour and observe the different species of deer and get first hand
knowledge of all aspects of deer farming after breakfast. Three course meal of beef,
lamb, or venison, pre dinner drinks. Hosts John and Betty, originally from
Scotland have travelled extensively overseas and having nine years experience in
hosting look forward to your stay with us.*

Directions: *Please phone.*

Continental breakfast consist of fruit, toast, tea/coffee,
Full breakfast is the same with a cooked course,
Special breakfast has something special.

Rotorua
Homestay
Address: 3 Raukura Place, Rotorua
Name: Ursula and Lindsay Prince
Telephone: (07) 347-0140 Please phone to confirm vacancy
Bedrooms: 1 Double with 1 single, 2 Single (2 bedrooms)
Bathroom: 1 Ensuite, 1 Private
Tariff: B&B (special) Double $70, Single $50, (Surcharge $5 for one night only);
Dinner by arrangement $20 with complimentary NZ wine

A warm welcome awaits you when you decide to stay with us at our spacious modern home right on Lake Rotorua. Our quiet, secluded home is five minutes by car from the city centre.

Two spacious guest rooms, each with private bathroom, well-cooked meals in a relaxed and informal atmosphere - the feeling to be amongst friends, is what we offer you. We will be happy to help you make the most of your Rotorua stay.

Feel free to make use of our extensive range of maps and guide books.

Relax on the deck, enjoy the tranquil lake and mountain scene, watch the waterbirds or explore the lake by Canadian canoe.

We are an active, middle-aged couple, who take an interest in world affairs, have travelled and lived overseas, and love the outdoors.

In our 7th year of home-hosting, we continue to enjoy sharing our home with guests.

Directions: *From Lake Rd turn on to Bennetts Rd, then first left on to Koutu Rd, then first right on to Karenga St. Now first right on to Haumoana St. and a left turn at the end brings you down Raukura Place to our door.*

209

Ngakuru, Rotorua

Farmstay
Address: "Te Ana" Poutakataka Road,
 Ngakuru, RD1, Rotorua. Please phone
Name: Heather and Brian Oberer
Telephone & Fax: (07) 333 2720
Beds: 1 Queen, 1 Double, 5 Single (3 bedrooms)
Bathrooms: 2 Ensuite, 1 Guests share
Tariff: B&B (special) Double $90, Single $60, Children negotiable - 12 & under
$35 B&B, Dinner $25 adult $10 child. 12.5 % GST included, 5% discount from
3rd night, Vouchers accepted May to August
Nearest Town: Rotorua 20 miles south

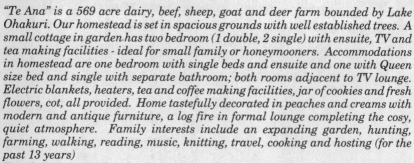

*"Te Ana" is a 569 acre dairy, beef, sheep, goat and deer farm bounded by Lake
Ohakuri. Our homestead is set in spacious grounds with well established trees. A
small cottage in garden has two bedroom (1 double, 2 single) with ensuite, TV and
tea making facilities - ideal for small family or honeymooners. Accommodations
in homestead are one bedroom with single beds and ensuite and one with Queen
size bed and single with separate bathroom; both rooms adjacent to TV lounge.
Electric blankets, heaters, tea and coffee making facilities, jar of cookies and fresh
flowers, cot, all provided. Home tastefully decorated in peaches and creams with
modern and antique furniture, a log fire in formal lounge completing the cosy,
quiet atmosphere. Family interests include an expanding garden, hunting,
farming, walking, reading, music, knitting, travel, cooking and hosting (for the
past 13 years)*
*Family "pets" include cats, dogs, trout, ponies, and three adult children who come
and go. Canoe and fishing rod are available, 4-wheel drive tour of farm, farm walks,
view cows being milked. Hot pools and attractions 10-30 minutes; an ideal base.
Complimentary wine and our own spring water with a 3-course dinner; fresh
vegetables in
abundance. Our home is smoke free.*
5% discount from 3rd night for direct bookings only.

Ngongotaha, Rotorua

Farmstay
Address: Please phone for directions
Name: Rex and Ann Wells
Telephone: (07) 3572-014
Beds: 1 Double, 2 Single (2 bedrooms) **Bathroom:** 1 Guests share
Tariff: B&B (full) Double $70, Single $40; Dinner $20. Vouchers accepted.
Nearest Town: Ngongotaha 3 km, Rotorua city 8 km

We farm 50 acres now having 200 Red deer, purebred Simmental cattle, Suffolk Sheep Stud. Our home is warm and roomy with central heating, electric blankets on all beds. Lovely rural and lake views from every room. Inside spa, full sized billiard table - Rex is keen to learn new shots!
We use home killed meat and vegetables with NZ wine at dinner.
Our families are grown up now so main interests include farm, dogs, photography and large roomy garden (in Gardens to Visit books).
Having stables, operate as 'Horse Motel'.
Close to golf course, lake, trout hatchery, Agrodome 1km, Whaka thermal area 12 kms. Rex has farmed all his life; Ann born in England, and both have travelled. We enjoy showing guests our way of life (Ann loves her 4 wheeled motorbike) and meeting friends the B&B way. We ask guests not to smoke in our home. Pick-up and deliver service is available - extra charge.

Ngongotaha, Rotorua

Homestay
Address: 11 Egmont Road,
Ngongotaha, Rotorua
Name: Joy and Brian Bell
Telephone: (07) 357-2088
Beds: 1 King, 2 Single (2 bedrooms)
Bathroom: 1 Guests share
Tariff: B&B (special) Double $60, Single $40.
10% discount for 3 nights or more (accommodation
only) on cash transactions. Dinner $20, Credit cards accepted, Vouchers accepted.

Our comfortable Lockwood style home is situated in a quiet tree lined street close to Lake Rotorua and the Waiteti trout stream, no traffic noise or sulphur fumes, 2km. from HW5 Auckland / Hamilton.
We are retired and share our home with Winston, our grey cat. Our son is in London, our married daughter lives locally. We are involved in church and community, also members of Probus and Stamp Club. Our pleasure is to entertain guests from home and overseas. You are assured of a warm, homely welcome, good home cooking and comfortable beds with electric blankets. You are welcome to share family dinner with us by prior arrangement. We are non-smokers and would appreciate guests not smoking in the house.
There is so much to do and see in and around Rotorua, we should be happy to help you make the most of your stay in this exciting part of New Zealand.
There is ample off-street parking.

211

Rotorua
Homestay
Address: 7 Walford Drive, Lynmore, Rotorua
Name: Selwyn and Dulcie Collins
Telephone: (07) 345 5778
Beds: 1 Double, 2 Single (2 bedrooms) **Bathroom:** 1 Private, 1 Family share
Tariff: B&B (continental) Double $60, Single $30, Dinner $20, Children under 12 half price, Campervans welcome. Vouchers accepted

Selwyn and Dulcie are now retired and enjoying their lovely sunny home and gardens. We enjoy bowls and golf and have seven grandchildren. In the past we have travelled abroad and have had many overseas tourists visit us. They seem to leave as friends, which is great.
Our guest accommodation is self-contained upstairs. Our street is quiet and we are but a short walk from the Redwood Forest with its many colour coded tracks. The lakes are a 5 minute drive up the road.
We welcome families and our outdoor living with gas barbecue has had lost of use by visitors. I love cooking but as we are often busy I would appreciate notice that you would like to have dinner with us. If you ring and get the answerphone please phone back after 5pm.
Directions: *Off the Tauranga / Whakatane Highway from Rotorua. Turn right up Tarawera Road, left into Hilton Road ext and right into Walford Drive.*

Rotorua
Homestay
Address: 9 Henare Place, Tihi-o-tonga, Rotorua
Name: Brian & Kate Gore
Telephone: (07) 347 9385 after 5pm
Beds: 1 Double, 2 Single (2 bedrooms)
Bathroom: 1 Guests share
Tariff: B&B (special) Double $70, Single $40, Children under 12 years half price, Dinner $25, Vouchers accepted

Greetings and Kia-ora! We are in our early 50's, young at heart, and have been enjoying home hosting for over 10 years. Our lovely new, spacious home is situated in Rotorua's quietest suburb and boasts panoramic views of the city and surrounding farmlands. Yet we are very close to forests, lakes, golf courses, tourist attractions, city and rural activities. We have travelled extensively overseas and throughout New Zealand and will happily advise you on places to visit while in our lovely country.
We both love the outdoors, tramping, sport, the arts, creating our new gardens, grandchildren and people. Brian hits a mean golf ball and Kate makes the best pavlova. Jade the cat is not impressed.
Rotorua being the heart of the tourist industry has much to offer, but we like to think we can share so much more to make your New Zealand holiday totally memorable.
Directions: *Please phone*

Mourea, Rotorua

Homestay
Address: Marijke's Lakeside Bed & Breakfast,
30 Okawa Bay Road, Mourea, R.D. 4, Rotorua
Name: Rein Klazes
Telephone: (07) 3624703
Beds: 2 Double, 1 Single (2 bedrooms) **Bathroom:** 1 Guests share
Tariff: B&B (full) Double $65, Single $40, Children half price, Dinner by arrangement $20. Credit cards: Visa/MC. Vouchers accepted
Nearest Town: Rotorua, 17km

You are invited to share our Okawa Bay lake-edge lifestyle. Rotoiti is a very scenic lake with a variety of watersports activities and good trout fishing. You can bring your boat and use our marina. A Canadian canoe is available.
The accommodation offered is a spacious triple room and a Kingsize waterbed room, bith wuth lovely views. The bathroom is guests' use only.
Your host speaks Dutch, English and German and is happy to find your holiday needs and to tell you about the variety of Rotorua's attractions and adventures. Okawa Bay is a 15 minutes drive from Rotorua and 30 minutes from Maketu Pacific Ocean Beach.
Directions: *From Rotorua take SH30, direction Tauranga. Go for Tauranga from the Whakatane turn-off another 4km on SH33. Turn right past the crest of a hill into Okawa Bay Road. Near the Yacht Club Reserve-end of the road turn into our driveway in front of the "steep grade, change down" -sign.*

Ngongotaha, Rotorua

Homestay
Address: 42 Parawai Road,
Ngongotaha, Rotorua
Name: Heather's Homestay
Telephone: (07) 357-5104
Beds: 1 Double, 2 Single (2 bedrooms)
Bathroom: 1 Private, 1 Guests share
Tariff: B&B (full) Double $60, Single $40,
Children half price 5 - 12 yrs, Vouchers accepted
Nearest town: Rotorua City 6 km

Haeremai. Welcome. My home is situated on the shores of Lake Rotorua, set amongst lovely old trees and gardens, in a quiet, private locality, 6km from City-centre.
The guest bedrooms open on to a balcony overlooking the lake. The upper floor is for guests' exclusive use so privacy is assured. I do not smoke but guests are welcome to smoke on the balcony. Major tourist attractions - the Agrodome (2 km), Fairy Springs and Rainbow Farm, Skyline Skyrides (3 km) and Rotorua's many other attractions, including good restaurants, are nearby. I am Rotorua born and bred, proud of my City and Maori heritage and enjoy sharing what local knowledge I have with guests. I have a friendly dog who lives outdoors and a cat who likes to share his kennel. I am a part time teacher at a local College. If I am not at home try 3481134 my work number.
Directions: *Only 2 km from Highway 5-Ngongotaha Road Roundabout.*

Ngongotaha, Rotorua

Homestay
Address: "Waiteti Lakeside Lodge",
2 Arnold Street, (off Waiteti Rd),
Ngongotaha, Rotorua
Name: Brian and Val Blewett
Telephone & Fax: (07) 357 2311
Beds: 3 Queen, 2 Single (4 bedrooms)
Bathroom: 2 Ensuite, 1 Guests share
Tariff: B&B (full) Double $75 - $90, Single $55 - $75,
Dinner $25 by arrangement, Credit cards accepted,
Vouchers accepted from April to October

A warm welcome awaits you at "Waiteti Lakeside Lodge", our new timber and stone home situated on the shores of Lake Rotorua and the mouth of the Waiteti stream in a secluded and tranquil setting with panoramic views of lake, city, forest and surrounding countryside.

No passing traffic or sulphur fumes. Comfort was our main priority in the beautiful guests rooms all with heating and electric blankets. Luxury ensuites with queen-size beds. The upper floor is designed exclusively for guests privacy, with bedrooms and spacious lounge having access onto balcony. The property is further enhanced by its attractive gardens and the Waiteti stream on its southern boundary with private access for trout fishing, boat ramp and jetty.

Originally from England, we have been in New Zealand for 38 years and as a fishing guide I skipper my own boat. We will arrange a Maori hangi and concert, white-water rafting, horse riding, or 4 wheel drive tours or you can relax on the deck, in the heated spa pool, or explore the lake and stream by Canadian canoe or dinghy. Fishing rods and golf clubs free to guests.

Directions: *Take Highway 5 from Rotorua, straight on at the roundabout, through Ngongotaha, 2nd turn right after railway crossing into Waiteti Road, right again into Arnold Street and we're on the left near footbridge.*

214

Rotorua
Homestay
Address: "Paradise", Valley Road,
R.D 2 Rotorua
Name: Neville & Shirley Mann
Telephone: (07) 357 5707
Beds: 2 Double, 2 Single (3 bedrooms)
Bathroom: 1 Ensuite, 1 Guests share
Tariff: B&B (Special) Double $60, Single $40, Children (under 12) $15, Dinner $25, Campervans welcome, Vouchers accepted
Nearest Town: Rotorua (8 km)

We welcome guests to our new spacious home set amongst lovely gardens with rural views, adjacent to a trout stream, 3km off SH5 on the scenic route to Rotorua. Enjoy a stroll amongst our sheep, and aviary birds, walk by the stream, or relax with refreshments and enjoy the peaceful setting.
We have two pedigree Tibetan terriers.
Guests rooms have electric blankets. One room has an ensuite, guests share a bathroom with shower, bath and separate toilet.
Our home is centrally heated. Enjoy an evening dinner with us or visit a Maori Hangi and concert. Rotorua is a tourist mecca. We have fly fishing at our door. 5 mins from Agrodome, Rainbow springs and Paradise Game Park and can help plan an exciting few days sightseeing. Our adult family live away. Our interests include gardening, art, photography. Having been involved in Education, hospitality industry and travelled widely we enjoy sharing our home with guests.
Directions: *Please phone.*

Rotorua - Rainbow & Fairy Springs
Homestay
Address: "Cambrook", 9 Barnard Road, Rotorua
Name: Betty C Price
Telephone: (07) 348 2485
Beds: 1 Double, 2 Single (2 bedrooms) **Bathroom:** 1 Guests share
Tariff: B&B (continental) Double $50, Single $30, Children $10, Dinner (3 course) Adult $15, Children $7.50, Vouchers accepted

My 1/2 acre property is enhanced by a trout stream on the boundary, grass tennis court, para pool, barbeque area, gardens, large trees and many shrubs. Very efficient bus route leaves from corner 100 metre away. Many interesting places to visit, good restaurants at hand, but I am very happy to provide a meal. Children are welcome and I have a cot and high-chair.
My interests are meeting people, bowls indoor & out, tennis, swimming, gardening and I have a group of ladies to 'Scrabble' every fortnight. My home is warm in winter, cool in summer and has a very relaxing atmosphere. If you like to 'lie in' you are welcome. If you need an early breakfast that's no problem. I love people and learning about other countries and experiences and can assure you of a comfortable and happy stay.
Directions: *Coming from North, Barnard Rd is opposite Rainbow and Fairy Springs.*

Rotorua

Farmstay & Homestay
Address: Peppertree Farm,
Cookson Road, R.D. 4, Rotorua
Name: Deane & Elma Balme
Telephone & Fax: (07) 3453718
Beds: 1 Double, 4 Single (3 bedrooms)
Bathroom: 2 Private, 1 Guests share
Tariff: B&B (continental, full on request) Double $75, Single $45, Dinner $25, Children half price, Campervans facilities available, Vouchers accepted
Nearest Town: Rotorua 8kms

Just ten minutes from the central city our charming Lockwood Home, in it's quiet rural tree clad setting overlooking Lake Rotorua, will provide you with a friendly welcome and homely atmosphere.

Upon your arrival you may care to enjoy a stroll around our small farm where you will see goats, sheep, cows, calves, horses, working dogs and chickens.

Before dinner, you may choose to enjoy your hosts' hospitality while relaxing on the verandah taking in the spectacular views. There is an excellent cuisine using fresh garden produce and served with New Zealand wine or we can arrange a visit to a Maori Hangi and Concert.

Our guest accommodation consist of two twin bedded rooms and one double room all with electric blankets and private bathroom facilities.

Horse riding and trout fishing can be arranged.

Your hosts are fourth generation New Zealander with a love of animals and the land, who wish to share the beauty of their surroundings with you.

Rotorua

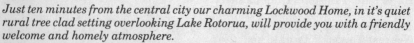

Homestay
Address: 228B Ranolf Street,
Rotorua
Name: Beverley Walker
Telephone: (07) 349 1437
Beds: 1 Double, 1 Single (2 bedrooms)
Bathroom: 1 Guests share
Tariff: B&B (full) Double $60, Single $35, Dinner $20, Children welcome. Vouchers accepted.
Nearest Town: Rotorua within 2kms of city centre.

I enjoy travelling and meeting people and offer friendly, personal hospitality in my comfortable and lovely home. Guest rooms feature reading lights and electric blankets on comfy beds and have use of own bathroom containing bath, shower and toilet. Off-street parking is available.

Although situated within 2km from City Centre, in a quiet residential area, I can provide dinner if required. There are two "Take-Away" shops, one block away, and 4 hotel restaurants within a five minute walk.

Rotorua has so much to offer. Thermal wonders that will intrigue and excite you, as well as being at the heart of Maori culture. Sailing, water skiing and fishing on picturesque lakes. Hunting and tramping in some of New Zealand's most beautiful bush hinterland and a wondrous array of other attractions, ranging from live sheep shows and trout in a natural environment through to the excitement and adventure of luge rides and white water rafting.

Directions: *Please phone.*

Owhata, Rotorua
Homestay & Self-contained Accommodation
Address: 13 Glenfield Road, Owhata, Rotorua
Name: Colleen & Isaac (Ike) Walker
Telephone: (07) 345-3882 (after 5pm) **Fax:** (07) 349-3456
Beds: Unit - 1 Double, 2 Single, (2 bedrooms) **Bathroom:** 1 Private.
Home - 1 Double (1 bedroom) **Bathroom:** 1 Family share
Tariff: B&B (continental) Double $50, Single $35, Dinner extra, Children half price, Unit: $50 2 persons & $10 extra persons. Vouchers accepted.

Situated in a quiet suburb only 10 minutes drive from Rotorua's city centre, 5 mins from Airport.
The unit is private and fully self contained with one double and one twin bedroom, separate lounge, bathroom, laundry and kitchen.
The house has a comfortable homely atmosphere with one double bedroom available with shared household facilities. Light breakfast included and other meals by arrangement. Guests have the opportunity of becoming one of the family. Colleen is a tutor at the local Waiariki Polytechnic. Ike has experience in farming and the paper industry. He is a keen fisherman and golfer. They have hosted many visitors and have travelled extensively themselves both within New Zealand and abroad. They enjoy meeting new friends and helping them make the most of their stay in New Zealand by arranging fishing, golfing, sightseeing and cultural experiences if required. Hosts own a small dog.
To avoid disappointment and to enable the best service to be offered 24 hours notice would be appreciated, especially if meal is required.

Ngongotaha, Rotorua
Homestay
Address: "Lake Edge Homestay" RD2, Rotorua
Name: Lake Edge Homestay
Telephone: (07) 332 3631
Beds: 2 Double, 3 Single (2 bedrooms)
Bathroom: 2 Ensuite
Tariff: B&B (special) Double $80, Single $45, Dinner by arrangement, Vouchers accepted
Nearest Town: Ngongotaha 4km

At Lake Edge Homestay, Jack and Dorothy Cunningham offer you a tranquil setting, in 2 acres of grounds, panoramic views. Bedrooms look out on Lake Rotorua. Variety of bird life including black swans. Private jetty (dock).
Dinner by arrangement. Vegetarians are catered for.
The queensized and single beds have woollen underlays and electric blankets.
Each room has its own private shower, basin and toilet; coffee and tea making facilities, radio and TV, extensive library of New Zealand books.
Interests include meeting people, trout fishing, pigeon breeding, philately, pet sheep. We are non-smokers.
We are close to Rotorua's tourist areas: Rainbow Springs Complex, Agrodome, horse riding, and golf courses nearby. Trout fishing available.
Our home is situated at the end of a no-exit road in a very peaceful rural area yet only 10 minutes from Rotorua City. 4 kilometres from Ngongotaha township.

Ngakuru, Rotorua

Farmstay
Address: "Lakehill", Whirinaki Valley Road
Ngakuru, R D 1, Rotorua
Name: John & Susan Shaw
Telephone: (07) 333 2829
Fax: (07) 346 0961
Beds: 1 Double, 3 Single (2 bedrooms, Triple and Twin)
Bathroom: 1 Ensuite, 1 Guests share plus extra toilet & handbasin
Tariff: B&B (full) Double $110, Single $55, Dinner $25. Credit Cards. Vouchers accepted 1 May to 31 August.
Nearest Town: Ngakuru is 30km south of Rotorua, off SH 30 or SH 5

Sue and I grow Calla Lilies as an export crop, tend an establishing chestnut orchard, farm a few bulls (plus sundry pets) and greatly enjoy the many and varied people who favour us with their presence.

We're in our 40's, non smokers, kids gone their own way, in a comfortable home, in large well kept grounds, with beautiful scenery and are, we hope, good company. Children over 12 are welcome.

We both enjoy tennis, there's plenty of spare racquets (even balls and a grass court) also a couple of sets of golf clubs, a fishing rod or two (trout) and a pool and barbecue for the Summer. The farm bounds Lake Ohakuri which has all year trout fishing (Spring and Autumn are the best times). Within 10 minutes there are hot pools, golf course and squash courts.

Our other interests include gardening, woodwork and Rotary. We can also offer guided fly fishing trips by prior arrangement.

If you come for dinner we will give you a three course meal with wine and a pre dinner drink but by all means BYO if you wish.

Directions: *Please phone.*

Okere-Falls, Rotorua
Countryhome Lake Stay
Address: "Waitui", Private Bag,
Okere-Falls, Rotorua
Name: "Waitui"
Telephone: (07) 362 4751
Beds: 1 Double, 2 Single (2 bedrooms)
Bathroom: 1 Guests share
Tariff: B&B (special) Double $70, Single $40,
Dinner $25, Vouchers accepted
Nearest Town: Rotorua

Okere-Falls village is approximately 20 minutes from Rotorua, past airport, on Highway 33 towards Tauranga.
Experience the peace and tranquillity of a lake stay in a countryhome atmosphere on a bush-clad peninsula overlooking Lake Rotoiti. Being elevated offers magnificent views from three quarters. We have a spacious and comfortable traditional style home. The locality offers beautiful bush walks near spectacular Okere-Falls on the Kaituna River, where there is white water rafting, fishing and local store. Telephone bookings are essential.
Directions: *Please phone.*

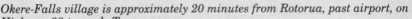

Rotorua
Homestay
Address: Magnolia Garden,
7 Meade St,
Whakarewarewa, Rotorua
Name: Janice and Maurice Lenihan
Telephone: (07) 347 0618
Beds: 1 Double, 2 Single (2 bedroom)
Bathroom: 1 Ensuite, 1 Private
Tariff: B&B (special) Double $80, Single $55, Dinner $25. Vouchers accepted except Jan & Feb.
Nearest Town: 2km from Rotorua City Centre

Welcome to the warm and friendly atmosphere of our home. Our 1/2 acre of garden is within walking distance of Whakarewarewa Thermal Reserve, Maori Arts and Crafts and Rotorua Golf Course.
We love helping our guests discover the variety of thermal activity, Maori Culture (including a concert at a Marae), trout fishing, and adventure available in Rotorua. On a clear night we are able to help our guests find the Southern Cross and Orion's Belt, and Jan offers a 40 minute walk in the Redwood Forest amongst native tree ferns. Day and half day bush walks by arrangement.
Come in and delight in our Art Deco guest rooms with comfortable beds, where complimentary tea, coffee and home made cookies are always available. Enjoy a leisurely breakfast and in the evenings fine restaurants and Maori Concerts are within walking distance or you may join us for a family dinner.
We will be happy to meet you at the airport, railway, or bus depot (no charge).
Directions: *5 mins from city centre. Last street on left South end of Fenton Street*

Ngongotaha, Rotorua
Country House
Address: Dalbeth Road,
Box 33 Ngongotaha
Name: Jan and Bruce Rykers
Telephone: (07) 357 4471
Beds: 1 Double, 5 Single (3 bedrooms)
Bathroom: 1 Ensuite, 1 Guests share
Tariff: B&B (full) Double $70, Single $40, Dinner $25 including wine, Children welcome. Vouchers accepted.
Nearest Town: Rotorua 8km - 10 minutes by car

Jan and Bruce welcome you to our warm and comfortable home in a rural garden setting but only 10 minutes from the city and major tourist attractions.
We have had many years looking after tourists from all parts of the world and have a wide knowledge of the area. Have an overnight stay or you may like to stay longer, there is so much to see. Leave it to us to help plan your sight-seeing, recommend restaurants or arrange collection for a Maori concert.
Waiting to greet you is our important family cat Hanibal.
Comments from our visitors book:
"Home and hospitality 100%".
"Our overnight stay highlight of our trip".
The house can be clearly seen at the start of a charming road.
From State Highway 5 at Ngongotaha Roundabout turn left. Continue until you pass through Ngongotaha village. Cross railway line and take first road on left - Dalbeth Road. We are first on left.

One of the differences between staying at a hotel and a B&B
is that you don't hug the hotel staff when you leave.

Westbrook, Rotorua

Homestay
Address: 378 Malfroy Rd, Rotorua
Name: Brian & Judy Bain
Telephone: (07) 347 8073
Beds: 4 Single (2 Bedrooms)
Bathroom: Family share
Tariff: B&B (continental) Double $55, Single $35, Children under 12yrs half price, Dinner $20pp (complimentary NZ wine), Vouchers accepted
Nearest Town: Rotorua 3km

We are retired farmers, of farming stock - live on city outskirts, yet only 3km from city centre.
We live in a warm comfortable Colonial style home with pleasant grounds. Having been for many years participating in farmstay and currently homestay, our interests include meeting the people, farming, politics, current affairs etc. Brian, a keen duckshooter all his life, is a member of Rotorua Host Lion's Club. Judy is interested also in crafts, gardening, sewing, millinery, homemaking etc.
Both guestrooms are well appointed with comfortable beds and electric blankets. As well as the friendly welcome at the front door much time can be spent over the meals table chatting with our guests. Our motto is "Home away from home"!
There is much to do in Rotorua and surrounds and we are happy to assist with your plans for "Things to do and see"! We will happily transport you to and from tourist centre if necessary. We look forward to your arrival.

Rotorua

Guest House
Address: 8 Whakaue St Rotorua
Name: Best Inn Rotorua
Telephone & Fax: (07) 347 9769
Beds: 4 Double, 10 Single (8 Bedrooms)
Bathroom: 8 Ensuite
Tariff: B&B (full) Double $95/$160, Single $75/$110, Children $30. Credit cards accepted.
Nearest Town: City Centre of Rotorua

We are proud to welcome you to Rotorua's brand new Bed & Breakfast "Best Inn Rotorua".
Newly built colonial style and opened in late 1994. All spacious rooms have their own private facilities. Superior suites are also available for your special occasion. Also, two private thermal baths (Japanese style) to relax you thoroughly.
Central location. Situated opposite to Queen Elizabeth Hospital. Walking distance to Lake front, city centre, restaurants, Tourism Rotorua and Government gardens. Off Fenton Street, but yet quiet and peaceful.
Fully cooked English-style breakfast.
We can arrange and reserve Hangi & Concerts, restaurants, sightseeing tours, trout fishing, all types of activities and ongoing travel.
Our Inn is fully thermally heated. Smoke free. Wheelchair access and facilities. Your hosts, Etsuko & Ian, have an experience in the travel industries in both NZ and overseas for many years. All visitors will be warmly welcomed with top quality service. Enjoy our personal touch.

Rotorua
Farmstay
Address: Fryer Road, Off Hamurana Rd Ngongotaha
Name: Enid & John Brinkler
Telephone: (07) 332 3306
Beds: 1 Queen, 1 Single (1 Bedroom) **Bathroom:** 1 Private
Tariff: B&B (full) Double $60, Single $30, Triple $80, Children $20, Dinner $15, Vouchers accepted
Nearest Town: Rotorua 14km, Ngongotaha 6km

We invite you to enjoy a little of 'the good life' at our hillside homestay. With magnificent lake and rural views, our large comfortable home is situated in 10 acres, part of which is a kiwifruit orchard. Adjacent to the guest bathroom, our upstairs guestroom has a queensize, plus a single bed.
In our early 50s, we are very much involved in education and enjoy relaxing in our peaceful rural environment which we share with 2 cats, 30 sheep and several chickens. Our hobbies are fishing, local history, theatre, gardening and travel. We love to meet fellow travellers.
Major tourist attractions are easily accessible from our property. Hamurana Golf Course, trout fishing and horse-riding are close-by.
You will find us 1km up Fryer Road, off Hamurana Road, on the route around Lake Rotorua. Fryer Road is well sign-posted, approximately 14km from Rotorua city centre. Please telephone in advance of arrival.

Lake Rotoiti, Rotorua
Homestay+Self-contained Cottage
Address: "Bushmere Lodge"
Te Akau Road Okere Falls
Name: Eric & Robyn Cameron
Telephone: (07) 362 4848
Beds: 1 Double, 1 Single (2 Bedrooms)
Bathroom: 1 Private, 1 Family share.
Cottage: 1 Double, 2 Single (3 bedrooms)
Bathroom: 1 Guests share. (Kitchen/Self catering or meals with us).
Tariff: B&B (Special) Double $100, Single $50, Dinner $25. Credit Cards accepted. Vouchers accepted
Nearest Town: Rotorua

Only 15 minutes drive from Rotorua's famous thermal wonderland, our home is situated on the Te Akau peninsula, nestled amongst native bush, on the edge of Lake Rotoiti, with our own jetty and boatshed.
A natural haven for birds, Tuis and Fantails are our constant companions.
All our rooms have wonderful lake views, and a cooked or continental breakfast is available. If you wish you are most welcome to join us for dinner.
We are in our late 40's and have spent all our lives involved in dairy and arable farming, and fruit growing.
We enjoy our watersports, and have available for our guests use a range of sailboards, kayaks, dinghy, and for a modest charge we can include water skiing, fishing, cruising, and trips to Rotoiti's famous hot mineral pools - accessible only by boat! There are many local attractions including the Okere Falls, thermal areas, Rhododendron gardens, bush walks and the Ohau channel.
We look forward to sharing with you the many wonderful features that made us choose Lake Rotoiti as our home.
Note: Building was not completed at the time of inspection, phone to confirm.

Rotorua
Homestay/Bed & Breakfast
Address: 10 Henare Place,
Tihi-o-tonga, Rotorua
Name: Lorraine & Basil Carter
Telephone: (07) 347 9967
Beds: 1 Double, 2 Single (2 Bedrooms)
Bathroom: 1 Guests share
Tariff: B&B (Special) Double $70,
Single $40, Children half price,
Dinner by arrangement $25,
Massage $30 hour
Nearest Town: Rotorua

Welcome to our home, "Woodhall" which is located in a quiet suburb of Rotorua with extensive views of the city and lake. Only 4km from the city centre and close to golf courses, tourist attractions, forest walks, trout fishing and restaurants. We are in our mid 50's with a grown family who live away from home. Basil is a trained masseur and what better than a relaxing therapeutic massage to finish off the day after looking at our beautiful tourist areas. Dine out or have dinner with us, the choice is yours.
We are non-smokers and ask guests not to smoke in our home.
If you require an evening meal advanced notice is needed.
We look forward to meeting you and making your stay an enjoyable one.
For directions, please phone.

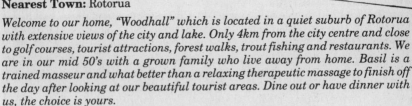

Hamurana, Rotorua
Farmstay
Address: Te Waerenga Road
RD 2 Rotorua
Name: Daniel's Farmstay
Telephone: (07) 332 3560
Beds: 1 Double, 4 Single (3 Bedrooms)
Bathroom: 1 Guests share + 1 Private 1/2 bath (toilet and vanity)
Tariff: B&B (full) Double $70, Single $40, Dinner $20, Vouchers accepted
Nearest Town: 20km north of Rotorua, 12km from Ngongotaha

Welcome to the Rotorua area, our farm and home. Our 70 acre red deer farm is a 20km scenic drive around the lake from Rotorua city.
Guests are welcome to a farm tour with an opportunity to feed a few friendly hinds and ride on a tractor. Our two friendly dogs and cat stay outdoors.
Our home has panoramic views of the lake and city. Upstairs which is for the exclusive use of guests has a twin room with balcony, double room, games room and bathroom. Downstairs there is a twin guest room with private toilet and vanity.
We are both non-smokers and thank guests for not smoking while inside our home.
Enjoy a true cultural experience, with earth hangi meal and concert on a Marae close by or pick-up to hotel.
Rod is a keen fisherman, Dianne is a teacher and we wish to extend our hospitality to visitors to Rotorua and the Bay of Plenty's many tourist attractions.
Directions: *Please phone for booking and directions.*

Rotorua
Farmstay
Address: RD4 Whakatane Highway
SH30 at the junction of Highway 33
to Tauranga & Rotorua
Name: Antrim House
Telephone: (07) 345 9218
Beds: 2 Double, 2 Single (3 Bedrooms)
Bathroom: 1 Guests share
Tariff: B&B (full) Double $70, Single $40, Children 10yrs and under half price,
Dinner $15. Credit cards. Vouchers accepted
Nearest Town: Rotorua

*Antrim House is a 70 year old house centrally located on a seven acre block of land.
The home of coloured sheep, Antrim House is a small farmlet which has chickens,
pigs, fruit trees and organically grown produce. Nestled in a lovely one acre
garden, Antrim House is a short ten minute drive from Rotorua.*
*Being only two minutes from Rotorua Airport we can collect and drop off our
guests. In addition we can arrange daily tours, a traditional hangi meals or any
of the other varied activities offered in Rotorua.*
We enjoy having guests and promise then a happy stay.

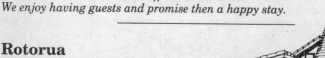

Rotorua
Homestay
Address: "Trehane"
230 Ranolf St Rotorua
Name: Helen
Telephone: (07) 346 3320
Beds: 1 Double, 4 Single (3 Bedrooms)
Bathroom: 1 Private, 1 Guests share, 1 Family share
Tariff: B&B (full) Double $60, Single $35, Children Maximum $65 a family,
Vouchers accepted
Nearest Town: Rotorua city centre 2km

*"Trehane" offers the peace of a quiet residential area while the thermal wonders
of Whakarewarewa, the Arikikapakapa Golf courses and a number of quality
Hotel Restaurants and eating places are only minutes away.*
*Downstairs is a Double Bedroom/Private Bathroom Facility while upstairs is
able to sleep 4-6 in family accommodation. Independent breakfast facilities are
available if preferred.*
A large lounge with our library of NZ books is yours to enjoy during your stay.
*"Trehane" is a smoke-free home and our guest accommodation is out of bounds for
Kiltie, our Bearded Collie dog.*
*Horizons continue to widen with our adult family overseas discovering their
English, Scottish and French heritage. Peace and privacy is important at
"Trehane". If, however, you would like some company, I will be delighted to share
with you my extensive knowledge of our beautiful city, district and country.*
The choice is yours. "Haere Mai ki Rotorua".
Directions: *Please phone 07 346 3320.*

Rotorua
Guest House
Address: 3 Toko Street
Rotorua
Name: Tresco International
            Bed & Breakfast
Telephone: (07) 348-9611
Beds: 5 Double, 2 Single (7 bedrooms)
Bathrooms: 2 Guests share
Tariff: B&B (full) Double $68, Single $45, Children under 12 half price. Credit cards. Vouchers accepted

New owners Gay and Barrie Fenton offer home style Bed and Breakfast hospitality. You will be welcomed into our home as our special guest, with a warm friendly greeting.
Our guest house is 2 blocks from the city centre and bus station. Star attraction of our thermally heated, non smoking home, is the Hot Mineral pool, which is ideal for travel weary visitors.
Our resident Cordon Bleu chef will start your day with a substantial continental and cooked breakfast. Tea and coffee making facilities are available 24 hours in our cosy TV lounge. We have ample off street parking, and laundry facilities in our thermally heated drying room.
We are happy to advise on and arrange tours, to ensure you get value for your dollar. We also take pride as Kiwi Hosts in guiding you through New Zealand on a top class Bed and Breakfast trail.
We look forward to making our home your home.

Rotorua
Homestay
Address: The Grange (Phone for directions)
Name: Marlene & John
Telephone: (07) 346 3306 (evenings)
Beds: 2 Double, 1 Single (3 Bedrooms)
Bathroom: 1 Private, 1 Guests share
Tariff: B&B (continental) Double $68, Single $40, Surcharge $5 1 night, Dinner $25. Electric heating, tea/coffee making facilities, electric blankets.
Vouchers accepted.
Nearest Town: City Centre 5 mins by car

Hi I'm a Kiwi and John is English. We have our magnificent dream home which we'd love to share with you. You're assured of a warm welcome. The very attractive setting, lovely views, peace and seclusion are an added incentive. Johns a chef/ tutor, should you require dinner it will be one to remember (24 hours notice necessary), $25pp. Glass of complimentary wine available. First class accommodation offered. We enjoy meeting people, our aim is to make your stay most enjoyable. We look forward to meeting new friends, and sharing our beautiful but homely house. John enjoys fishing and playing golf. I enjoy music and needlework. We look forward to meeting you.

Rotorua
Homestay
Address: "Kareanui",
Iri Irikapua Parade, Hinemoa Point,
Rotorua (Postal: Box 10 Rotorua)
Name: Gail Hodgkinson
Telephone: (07) 345 4024
Beds: 1 Double, 2 Single (2 Bedrooms)
Bathroom: 1 Guests share
Tariff: B&B (continental, full by request) Double $75, Single $45, Dinner $15 to $20 by arrangement. 3rd bedroom can be made available. Campervans welcome. Vouchers accepted between March-October,
Nearest Town: Rotorua 5.5km

Kia Ora - Greetings
Kareanui is situated in a semi-rural location on historic Hinemoa Point, a well known landmark on the shores of Lake Rotorua. It is set on half an acre of lawn and cottage gardens with stunning panoramic views of the city and lake.
This unique setting was why I built my two-storied, award winning home in 1992. I wish to cater for travellers who like to relax in the comfort of a private home, and my guests have exclusive use of the top floor bedrooms and facilities.
I have six children who have now left home and I enjoy meeting and entertaining people of all ages and cultures. I am Rotorua born and bred and look forward to sharing my knowledge of the area with my guests.
Messages can be left on my answerphone, but bookings must be confirmed before arrival and I would appreciate 24 hours notice if you wish to dine with me.

Rotorua
Homestay
Address: 23 Utuhina Rd Rotorua
Name: Eddie & Judy Jackson
Telephone: (07) 347 8311
Beds: 1 Double, 2 Single (2 Bedrooms)
Bathroom: 1 Guests share
Tariff: B&B (full) Double $65, Single $45, Children under 12 years half price, Dinner $25, Vouchers accepted

We are an outgoing couple with a grown family living away from home. Now Eddie and I (and our Cat) would like to share our home with you. Our home is double storied, with the downstairs area being exclusively for guest use. This comprises a twin bedroom, and a double bedroom with lounge facilities including TV, guest share bathroom, tea and coffee making facilities and a fridge for guest use. A washing machine is also available at a small extra charge. Each bed is supplied with electric blankets, and each area is heated. A continental or full breakfast is available. You are welcome to join us for a home cooked dinner on request.
We are situated 4km from the city centre, and only 15 minutes from all of the attractions of Rotorua including the nearest golf course.
Rotorua is the Heartland of New Zealand Forestry and Logging on which we can provide a great deal of information.
Directions: *Please phone.*

Lake Okareka, Rotorua
Lake Stay+Self-contained Accommodation
Address: 7 Steep Street Lake Okareka
Name: Cathy & Eddie Lines
Telephone: (07) 362 8112
Beds: 3 Double, 2 Single (3 Bedrooms) **Bathroom:** 1 Ensuite, 1 Family share,
Tariff: B&B (full) Double $80, Single $60, Dinner $25
Nearest Town: Rotorua

12 minutes from Rotorua New Zealand's No 1 tourist centre you can enjoy the peace and tranquillity of lake edge living. Lake Okareka with a population of 800 has unspoilt beauty of native bush farmland forest wildlife and uncrowded waters. Whilst on a major tourist route there are no hotels or motels. 10 minutes drive and you can experience the famous Lake Tarawera, Buried Village and Blue and Green Lakes. These together with Lake Okareka's attractions open up the great outdoor opportunities to Rainbow Trout fishing, lake cruises which can include thermal activity, water skiing, swimming, canoeing, bush walking tennis and horse trekking. Dinghy canoes and fishing tackle by arrangement. Also available separate quality cedar shingle self contained apartment which sleeps 4.
Directions: *From Rotorua take SH 30 east. At AA sign posting turn right into Tarawera Road. Travel 6km to AA sign turn left into Loop Road. Take second on left Steep Street turn right into 4th driveway.*

Rotorua
Homestay
Address: 36 Malfroy Road
Rotorua
Telephone: (07) 348 7418
Beds: 1 Double, 2 Single (2 Bedrooms)
Bathroom: 1 Guests share
Tariff: B&B (continental) Double $60, Single $35, Dinner $20, Vouchers accepted
Nearest Town: Rotorua

Welcome to Rotorua.
My home is an attractive new two storeyed town house with thermal heating which makes it very warm and comfortable. My guest accommodation consists of one twin bedded room and one double room, all beds have electric blankets and guests share the guest bathroom plus extra toilet and hand basin.
As I am situated within 1km of Rotorua city centre there are plenty of restaurants and takeaways within walking distance, or I can provide dinner if required.
Rotorua is situated in the heart of the thermal region with Maori culture and many tourist attractions. Bush walks in the Redwood Forest, lakes for trout fishing, sailing or water skiing, parks and golf course are all very handy.
Directions: *Please phone.*

Tariffs are constant for this year. However some
may have had to change slightly. Always check.

Ngongotaha, Rotorua
Homestay+Self-contained Accommodation
Address: Leonard Rd Ngongotaha (P.O. Box 14 Ngongotaha)
Name: Alf & Raema Owen
Telephone: (07) 357 4913
Beds: 1 Double, 2 Single (2 Bedrooms) **Bathroom:** 1 Guests share
Bedsit is fully self-contained and has 1 double bed **Bathroom:** 1 Private
Tariff: B&B (continental) Double $60-70.
Nearest Town: Rotorua

Come and enjoy the tranquil rural setting of our two acre block and the panoramic views of Lake Rotorua and environs from our conservatory windows and comfortable home.

Enjoy fly fishing in the Waitete Stream or visit any of the many attractions that Rotorua has to offer.

We have travelled extensively and are Kiwi hosts who enjoy meeting people and are happy to arrange any activity you may desire including Maori concerts and tourist activities.

We are retired and been home hosting for seven years. Our interests are building, Lions, yachting, fishing, gardening and bushwalks.

You can be self sufficient in your own bedsitter with double bed, full kitchen, bathroom facility and lounge dining; or be guests in our comfortable home with twin or double bedroom, own bathroom.

We have ample off street parking. Advance notice appreciated to avoid disappointment. We look forward to your visit. We aim to please. There is an answerphone for your convenience.

Scrivener Rotorua
Homestay
Address: 2 Grand Vue Rd,
Rotorua
Name: Keszthely
Telephone: (07) 348 7430 or 347 0828
Fax: (07) 346 2746
Beds: 1 Double (1 Bedroom)
Bathroom: 1 Ensuite

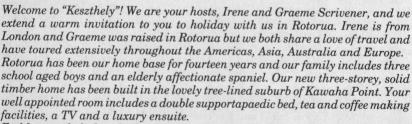

Tariff: B&B (full) Double $75, Single $50, Dinner $20, Vouchers accepted
Nearest Town: Rotorua

Welcome to "Keszthely"! We are your hosts, Irene and Graeme Scrivener, and we extend a warm invitation to you to holiday with us in Rotorua. Irene is from London and Graeme was raised in Rotorua but we both share a love of travel and have toured extensively throughout the Americas, Asia, Australia and Europe. Rotorua has been our home base for fourteen years and our family includes three school aged boys and an elderly affectionate spaniel. Our new three-storey, solid timber home has been built in the lovely tree-lined suburb of Kawaha Point. Your well appointed room includes a double supportapaedic bed, tea and coffee making facilities, a TV and a luxury ensuite.

Feel free to take light refreshments in our secluded garden and listen for the native tuis, or spend time with us in our home. We'd enjoy hearing about your travels! Our homestay is conveniently located just five minutes drive from the town centre, 1.8km from State Highway 5 and we are close to famous Rotorua attractions. Please phone for directions and to ensure a reservation. See you soon!

Rotorua
Bed & Breakfast
Address: 51 Lytton Street
Name: Hannah & Jim Sharpe
Telephone: (07) 348 7677
Beds: 1 Double (1 Bedroom) **Bathroom:** 1 Ensuite
Tariff: B&B (full) Double $60, Single $40, Vouchers accepted

We are a recently retired couple who enjoy meeting travellers, having ourselves travelled widely throughout the world.
Our house, which is in a quiet area, is very convenient being just ten minutes walk from Rotorua Town Centre and the same distance to Whakarewarewa Thermal Wonderland and the Maori Cultural Centre.
Being just one street away from the main tourist thoroughfare we are just a short stroll from restaurants, fast-food outlets and entertainments.
Guest accommodation comprises; large bedsitter with elevated pleasant views, ensuite bathroom, television, electric blankets, tea and coffee making facilities and own entrance. Guests may wish to relax in the garden which is very private.
Join your hosts for breakfast or if you prefer have breakfast brought to your room. The numerous tourist attractions in and around Rotorua offer a wide choice of things to do and we will be happy to help with advice and suggestions.
Good off-street parking.
Pet: Adorable Maltese terrier 'Tia"

Rotorua
Homestay
Address: 18 Walford Drive, Lynmore, Rotorua
Name: Don & Anne Speedy
Telephone: (07) 345 5385
Beds: 1 Double, 2 Single (2 Bedrooms) **Bathroom:** 1 Private
Tariff: B&B (full) Double $70, Single $40,
Dinner by arrangement ($15 to $25), Vouchers accepted
Nearest Town: Rotorua 5km

Experience Kiwi hospitality in the comfortable smoke-free environment of our modern, all-timber home, situated in an exclusive residential area of Rotorua, 5km from the Tourist Information Centre. Our home has extensive lake and forest views and is a five minute walk from Whakarewarewa Forest Park.
We accept only one booking per night and our guests have their own bathroom, toilet, and TV lounge, with direct access to the Conservatory and Spa. Off-street parking and modern laundry facilities are available, with local sightseeing, forest walks, fishing and sailing trips by arrangement.
Your middle-aged, well-travelled hosts, would welcome the opportunity to return some of the hospitality they have enjoyed overseas. Anne works full time and is a keen gardener, while Don is a semi-retired surveyor who enjoys tennis, sailing, and his Masonic Lodge.
Messages can be left on our answerphone, but bookings must be confirmed before arrival, and we would appreciate 24 hours notice if you wish to dine with us.

Guests share means you may be sharing the bathroom
with other guests, especially at peak season.

Rotorua
Homestay
Address: 10 Iles Rd, Rotorua
Name: Patricia & Ron
Telephone: (07) 345 6451
Beds: 4 Single (2 Bedrooms)
Bathroom: 1 Guests share, Family share toilet
Tariff: B&B (continental) Double $60, Single $35, Children under 12yrs half price, Dinner $15. Credit cards: Visa/MC/BC. Vouchers accepted
Nearest Town: Rotorua

We invite you to share our home in lovely Lynmore, Rotorua. We are only a short stroll away from beautiful forest walks in the Redwood Grove Forest Park and 4 minutes drive from the central city, 10 minutes from the airport.

We offer free pick up and delivery from your bus, train or plane. We have two bedrooms with two single beds in each with electric blankets, heaters and radios in each room.

The shower, large bathroom (with bath) and toilet are all separate. Relax in our heated spa pool (available all year round - no extra charge) or cool off in our inground swimming pool (summer).

We are both in our mid 40's with no children living at home and enjoy meeting people from differing lifestyles and cultures.

Patricia belongs to Zonta International, is a nurse and a therapeutic massage therapist (tariff on request) whose interests include windsurfing, spinning, knitting, walking and jogging.

Ron is involved in video production and photography, specialising in weddings, conferences, corporate assignments, computer graphics and animations, his hobbies include windsurfing.

We would love to share our home with you and help make your stay in Rotorua a happy experience.

Kaharoa, Rotorua

Country Stay
Address: Malrex Manor,
Kaharoa Road, R.D. 2, Rotorua
Name: Vida Whale
Telephone & Fax: (07) 332 2313
Beds: 3 Queen, 3 Single (3 Bedrooms
/ 1 Queen & 1 Single in each room)
Bathroom: 1 Guests share, 1 Family share
Tariff: B&B (full) Double $70-$80,
Single $35-$40, Children half price, Dinner by arrangement $20, Campervans
$20. Discount for extra nights. Vouchers accepted
Nearest Town: Ngongotaha, Rotorua

Come and relax in my spacious home in the country.
*In the afternoons, the Breezeway is a sunny area where you can write, watch TV
or simply rest. In the lounge you can use the pooltable, organ or piano. If you want
gentle exercise you can wander around 11 acres and see Santa Gertrudis crossbred
cattle, or feed an assortment of hens.*
*As there is so much to do and see around Rotorua why not stay a few days, and I
will help you with your itinerary. I am only 10 mins from Rainbow Springs, the
Agrodome, and the Farmhouse horse riding. The Kiwi Outback is 8km away,
where you can go hunting, or be guided through virgin bush and enjoy a venison
BBQ. I can transport you to and from Rotorua if needed.*
Directions: *Through Ngongotaha, 5km to Tauranga Direct, 5km to Kaharoa
Road (right), 3km, past school and Kapukapu Road, up drive on right.*

Rotorua

Guest House
Address: 'Morihana',
20 Toko Street, Rotorua
Name: Bob & Janice Witheford
Telephone & Fax: (07) 348 8511
Beds: 2 Double, 1 Triple, 1 Twin,
3 Single (7 bedrooms)
Bathroom: 1 Ensuite, 2 Guests share
Tariff: B&B (special) Double with ensuite $80, Double/Twin $70, Triple $90,
Single $45, Dinner $20. Credit Cards Visa, MC, JCB. Vouchers accepted except
for room with ensuite.

*'Haere Mai. 'Morihana' means Bright and Shining, the atmosphere is just that.
Our renovated 1910 home offers travellers a haven to wander through NZ's
geothermal Lake District.*
*Situated 1km from the city centre we provide transport to/from bus and train
depots in our courtesy car.*
We have 7 guest bedrooms and one of our double bedrooms offers full ensuite.
*Conversation is warm and friendly in the TV/video lounge-library. There aren't
any strangers at the breakfast table where a delectable cooked/continental menu
changes daily, tempting even the most discerning tastebuds.*
*Enjoy the garden-spa or indoor pool. There's a BBQ outside or we'll cook dinner
for you (by arrangement). Full laundry facilities. Off street parking.*
Come be our guest and meet Libby the Lassie look-alike.
Directions: *From Fenton Street turn into Malfroy Road then 1st right into Toko
Street. 'Morihana' is only 50m on the right.*

West Taupo
Farmstay +
Self-contained Accommodation
Address: 'Apple Tree Bridge Farm',
Highway 32,
RD Mangakino (nr Taupo)
Name: James and Virginia Dysart
Telephone: (07) 372 8232
Beds: 4-6 in cottage, 1 twin in homestead
Tariff: B&B Double $100, Single $50, Dinner $20;
Self contained Cottage (linen provided) sleeps 4-6 $130 per night, 1 week $400, meals arranged as extra if required, Dinner $20, Campers, Caravans, & Campervans welcomed.

We welcome visitors to our farm in the Taupo Region. The self contained cottage sleeps 4-6 comfortably. A family's needs met including a microwave oven & coal and wood burning range for winter that burns continuously. Electric blankets on beds. The homestead offers a twin bedded room, guests share bathroom, living and meals with the family.

The farm is 500 acres, sheep, cattle and pine trees. Situated at the North west end of Lake Taupo. It is an ideal base being central; trout fishing, photography pursuits, golf, hot pools, skiing in winter. The Pureora Forest Park is close by for walking, bird watching and taking a picnic. The Waitomo Caves, Rotorua and Mt Ruapehu are an easy days trip away.

Horse riding on the farm is available. Farm activities change with the seasons and such things as lambing, mustering with sheep dogs, haymaking, and various other farm activities can be observed or participated in by the visitor.

Simply phone us to book or write and you will receive a detailed map. We are very easily located, directions are not difficult.

Taupo
Homestay
Address: "Woodlands" 801 Oruanui Rd, R. D. 1, Taupo
Name: Donna and Mike Smith
Telephone & Fax: (07) 377 6451
Beds: 1 Double, 3 Single (2 bedrooms) **Bathroom:** 2 Private
Tariff: B&B (special) Double $75, Single $45, Children half price,
Nearest Town: Taupo – 18 kms to the south

We are situated at the north end of Oruanui Road, some 18 km north of Taupo but very handy to SH1. We have recently sold our farm retaining 13 acres around the house so remain surrounded by farming activities which visitors are welcome to explore. The home is a 2 storey Lockwood offering pleasant and peaceful rural views. Mike is the Executive Secretary of the Farm Forestry Assn. Taupo is centrally situated and has much to offer. It is clean, crisp and pretty town offering a wide range of tourist activities such as trout fishing, boating, thermal swimming, golf courses that are never closed by weather and numerous walks.
Directions: *Turn off S.H.1 apprx 9km North of Wairakei (Oruanui Road), "Challenge" fertilizer shed on corner. Apprx half a kilometre along on right. Please phone first.*

Te Moenga
ACACIA BAY LAKE TAUPO, NEW ZEALAND

Taupo
Farmstay
Address: Reeves Road,
Acacia Bay, Taupo
Name: Jay and Bruce McLeod

New Zealand Association
FARM & HOME HOSTS

Telephone & Fax: (07) 378-7901
Beds: 1 King, 1 Queen, 1 Twin (3 bedrooms) **Bathroom:** 3 Ensuite
Tariff: B&B (continental) Double $90, Single $50, Dinner $25 (includes wine),
Children half price; Campervans welcome $25, Vouchers accepted

*Jay and Bruce extend a warm welcome to share the unique experience of staying
at Te Moenga Park. Te Moenga is a working deer, sheep, and cattle farm
overlooking the lake and located minutes from central Taupo, boat harbour, three
golf courses, and all the major tourist and sporting attractions. From your own
private suite to the glorious views of Lake Taupo you will find your accommodation
unequalled. We pride ourselves that we offer complete privacy and perfect comfort.
However if it is your wish more adventurous activities ranging from scenic bush
and farm walks through to fishing and all the recreational activities the region
offers can be readily arranged.*
*Te Moenga homestead is spacious, well appointed, and set in large park like
surroundings, all suites have their own private lounge, TV etc.*
*Your hosts have travelled widely and have a detailed knowledge of the region and
are able to ensure a memorable experience.*
Directions: please phone.

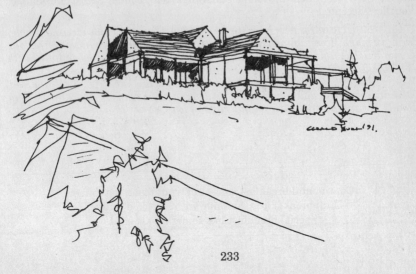

Taupo
Homestay
Address: 23 Rokino Road, Taupo
Name: Colleen and Bob Yeoman
Telephone: (07) 377 0283

Beds: 1 Double, 3 Single (3 bedrooms, cot available)
Bathroom: 1 Private, 1 Guests share
Tariff: B&B (full) Double $80, Single $45, Children half price, Dinner $25.
Campervans welcome. Vouchers accepted June to October.
Nearest Town: Taupo 2kms (20 minute walk) 5 minute walk to Lake.

Your hosts Colleen and Bob extend a warm welcome. We offer comfortable beds and pillows, electric blankets and luxurious duvets. Guest bathroom for twin room and single room upstairs. Own shower and toilet for double bedroom downstairs. Please feel free to use laundry and ironing facilities. Enjoy our billiard room, spacious lounge and sun deck with panoramic views of Lake and mountains. We are familiar with boating and fishing, keen golfers, have interesting books on New Zealand, member of CWI. Recently retired from farming.

Taupo is a lovely place to catch your breath, to relax, to enjoy some pleasant walks. Taupo has many splendid restaurants, or you may prefer to share a three course dinner with your hosts and enjoy complimentary wine.

We are situated en route to Wellington, Auckland and Hawkes Bay. Guests can be met at Taupo Airport and off public transport.

Directions: *Turn into Huia Street from lake front, take fourth turn on right into Rokino Road.*

Taupo
Homestay
Address: 77A Wakeman Road, Acacia Bay, Taupo
Name: Joan & Eric Leersnijder
Telephone: (07) 378 3861
Beds: 1 Double, 2 Single (2 bedrooms)
Bathroom: 1 Private
Tariff: B&B (continental) Double $65, Single $40, Dinner $25, Children $20, Vouchers accepted

We are retired farmers who have travelled extensively and enjoy meeting people. We have magnificent, uninterrupted views of the lake and surroundings from our home, which is situated in a quiet area of Acacia Bay, and only a few minutes walk from the beach and our hobbies are sailing and fishing.

We are about 6km from Taupo and about the same distance from 3 golf courses.

Directions: *Vehicular access is the road going down between 95 - 99 Wakeman Road. We are the last house on this right of way.*

Continental breakfast consist of fruit, toast, tea/coffee,
Full breakfast is the same with a cooked course,
Special breakfast has something special.

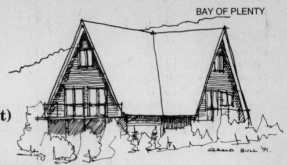

Taupo (North-West)
Farmstay
Address: 1218 Mapara
Road, R.D. 1, Taupo
Name: Guido & Dianne Jakschik
Telephone: (0737) 81305, **Mobile:** 025 740 187
Beds: 2 Double, 2 Single (2 bedrooms) **Bathroom:** 1 Family share (large)
Tariff: B&B (Full) Double $60, Single $35, Dinner $25, Children under 12yrs
1/2 price, infants free, Vouchers accepted

*Guido (originally from Germany), Dianne, Benjamin (10) and Natasha (9)
welcome you. We like chatting over good food and New Zealand wine.*
*Our farmlet, 8 1/2 hectares, is surrounded by sheep, beef and deer farmers - we
rear calves, nurse cows and pet lambs. Outside German Shepherd, one kitten.*
*We are a career minded couple, B.Sc in Agriculture, land agent and working
nurse, we have travelled and worked around the world. Can organise scenic tours.*
*Lake Taupo offers daily cruises with entertainment and fishing. Have your
rainbow or brown trout smoked or served hot and fresh!*
Taupo offers many recreational activities:
*AC Baths - swim, soak in natural thermal water, slide, private pools, sauna,
Barbeque.*
Dancing Club - Modern, rock-round ballroom dancing on Saturday nights.
*Wairakei Tourist Park - thermal area, Huka Falls, Geysers, silica terraces, jet
boating, horse trekking, craft shops, scenic walks and tramping. Bungy Jumping.
Hunt for sika, red deer or wild pigs.*
*Ski at Mt Ruapehu, Ngauruhoe or Tongairiro or tramp them during summer.
Canoeing, kayaking, water ski-ing, windsurfers, white wate rafting, tennis and golf.
We wish you a nice time here in Taupo.*
Directions: *1.5 km from Town Information Centre North on State Highway 1,
turn left 8 km (West) Poihipi Rd left 2.7 km 1218 Mapara Road left "A" framed
house.*

Taupo
Homestay
Address: 98 Wakeman Rd., Acacia Bay, Taupo
Name: Bob & Marlene Leece
Telephone: (07) 3786099
Beds: 1 Double, 2 Single (2 bedrooms) **Bathroom:** 1 Guests share, 1 Private
Tariff: B&B (continental) Double $75, Single $40, Children half price, Vouchers
accepted
Nearest Town: Taupo

*We have a large Lockwood home 6km from town in Acacia Bay with panoramic
views of lake and mountains. Also two beautiful middle aged Burmese cats.*
*We offer two large rooms, one with a queen size waterbed, the other with 2 single
beds with electric blankets. Own guest facilities, bath, shower, toilet. You are
welcome to smoke, but not in our home please.*
Please phone for directions.

Taupo

Homestay
Address: 30 Rokino Road, Taupo
Name: Betty & Ned Nolan
Telephone & Fax: (07) 3770828
Beds: 4 Single (2 bedrooms) **Bathroom:** 1 Ensuite, 1 Family share
Tariff: B&B (full) Double $70, Single $50 (discount for subsequent nights), Dinner $25. Vouchers accepted.

We have a spacious home on an elevated section with expansive views of the ranges, lake, mountains and town in a quiet area but only minutes from town, restaurants and lake.
We are retired farmers who enjoy meeting people and have been hosting farmstays since 1980.
We have travelled extensively and have varied interests which include fishing and have our own boat.
We have two mountain bikes for use.
Betty enjoys cooking and you are assured of a great welcome and relaxing stay.
Directions: *From lake front turn up Taharepa Road, left down into Rokino Road. We are on your right up a tree clad drive.*

Taupo

Self-contained Accommodation
Address: Riverway Cottages, 16 Peehi Manini Rd, Waitahanui RD2, Taupo
Name: Joyce and John Johnson
Telephone: (07) 378 8822
Beds: 2 Double, 1 Single (2 bedrooms) **Bathroom:** 1 Private
Tariff: B&B (continental) Double $70, Single $45, Dinner $20, Children half price
Nearest Town: Taupo

Riverway Cottages are situated 100 yds from the famous Waitahanui River, and 200 yds from beautiful Lake Taupo. They are older-type properties, one John and Joyce live in, and the second, comprises lounge with TV, kitchen with fridge, freezer, microwave, and conventional ovens, separate dining room, two double bedrooms and bathroom. There is a deck to relax on in summer, and perhaps enjoy a BBQ with us, with complimentary pre-dinner drinks - as evening dinner is optional. In winter there are gas and electric fires, and electric blankets on all beds, for the comfort of our visitors. We have ample parking space, for visitors driving around beautiful New Zealand.
For interested fishermen, John has been a successful Trout Fly Fishing Guide for 18 years, and can take you to some "magic places", and may be booked by the hour or by the day. Joyce is a keen badminton player.
Come and visit Waitahanui. We'd love to meet you.
Directions: *Please phone for directions - and we will pick up if needed.*

Taupo

Homestay
Address: "Pataka House" 8 Pataka Road Taupo
Name: Raewyn & Neil Alexander
Telephone: (07) 378 5481
Beds: 1 Queen, 4 Single (3 Bedrooms) **Bathroom:** 1 Guests share + powder room
Tariff: B&B (full) Double $80, Single $45, Children half price, Campervans welcome

Welcome to "Pataka House". We love to meet overseas people as well as New Zealanders. Eight years ago we opened our farm house to visitors from around the world and now we find the world a much more closely-knit community, full of friendly faces.
Today our home is in Taupo where Neil and I live in a quiet bright, airy spacious abode. There are three double downstairs bedrooms for visiting travellers - two with beautiful lake and mountain views. Feel free to use laundry facilities. Our home is centrally heated and in winter a wood-fire is continuously burning. The living area has a sunny outlook with french door opening onto a private courtyard and garden. In summer there is an outdoor swimming pool and entertainment barbecue are available. A roomy carpark.
We live 200 metres from Lake Taupo and within easy walking distance to many excellent restaurants. Guests can be met. Please phone your bookings or write for reservations.

Taupo

Country Homestay
Address: "Te Awanui" 1506 Poihipi Rd Taupo
Telephone: (07) 377 6040
Beds: 1 Queen, 2 Single (2 Bedrooms) **Bathroom:** 1 Guests share
Tariff: B&B (full) Double $90, Single $45, Children 5 to 12yrs half price, Dinner $25, Vouchers accepted
Nearest Town: Taupo

Welcome to "Te Awanui" our home in the country, 15km from Taupo.
We recently moved here (after selling our farm at Tirohanga) and have semi-retired on an 145 acre farm with sheep, cattle and horses.
We are still very involved with equestrian horses competing, schooling, breeding and students for lessons.
Our home is spacious and comfortable with quality accommodation. We welcome you to have with us a delicious three course dinner with complimentary wine, or if you prefer, only Bed and Breakfast.
My husband enjoys playing golf, we also love fishing the beautiful Lake Taupo. We have both travelled extensively and enjoy meeting people from other countries.
Taupo is a refreshing, lovely place to stay, it has much to offer. We are able to advise or arrange most activities.
We look forward to meeting you, our directions are simple. 1506 Poihipi Road. Please phone (07) 377-6040
We ask guests not to smoke inside our home.

Taupo

Homestay
Address: Please phone
Name: Ian & Veronica Cook
Telephone: (07) 377 1447
Beds: 1 Double, 2 Single (2 Bedrooms)
Bathroom: 1 Private, 1 Family share
Tariff: B&B (full) Double $70, Single $35,
Dinner $20, Vouchers accepted (midweek only)
Nearest Town: Taupo

Our warm and comfortable home is situated within easy walking distance of the lake and close to the town and other places of interest, with a beautiful view of lake and mountains.

We are in our mid sixties, with a grown family and wide interests which include blue water sailing, fishing and golf. We have both travelled extensively, and enjoy welcoming overseas and NZ guests to our home.

We are non-smokers, have two small terriers, and a 9 metre keeler yacht which can be available to take visitors out on the lake.

Breakfast and dinner are served in our pleasant dining room or (weather permitting) outside on the deck. We offer a choice of continental or full breakfast the timing of which is flexible.

Taupo is a charming town with plenty to see and do, and we look forward to sharing it with you.

Taupo

Farmstay
Address: Watership Down Lodge,
Whangamata Road, RD 1, Taupo
Name: Roland & Clair Ellis
Telephone: (07) 377 3553
Beds: 2 Double (2 Bedrooms)
Bathroom: 2 Ensuite
Tariff: B&B (full) Double $100, Single $60,
Children same, Dinner $30,
Vouchers 1st May-30th September accepted
Nearest Town: Taupo 20km

Roland and Clair purchased Watership Down, at Kinlock, as a 360 acre bare block, which has now been transformed into a sheep and beef farm. The house located in quiet surroundings has magnificent views of Lake Taupo, Mount Ruapehu and Mount Ngauruhoe. Built of macrocapa timber beams the house has great character with the two double bedroom and ensuite bathrooms offering guests every comfort.

Roland an ex cavalry officer and ardent fly fisherman can help fishermen with professional guides or his own local knowledge, whilst Clair enjoys helping guests plan any of the many activities available locally or a quiet day's sightseeing. Both are seasoned travellers in New Zealand and world wide.

Clair's enjoyment of cooking provides an excellent three course dinner including fine New Zealand wine. The area is ideal for fishing, golf (4 courses), riding, rafting, bush walks, bird watching, with skiing 1 1/4 hours away. Enjoy a farm tour with great view.

Directions: *Please phone*

Taupo

Rural Homestay - close to Taupo town
Name: "Awahuri" - River's Bend. William & Suzanne Hindmarsh
Telephone: For directions and enquiries (07) 378 9847
Beds: 2 Double/Twin, 1 Single (2 Bedrooms)
Bathroom: 1 Ensuite, 1 Family share
Tariff: B&B (full) Queen & Twin ensuite $135, plus extra bedroom $45, 3/4 & Twin $95, Single $70, Dinner by arrangement $30pp

We've lived in Taupo since 1964, in the same secret place. Our extended house is set in a three acre (11500m²) garden, with three 'lakes', amazing bird life, 30 year old trees, and over 300 Camellias, Rhododendrons and Roses etc. Our 8.5 acre (3.5 ha) property borders the Waikato River, with superb views, yet it's only minutes from Taupo town.

Your independent accommodation is on the East side of the house. It invades part of the garden, is very tranquil and sunny. Your large bedroom contains a queen sized double bed plus single bed and a lovely double bay window. The ensuite bathroom is right beside and the extra bedroom nextdoor. Maybe you could consider staying a few days — the atmosphere is tasteful, beguiling, and smoke free!

*And Suzanne's **evening meals**, ... well, you'll just have to try them to find out how brilliant they really are, won't you? But please arrange to eat with us at least four hours in advance. Breakfast, full or continental, will be served in the dining room, times to suit.*

We have wide interests, from classic cars to gardens; from philosophy to politics. All sporting facilities are close including our own grass tennis court and a swimming hole in the river nearby. We have gear for Rainbow trout fishing on our river boundary.

It is important that you give reasonable notice when you would like to stay with us. We will then have time to prepare for your visit, and we look forward to meeting you.

Would you like three weeks free B&B for two people?
Complete the page at the front of the book.

Taupo

Homestay
Address: "Kooringa"
32 Ewing Grove, Acacia Bay, Taupo
Name: Rob & John Mosley
Telephone: (07) 378 8025
Beds: 1 Double, 2 Single (2 Bedrooms)
Bathroom: 1 Private (one party only taken at a time)
Tariff: B&B (continental) Double $75, Single $45, Children half price, Dinner $25, Vouchers accepted April to October.
Nearest Town: Taupo

"Kooringa" is situated in sheltered Acacia Bay surrounded by bush and gardens with magnificent uninterrupted views of Lake Taupo and Mount Tauhara. The guest rooms are tastefully furnished with private bathroom, toilet, laundry and kitchenette plus family room with TV. There are 2 bedrooms - one has a double bed - the other - 2 singles. We are retired professional people who have travelled extensively, lived overseas and now enjoy a very relaxed lifestyle in this beautiful tranquil area. We are only 2-3 minutes stroll from the Lakeside and some of the loveliest bush walks in the area. We are within easy distance of 3 golf courses - hot pools, mini golf and numerous other attractions. We assure you of a warm welcome and comfortable stay, with a candlelight dinner overlooking the Lake if desired.
Directions: *Please phone.*

Taupo

Homestay
Address: "Lakeland Homestay" 11 Williams Street
Name: Lesley & Chris
Telephone: (07) 378 1952
Beds: 1 Double, 2 Single (2 Bedrooms) **Bathroom:** 1 Family share
Tariff: B&B (continental) Double $70, Single $40,
Children half price, Campervans $25, Vouchers accepted
Nearest Town: Taupo

We invite you to stay in our home, within walking distance to the town (1km) and lake. Our street is small and quiet. We enjoy views of the lake and mountains and stunning sunsets. Our garden has mature trees and shrubs that attract a variety of birds including tuis.
Our home has three bedrooms upstairs with balconies overlooking the garden. Guest bedrooms have electric blankets available. We request no smoking in the house.
We are avid golf and fishing enthusiasts, being members of the Taupo Golf Club. We go trout fishing as often as time allows. We have both travelled to Europe and England. For the snow skier we are approximately an hour from the skifields.
Directions: *Travelling from north turn left at the only set of traffic lights, take Heathcote Street on the left and right into Williams Street. Travelling from south turn right into Rifle Range Road (Firestation) and left into Williams Street after crossing Heu Heu Street.*

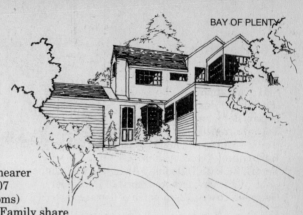

Taupo
Homestay
Address: 10 Pataka Rd
Name: Robbie & Stan Shearer
Telephone: (07) 378 7007
Beds: 4 Single (2 Bedrooms)
Bathroom: 1 Private, 1 Family share
Tariff: B&B (special) Double $75, Single $50, Dinner $25 incl. wine
Nearest Town: Taupo

We welcome you to our comfortable home nestled in a tranquil mature garden. Situated a hundred metres from the lake opposite the snow-capped mountains of National Park we are only a leisurely stroll along the lakefront to town. Our home is comfortably furnished with a hint of old world charm. Guest bedrooms are attractive and comfortable with matching bathroom facilities. You are welcome to use our laundry, barbeque terrace, garden and spa pool terrace.
We are a retired couple who enjoy travel, people, good food, golf and hospitality. We were honoured with the New Zealand Travel Association Courtesy Award for the Lodge and restaurant we operated for many years in Taupo. We can advise you how to share our beautiful environment with skiing, golf, boating, trout fishing, water skiing, thermal areas, hunting and whitewater rafting (to mention only a few) all close by.
Directions: *Please phone mornings - we can collect you from airport or coach depot if required.*

Taupo
Farmstay
Address: "Ben Lomond" 1432 Poihipi Rd, R.D.1 Taupo
Name: Jack & Mary Weston
Telephone: (07) 377 6033
Beds: 4 Single (2 Bedrooms) **Bathroom:** 1 Guests share
Tariff: B&B (full) Double $90, Single $45, Children half price, Dinner $25 includes wine, Vouchers accepted
Nearest Town: Taupo 15km west

Ben Lomond is a 700 acre sheep and cattle farm 15km west of Taupo. We have farmed the land for the last 33 years and offer you a pleasant farmstay in our comfortable home.
Our interests include equestrian and fishing and we can advise you on the local spots of interest which are wide and varied in the Taupo District.
Jack and I have both travelled widely within New Zealand and overseas and enjoy making new friends.
Our 3 sons have grown up and virtually left home and we offer you 2 twin rooms and 1 bathroom for guest use only. We have the usual farm animals of which 2 dogs wander in and out.
You are welcome to dine with us but please ring and "make a date". We prefer non-smokers.
Directions: *Please phone.*

Te Rangiita, Turangi

Homestay
Address: Raukawa Lodge,
SH1, Te Rangiita
(Postal: PO Box 195, Turangi)
Name: John and Sarah Sage
Telephone & Fax: (07) 386 7637
Beds: 1 Queen, 2 Single (2 bedrooms)
Bathroom: 1 Guests share
Tariff: B&B (full) Double $70, Single $40, Dinner $20pp, Children under 10 half price. Vouchers accepted April to December.
Nearest Town: 12km north of Turangi on SH 1

Kia Ora - Our home is halfway between Auckland and Wellington on State Highway One - close to the mountains but closer to the lake with a rural outlook reaching to the Kaimanawa Ranges. We are minutes to the Tauranga-Taupo River for trout fishing, surrounded by beautiful walking treks or tranquillity and peace for an artist. Whatever your interest the Central Plateau can ably cater for all tastes in all seasons.

We offer comfortable accommodation with electric blankets and duvets; your own tea/toast making, washing and toilet facilities; conservatory with wood burner in the games room. We serve simple New Zealand fare - invariably smoked trout or barbequed leg of lamb with an inviting aroma of freshly baked bread.

We have travelled extensively at home and abroad, are keen golfers, fisherpersons and gardeners - and ... followers of rugby. Our family at home, Abby and Sophia, are two Old English Sheepdogs, who always welcome new faces.

Please phone for directions and availability.

Turangi

Self-contained Accom
Address: 72 Taupehi Road,
Turangi
Name: Jean & Leslie Bird
Telephone: (07) 386-7518
Beds: 1 Double (Queen),
2 Single (2 bedrooms)
Bathroom: 1 Ensuite.
Tariff: B&B (full) Double $75, Extra person $30 each, Dinner by arrangement

We have a modern home, with a self-contained apartment attached which has 1 Queensize bed and two single beds all innerspring mattresses with Woolrest Sleepers and feather duvets. Own kitchen facilities, dining area, sitting room with own TV, electric fan heating, ensuite bathroom and carport. Laundry available. We have a solar-heated swimming pool, private spa pool and barbeque area. Our home is close to the Tongariro River, Tongariro National Park and Lake Taupo. These areas cater for trout fishing - lake and rivers, tramping, ski-ing and other outdoor activities. We have spent 10 years in the tourist industry and have travelled extensively in New Zealand and overseas, and are now retired and can offer our hospitality to New Zealand and overseas visitors.

We and our Cocker Spaniel Katie will be pleased to greet you.

Directions: *Please phone.*

Turangi
Homestay
Address: Omori Road, R.D. 1, Turangi
Name: Joy Wardell
Telephone: (07) 386-7386
Beds: 2 Single (1 bedroom) **Bathroom:** 1 Private
Tariff: B&B (full) Double $60, Single $40, Dinner $20

My home is 16 km West of Turangi (off State Highway 41) with magnificent views across Lake Taupo and over the surrounding farmland and bush clad mountains. I share a property with my family whose home is next door to mine and we all enjoy meeting and entertaining people. It gives me much pleasure to cook and serve tasty meals for my numerous guests.

We have a few sheep and there are deer and goats on an adjoining property. There is a private study with television for the use of guests if required.

You need travel only short distances to the many attractions of this area, e.g. Mountains - Ngaruahoe, Ruapehu and Tongariro, the Tongariro River and of course Lake Taupo itself. Activities such as trout fishing, bush walking, ski-ing, rafting, jet boating and many more can be enjoyed or if you prefer just relax and enjoy the fresh air and country atmosphere.

Turangi
Homestay + Self-contained
Accommodation
Address: 1 Poto Street, Turangi
Name: Jack and Betty Anderson
Telephone: (07) 386 8272
Beds: 1 Queen, 1 Double, 2 Single (3 bedrooms) + Cottages sleep 5 & 7.
Bathroom: 1 Ensuite, 1 Private, 1 Family share.
Tariff: B&B (full) Double $65, Single $40, Dinner $20 (by prior arrangement), Children under 12 half price, Self catering cottages $50 Double

Welcome to our relaxed lifestyle beside the Tongariro River, away from traffic noise, with bush walks and fishing pool nearby. Upstairs is a queen bedroom with ensuite, ensuring your privacy, and a twin room. Downstairs, with private bathroom is a double bedroom. For travellers preferring independence, our self-contained 2 bedroom cottages are adjacent. Laundry facilities available.

Breakfast, leisurely, of your choice. Meals contain fresh vegetables in season. Vegetarians catered for. Off street parking. No smoking inside please.

With both children away, we can share our interest in flying, golfing, skiing, and trout fishing. From our central North Island location enjoy day trips to Tongariro National Park, Taupo, Rotorua and Napier. Thermal baths are nearby. We can show you volcanoes, mountains and lakes from our 4 seat Cessna aircraft. Guided rafting, horse treks, river and boat fishing arranged. Maps of walking tracks and pools available. We can meet your bus.
Directions: *Please phone*

Turangi
Homestay + Self-contained flat
Address: Tongariro View,
4 Main Road, Turangi
Name: Bob & Lillian Bebbington
Telephone: (07) 386 0161
Beds: 1 Double, 2 Single (2 bedrooms)
Bathroom: 1 Guests share.
Plus 2 bedroomed self contained flat, 1 double, 4 bunks
Tariff: B&B (continental) Double $80, Single $70, Flat: Double $75, $10 each extra person, Dinner $20
Nearest Town: Taupo 53km north on SH1

My wife and I will be pleased to welcome you to our modern home overlooking the Bridge Pool on the Tongariro River, 10 minutes from Lake Taupo and close to the ski fields of the central North Island. Our three storey home has panoramic views, in a beautiful situation with a wide variety of outdoor activities on river, lake and mountain. Guest lounge and bedrooms on top floor via a spiral staircase, comfortable beds have inner spring mattresses with electric blankets. Guest bathroom on middle floor.

Flat on ground floor has all facilities including laundry with cooker plus microwave colour television and fridge/freezer. Fully furnished suitable for families or groups for long stays.

Complementary tea, coffee and milk provided on arrival.

*Guided trout fishing on the river, fly tying and casting tuition by host is available.
All meals by arrangement B&B only.*

Directions: *Drive North past Turangi on SH1, 2nd house on right over Tongariro River bridge.*

Turangi
Homestay
Address: 8 Tongariro Street, Turangi,
Postal: P.O. Box 290, Turangi
Name: Carol & Frank Harwood
Telephone & Fax: (07) 386 6404
Beds: 1 Twin, 1 Single (2 bedrooms)
Bathroom: 1 Private, 1 Family share.

Tariff: B&B (continental) Double $75, Single $45 Dinner $20. Vouchers accepted.

Our comfortable cottage is open plan living with a small back yard facing the morning sun. We are both keen gardeners and our evening meals often have our own freshly picked vegetables. Special diets can be catered for, eg. low cholesterol, vegetarian. Packed lunches are available on request for day trips.

I am interested in most crafts and often have a selection of garments for sale. We both love the outdoors and are experience in the local bush walks. Frank and I are both professional fishing guides and Hardy Instructors, fishing trips can be arranged at additional cost.

*There are always plenty of fishing books and manual in our book shelves to read.
The Tongariro River is only 3 minutes from the house.*

Turangi town-ship offers a variety of good restaurants.

Frank and I have travelled extensively and welcome the opportunity to meet overseas visitors

Tokaanu, via Turangi
Braxmere Fishing Lodge
Self-contained Accommodation
Address: Waihi Road,
PO Box 11, Tokaanu
Name: Brian Jones
Telephone: (07) 386 8011
Fax: 386 7513
Beds: 14 double and 14 single bedrooms, 1 each per unit)
Bathrooms: 1 private in each unit
Tariff: B&B (full) Double $90, Single $60, Dinner $20, Children $9, Campervans $7 per head. All prices inclusive GST.
10% discount for "Over 60's". Visa and Bankcard accepted. Vouchers accepted.
Nearest Town: 2 kms Tokaanu (Village) 7 kms Turangi.

'Take a Break' half way between Auckland and Wellington on state Highway 41. Braxmere Fishing Lodge is situated on the Southern shore of Lake Taupo, near the attractive Maori Village Waihi, 30 minutes Whakapapa Ski fields and 10 minutes from the delta of the mighty Tongariro River - world renowned for Trout fishing. There are many bush walks, Tongariro River, small Trout streams, Trout Hatchery, Lake Rotoaira, Tokaanu, Thermal park and pools, 18 hole golf course, horse trekking, restaurants and Turangi township.

We offer 11 self-contained units with 1 double and single in separate bedroom and 2 single beds in the Kitchen / TV Living Room. All units have an individual view of the Lake and are thermally heated. There are also 2 separate houses with double bedrooms, single bunk rooms, thermal pools and barbecue.

In addition, we have a thermal pool, barbecue, wharf, launching ramp, hire boats, fishing gear, laundry facilities, drying rooms for skiers gear and motor home sites. Please mention the B&B Book when booking.

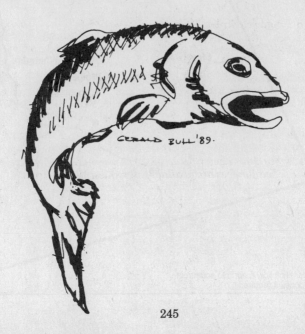

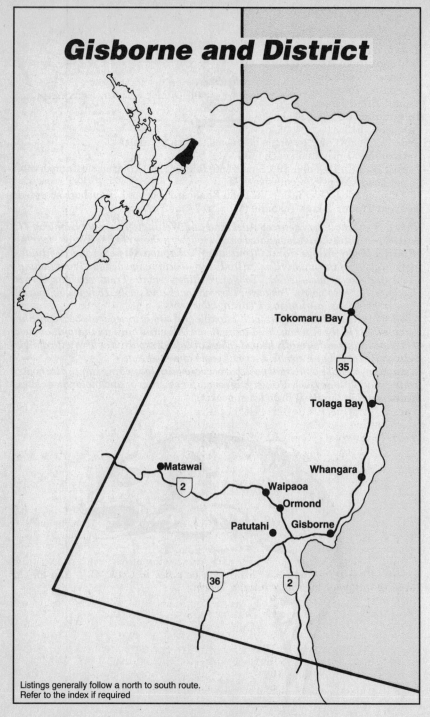

Gisborne and District

Tokomaru Bay

35

Tolaga Bay

Matawai

2

Waipaoa

Whangara

Ormond

Patutahi

Gisborne

36

2

Listings generally follow a north to south route.
Refer to the index if required

Tokomaru Bay
Farmstay
Address: "Tironui", Mata Road, Tokomaru Bay
Name: David & Caroline Jefferd
Telephone: (06) 864 5619
Beds: 1 Double, 1 Single (1 bedroom) **Bathroom:** 1 Family share
Tariff: B&B (full) Double $60, Single $40, Dinner $20, Children half price. Campervans welcome. Vouchers accepted
Nearest Town: 11km from Tokomaru Bay, 84km north of Gisborne

We have two young children, aged 6 and 8, and live on an 830 hectare sheep and cattle property 11km from the Tokomaru Bay village and beach.
Tokomaru Bay is a typical east coast village which is becoming increasingly renowned for its Maori culture and crafts, and for other cottage industries. As well there are the wonderful sandy beaches which are still relatively quiet during our hot summers.
Our farm is typical of many hill country farms and where possible we will endeavour to show our visitors farm activities that are of particular interest to them.
We have a swimming pool and tennis court which visitors are welcome to use. No smoking inside.
Directions: *Please phone*

Tolaga Bay
Farmstay
Address: "Kaiaua", Tolaga Bay, Gisborne District
Name: Helen & Ian Salmon
Telephone: (06) 862 6758
Beds: 2 Double, 1 Single (3 bedrooms)
Bathroom: 1 Guests share
Tariff: B&B (continental) Double $60, Single $40, Dinner $20pp, Campervans $15. Vouchers accepted.
Nearest Town: Gisborne 63 km on S.H.35

Our home is a large country homestead overlooking the sea on our son's sheep and cattle station on the East Coast, north of Gisborne.
The homestead has recently been completely renovated and is very warm and sunny and is set in a beautiful bush garden . There is a tennis court available for guests' use. For those who like walking there are beautiful bush walks through native bush and out on to Marau Point which gives magnificent views along the coast to East Cape and Mount Hikurangi, the first places in the world to receive the sun each day.
A short driving distance away there are a number of historical places from Captain Cook's first landing. Walks can be taken to Cooks Cove and an old whaling station at the end of Kaiaua Beach.
A warm country welcome is assured.
Directions: *Please phone for full directions.*

Private bathroom is for your use exclusively,
Guests share means you may be sharing with other guests,
Family share means you will be sharing with the family.

247

Whangara, Gisborne

Farmstay
Address: "Hikatu",
Waiomoko Road,
Whangara, RD3,
Gisborne. Please ring.
Name: Ian and Sue Fraser
Telephone: (06) 862-2850
Beds: 1 Double, 2 Single (2 bedrooms)
Bathroom: 1 Private, 1 Guests share
Tariff: B&B (full) Double $60; Single $30; Dinner $15.
Nearest Town: 34 km from Gisborne Highway 35

We live in the old family homestead which was built in the early 1900s. It is a comfortably sunny old place that we have renovated over the years and happily still retains the old world atmosphere we enjoy so much and would like to share. Our two rooms are never booked simultaneously unless our visitors are travelling together. Consequently the guest bathroom is shared with friends only. Our garden would be of particular interest to gardeners and garden lovers alike as we have spent many years creating a varied and interesting place.
There is a swimming pool and a tennis court (not Wimbledon).
The farm runs a Hereford stud, sheep, and various other animals. You are welcome to watch seasonal work in progress or ramble over the farm. Light lunch available. For those who wish to enjoy the country way of life, a peaceful garden, or just get away from it all, Hikatu is just that tranquil spot.

Matawai, Gisborne

Farmstay
Address: Moanui Station, R.D. Matawai, Gisborne
Name: Mark & Jane Johnson
Telephone: (06) 8678586
Beds: 1 Double, 2 Single (2 bedrooms) **Bathroom:** 1 Guests share
Tariff: B&B (full) Double $50, Single $30 Dinner $20, Vouchers accepted
Nearest Town: Gisborne 90km, Opotiki 80km

Our home is a typical station homestead, rimu panelled, large kitchen which is the hub of our lifestyle. Our station of 2000 acres involves sheep, cattle and deer. The Moanui Valley is a hunters paradise with deer, goats, pigs and fishing so you are welcome to do your own thing or join us in our farming activities. It will be an experience of High Country farming and hospitality and we welcome you to share it with us. Please phone before hand.
Directions: *From Gisborne of State Highway 2 go past Matawai approx 10km and take a road on your left marked Rere, Koranga Valley Road and Moanui Valley Road travel for about 2 minutes and then take the Moanui Valley Road on you right and travel for 15km - this is metalled - there is a sign on our gateway rails "Moanui" and a driveway among trees to our home on the side of a hill.*

THE WILLOWS

Waipaoa, Gisborne

Farmstay
Address: "The Willows",
Waipaoa, R.D. 1,
Gisborne
Name: Rosemary & Graham Johnson
Telephone & Fax: (06) 862 5605
Beds: 2 Double, 3 Single (3 bedrooms) **Bathroom:** 1 Guests share
Tariff: B&B (full) Double $55, Single $40, Dinner $25, Vouchers accepted
Nearest Town: Gisborne 20km

Our home is probably best described in the American Colonial Style with a panelled entry and dining room of our own oak timber milled from trees of which we have some lovely specimens planted by our forefathers. We enjoy the amenities available in the city and also the country life on our 440 acre property involving deer, cattle, sheep, grapes and cropping.
We enjoy meeting people and look forward to your visit. We welcome you to have dinner with us, or if you prefer only Bed & Breakfast.
We would appreciate if you could ring prior to your arrival.
Directions: *We are situated 20km north of Gisborne on SH2 through to Opotiki and the Bay of Plenty - approx 6km from the Ormond Store or 9.5 km from Te Karaka. We have a sign "The Willows" at the end of our driveway. A good landmark is the curved Kaiteratahi Bridge and we are 1 mile north of that. Our house is white with a black tiled roof situated on a hill overlooking the Waipaoa River.*

Gisborne

Homestay
Address: 159 The Esplanade, Gisborne
Name: Alec & Barbara Thomson
Telephone: (06) 868-9675
Beds: 1 Double, 2 Single (2 bedrooms)
Bathroom: 1 Family share, Separate toilets
Tariff: B&B (full) Double $55, Single $40, Dinner $15, Children reduced rate.
Tariff of 10% discount for any bowlers staying with us when participating in local tournaments). Vouchers accepted.

Our home is situated overlooking the Waimata River, with river views from each guest room.
We are also a short and pleasant walking distance from the city shopping area, Museum and Art Centre and Lawson Field Theatre, where Gisborne stages many entertaining productions.
Alec and I enjoy meeting people and we look forward to welcoming all who wish to spend time with us.
Off street parking is available.
We are both active members of lawn and indoor bowling clubs.
We also enjoy a game of bridge.

249

Gisborne

Homestay

Address: "Fawn Ridge",
29 Richardson Ave, Gisborne
Name: Kathlyn and Bryan Thompson
Telephone: (06) 868 8823
Beds: 2 Single (1 bedroom) **Bathroom:** Private
Tariff: B&B (continental) Double $60, Single $45. Vouchers accepted all year.

Our home is situated in a private semi rural hill setting of 4 hectares with sweeping views of Young Nicks Head but is only 15 minutes walk to city centre.
We run a few deer, sheep, chooks and are growing various different trees.
We are a working family with one teenage son plus a cat. Our house is 12 years young with stairs. The guest bedroom has single beds with electric blankets and adjoining bathroom and toilet. The family room has TV for your own use and kitchen where you can help yourself to tea and coffee. The bedroom opens onto a deck overlooking a secluded garden.
Gisborne has much to offer in the way of sandy beaches, pleasant year round climate and access to numerous leisure activities. It is an easy 20 minutes drive to famous Eastwood Hill Aboretum (a must to see).
We request that you phone the evening prior to your arrival.

The standard of accommodation in *The New Zealand Bed and Breakfast Book*
ranges from homely to luxurious,
but you can always be sure of superior hospitality.

Patutahi, Gisborne

Farmstay
Address: "Repongaere"
Lavenham Rd, Box 116
Patutahi, Gisborne
Name: Midge & Michael Dods
Telephone & Fax: (06) 862 7717
Beds: 2 Queen, 2 Single (3 bedrooms)
Bathroom: 1 Ensuite, 1 Private, 1 Guests share
Tariff: B&B (full) Double $120-$150, Single $100, Dinner by arrangement.
Major credit cards accepted.

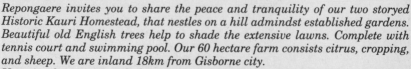

Repongaere invites you to share the peace and tranquility of our two storyed Historic Kauri Homestead, that nestles on a hill admindst established gardens. Beautiful old English trees help to shade the extensive lawns. Complete with tennis court and swimming pool. Our 60 hectare farm consists citrus, cropping, and sheep. We are inland 18km from Gisborne city.
Upstairs three spacious bedrooms, two with queensized beds and verandahs, one twin. Electric blankets. While downstairs the traditional dining room and drawing room set off many interesting antiques.
New Zealand dishes are speciality, featuring seafoods, game, lamb, accompanied with locally grown fresh fruits and vegetables. A selection of New Zealand wines are served with your dinner.
Eastwood Hill Aboratum, beautiful beaches, winery, boutiques, golf courses, fishing rivers in close vincity.
We both enjoy travel, sports and meeting our guests.
Brochure available.
Directions: *Please ring for directions and reservations. Transfers available.*

251

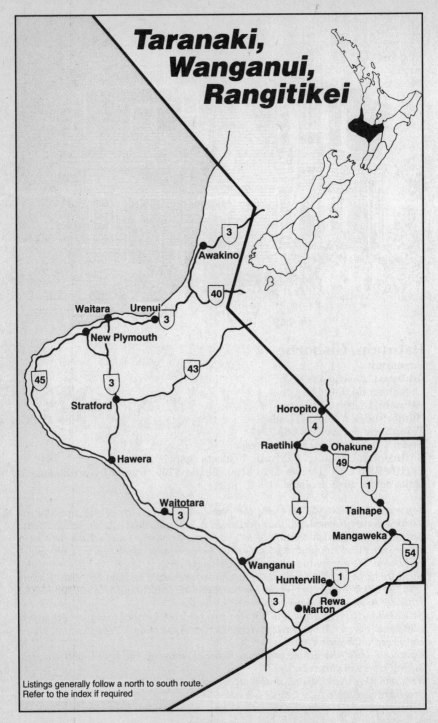

Taranaki, Wanganui, Rangitikei

Listings generally follow a north to south route.
Refer to the index if required

Awakino
Farmstay
Address: Maunganui Road, Awakino. Postal: Private Bag, Mokau
Name: Nawton and Sherryl Telfer
Telephone: (06) 752 9835 **Fax**: (06) 7529-849
Beds: 1 Double, 4 Single (3 bedrooms) **Bathroom**: 1 Guests share
Tariff: B&B (full) Double $50, Single $25, Dinner $15. Vouchers accepted.

*We have a coastal property carrying 6000 sheep, 600 cattle and 300 deer. The farm
surrounds the 1500 acre Stewart Russell native reserve.*
*We have a large five bedroom home, with an indoor heated swimming pool, spa
pool and sauna which is available at all times.*
All meals available. Lunch, morning and afternoon teas free.
Directions: *Please phone.*

GERALD BULL '92

Awakino
Homestay+Self-contained Cottage
Address: Awakino R.D., Mokau
Name: Eileen Knight
Telephone: (06) 752 9875
Beds: 1 Double, 2 Single (2 bedrooms),
plus self contained cottage
Bathroom: 1 Guests share
Tariff: B&B (full) Double $50, Single $30, Dinner $15, Children free Campervans
$20. Vouchers accepted.
Nearest Town: Equal distance Te Kuiti or Waitara

*Welcome to Awakino a comfortable drive to New Plymouth to the south, or Te
Kuiti's spectacular limestone country to the north. I love greeting strangers and
farewelling them as friends. I provide comfortable beds, bacon and eggs or fruit
and cereal breakfast. Also available farmstyle evening meals. In season there's
trout fishing or whitebaiting on the Awakino River, only yards from the house, or
surf-casting and spinning for kahawai at the rivermouth five minutes drive away.
Check out the spectacular drive through native bush to Waikawau beach with
access through a historic tunnel. If you prefer total relaxation enjoy my spacious,
though not always disciplined garden and share an interest in birds, fish and
flowers. For independent folk my warm and cosy cottage will sleep six people. It
is available long or short term. Enjoy a super spa, trampoline, tree hut etc.*
Directions: *2km north from Awakino township. First house on the right over the
Waikawau bridge. A hop, skip and jump from the Main Road.*

Urenui
Farmstay
Address: Beach Road Urenui **Postal:** RD 44
Name: Toon & Helen Welvaert
Telephone: (06) 752 3313 **Fax:** (06) 752 3476
Beds: 1 Double or 2 Single (1 Bedroom) **Bathroom:** 1 Ensuite
Tariff: B&B (full) Double $55, Single $30, Children $15, Dinner $20, Vouchers accepted
Nearest Town: Waitara

You are invited to join us and a menagerie of birds, bees, trees and 3 small children our 7 ha lifestyle block 35km north of New Plymouth.
Our property extends to a secluded beach called Honeymoon Bay, where you can swim, fish, stroll or just sit. Numerous beaches extend up and down to coast from here, and the Urenui River mouth with Domain and 9-hole golf course are just 1km down the road.
We also have high county horse trekking and the White Cliff walkway within 10 minutes drive from here.
Eat in with us, or out at one of 2 small restaurants in the village 2km away.
Directions: *2km north of Urenui on State Highway 3, turn seaward onto the Beach Rd (Direction Motor Camp) and we are about 200 metres down to the right hand side.*
There is nothing military about us, the sign 'Den Troop' on the gate is Flemish for 'The Tropics'.

Waitara
Farmstay
Address: Tikorangi Road, 43 R.D. Waitara
Name: John & Anne Megaw
Telephone: (06) 754 6768
Beds: 1 Double, 2 Single (2 bedrooms) **Bathroom:** 1 Guests share
Tariff: B&B (full) Double $55, Single $30, Dinner $15, Vouchers accepted
Nearest Town: Waitara

Our three bedroomed cosy brickhouse is situated on a hill with panoramic views of Mt Egmont, the Waitara River Valley farmlands and a glimpse of the sea and is 8 kilometres from Highway 3 turnoff.
We live on a dairy farm where we milk 180 cows, have tunnel houses for melons and courgette growing, and have shade houses for begonias and ferns. Visitors are welcome to participate in any farm activities, or wander to the river or up on the hills if they wish.
Taranaki has much to offer scenically with parks and gardens, the mountain and coastline plus numerous walkways. The McKee Energy Field, Waitara Petrolgas, and Motonui Synfuel Plants are all close to Waitara.
Directions: *Travel on Highway 3 to Waitara, turn inland to Tikorangi on Princess St to Ngatimaru Road. Continue to very end of Ngatimaru Road, 8 kms from turnoff Highway 3 and turn right on no exit road. Our house is second on the left.*

Always telephone ahead to enquire about a B&B. It is a nuisance for you if you simply arrive to find someone already staying there.
And besides hosts need a little time to prepare.

Waitara
Farmstay
Address: 2 Armstrong Ave, Stonehaven Gardens, Waitara
Name: Bev & George Moratti
Telephone & Fax: (06) 754-6164
Beds: 1 Double, 2 Single (2 bedrooms) **Bathroom:** 1 Guests share
Tariff: B&B (full) Double $55, Single $35, Dinner $15, Vouchers accepted
Nearest Town: Waitara 2kms. New Plymouth 10kms south.

STONEHAVEN GARDENS
Our 13 acre farmlet is situated on the outskirts of Waitara - 2 minutes from the shopping centre and 10 minutes from New Plymouth. We have a new home in pleasant and tranquil surroundings in one and a half acres of garden. A piedmontese beef stud takes up the rest of the property. We are keen horticulturalists and try to grow most of our own plants and shrubs.
The Petrochemical Industrial sites are only minutes away as are several beaches, walkways and picnic spots. We are interested in travel and enjoy meeting people from both within New Zealand and from overseas. Non-smokers preferred.
Directions: From SH3 turn onto Princess Street towards Waitara - 1st left at Armstrong Ave.

New Plymouth
Homestay
Address: 30 Heta Road, New Plymouth
Name: Gerry & Beryl Paulin
Telephone: (06) 758 2900
Beds: 1 Double, 2 Single (2 bedrooms) **Bathroom:** 1 Guests share
Tariff: B&B (full) Double $55, Single $35, Dinner $20, Vouchers accepted

Welcome to our home.
We are a newly retired couple so have time to look after you in a comfortable modern home in a quiet suburb with mountain, sea and rural views. We have been hosting with "The Book" since 1988 and have enjoyed meeting people from many countries. We look forward to sharing our home with you
We have travelled New Zealand from Cape Reinga to Stewart Island many times and will be able to help you plan your holiday.
We have also travelled extensively overseas and will enjoy hearing about your journeys.
As retired cut flower growers, our interests are gardens, horticulture generally and our own garden.
Gerry has a special interest in Pukeiti Rhododendron Trust Gardens and he relaxes on the golf course. Beryl enjoys needlework, knitting, floral art and cooking.
Directions: *Please phone*

New Plymouth

Homestay
Address: "Blacksmith's Rest",
481 Mangorei Road, New Plymouth
Name: Evelyn & Laurie Cockerill
Telephone: (06) 758 6090
Beds: 1 Queen, 3 Single (2 bedrooms)
Bathroom: 1 Private, 1 Family share (guests have priority)
Tariff: B&B (full) Double $50, Single $30, Dinner $17,
Children under 12 $15, Campervans welcome, Vouchers accepted

Welcome to New Plymouth.
Our home is situated on two acres next to New Plymouths well know Tupare gardens in a rural area but within the city boundary.
Taranaki is world renowned for its beautiful parks and gardens - the Pukeiti Rhododendron Trust gardens are only twenty five minutes drive away and Mt Egmont can be reached within 20 minutes.
As Laurie is a blacksmith / farrier we are interested in all aspects of horse sports. We have a large garden and also keep a few sheep.
We were both born and brought up in the South Island and have travelled widely around New Zealand and overseas and enjoy meeting people from all walks of life. We have a cat and a small dog which lives outside, as well as a small pony. There is plenty of off street parking.
Mangorei Road can be easily found from North or South off SH 3 when entering New Plymouth.

New Plymouth

Homestay
Address: 39 Plympton Street,
Brooklands, New Plymouth
Name: Neal Spragg: Brooklands B&B
Telephone: (06) 753 2265
Beds: 1 Double, 2 Single (2 bedrooms)
Bathroom: 1 Private
Tariff: B&B (full) Double $55, Single $35. Vouchers accepted.

My home is located in a peaceful and tranquil setting overlooking a bush clad walkway leading to the renowned Pukekura and Brooklands Parks. The guest wing consists of bathroom and toilet facilities, two bedrooms, one queen size and the other a twin room. I request no smoking in the house.
Being only minutes from central city you may choose to spend time at our museum, art gallery or library or perhaps take in a movie at the cinema complex. Also nearby and worthy of a visit are the sports stadium, aquatic centre, harbour and beaches.
Taranaki offers a unique diversity of attractions and landscapes, the picturesque Mount Egmont, expansive views of the Tasman Sea, beautiful parks, rhododendron gardens, rich dairy farmlands and energy fields.
I enjoy sharing my comfortable home with visitors from abroad and New Zealand travellers. I offer you a warm and friendly welcome and a relaxed stay in New Plymouth.

New Plymouth

Homestay
Address: 11 Tamati Place,
Merrilands, New Plymouth
Name: Ashley & Evelyn Howan
Telephone: (06) 758-8932
Beds: 1 Double, 4 Single (3 bedrooms)
Bathroom: 1 guests share
Tariff: B&B (full) Double $50, Single $30, Vouchers accepted

We welcome you to New Plymouth, and offer hospitality in a comfortable modern home, with an unobstructed view of Mount Egmont.
We are a newly retired couple who enjoy meeting and entertaining people from all countries. Our home is located in a quiet cul-de-sac.
Guests have their own shower, toilet and bathroom (spa bath). The beds have electric blankets and innerspring mattresses.
Taranaki has a host of things to do and see, being a popular tourist destination. All Taranaki's main attractions are within easy reach of New Plymouth.
We will provide either a continental or cooked breakfast. Evening meals can be enjoyed at your choice of a variety of good restaurants.
No pets please, and we request no smoking in the house.
We will do our best to make your stay enjoyable.

New Plymouth

Homestay
Self-contained Beach Cottage
Address: "River Glen",
313 Mangorei Road, New Plymouth
Name: Val & Martin Massey
Telephone: (06) 758-3995
Beds: 1 Double, 1 Single (1 bedroom)
Bathroom: 1 Private
Tariff: B&B (special) Double $50, Single$ 25, children 1/2 price, Dinner $15 by arrangement, Cottage price on application. Vouchers accepted.
Nearest Town: New Plymouth

We invite you to come and enjoy our hospitality, beneath the shadow of Mount Egmont, relax amid our beautiful lakes and gardens, or laze on our popular beaches.
Retired, with a grown-up family, we can spend time with our hobbies, growing flowers, craftwork and fishing. Our home is modest and comfortable, set on 4 acres within the city boundary, overlooking the Waiwhakaiho River.
The room has toilet and shower. Guests are invited to use our swimming and spa pools, games room and barbeque.
We offer a courtesy car to and from public transport, and scenic tours can be arranged.
Our Beach Cotttage is 20 minutes drive North of New Plymouth, with good fishing, river and sea swimming and adjacent golf course.
Breakfast is special and guests are invited to dine with us.
Directions: *Travelling North on State Highway 3, turn right in Mangorei Road. We are 2.2 km on right. Travelling South along Northgate, turn left at Mangorei lights, we are 2.8 km on left.*

New Plymouth
Farmstay
Address: "Mountain Dew" Farmstay,
606 Carrington Road,
R.D. 1, New Plymouth
Name: Marion & Geoff Rivers
Telephone: (06) 753-5123
Beds: 2 Double, 2 Single (2 bedrooms) **Bathroom:** 2 Private
Tariff: B&B (full) Double $70, Single $40, Dinner $18, Vouchers accepted weekdays.
Nearest Town: 12 km from New Plymouth

We live 12 km out overlooking New Plymouth city. Have extensive views over surrounding countryside with Mt Egmont (Taranaki) to the South and Tasman Sea to the North. On a clear day panoramic views of the central mountains can be enjoyed. Accommodation is upstairs and includes large lounge with balcony. Guests have s.c. kitchen, T.V.

We have a 160 acre (62 h.a.) dairy farm. Go walking in peaceful surroundings. Pleasant 1 hour walk or 10 min drive to world renowned Pukeiti Rhododendron Park. 5 mins to historic Hurworth Cottage, close to private zoo, 10 mins to 18 hole country golf course. Tramp in the National Park or climb the mountain. Great surf $ swimming beach 10 mins away. Indoor aquatic centre, historic Pa site nearby. Well travelled active outdoor hosts prepared to show guests around for small fee. Adults only. We are non-smokers and share our home with 2 lovely cats and sweet poodle.
Directions: *Please phone for reservation and directions. Courtesy car to plane, bus or city.*

New Plymouth
Homestay

BALCONIES BED & BREAKFAST

Address: 161 Powderham Street
New Plymouth
Name: 'Balconies'
Telephone: (06) 757 8866
Beds: 2 Double, 3 Single (3 bedrooms)
Bathroom: 1 Guests share
Tariff: B&B (special) Double $60, Single $40, Children under 15 yrs 1/2 price, Credit cards accepted, Vouchers accepted.
Nearest Town: Short walking distance to City centre

John and Annamarie welcome you to picturesque New Plymouth.
'Balconies' is situated just 1/2 km (5 minute walk) from the New Plymouth city shopping area. Our warm, comfortable 110 year old character-style manor offers three tastefully decorated guest rooms, large guest bathroom, separate toilet facilities and spacious lounge. The guest rooms are all downstairs, all beds have electric blankets and each room is electrically heated.
Within walking distance are the art gallery, library and museum, glass-blowing studio, Heritage Walkway, indoor pool complex and the beautiful Pukekura and Brooklands Parks.
After a comfortable nights sleep you will be served a generous fully cooked and / or continental breakfast.
We are also happy to provide complimentary refreshments, courtesy transport and laundry facilities. Ample off-street parking is available.
Join us, we look forward to your company, your comfort and satisfaction are No 1 to us. We are non-smokers who enjoy a drink or two and a good joke.

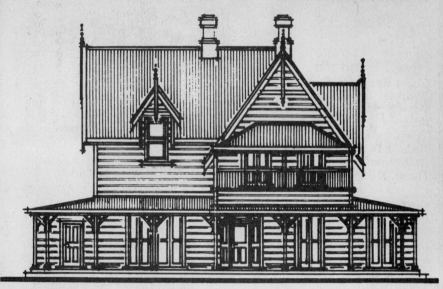

Henwood House - *Built 1890* -

New Plymouth
Colonial Homestead
Address: "Henwood House" 122 Henwood Road RD2 New Plymouth
Name: Lynne & Graeme Axten
Telephone: (06) 755 1212
Beds: 3 Queen, 4 Single (5 Bedrooms) **Bathroom:** 3 Ensuite, 1 Guests share
Tariff: B&B (full) Double $75-$90, Single $55-$70, Dinner $25. Credit cards:
Visa, M/C.
Nearest Town: New Plymouth 5km

Henwood House nestles in 2 acres of grounds featuring many mature native and exotic trees. The gracious colonial homestead built in 1890 has been restored by the owners who welcome guests to this rural retreat only minutes away from the city centre.

Relax in our grand lounge with its high ceilings, polished floors, panelling and two open fireplaces. Tall french doors open onto wide verandahs which overlook the gardens.

Upstairs are five spacious guest bedrooms (three with ensuite) furnished with quality beds and antique furniture. The Fitzroy Suite features its own fireplace and exclusive balcony with views over the countryside to the sea. Guests have a refrigerator and tea and coffee making facilities. Enjoy a leisurely breakfast served in our large country kitchen, continental or cooked.

We share our home with our 12 year old daughter Lauren, Basil a Golden Retriever and Smokey the cat. We ask guests not to smoke indoors. We look forward to meeting you.

Directions: *Henwood House is 3km up Henwood Road off State Highway 3 from Bell Block township.*

New Plymouth
Guest House
Address: 32 Carrington Street,
New Plymouth
Name: Carrington Guest House
Telephone: (06) 758 2375
Beds: 2 Double, 1 Single (3 bedrooms)
Bathroom: 1 Guests share
Tariff: B&B (continental) Double $58, Single $38, Children half price.

Ian and Linda invite you to stay with us in our comfortable house built around 1860.
Carrington Guest House is situated close to the heart of New Plymouth city and is just a short stroll to our beautiful Pukekura and Brooklands Parks.
Our home offers upstairs accommodation for guests consisting of 3 elegant bedrooms. All beds have electric blankets. Guests share bath / shower and toilet facilities. A large comfortable lounge with TV and video for relaxing and separate dining room.
Complimentary tea / coffee / milo / fruit juice and biscuits are available 24 hours. BBQ facilities and fenced swimming pool.
You will be served a continental breakfast offering a choice of fruit juice, cereals, fruit, toast and tea or coffee.
Off-street parking. Courtesy transport available.

Stratford
Homestay
Address: "Woodhill"
Mountain Road South (SH 3), RD23, Stratford
Name: John and Elaine Nicholls
Telephone: (06) 765-5497
Beds: 1 Double, 4 Single (3 bedrooms)
Bathroom: 1 Guests share
Tariff: B&B (full) Double $65, Single $40, Children $15; Dinner $25; Campervans $25 (up to 4 people), Vouchers accepted
Nearest Town: 46 km south of New Plymouth on State Highway 3

Come and enjoy the tranquility and beauty of the countryside in the heart of Taranaki. Our home is nestled in two acres of old English gardens and is over a hundred years old.
Each bedroom opens out onto the gardens and there is a separate guest bathroom. We offer you warmth, hospitality and a haven from the stresses of everyday life. After a generous, leisurely breakfast enjoy a walk in the gardens or a swim in our large, outdoor pool. In the evenings you are welcome to join us for dinner, or if you prefer there are several restaurants in Stratford.
Our home is only 3 km from Stratford and 15 km from the Stratford Mountain House.
Stratford offers a wide range of activities including a pleasant golf course, lawn bowls and all types of mountain sports. For garden enthusiasts there is the Taranaki trail of gardens of which our home is a participant.
Directions: *We are situated 3 km south of Stratford on State Highway 3, adjacent to the Ngaere railway overbridge.*

Stratford

Farmstay Bed and Breakfast &
Self-contained accommodation
Address: Stallard Farm, SH 3 Stratford Nth 1 km RD24
Name: Billie Anne & Corb Stallard
Telephone: (06) 765 8324
Beds: Comfortable Double, Twin and Single rooms, T.V. Electric blankets.
Bathroom: 1 Ensuite, 2 Guests share
Self-cont. 1 bedroom flat sleeps 4
Tariff: B&B (special) Double $60, Single $36, Children $15, Self service guest kitchen, Cot available. Credit Cards:Visa & M/C. Vouchers accepted.
Nearest Town: Stratford 1 kilometre

Built on the turn of the century, this elegant country house, with its extensive gardens and farm walks, offers Old English B&B in the true sense. BBQ. Boating on the lake.
Completely private if desired, making use of the fully equipped guest kitchen, or settle in as a home away from home. Local restaurants are excellent 1km.
The Aga cooker in the main kitchen ensures a warm glow throughout the house in winter, and provides a hearty cooked breakfast, or a light breakfast may be chosen. Complimentary tea and coffee, biscuits etc (continuous self-service). Laundry facilities (small charge). TV in rooms, Pooltable.
The area offers: Mt Egmont skiing 15 minutes; Trout fishing; Walkways; Museums; Golf, Houseboat trips; White water rafting; Famous gardens; Farm visits; Helicopter sightseeing; Shopping in Stratford local centre or just lazing. Free farm visit. Family all grown. Cat Fluffy lives outside.
Directions: *1 km Stratford, north on State Highway 3.*

Hawera

Address: Turuturu Rd., Hawera
Name: Ian & Diana Rowe
Telephone: (06) 278 4037
Beds: 1 Double, 2 Single (2 bedrooms)
Bathroom: 1 Family share
Tariff: B&B (full) Double $55, Single $35, Children $20, Dinner $20. Vouchers accepted.

We are a semi retired farming couple with an adult family of three boys all of whom have left home. Having retired from sheep and beef farming we now enjoy a small acreage and our new home five minutes out of Hawera.
Hawera and the surrounding district offer many attractions. The renowned Tawhiti Museum is 3 minutes away, Mt Egmont, the beautiful Lake Rotorangi, two good golf courses and others with a few miles, bowling clubs, bridge club. The Annual Taranaki Rhododendron Festival is a very popular attraction, many of the lovely gardens in and around Hawera.
We both enjoy people, bridge, golf, bowls, craft and farming activities.
Please phone for directions.

Hawera
Homestay
Address: Wynyard Street
Normanby, Hawera
Name: Noeline & Eddie Bradley
Telephone: (06) 272 8206
Beds: 1 Double, 2 Single (2 Bedrooms upstairs)
Bathroom: 1 Guests share
Tariff: B&B (full) Double $60, Single $35, Dinner $20.
Vouchers accepted.
Nearest Town: Hawera

Our home is centrally situated just off State Highway 3 - only 6 kilometres north of Hawera. It is in a semi-rural area, handy to town, restaurants etc, yet peaceful and quiet. We have a few acres where we rear calves.
We are active semi-retired (sheep and dairy) farmers who know the district well. Local scenic tours and farm visits could be arranged and advice given about local points of interest.
Hawera is a farming centre the home of the large Kiwi Dairy Company, it is also the centre for the many other attractions of South Taranaki - lakes and mountain walks (Mount Egmont is less than 30 minutes away), an excellent museum, garden tours especially October / November Rhododendron Festival etc.
There are several fine golf courses, many bowling greens and a local racecourse. We both enjoy sport - we also enjoy meeting people.
Please phone for directions.

Hawera
Farmstay
Address: "Riverlea Downs" Wirihana Rd
(PO Box 227 Hawera)
Name: Marian & John Murphy
Telephone: (06) 278 7864
Beds: 1 Queen, 1 Double, 1 Single (2 Bedrooms
/Brm 1:1 Queen+1 Single, Brm 2: 1 Double)
Bathroom: 2 Private
Tariff: B&B (full) Double $60, Single $40, Children $25, Dinner $25pp,
Vouchers accepted
Nearest Town: Hawera

Welcome to South Taranaki Heartland.
We live on a dairy farm approx 5 mins from the township of Hawera situated midway between New Plymouth and Wanganui on State Highway 3.
Our spacious home with its upstairs guest area is set in sheltered tranquil grounds with vistas of Mt Egmont.
Sth Taranaki has many attractions including 3 golf courses within 15 mins drive. The close proximity of our majestic mountain with its bush walks, climbing and skiing. Numerous beautiful gardens to visit a feature of our province.
Hawera offers a choice of bistros and restaurants.
Please phone for reservations and directions.

Waitotara

Farmstay
+ Self-Contained Accommodation
Address: Ashley Park, PO Box 36,
Waitotara, Wanganui
Name: Barry Pearce and Wendy Bowman
Telephone: (06) 346-5917, Fax: (06) 346 5861
Beds: 1 Double, 4 Single (3 bedrooms) **Bathroom:** 1 Guests share
Tariff: B&B (full) Double $60, Single $40; Dinner $20; Power points for caravans and campervans with full facilities; Cabins available; Self-contained unit for 7 people; Two fully equipped motels, each sleeping 5. Double $65, Vouchers accepted

We are 2 km from Waitotara village and 8 km to the beach. We have a mixed farm, sheep cattle, deer and cropping. We have a large, comfortable home set in an attractive garden with a swimming pool and avaries with exotic birds and pheasants. Also in the garden is an antique and craft shop which also serves Devonshire teas and sandwiches from 9 am_5 pm daily.
Situated 100 metres from the house and garden is a 4-acre park of native and English trees, surrounding a picturesque lake with waterfowl.
We like to serve New Zealand fare and hope you enjoy the tranquility of the countryside. Guests are welcome to observe farm activities where possible and there are scenic drives locally.
Directions: *We are situated 32 km north of Wanganui and 12 km south of Waverley on State Highway 3.*

Wanganui

Homestay
Address: 156 Great North Road Wanganui
Name: Janet Dick
Telephone: (06) 345 8951
Beds: 2 Single (1 Bedroom) **Bathroom:** 1 Private
Tariff: B&B (continental) Double $55, Single $35, Dinner by special arrangement, Vouchers accepted, Cooked breakfast on request
Nearest Town: Wanganui

My home is a four year old Lockwood set amongst mature trees, two kilometres from the centre of Wanganui on the main Wanganui / New Plymouth Highway.
I have travelled extensively overseas and enjoy meeting and conversing with people from all countries. I have a small flower growing business and my many interests include sport, tramping, gardening, bridge and travel.
Wanganui has many attractions including excellent golf courses and sporting facilities the Regional Museum and superb Serjeant Art Gallery and the scenic Wanganui River which offers something for everyone from sedate paddle steamers cruises to kayaking the rapids. Or take a day trip by jet boat to see the famous Bridge to Nowhere, the Drop Scene and the Settlement of Jerusalem. Wanganui also has a good variety of restaurants, both licensed and BYO.
I look forward to meeting you.
Directions: *2km up SH 3 from Wanganui towards New Plymouth.*

Horopito - Tongariro National Park

Homestay (B&B or self-catering) + Self-contained Accommodation
Address: Matapuna Road, Horopito, R.D. 6, Raetihi
Name: Conon & Jackie Fraser
Telephone: (06) 385-4495
Beds: 2 Double, 4 Single (2 bedrooms)
Bathroom: 2 Ensuite
Tariff: B&B (continental, full) Double $82-$90, Single $66-$70, Dinner $15-20, Children half price, No B&B during ski season, self-catering only. Campervans welcome $20 up to 4 people.
Self-contained cottage: 1 Double, 6 Single (3 bedrooms), full facilities, self-catering. Tariff: $25 per adult, chn half: min. hire $125 per night. 10% discount midweek, 20% out of ski season. One day free for a whole week's stay. Vouchers accepted.
Nearest Town: Raetihi & Ohakune, both 16km

Our recently built, warm and comfortable home is right on the boundary of Tongariro National Park. The two guest rooms, one with its own balcony, are spacious and have glorious views of Mount Ruapehu. Extensive decking overlooks the Park.
We have 3 hectares of beautiful bush, pond, streams and paddocks with a few sheep and ducks.
Guests sometimes prefer to bring their own sleeping bags and to cook their own meals in our kitchen, which has two sinks, a microwave and two ovens and we reduce the tariff accordingly to $25 per person - minimum hire per room $75, or $50 out of the ski season.
Both Mounts Ruapehu and Taranaki can be seen from our self-contained and comfortable cottage. Table tennis and a Pool table are in the barn, and there is a sandpit and indoor family games and books.
We are in our early 60s and our children have all left home. We enjoy our environment of beech forest and mountain, tramping, bird-watching, writing and photography. We know New Zealand well and enjoy having people to stay.
Write for leaflet or phone. We are 2.2km from S.H. 4 and are easy to find.

Horopito

Self-contained Farmstay Accommodation
Address: "Lahar", Matapuna Rd, Horopito, Raetihi
Name: Brent & Noeline Bishop
Telephone: (06) 385 4136
Beds: 2 Double, 3 Single (2 Bedrooms) Cot available **Bathroom:** 1 Private
Tariff: B&B (basket) Double $80, Single $60, Additional adult $20, Children half
price, Dinner $20, Campervans $25, Vouchers accepted
Nearest Town: Raetihi or Ohakune both 16km

*"Lahar Farm" (1,400 acres) offers you the rural NZ that few get to experience,
inland high country splendour (3,000ft), volcanic majesty, native podocarp forest,
pristine mountain streams, native birds, guided hunting, enjoy pure unsullied
spring water, idyllic farm pasture peppered with the ongoings of farm animals.
For those who choose to do more than just rest, read and feed, Lahar bounds the
Tongariro World Heritage / Cultural National Park; an adventure and nature
tourism area.*

*Lahar's Log Chalet is built with privacy and luxurious self-sufficiency in mind,
secluded within its own bush clearing, a minute's drive away across our farmland.
An aura of calmness is created by the hand scribed Douglas Fir logs. The ground
floor kitchen is fully equipped with adjacent dining and lounge area, two spacious
tastefully appointed bedrooms open off the hand-crafted log stairway. A breakfast
basket is available and you may choose to enjoy genuine country hospitality at an
evening meal with us and our family.*

Directions: Only 2km off State Highway 4, please phone.

Raetihi

Farmstay
Address: State Highway 4, P O Box 91, Raetihi
Name: Brian & Pixie Chambers
Telephone: (06) 385 4310
Beds: 2 Single (1 Bedroom) **Bathroom:** 1 Private
Tariff: B&B (full) Double $60, Single $35, Dinner $20. Vouchers accepted

Our four children have left home to pursue their own careers and we now enjoy making new friends and sharing our lives with them.
We have a 1600 acre farm on which we run sheep, cattle and deer.
There is an outdoor swimming pool, set in idyllic garden surroundings and an indoor spa pool for the cooler season. As we both enjoy gardening, our home is set in gracious, peaceful surroundings, with a panoramic view of mountains and farmland. This is often described by visitors as a "million dollar view". One of the first pleasures you will notice is the crisp, clear, mountain air.
We are 30 minutes from the Turoa Ski Resort and scenic mountain drive. There is also a lovely golf course to enjoy nearby.
Brian runs his own stock and station business and enjoys taking visitors with him on his trips to buy stock from farmers in the district.
Accommodation is twin bedroom, with private shower and toilet.
Directions: *1 km North of Raetihi.*

Raetihi

Farmstay, Shearers Quarters
Address: Pipiriki Road, R.D. 4, Raetihi
Name: Ken & Sonia Robb
Telephone: (06) 385-4581
Beds: 1 Double, 2 Single (2 bedrooms) **Bathroom:** 1 Ensuite, 1 Family share
Tariff: B&B (full) Double $60, Single $35, Children 1/2 price, Dinner $20, Vouchers accepted.

We welcome you to our 1,000 acres of hill country farm in the quiet, picturesque Mangaeturoa Valley just 10 minutes from Raetihi where Ken runs Romney sheep and Simmental cattle.
Our home is set in a spacious garden to which native NZ birds love to visit and offers superb views of the surrounding countryside and Mt Ruapehu.
Our interests include travel, flying, photography and gardening. There are many activities available locally throughout the year, skifields, jetboating from Pipiriki on the Wanganui river, scenic tramps or maybe a farm tour with Ken if your time permits.
Your accommodation is a double room with very comfortable queen bed and feather duvet and ensuite. Twin room has share facilities with your hosts. A cot is available and there is a spa pool which guests are welcome to use. Dinners are prepared from home grown meat and vegetables served with NZ wine. Cooked or continental breakfast.
We are 6 1/2 km from Raetihi pn Pipiriki Road.

Continental breakfast consist of fruit, toast, tea/coffee,
Full breakfast is the same with a cooked course,
Special breakfast has something special.

Ohakune
Homestay/Farmstay
Address: "Mitredale",
Smiths Road, Ohakune
Name: Audrey and Diane Pritt
Telephone: (06) 385 8016
Beds: 1 Double, 2 Single (2 bedrooms)
Bathroom: 1 Family share
Tariff: B&B (continental) Double $60,
Single $35, Children - 25%;
Dinner $20, Campervans $20,
Vouchers accepted
Nearest Town: Ohakune 6 km, Raetihi 9 km

We are farmers who farm sheep and bull beef in a beautiful peaceful valley with magnificent views of Mt Ruapehu.

The Waimarino is an excellent area for holidaying summer or winter. Tongariro National Park offers excellent walks, opportunities for photography and great skiing at Turoa and Whakapapa. The rivers offer good sport for fishermen and an excellent 18-hole golf course only 3 km from our door.

We are keen members of the Conservation body Ducks Unlimited. We have two guest-rooms - one with two single beds, the other a double bed. All equipped with electric blankets.

The home is heated with a log-fire and open fire - excellent for drying gear after a day's skiing, a comfortable, cosy atmosphere to relax in.

We offer dinner with the traditional farmhouse fare or just breakfast - gives you the opportunity to sample our excellent home-made jams.

We enjoy sharing our lifestyle with others so come and spend some time on the farm.

Directions: *Take the Raetihi Road (State Highway 49) at Ohakune Hotel corner, travel 4 km to Smiths Road, second side road on the left. An unsealed road. We are the last house 2 km at the end of the road.*

Ohakune

Self-contained Accommodation
Address: "South Fork" 3209 Raetihi-Ohakune Road, Ohakune
Name: Noeline & Trevor Reynolds
Telephone & Fax: (06) 385-8412
Beds: 1 Double, 6 Single (3 bedrooms) Bathroom: 2 Private
Tariff: B&B (full) Double $70, Single $40, Dinner $25, Children $20. Vouchers accepted.
Nearest Town: Ohakune

"South Fork" is sited on 11 acres of quiet park-like grounds with close-up views of Mt Ruapehu. A good half way stop between Auckland and Wellington.

Our self-contained luxury accommodation includes kitchen, dining, lounge with extensive golf course and garden views, plus T.V. There are two bedrooms; one with a double bed, and an alcove with 2 single beds. And a third bedroom with 4 beds. Also included are full bathroom and laundry facilities. The kitchen has quality fittings throughout.

You are welcome to wander around our spacious gardens. Activities in our area include skiing in winter, scenic mountain walks, Jet boating, white water rafting, sailing, trout fishing and horse trekking. We are happy to advise on others.

Directions: *From Waiouru on S.H.1, turnoff to Ohakune. Turn left at the BP Fuel Station travel about 5 km to a reflectorised hanging sign reading "South Fork" on your left. Proceed up the tree-lined drive.*

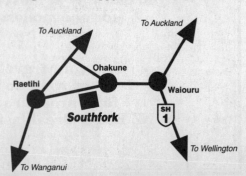

Taihape

Homestay
Address: 12 Lark Street, Taihape
Name: Jack and Joyce Gilbert
Telephone: (06) 388-0915
Beds: 2 Single (1 bedroom)
Bathroom: 1 Family share, (separate toilet)
Tariff: B&B (full) Double $60, Single $35, Dinner $20. Vouchers accepted

We are a retired farming couple with a grown up family. We offer you a warm and friendly welcome to our home which is surrounded by a large garden of flowering shrubs and roses.

Our home, situated on the hill, has panoramic views of extensive farmlands with the Ruahine Ranges in the background. Our guest room has twin beds with electric blankets. Dinner would be by arrangement.

Taihape, situated on SH1, is only 2 hours 30 mins drive from either Wellington or Rotorua. A one hour drive would take you to the Ruapehu Ski Fields or Lake Taupo (renowned for its trout fishing). We can arrange a farm visit, tramping, all types of rafting and jet boating. Titoki Point Gardens or Cross Hills Rhododendron Gardens are well worth a visit.

Our son runs the home farm (700 hectares) of sheep, cattle.

Our hobbies are spinning (Coopworth fleece), knitting and gardening. We have no cats, dogs or small children.

Taihape

Homestay
Address: "Korirata", 25 Pukeko Street, Taihape
Name: Patricia & Noel Gilbert
Telephone: (06) 388 0315
Beds: 4 Single (2 bedrooms, electric blankets on every bed)
Bathroom: 1 Guests share
Tariff: B&B (special) Double $60, Single $40, Primary children half price, Dinner $20, Campervans facilities available, Credit cards accepted, Vouchers accepted

A warm welcome to Taihape, where we are situated on top of the hill with panoramic views of Mt. Ruapehu, the Ruahines and extensive farming country. Warmth and comfort is a feature in tranquil surroundings for instant relaxation. The entire section - three-quarters-of-an-acre - has been landscaped with shrubs, hydroponic and orchid houses, and a large area planted in chrysanthemums. Dinner and lunch are available on request and almost all types of meals are available. Meals with hosts using our home grown produce - cooking is a hobby. Separate toilet and bathroom available for guests. Farm visits, tramping, rafting, fishing, bunjee jumping and jet boating can be arranged and most are within 1/ 2 hour. One hour to Ruapehu (skiing), one hour to Lake Taupo, 2 1/2 hours to Rotorua or Wellington, 40 minutes to Titoki Point and other well known gardens. Noel has retired from the farm to horticulture and Pat teaches.
Directions: *Please phone.*

One of the differences between staying at a hotel and a B&B
is that you don't hug the hotel staff when you leave.

Taihape
Farmstay
Address: Utiku South Road, Utiku, Taihape
Name: Blair and Dot McLeod
Telephone: (06) 388 0439
Beds: 1 Double, 1 Single (2 bedrooms) **Bathroom:** 1 Private, 1 Family share
Tariff: B&B (full) Double $70, Single $40, Dinner $25, Vouchers accepted
Nearest Town: Taihape 11 kms

Welcome to our piece of clean green NZ.
We are: Conveniently situated between Taupo and Wellington.
Just one kilometre off State Highway 1
Owners of 1200 acres of sheep / cattle breeding hill country.
Interested in breeding and training sheepdogs, spinning and knitting,
gardening, travelling and meeting people.

We offer: A warm, sunny, cozy, smoke-free home.
Stunning rural and mountain range views
Very comfortable, warm beds
A relaxing, tranquil stopover
Delicious 3 course meals using home cooking and farm produce
Complimentary morning or afternoon tea
Kiwi hospitality - Dot is a Kiwi Host
Breakfast in bed if desired.

You can: Get away from the rush and hustle
Roam on the farm & experience farm life (with a packed lunch if required)
Wander in the garden and absorb the views
Or take advantage of more adventurous activities the region offers
- bungy jumping, white water rafting, mountain flights, etc.
Please phone in advance as late bookings are sometimes not convenient.

Taihape
Homestay
Address: "Papa Pottery and B&B"
24 Huia Street, Taihape
Name: Lindsay and Cathy Baine
Telephone: (06) 388 0318
Beds: 3 Double, 3 Single (4 bedrooms)
Bathroom: 1 Guests share
Tariff: B&B (special) Double $60, Single $35, Children $15, Dinner $20, Visa, Mastercard, Bankcard accepted, Vouchers accepted

We are a young couple and have recently moved from Wellington to operate a pottery studio. You may enjoy watching pots created during your stay.
Built as a doctors residence, our lovely 1910 two storey home, is situated near the centre of Taihape. Taihape is an ideal stop over between Auckland and Wellington. It has many attractions to offer; for example, rafting, bungy jumping, trout fishing, jet boating, kayaking, and excellent golf courses are all close at hand. We are also centrally placed for visits to the many famous gardens of the Rangitikei region, and only one hours drive to Turoa Skifields.
We offer you a warm and comfortable stay. Lunch and dinner can be provided by arrangement and we cater for vegetarians as well. Being non-smokers we ask that guests refrain from smoking indoors.
We look forward to having you stay with us.
Directions: *Huia Street - turn at the Post Office.*

Mangaweka
Farmstay/Self-contained Accm.
Address: "Mairenui Farm Holidays",
Ruahine Road, Mangaweka 5162
Name: Sue and David Sweet
Telephone & Fax: (06) 3825 564
Beds: 2 Double, 2 Single (3 bedrooms) Bathroom: 2 Ensuite, 1 Family share
Tariff: B&B (special) Double $95, Single $62, Dinner $28, Campervans: $5 per
person. Credit Cards: Visa, M/C. Vouchers accepted.
Nearest Town: Mangaweka

*We have a sheep and cattle farm situated on a scenic through route from
Mangaweka to Palmerston North. As well as the farm animals we have two cats
and Benji, the lovable cockerspaniel.*

*Two rooms have their own verandahs and ensuite bathrooms, the double with a
sunken bath, the twin with ensuite shower and toilet. Each room has tea and coffee
making facilities, and home-baked biscuits are provided.*

*We have a concrete tennis court, horse riding, farm walks and river swimming. We
can arrange trout fishing, white water rafting, jet boating, bungy jumping and
garden visits, with Titoki Point, Cross Hills, Rathmoy and The Ridges nearby.
Alternatively we offer you a peaceful rest in the beautiful countryside!*

*There is an excellent cuisine, and good New Zealand wines are provided.
Complimentary pre-dinner drinks are served in the comfortable living room in
front of a roaring maire fire or on the large sunny verandah. Filter coffee, espresso
or capuccino are specialities of the house. We enjoy meeting people of all
nationalities and both French and German are spoken.*

*Self-contained architect-designed accommodation sleeps 4. Everything provided
except food & drink. Catered meals available at homestead. Tariff $70 Double,
$15 each extra person.*

Directions: *The farm is situated 12 km from Mangaweka and 84 km from
Palmerston North on Ruahine Road (look for the teal and yellow Heritage Trail
sign on SH1 turn-off). We are 3 hours from Wellington or Rotorua.*

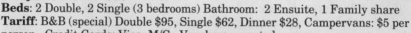

Tell other travellers about your favourite B&Bs

Mangaweka
Farmstay
Address: 'Cairnmuir Farmstays',
State Highway 1, Mangaweka
Name: David and Elizabeth Buchanan
Telephone: (06) 382-5878
Beds: 1 Double, 2 Single (2 bedrooms) **Bathroom**: 2 Private
Tariff: B&B (full) Double $95, Single $55, Dinner $28, Children by negotiation,
Vouchers accepted
Nearest Town: Taihape 16 kms South, Mangaweka 5 kms North

*Our country home is situated conveniently on Highway 1 and offers you a
comfortable, relaxed, and fun-filled time. We live on a 735 hectare sheep & cattle,
steep hill-country property with panoramic views of the Rangitikei district.*
*Our attractively decorated and spacious home has a welcoming atmosphere. The
open fire and pleasant living room gives everyone time to share pre-dinner drinks
and absorb the rural lifestyle.*
*Massed plantings of flowers, trees, and shrubs are a haven for bellbirds and tuis,
with waterfowl appreciating the landscaped ponds.*
*We enjoy sharing our horticultural interests with others and several gardens of
world renown are within easy driving distance.*
*Cairnmuir cuisine is noted for its excellence and flair, using home-grown produce.
Quality NZ wines are provided. Special coffees and tea are served with oven fresh
baking and there is a breakfast of your choice.*
*Mangaweka has unique opportunities for all to have a restful break from city life
- trout fishing, white water rafting, jet boating, bungy jumping, golf, bush walks,
or tennis on our concrete court.*
"A treat of a life time. We leave so that we may return"
- F. Guiliano, U.S.A.

Hunterville

Self-Contained Accommodation
Address: "Otairi", RD 2, Hunterville
Name: David and Vicky Duncan
Telephone: (06) 322 8027
Beds: 1 Double, 8 Single (6 bedrooms) Bathroom: 3 Guests share
Tariff: B&B (continental) Price on application
Nearest Town: Hunterville

We invite you to say in "Otamaire", a lovely architect designed 50 year old home set in landscaped gardens, 15 minutes off State Highway One. "Otamaire" was until recently our home and is part of an historic sheep and beef cattle station of 12,000 acres which has been farmed by four generations of the Duncan family. We have moved to the 100 year old homestead 1 km away and "Otamaire" is available to guests who wish to have the privacy of the self-catering option with all comforts and still be part of a farming operation. The house is large and well appointed. Spa bath, dishmaster, automatic laundry, television, gas fired AGA cooker, wall panel electric heaters, open fires (wood supplied), fully carpeted, linen, towels and all other requirements. Daily delivery from Hunterville. Housekeeping services available on request.

The garden has roses, mature trees, sweeping lawns and a grass tennis court. All well maintained. There is a stable complex and reliable mounts and good rides can be arranged. The Turakina River runs behind the house with good swimming holes. Other activities could include garden tours of well known Rangitikei Gardens, "Rathmoy", "The Ridges", Cross Hills, Westoe and Titoki especially in the spring. Nearby Lake Namunamu is a 20 minutes walk away for swimming, row boats, & trout fishing.

We are 2 1/2 hours from Wellington, 2 1/2 hours from Taupo, 1 hour from Palmerston North, 1 hour from Wanganui, 1 1/2 hours from Ruapehu Skifield, 1/2 hour from Rangitikei River for rafting, trout fishing and jet boating and bunji jumping.

Please phone for precise directions, brochures and tariffs.

Please let your hosts know if you have to cancel.
They will have spent time preparing for you.

---

*V*ENNELL'S
FARM STAY
HOMESTEAD ACCOMMODATION

Hunterville
Farmstay
Address: Vennell's Farmstay,
Rewa, R.D.
Name: Phil & Oriel Vennell
Telephone: (06) 328-6780 or if no reply try 328-6769
Beds: 1 Queen, 4 Single (3 bedrooms - electric blankets)
Bathroom: 1 Ensuite with Queen, 1 Guests share.
Tariff: B&B (full) Double $80, Single $40, Dinner $25 includes
complimentary pre-dinner drinks, Children welcome.
Nearest Town: Hunterville

*We are third generation farmers on a sheep, cattle and cropping hill country farm.
Our spacious, modern and comfortable home is in a tranquil setting of mature
trees and garden with swimming pool. We have a family room with pool table and
cosy living room with a large open fire. Beautiful rural views can be seen from our
home and surrounding hills. We are situated just off State Highway One near
Hunterville on the scenic route to Feilding and in the centre of Rangitikei Private
Gardens. We are 3 hours drive from Rotorua, 1 1/2 hours from Mt Ruapehu
skifields, 2 1/2 hours from Wellington and 30 minutes from Manfield motor
sports, equestrian and Fielddays.. Trout fishing, rafting, jet boating, bungy
jumping can all be enjoyed on the nearby Rangitikei river.*
*Our interests include current affairs, fishing, boating, gardening, sport, general.
Collection from public transport arranged.*
*We love sharing our home with friends. Approved Farmstay hosts since 1980.
Longer stays welcome.*
Directions: *Please phone for directions.*

Hunterville
Farmstay
Address: "Homecroft", R.D. 5, Hunterville (Please phone)
Name: Kathryn & Philson Marsh
Telephone: (06) 322 9890
Beds: 2 Single (1 bedroom - extra beds in separate room can be arranged)
Bathroom: Family share
Tariff: B&B (full) Double $60, Single $35, Children 1/2 price, Dinner $20,
Vouchers accepted
Nearest Town: 12 km North of Hunterville, 1 min from SH1

*We have three young children and offer true "home" hospitality. You can take part
in family activities or be alone if you so wish. We farm 1100 acres, running sheep
and cattle and guests are welcome to participate or observe farm activities, or to
just relax and enjoy the unique scenery that the Rangitikei valley offers. Heli-
jetting, Jet-boating (Philson drives for a local tourist operation), horse riding,
bungy-jumping, scenic flights and some of New Zealands best gardens are all
within 10-20 mins, as are fishing, golfing, and swimming opportunities. The
Turoa ski-field is one hour north, Wellington 2 hours south.*
*Our home is a warm, spacious and traditional farmhouse set amongst established
trees and garden. We are flexible and mindful of individual guests needs. Picnic
hampers and lunches can be provided at a moment's notice.*
Please phone for directions.

Hunterville
Farmstay
Address: 'Drysdale', RD2, Hunterville
Name: Sharon and Bernard Lilburn
Telephone: (06) 322 8595 **Fax:** (06) 322 8392
Mobile: 025 425 913
Beds: 1 Double, 2 Single (2 bedrooms) **Bathrooms:** 1 Ensuite, 1 Family share
Tariff: B&B (full) Double $60, Single $35, Children half price, Dinner $25, Campervans $10, Credit cards accepted, Vouchers accepted
Nearest Town: Hunterville

'Drysdale' is a lovely, large, turn of the century homestead with spacious mature gardens and an asphalt tennis court. Part of a 2100 ha hill country property set in the Turakina Valley, 25kms pleasant drive off SH.1 from Hunterville.
We are pleased to be able to share our well heated and spacious home and this beautiful valley with visitors. We have 3 young children and enjoy meeting people. Having both travelled extensively we are now able to repay some of the kindness shown to us in our travels.
We are 5th generation farmers of the property, that offers much to the traveller in the way of walks, native scenery or the chance to just be restful!
There is action with jetboating, bungi jumping, river rafting, golfing (all 35-45 minutes) and skiing (1 hour to Turoa). We are also close to five public gardens (30-60 minutes).
Electric blankets on beds. Dinner by arrangement. Separate bathroom and shower.
Directions: *Please phone.*

The standard of accommodation in *The New Zealand Bed and Breakfast Book*
ranges from homely to luxurious,
but you can always be sure of superior hospitality.

Marton
Farmstay
Address: "Tataramoa",
R.D. 2, Howie Road, Marton
Name: Janice and Des Gower
Telephone: (06) 327- 8778
Beds: 1 Double, 6 Single (4 bedrooms)
Bathroom: 2 Guests share.
Tariff: B&B (continental) $35 per person, Small children half price, Dinner $18 per person, Light snack on request, BYO. Vouchers accepted.

Tataramoa is a 138 year old large wooden homestead set in peaceful landscaped gardens, surrounded by spacious beautiful mature New Zealand bush filled by many native birds. We have 1000 acres on which we run sheep, cattle and deer and we also have cropping paddocks. There are great opportunities for interesting walks around the flats, hills and valleys.
Centre of garden and heritage homes. Close to Palmerston North and Wanganui. We have a friendly and homely atmosphere with a very welcome cosy log fire. Traditional New Zealand farm roast dinner with private lounge or billiard room if preferred. We enjoy opening our home to visitors from all over the world, with ample space for you to relax and unwind. Tataramoa welcomes you.
Directions: *From Marton township turn at Westpac to Wanganui for 3 miles. Turn right at Fern Flats Road proceed and turn left at Waimutu Road. Proceed until 'Tataramoa" signpost. Farm at end of road through avenue of trees.*

Marton
Farmstay
Address: "Dunollie"
Bonny Glen RD2, Marton
Name: Melva McDougall
Telephone: (06) 327 6771
Beds: 1 Double, 2 Single, (2 bedrooms)
Bathroom: 1 Family share
Tariff: B&B (full) Double $50, Single $30, Dinner $20, Vouchers accepted
Nearest Town: Marton

My home is the one we built 34 years ago; sunny and spacious with a pleasant garden. Our son Peter runs the farm, he has 220 milking cows which are milked in a modern rotary milking shed. We have calves and sheep and some grain (wheat and barley) is grown.
I have 2 cats, and a dozen red hens. I am interested in spinning, weaving and pottery.
Rangitikei District is noted for its gardens; there are several that I can arrange for you to see if you wish.
We are 20 miles from Wanganui, 35 minutes from Palmerston North and two and a quarter hours from Wellington.
Welcome to our district.
Directions: *Please phone*

Marton

Historic Home, Farmstay + Self-contained Accommodation
Address: "Maungaraupi", Leedstown Road, RD 1, Marton
Name: Ken and Hilary Cavanagh
Telephone: (06) 327 7820 **Fax:** (06) 327 8619
Beds: 4 Double, 2 Single (5 bedrooms)
Bathroom: 3 Ensuite, 1 Guests share
Tariff: B&B (full) Double $90 - $120, Single $50. Dinner $25.
Vouchers accepted
Nearest Town: Marton or Hunterville. On State Highway One 15 minutes
north of Bulls, 10 minutes south of Hunterville.

Let Historical Maungaraupi take you back to an era when life was enjoyed in good style.

Hilary and Ken invite you to come and experience a unique lifestyle of a 10,000 square foot two storey tudor style home set in five acres of native bush, extensive lawns and lovely gardens. Enjoy the romantic touch of strutting peacocks, doves and abundant native bird life, savour the extensive view of the Ruahine Ranges and rolling farm land, relax in front of one of the open fireplaces, and dine in style at a 16 seat antique five legged Kauri table.

Built in 1906 of quality native timbers with 11 bedrooms, a huge farmhouse kitchen, magnificent entrance hall and stairway, billiard room, library, turret, schoolroom, and wide sweeping verandahs, you can relish an almost forgotten bygone era.

The guest rooms are sunny and attractive with electric blankets on all beds. Three double rooms have ensuite bathrooms, and one has its own private balcony.

Adjoining the homestead is a self-contained unit with modern facilities and Kent fire. Sleeping accommodation for six. Meals can be arranged with your hosts if that is your preference.

The atmosphere at Maungaraupi is friendly and relaxed and guests are free to relax about the house, take a bush or farm walk, play billiards, tennis or croquet or travel a short distance to play golf, visit well-known gardens, or fish, white water raft or jetboat on the scenic Rangitikei River. Take a guided fly fishing trip to trout filled pools, try pig hunting, or a deer stalking safari for that experience of a lifetime. Mount Ruapehu's Turoa Skifield is 1.5 hours drive away, Wanganui 30 minutes, Palmerston North 40 minutes, and Marton or Hunterville 10 minutes. There isn't anywhere quite like breathtaking grand Maungaraupi, a gift from the past, a tribute to an era when style was the thing.

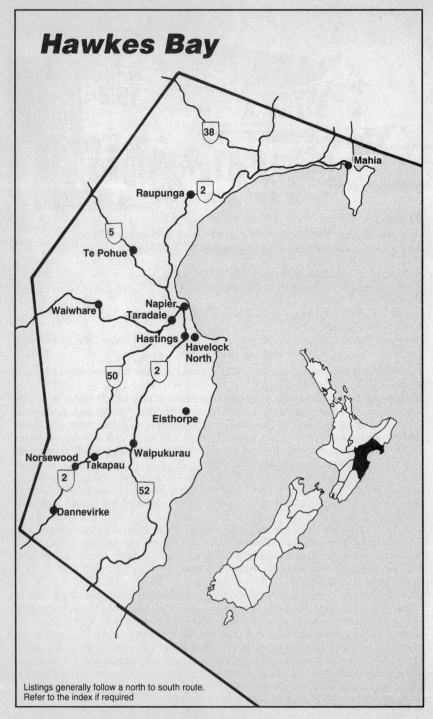

Hawkes Bay

Listings generally follow a north to south route.
Refer to the index if required

Mahia

Farmstay/Self-contained Accommodation
Address: Tunanui Farmstay,
Tunanui Road, Opoutama-Mahia
Name: Ray and Leslie Thompson
Telephone: (06) 837 5790
Beds: 2 Double, 2 Single, (2 bedrooms) **Bathroom:** 1 Private
Tariff: B&B (full) Double $60, Single $40, Dinner $25, Children reduced rate,
Cot and highchair available. Reasonable weekly rates on request. Campervans
welcome $20. Horse riding $20pp per hour. Vouchers accepted.
Nearest Town: Wairoa 50km, Opoutama store and petrol station 6km, Mahia
Beach store 12km

*Our family of four, farm a hill-country property of 3200 acres running sheep and
beef, overlooking the beautiful Mahia Peninsula. We enjoy meeting people and a
warm friendly welcome awaits you.*
*Our fully self-contained chalet-type holiday home is set in our large landscaped
gardens with sea views.*
*This comfortable and homely open plan accommodation, has upstairs, a fully
equipped kitchen, including microwave, fridge freezer and oven, dining and
sitting areas and the main bedroom has a great outlook over Mahia Peninsula.
The second bedroom, bathroom and laundry are downstairs. A lovely sunny
verandah off the north facing side, has built in seating and a BBQ looking into
part of the garden.*
*A short walk through the garden leads you up to our home, where you can by
arrangement, join us for breakfast, drinks or dinner.*
*Our large comfortable family home, was once a small farm house which has been
architecturally redesigned to take in great views.*
*Guests are welcome to use our tennis court, which is suitable for social tennis and
to wander around our country garden. Horse riding is also available by
arrangement, horses being a family interest, and there are great bush and farm
walks. Or take a dip in a river swimming hole or fly fish for trout in our catch and
release stream.*
*Nearby attractions include: 9 hole golf course where clubs can be hired, Craft
studio, garden and Marae visits. Scenic flights and fishing trips can be arranged.
Hot mineral pools and bush walks at nearby Morere Hot Springs, and Mahia is
renown for its beaches.*
*Many of our visitors comment, they wish they had allowed time for a longer stay.
We only take one booking at any one time so we would appreciate it, if you would
ring prior to your arrival. If you can not get us during the day, as we are often
outside, try ringing before 8 am, at lunch time or after 6pm.*
Directions: *At Opoutama, follow the Mahanga Road for 2km, turn left into
Tunanui Road, we are 4km up the road.*

Raupunga
Fishermen's Farmstay
Address: "Waikohe" RD4,
Raupunga, Northern Hawkes Bay
Name: Brian and Janice Batson
Telephone & Fax: (06) 838-6969
Beds: 1 Double, 4 Single (3 bedrooms)
Bathroom: 1 Guests share
Tariff: (full) On application
Nearest Town: Wairoa

We are situated in a very remote farming area adjacent to the Urewera National Park and a one-hour drive north-west of Wairoa. We farm an 815 acre sheep and cattle property. Recently we diversified into a Sportsmen's Lodge catering for trout fishermen worldwide which has proved very popular and successful.

Our isolated lakes and rivers are well-stocked with quality rainbow and brown trout and guests like the fact that they can fish all day without seeing another angler. Our ranch style home, at an elevation of 1500 ft has panoramic views of the countryside. This is complemented by well-manicured gardens, fish pond with waterfall, swimming pool, concrete tennis court and spacious patio ideal for outdoor meals.

Whether you require fishing services, relaxation, bush walks, mustering, shearing, or visiting the Urewera National Park, we can assure you a warm and friendly hospitable stay.

Due to our isolation, we recommend a minimum stay of two days. Please phone for directions.

Napier
Homestay
Address: 19 Alamein Crescent, Napier
Name: Pam & Bill McCulloch
Telephone: (06) 843 6744
Beds: 1 Kingsize, 4 Single + Cot (3 bedrooms)
Bathroom: 1 Guests share, 1 Family share
Tariff: B&B (continental) Double $70, Single $35, Dinner $20, Children under 12 half price, Vouchers accepted.

We are retired and enjoy sharing our home with visitors from New Zealand and overseas. We have hosted many through our involvement with Rotary, and the Friendship Force, and are a Kiwi Host homestay offering a warm welcome and quality service.

Off-street parking available, or we can meet your plane, train, or bus.

Our rooms have comfortable single beds or a king-sized double bed, with electric blankets. Cot and high chair available. Bathroom facilities are shared.

Continental breakfast is provided at a time to suit you. Please join us for dinner any evening by arrangement, and feel free to relax with us in the lounge over coffee. We have a well-kept garden with swimming pool, and one handsome cat.

Napier has many tourist attractions, suitable for a good family holiday, an excellent climate, plenty of sunshine, attractive shops and restaurants.

Being non-smokers ourselves, we thank you for not smoking in the house.

Tell other travellers about your favourite B&Bs

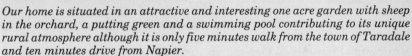

Taradale, Napier

Homestay
Address: "Victoria Lodge",
50 Puketapu Road, Taradale
Name: Don and Sheila Copas
Telephone: (06) 844-2182 (h), 835-7933 (w)
Beds: 1 Double, 3 Single (3 bedrooms)
Bathroom: 1 Guests share
Tariff: B&B (full) Double $50, Single $25, Children
half price; Dinner $20, Vouchers accepted
Nearest Town: Napier 10 km

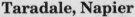

Our home is situated in an attractive and interesting one acre garden with sheep in the orchard, a putting green and a swimming pool contributing to its unique rural atmosphere although it is only five minutes walk from the town of Taradale and ten minutes drive from Napier.

The climate of Hawkes Bay justifies the title of "Sunny Napier" and the area in and around the city has much to offer of interest and activity, i.e. sailing, fishing, windsurfing, bush walks, wine trail etc.

Napier is also well endowed with tourist attractions _ museums, aquarium, Marineland and can lay a claim to being the 'Art Deco' centre of the world.

We love to entertain and you will be assured of a warm welcome at our comfortable family home from us and our dogs and cat.

Directions: *10 km west from Napier. Area maps are available from the Information Centre on Marine Parade or the A.A. Centre in Dickens Street, Napier or phone us for directions.*

Napier

Farmstay
Address: "Hilltop Farm", Puketitiri Road, R.D.2, Napier
Name: Jean & Bob Wilson
Telephone: (06) 844-3205 (after 5pm)
Beds: 3 Single (2 bedrooms) **Bathroom:** 1 Guests share
Tariff: B&B (continental) Double $50, Single $30, Dinner $20, Children half price, high chair & cot available. Vouchers accepted.
Nearest Town: Napier

We live close to the two Hawkes Bay cities of Napier and Hastings. It is approximately a 20 minute drive to the Napier Post Office and 25 minutes to Hasting Post Office. The Hastings area is known as the "fruit bowl" of New Zealand.

Our home is only a few years old, is spacious and comfortable and guests have separate bathroom and toilet facilities. It is situated on 60 acres of farm land, on which sheep and a few cattle are run and has panoramic views of Napier and Hawkes Bay. We also have a swimming pool and outdoor spa pool. The following attractions are within easy distance, the gannet colony, local beaches, Marineland, aquarium, native bush reserves and scenic walkways and visits to local winemaking breweries.

Napier

Homestay
Address: 7 Charles Street, Westshore, Napier
Name: Sheila & Rob Comrie
Telephone: (06) 835 9679
Beds: 1 Double, 2 Single (2 bedrooms) **Bathroom:** 1 Guests share
Tariff: B&B (full) Double $55, Single $30, Children half price, Dinner $15pp,
Vouchers accepted

We have recently retired from farming life and having travelled overseas and enjoyed B & Bs, we would be pleased to share our comfortable modern home with people who enjoy a homely atmosphere.
From the house you step out on to a pleasant, safe beach and are only 5 minutes drive from central Napier or the Airport. Hastings, Taradale and Havelock North are all within a 30 minute drive.
Accommodation, on the ground floor, consists of lounge, dining room, two double bedrooms, guest bathroom and separate toilet. Kitchen available for tea making. Laundry available. Restaurants handy or dinner by arrangement. We sleep upstairs.
All local attractions available including beach walks, windsurfing and sailing almost on the doorstep. Off street parking.
Directions: *Please phone. Pick-up from Airport, Station or Bus dept if required.*

Napier

Hotel Prive
Address: 415 Marine Parade,
P.O. Box 871, Napier
Name: Mon Logis
Telephone and fax: (06) 835-2125
Beds: 2 Double, 4 Single (4 bedrooms) **Bathroom:** 4 Ensuite
Tariff: B&B (special) Double $140, Single $110, Dinner $50.
 Credit cards accepted

A little piece of France nestled in the beautiful wine growing region of Hawkes Bay. This Grand Colonial overlooking the Bay is only a few minutes walk from the city centre.
Frenchman Gerard Flaschner and his wife Jacqueline, a New Zealander, have modelled Mon Logis on the small privately owned french Hotel. Charm, personal service and french cuisine are the specialities.
Four delightful guestrooms upstairs each with ensuite, iron bedsteads, feather duvets, lace covers and fine cotton linen.
Gerard's freshly baked continental breakfast is the speciality, while the English cooked one takes on new meaning at Mon Logis, whichever is chosen will be served to your room.
Dining in the evening, by prior arrangement, is in true La Table d'hote style, enjoyed in grand manner, a five course meal, using the best of local produce and wines.
All perfectly designed for your comfort and relaxation Mon Logis is a non-smoking establishment and does not cater for children.

Napier
Homestay
Address: 17 Cobden Road, Napier
Name: Kay & Stewart Spence
Telephone: (06) 835 9454
Beds: 2 Double, 4 Single (3 bedrooms)
Bathroom: 2 Ensuite, 1 Family share
Tariff: B&B (special) Double $65, Single $45, Dinner $20. Vouchers accepted.

Our early colonial, two-storeyed home with comfortable and modern facilities is pleasantly situated in a sunny position on Napier Hill. The home is set in attractive grounds spread over almost an acre, in a quiet area - just a 10 minute walk from the Napier City Centre.

Two guest rooms include a double bed and a single bed and ensuite bathrooms, one suite also includes a sitting room and a twin room with share bathroom facilities.

All rooms are spacious with lounge chairs and tea making facilities. Beds have electric blankets and woollen underlays.

We have been welcomed into private homes in New Zealand and overseas and wish to extend a warm welcome to you to share our home in the Art Deco city in sunny Hawkes Bay.

We will be happy to meet you at the Hawkes Bay Airport, Napier Railway Station or city bus depot.

Directions: *Bluff Hill Lookout area off Thompson Road. Please phone.*

Napier
Bed & Breakfast
Address: 9 Milton Terrace, Napier (The Art Deco City)
Name: Helen & Robert McGregor
Telephone: (06) 835 7434
Beds: 1 Double (1 bedroom) **Bathroom:** 1 Private
Tariff: B&B (full) Double $60, Single $40. Credit cards: Visa/MC. Vouchers accepted

Enjoy a room with a view!
When visiting Napier, you are welcome to stay with us in our modern two-storeyed home set in an attractive garden on the sunny northern side of Napier's beautiful hill. The guestroom is fully appointed and has a fine view over Hawke Bay. You will have your own private bathroom.
Cooked or continental breakfast provided. We will be happy to collect you from the airport, bus depot or railway station. We ask guests not to smoke in the house. Laundry facilities available at no charge. Visa or Mastercard accepted.
We are in our fifties, enjoy entertaining, and having experienced home hosting overseas, we are firm believers in its advantages. Our interests are travel, gardening, the arts, local history and the preservation of Napier's famous Art Deco architecture.
Please telephone or write beforehand.

Napier
Farmstay
Address: Te Awatea,
Omarunui Road, Napier
Name: Janice McLeod
Telephone & Fax: (06) 844 2216
Beds: 1 Double, 2 Single (2 bedrooms) **Bathroom:** 1 Private, 1 Family share
Tariff: B&B (full) Double $65, Single $35, Dinner $20, Children half price, Campervans facilities. Vouchers accepted.

Gracious old homestead set in two acres of landscaped gardens. Peaceful surrounds with swimming pool and tennis court.
Centrally situated 4 minutes Taradale 10 minutes Napier / Hastings. Golf, wineries, trout fishing in the immediate vicinity. Handy to all other Hawkes Bay attractions. Cooked breakfast included in tariff. Lunch and dinner by arrangement. Picnic lunches available.
Guests are welcome to enjoy the hospitality, good food and to relax in the tranquil surrounds.
Directions: *2km from Highway 50 turn-off. Phone for further information. Collection from airport, station or bus terminal can be arranged if required.*

Napier

Boutique Hotel, Self-contained Accommodation

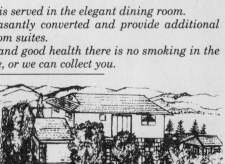

Address: "Anleigh Heights" 115 Chaucer Road North Napier
Name: Allan & Anne Tolley
Telephone: (06) 835 1188
Beds: 8 Double, 8 Single (12 Double Bedrooms)
Bathroom: 3 Ensuite, 2 Private, 1 Guests share
Tariff: B&B (special) Double $90-$150. Credit cards.
Nearest Town: 5 mins drive to Napier CBD

Experience the character and charm of a bygone era. Anleigh Heights offers quality accommodation in Napier's grandest historic home. Situated high on the Napier hill, next to the hospital, our home has commanding views over Hawkes Bay. We have recreated the cossetted lifestyle of the Edwardian House Party for our guests;
- you are greeted at the door by your hosts or family dog
- your rooms are named not numbered
- tea and coffee is served on a silver tray, in fine china, with tea strainers and silver pots
- open fires, flowers, antique furniture and personal possessions all make you feel as if you're part of the household
- breakfast is a house speciality and is served in the elegant dining room.
The original stables have been pleasantly converted and provide additional family accommodation in two-bedroom suites.
For reasons of historic preservation and good health there is no smoking in the house. Off-street parking is available, or we can collect you.

Napier

Homestay

Address: 4 George Street, Hospital Hill, Napier.
Name: Noel and Nancy Lyons
Telephone: (06) 835 1812
Beds: 1 Double, 2 Single (2 bedrooms)
Bathroom: 1 Guests share
Tariff: B&B (continental) Double $60, Single $35. Vouchers accepted.

Our modern home is situated in a quiet area with extensive views across the Bay. We are 5 min from the city renowned for the 'Art Deco' buildings, and a short distance from the many Hawkes Bay wineries.
We offer comfortable accommodation with your own lounge if you wish for quiet times on your own. All beds have electric blankets. Laundry and tea making facilities available.
We have travelled extensively and welcome the opportunity to meet overseas visitors. We look forward to sharing our knowledge of the area with you.
Our interests are travel, gardening, live theatre, bowls and embroidery.
A comfortable holiday home at Mahia Beach, 2 1/2 hours drive north of Napier is available for a relaxing holiday. Safe swimming beach at your front door.
Directions: *Please phone. Free collection from Airport, Station or Bus dept if required.*

Hastings
Farmstay
Address: Wai-iti Farms,
Maraekakaho Road, Hastings
Name: Jan Graham and Dick Black
Telephone: (06) 879-7951
Beds: 1 Double, 2 Single (2 bedrooms)
Bathroom: 1 Private
Tariff: B&B (continental) Double $60, Single $30, Children half price, Dinner $20, Vouchers accepted
Nearest Town: Hastings 12km

Last century our house began life as a ploughman's cottage but like Topsy has grown to gracious and generous proportions.
We have spacious lawns and an attractive garden which hosts a variety of pets from peacocks to puppies.
Hundreds of school children, parents and teachers visit us every year to enjoy a variety of farm experiences and animals which our guests would be most welcome to enjoy also.
Swimming pool available.

Hastings
Farmstay
Address: Millstream,
RD 4, Hastings
Name: Maureen Harper
Telephone & Fax: (06) 878 9944
Beds: 2 Double, 2 Single (2 bedrooms)
Bathroom: 1 Ensuite, 1 Private
Tariff: B&B (continental) Double $60, Single $30, Dinner $15, Children $15, Campervans welcome, Vouchers accepted
Nearest Town: 25km south of Hastings on main Highway 2 to Wellington, 11km Waipawa (south)

Nestled among the beautiful hills of New Zealand's "fruit basket" and premium wine country, my countryside villa is a haven for fresh air, relaxation, and delicious home cooked meals. This sprawling, 20 ha property is adorned with beautiful trees, a quiet stream, and abundant lawns and gardens. Horse trekking is available on site and guests can view one of NZ's few miniature horse herds. I have a few cattle and sheep, and guests are welcome to participate in farm activities that change seasonally. My comfortable home features a large living area, sundeck, cozy fireplace, and nooks to relax or read in. Delicious continental breakfasts served, and my homemade bread (made from local wheat) is addicting! Wholesome and generous dinners can be added to accommodation by arrangement. All guests will enjoy complimentary tea or coffee on arrival, and children and pets are welcome. Pick-up in Hastings can be arranged for a minimal fee.

Hastings
Homestay
Address: 115A Frederick St Hastings Hawkes Bay
Name: Doug & Barbara McConchie
Telephone: (06) 878 4576
Beds: 1 Queen, 2 Single (2 Bedrooms) **Bathroom:** 1 Guests share
Tariff: B&B (special) Double $70, Single $35, Children half price, Dinner $20, Vouchers accepted
Nearest Town: Napier

We are a retired couple with three of our four adult children living in Australia. We have a Siamese cat.

Our home is modern, attractive and peaceful, being in a back garden setting away from traffic noises. It has a guest wing with ranchslider entry. A short walk will take you to the centre of the city or to parks. A fifteen minute drive will take you to golf courses or up Te Mata Peak to wonderful views. A gannet sanctuary at Cape Kidnappers is a great trip. Plenty of wineries, fruit orchards, picnic spots or walks around. A five minute drive will take you to the picturesque village of Havelock North. We enjoy meeting people and judging by the letters we get, people enjoy being with us. We give you your choice of breakfast. Continental, cooked or special. Long stays discounted.

No smoking inside please. Married couples with or without children and single, separate bedroom folk are extremely welcome.

Directions: *Coming from Napier take the main highway south and upon reaching Hastings, Frederick St is the second street off on your left. Drive down until you have crossed the railway line. 115a is just past the next intersection on your right, and down a driveway. Turn into the first gateway off and you are there. Wellington is 3 1/2 - 4 hrs south and if coming from there by train or bus, ring and we will meet you. If coming by car from Wellington, drive across Hastings City and ask directions by phone.*

Waiwhare
Country Farm Homestead
Address: "Mangawhare",
Waiwhare, Taihape Road,
PO Box 159, Hastings
Name: Pat and Brian Tolley
Telephone: (06) 8742-875
Beds: 1 Double, 6 Single (4 bedrooms)
Bathroom: 1 Guests share
Tariff: B&B (full) Double $55, Single $30, Dinner $15, Children half price; Campervans $20 up to 4. Vouchers accepted.
Nearest Town: Hastings 50 kms

A warm welcome awaits guests at Mangawhare (sheep and cattle farm) at our large historical Elizabethan homestead which is situated just off the Napier/ Taihape (Gentle Annie) Road, 60 km from Napier, 50 km from Hastings.

Nearby there are deer farms, one with bow hunting a speciality. Water rafting and hunting also available in close proximity with native bush walks, fishing and golf and squash facilities within easy access. In season there are local country gardens open to public viewing. We are also classic car enthusiasts (Daimler).

Directions: *Taihape Road turn off at Fernhill (State Highway 50) follow Taihape Road to Glenross, River Roads cross roads. Mangawhare is situated 1 km on the Glenross Road, first on the right with our name on the mailbox. Likewise 100 km from Taihape on the Taihape/Napier Road.*

Clive, Hastings
Homestay
Address: "Riverbank House", 524 State Highway 2, Hastings North.
Postal Address: Box 38, Clive, Hawkes Bay.
Name: Paul & Di White
Telephone: (06) 870 0759
Beds: 3 Double, 2 Single (4 Bedrooms) **Bathroom:** 2 Guests share
Tariff: B&B (full) Double $60, Single $35, Children half price, Dinner by arrangement $20pp, Vouchers accepted
Nearest Town: Equidistant from Napier and Hastings

Our property is centrally situated midway between Napier and Hastings just a few minutes pleasant drive from either city. The location is semi rural bordering the Clive River ideal for visiting local wineries, the Gannet Colony and all attractions of Hawkes Bay.
We have 1 1/2 acres of tranquil lawn and gardens with a large in ground swimming pool and spa adjoining a delightful studio cottage where guests can relax, read or enjoy a quiet glass of Hawkes Bay wine.
In the main house we offer twin or double rooms with queen size beds with electric blankets for winter warmth and private bathroom facilities for guests.
Both of us have had many years involved in the local restaurant and wine industries and look forward to helping you plan your stay in Hawkes Bay.
Directions: *From north take State Highway 2 along Marine Parade to Clive. 2.5km past Clive look for sign on right.*
From Hastings follow State Highway 2 from northern boundary for 5km, look for sign on left.

Hastings/Havelock North
Homestay/Farmstay
Address: Wharehau R.D. 11, Hastings
Name: Ros Phillips
Telephone: (06) 877-4111
Beds: 7 Single (4 bedrooms) **Bathroom:** 1 guests share
Tariff: B&B (full) Double $60, Single $30, Dinner $20, Children half price (cot and high-chair available), Campervans welcome, Credit cards accepted, Vouchers accepted
Nearest Town: Hastings,Havelock North

Having enjoyed many homes on overseas travels I welcome visitors to our peaceful farmhouse. "Wharehau" is 20 minutes from Hastings, Havelock North or Waipawa. We have a Hereford and Romney stud. Farm tours are available with fabulous views of Hawkes Bay. There is also 50 acres of native bush and an excellent fishing river, the Tukituki, nearby.
Ros is actively involved in the day to day running of the farm, enjoys gardening and is a keen cook. The farmhouse has three bedrooms and guest bathroom upstairs, and one guestroom downstairs with shared facilities. Children welcome.

Many homes have facilities for campervans. The ideal camping spot with electricity, bathroom, laundry and friendly hospitality.
Tell campervanners about this when you see them.

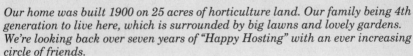

Havelock North

Homestay/Farmstay
Address: "Peak View" Farm,
Middle Rd., Havelock North
Name: Dianne & Keith Taylor
Telephone: (06) 8777408
Beds: 1 Double, 2 Single plus cot & highchair (2 bedrooms) **Bathroom:** 1 Family share
Tariff: B&B (full) Double $55, Single $35, Dinner $20, (2 course $15), Children half price. Credit Cards: Visa & M/C. Vouchers accepted.
Nearest Town: Havelock North 1 km, Hastings 6km

Our home was built 1900 on 25 acres of horticulture land. Our family being 4th generation to live here, which is surrounded by big lawns and lovely gardens. We're looking back over seven years of "Happy Hosting" with an ever increasing circle of friends.
We enjoy meeting people - our aim is to provide a pleasant and memorable stay. Interested in caravanning, tramping and bushwalks. Keith enjoys fishing, Dianne sewing, gardening and genealogy. One friendly cat. Dianne is a Kiwi Host.
We offer comfortable accommodation. All beds have electric blankets. Dinner with us be assured of wholesome and generous meals with local wines our compliments. Afterwards share an evening of relaxation and friendship or browse through our many New Zealand books. Also can advise on travel throughout New Zealand from own experiences.
Handy to winerys, tennis and squash courts, indoor and outdoor pools, short drive to Te Mata Peak with panoramic views. Napier 25 minutes away.
No smoking inside please.
Be welcomed with tea or coffee.
Laundry facilities available.

Havelock North

Homestay
Address: 4 Waikonini Place, Havelock North
Name: Sonia and Martin Heesterman
Telephone: (06) 8774-190
Beds: 1 Double, 2 Single (2 bedrooms) **Bathroom:** 1 Guests share
Tariff: B&B (Full) Double $50, Single $25, Vouchers accepted
Nearest Town: Hastings

Our spacious sunny home is situated in a quiet cul-de-sac with views to Napier and the coast and only a five minute walk to the Havelock North shopping centre. We are in our late fifties, our three children are all married and no longer live at home.
We have travelled extensively overseas using the Bed & Breakfast system. We endeavour to make our guests feel welcome in our home and our beautiful surrounding countryside.
We are close to the twin cities of Hastings and Napier and our area has much to offer the tourist. We have an inground saline swimming pool, guest sitting room, and off-street parking is available. No smoking in the house.

Havelock North

Self-contained Accom B&B
Address: "The Birches",
39 Tanner Street, Havelock North,
Name: Margaret and Geoff Fuller
Telephone: (06) 877-8391
Beds: 2 Single (1 bedroom)
Bathroom: 1 Ensuite
Tariff: B&B (special) Double $75, Single $50

"The Birches" is situated 1 km from the centre of Havelock North with views towards the mountains.
Havelock North is a very pleasant residential and shopping area, surrounded by orchards and vineyards. The twin cities of Hastings and Napier are within easy driving distance (S.H.2)
Hawkes Bay is an attractive district offering a wide range of activities for visitors, and many types of commercial tours. We are a retired couple who have enjoyed travelling in New Zealand and overseas, and have special interests in the arts. Geoff is an artist / designer.
Our well appointed accommodation is separate and self-contained, with off-street parking.
Continental or cooked breakfasts. Laundry facilities available (extra charge). No pets. No smoking inside please.
Directions: *From the centre of Havelock North follow Joll Road to the end, turn left into Tanner Street to number 39. The house is at the top of the drive up the hill. Please phone or write beforehand.*

Havelock North

Homestay
Address: Waimarama Road,
R.D.12, Havelock North
Name: Joan & Nigel Sutton
Telephone: (06) 877 6852
Beds: 1 Double, 3 Single (3 bedrooms)
Bathroom: 1 Guests share
Tariff: B&B (full) Double $75, Single $45, Dinner $25 includes wine & pre dinner drinks. Vouchers accepted.
Nearest Town: Hastings

Our comfortable family home is set in ten acres of rolling hill country in the beautiful Tuki Tuki River Valley close to Te Mata peak, yet only five minutes from Havelock North, ten minutes from Hastings and fifteen minutes from Napier.
Two of Hawkes Bay's nicest beaches are about fifteen minutes pleasant driving along Waimarama Road.
We have a number of friendly animals including kunekune pigs, sheep, horses, cats and a dog and a small flock of homing pigeons.
We can help you plan your enjoyment of Hawkes Bay's numerous attractions or you can take a stroll with us to the river, meeting and feeding the animals on the way, laze by the pool, play tennis on the grass court, fish for rainbow trout or relax in the outdoor spa. Dinner, served with local wine, is a pleasant time to get to know one another. Being non smokers we would appreciate you not smoking indoors.

Havelock North
Guest House
Address: Middle Road RD 2 Hastings Hawkes Bay
Name: Providencia
Telephone: (06) 877 2300
Fax: (06) 8772300
Beds: 2 Double, 3 Single (4 Bedrooms)
Bathroom: 1 Guests share (bath & shower)
Tariff: B&B (special) Double $130, Single $100,
Dinner $45 (including wine). Credit cards.
Nearest Town: Havelock North - 5 mins drive (3km from village)

Built in 1903, historic Providencia was moved to its present rural site by its new owners.

The 4500 sq ft home still retains many of its original features - solid kauri and rimu panelling, exquisite leadlight windows and doors and wide verandahs.

Providencia is in the heart of the Hawkes Bay wine growing area and is minutes away from excellent fly fishing (a guide can be arranged) paragliding, bush walking, horse riding, polo, parachuting and beaches.

We can pack a wonderful picnic hamper for your day trips. We'll cook your catch.

Providencia has been restored for the comfort of our guests. However, in order to preserve its unique heritage value, there are no ensuites - but sharing a bathroom in such a special house means you won't find it a problem.

Dining in the evening is by prior arrangement and we use the very best of regional produce.

Having travelled widely your hosts Janet and Raúl Maddison-Mejias lived in Sydney and South America for the past 15 years or so.

We are a non-smoking establishment inside and children N/A. Se habla Espanōl.

Note: Building was not completed at the time of inspection, phone to confirm.

Would you like a weeks free B&B for two people?
Please complete and send us the comment form supplied by your host.

Elsthorpe
Farmstay+Self-contained Accommodation
Address: "Paeroa Station" Kokatawai Road
Elsthorpe Postal: Box 900 Hastings
Name: Barbara & John Bibby
Telephone & Fax: (06) 858 4241
Beds: 5 Single (3 Bedrooms)
Bathroom: 1 Guests share
Tariff: B&B (continental) Double $90, Single $50, Children under 12 half price,
Dinner $25, Campervans facilities available, Vouchers accepted
Nearest Town: Waipawa 35km, Hastings 55km

We welcome you to join us on "Paeroa Station" in Central Hawkes Bay. Our large comfortable homestead overlooks the garden and farm in a peaceful setting. A Landrover tour provides you with outstanding views of Hawkes Bay from the Ruahine Ranges to the sea and an insight into farming our 3000 acres of sheep, beef cattle, forestry and our 150 acres native bush reserve. Relax afterwards in our swimming and spa pools and enjoy friendly hospitality at our table, delicious home cooked meals of local produce and a peaceful comfortable sleep.
You can participate in the faming activities enjoy bushwalks, troutfishing, the beach 5 minutes away or 45 minutes comfortable drive to the excellent selection of Hawkes Bay vineyards, gannet sanctuary and many other attractions of Hastings and Napier.
We also have a self-contained 4 bedroom holiday house available sleeps 14 - enquire by phone.
Leave SH 2 at either Hastings or Waipawa to drive to us.
Ring ahead for directions and bookings.

New Zealand Association
FARM & HOME HOSTS

Waipukurau
Farmstay
Address: "Oakworth", Station Road, RD1, Waipukurau
Name: Marilyn and Trevor Jane
Telephone: (06) 855-8255
Beds: 1 Double, 3 Single (2 bedrooms)
Bathroom: 1 Ensuite, 1 Guests share
Tariff: B&B(full) Double $60, Single $40, Children half price, Dinner $15 per person, Campervans welcome, Vouchers accepted
Nearest Town: Waipukurau 16 km

Marilyn and Trevor welcome you to "Oakworth Farm" in sunny Central Hawke's Bay. Enjoy a friendly, relaxing stay on our sheep and cattle farm.
Our large comfortable home, is set in attractive grounds. Experience country hospitality, with quality meals of fresh farm produce, and NZ wines. Look around the farm, relax by the pool in summer, and spend the evenings chatting with the family.
Our interests include travel, crafts, computers and meeting people. We have two cats and a fox terrier.
We are close to two golf courses and trout rivers are nearby. Bush walks, deer farms, limeworks, Heritage Trail, gardens and Norsewood are just some of the interesting things to see in the locality.
Directions: *Turn off State Highway 2 at Fraser Road, by "Richmonds" sign, 15 km south of Waipukurau. Travelling north, 4 km from Takapau crossroads, turn left at railway line into Station Road, 4th house. Children welcome.*

Waipukurau

Farmstay
Address: "Tukipo Terraces",
P O Box 114, Takapau 4176, Hawkes Bay
Name: Bay and Shona de Lautour
Telephone: (06) 855-6827
Fax: (06) 855 6808
Beds: 2 Double, 2 Single (2 large, beautifully appointed suites)
Bathroom: 2 Ensuite
Tariff: B&B (special) $50 per person; Dinner $25pp includes wine and pre-dinner drinks. 24 hr rate including all meals $90 pp. (GST included in tariff),
Children under 12 half price, Visa/MC accepted
Nearest Town: Waipukurau 20 km, Takapau Village 8kms

A warm welcome awaits you at Tukipo Terraces, our beautiful home set in a large developing garden with panoramic views across to the mountains.

Relax and enjoy finest food and wine with us in idyllic surroundings. Tennis court, swimming, trout fishing. Rod & racquets for guest use. Pet Fox terrier.

We farm sheep, cattle and deer, are both involved in many off-farm activities and have travelled widely overseas.

Our property is on Highway 50, the picturesque alternate route between Napier and Takapau which passes through the Heritage trail area encompassing beautiful gardens open to the public, native bush walks and the historic village of Onga Onga.

Directions: *From south on Highway 2, 30 kms north of Dannevirke turn left onto Highway 50, travel 5 kms, on right just at end of long line of mature pines.*
From north, on Highway 50, 22 kms from Tikokino, first on left over Tukipo stream.

One of the differences between staying at a hotel and a B&B
is that you don't hug the hotel staff when you leave.

Private bathroom is for your use exclusively,
Guests share means you may be sharing with other guests,
Family share means you will be sharing with the family.

Waipukurau

Farmstay
Address: Hinerangi Station,
Hinerangi Road, R.D. 1, Waipukurau
Name: Caroline & Dan von Dadelszen
Telephone: (06) 855 8273

Beds: 1 Double, 2 Single (2 bedrooms) **Bathroom:** 1 Guests share
Tariff: B&B (special) Double $80, Single $50, Dinner $20, Children $18.
Vouchers accepted.
Nearest Town: Takapau 11km, Waipukurau 20km

*Hinerangi is an 1800 acre sheep, beef and deer station situated amongst the
rolling hills of Central Hawkes Bay. There are magnificent views of the Takapau
plains and the Ruahine ranges to be had from various vantage points on the farm.
We are happy to show and explain to guests what is happening on the farm while
you are here.*
*Our large colonial homestead has a full sized billiard table and there is a tennis
court and swimming pool in the garden for guests to enjoy. Our home is spacious,
comfortable with a private entrance for visitors to come and go as they please. You
are welcome to join us for dinner and an evening by the fire.*
*There are several beaches, bush walks and trout fishing streams within an hours
drive and for golfers the Takapau golf course is 10km away.*
We are 8km off State Highway 2.
Directions: *Please phone.*

New Zealand
Association
FARM & HOME
HOSTS

Waipukurau

Farmstay
Address: "Mynthurst", Lindsay Road,
RD3, Waipukurau
Name: David and Annabelle Hamilton
Telephone: (06) 857 8093

Beds: 1 Double, 1 Twin, 1 Single, 1 cot (three bedrooms) **Bathroom:** 1 Private
(We only host one group at a time).
Tariff: B&B (Special) Double $100, Single $55, 24hr rate (includes all meals)
$95p.p. Dinner $25, Children under 12 half single rate, under 12 months free.
Nearest Town: Waipukurau/Waipawa 9 km

*Welcome to Central Hawkes Bay. Join us on our sheep and bull beef rearing farm
situated 5 miles (9 kms) from S.H.2 between Waipukurau and Waipawa. Our
homestead is large and overlooks the garden and farm, with distant views of the
Ruahine Mountains. Enjoy local produce with delicious home cooked meals and
sleep peacefully in beds that are all provided with electric blankets. You are
welcome to participate in all the farming activities or just relax beside the pool.
There are trout streams nearby, with golf and horse riding easily arranged.*
*We are approximately 30 minutes drive from wonderful mountain walks or
picnics beside the sea. A comfortable trip brings you to the excellent selection of
Hawkes Bay Vineyards and many other attractions of Hasting and Napier.
Children welcome.*
*Please phone ahead for bookings to avoid disappointment. Arrangements can be
made to collect guests from Napier/Hastings Airport or coach depots.*

Takapau/Norsewood

Farmstay
Address: "Kilbirnie" Byrne Road,
Takapau 4176, Central Hawkes Bay
Name: Jill & John Grant
Telephone: (06) 8558325
Beds: 1 Double, 2 Single (2 bedrooms)
Bathroom: 1 Guests share
Tariff: B&B (special) Double $55 (exclusive use of suite $65), Single $35, Dinner
$18pp, Children and pets by arrangement, Vouchers accepted
Nearest Town: 25km south of Waipukurau, 32km north of Dannevirke

*Kilbirnie, adjacent Highway 2 between Napier and the Wellington Ferry, offers an
ideal opportunity to experience country hospitality in a special part of New
Zealand. We aim to make your stay memorable by providing a generous selection
of interesting foods, including decadent desserts, crisp sheets on a comfortable
antique bed and a guest lounge containing TV, frig, tea making facilities and
unusual NZ books to read by the fire. You may be as sociable or private as you wish.
Views extend over the gardens towards Napier with Art Deco, Heritage Trails,
gannets and wineries or to the Ruahine Mountains and Norsewood Scandinavian
Village with museum and Knitwear factory.*
*We are happy to demonstrate shearing, dogs working or just walk over the farm
to the duck pond, sharing local knowledge, pioneering anecdotes and conversation.
Pamper yourself - stay at Kilbirnie.*
Directions: Turn left off Highway Two 4km south of Highway 50 intersection
at Takapau or, from Wellington fourth turn on right after Norsewood.

Norsewood

Farmstay
Address: Arthur Road, RD, Norsewood
Name: Wayne & Helen Hermansen
Telephone: (06) 374 0735
Beds: 1 Double, 1 Single (1 Bedroom) **Bathroom:** 1 Private
Tariff: B&B (full) Double $55, Dinner $15pp BYO if required, Vouchers accepted
May to October
Nearest Town: Norsewood

*Guests will be warmly welcome to our spacious home where you can relax and
enjoy the peace of the country and the view of the Ruahine Ranges, or be included
in the family and farm activities.*
We live on a bull fattening block and have a Town Supply Dairy farm.
*We are only 2km from Norsewood, which is a one hour drive to either Palmerston
North or Hastings on SH 2.*
*Our district is steeped in Scandinavian History with a very interesting museum.
Tours of Norsewear Woollen Mills can be arranged. The golf course is just around
the corner, or you can do a day tramp up the Ranges.*
*The men run a hay contracting business and you are welcome to watch the
harvesting and join us for meals in the paddock most evenings in the summer.*
Interests include gardening, reading, machinery, tramping.
We enjoy people, love entertaining and a good game of cards, especially 500.
No pets, no smoking please.
Directions: *Please phone.*

Dannevirke

Homestay
Address: 42 Victoria Avenue,
Dannevirke
Name: "Glendane"
(Norma and Ian Pedersen)
Telephone: (06) 374-6453
Beds: 1 Double, 3 Single (2 bedrooms)
Bathroom: 1 Private   (we take 1 party only at a time)
Tariff: B&B (continental) Double $60, Single $35; Dinner
$20 by arrangement, Vouchers accepted
Nearest Town: 1 km west of Dannevirke

Our lovely modern home is set in one acre of beautiful garden and being on the outskirts of town has a rural view with our Ruahine Ranges in the background. It is very quiet and restful, a great place to break your journey.

You can walk to town in ten minutes or head in the other direction and have a refreshing walk in the country. On returning you are assured of a quiet relaxing evening. We have no children or pets.

You may enjoy dinner with us or bed and breakfast only if you prefer.

Apart from our interests in gardening and farming we make from pure natural wool our own handspun, handmade woollen goods - jerseys, vests, hats, scarves, etc and these original garments are for sale.

Directions: *Please phone.*

Always telephone ahead to enquire about a B&B. It is a nuisance for you if
you simply arrive to find someone already staying there.
And besides hosts need a little time to prepare.

Dannevirke

Homestay
Address: "Inverness",
4 Allan Street, Dannevirke.
PO Box 314, Dannevirke.
Name: Graham & Sally Ramsden
Telephone & Fax: (06) 374-7220
Beds: 1 Double, 4 Single (3 bedrooms)
Bathroom: 1 Ensuite, 1 Family share
Tariff: B&B (full) Double $70, Single $40, Children 12 and under half price.
Vouchers accepted.

Historic "Inverness" is a picturesque English Cotswald style home, welcoming, cosy and comfortable, set in 1/2 an acre cottage style garden with protected trees and a swimming pool.

We are actively involved in hill country sheep and cattle farming. Graham commutes to the farm each day. The other member of our household is Arbuckle, a cairn terrier.

Dannevirke and the surrounding area offer a variety of rural pursuits including fishing, caving, bushwalks plus local crafts, wood-turning, pottery, spinning and weaving. Being non-smokers ourselves we thank you for not smoking in the house and welcome you as our guests and hope you leave as our friends. We offer free pick up from bus terminal or railway station.

Directions: *To reach "Inverness" when coming from the North turn right into Cole Street (at North School), then left into Allan Street. When coming from the South, turn left into Miller Street or Allardice Street, then right into Queen Street which later becomes Allan Street.*

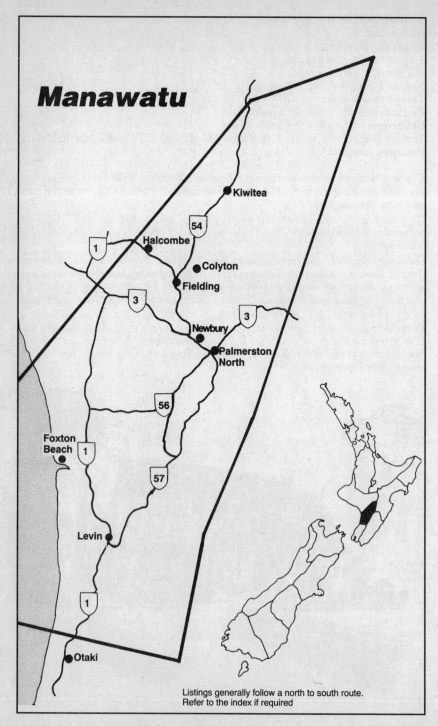

Manawatu

Kiwitea

54

1

Halcombe

Colyton

Fielding

3

Newbury

3

Palmerston
North

56

Foxton
Beach

1

57

Levin

1

Otaki

Listings generally follow a north to south route.
Refer to the index if required

Kiwitea, Feilding

Homestay
Address: "Tirohanga", Kiwitea, RD 7, Feilding
Name: Shirley and John Bird
Telephone: (06) 328 9866
Beds: 4 Single (2 bedrooms) **Bathroom:** 1 Guest share
Tariff: B&B (full) Double $60, Single $35, Children half price,
Dinner $20 each, Vouchers accepted
Nearest Town: Feilding

*We have 5 acres of land. "Tirohanga" meaning "View", has large garden with
views, south to Kapiti Island, and east to Ruahine and Tararua Ranges. Sometimes
fabulous sunsets.*

*We have travelled overseas, especially Britain, where John's father lived for 21
years before settling in New Zealand. Three sons, two daughters (all married) and
seventeen grandchildren make up our family. John spends some time helping out
on two Hill Country farms we own with two sons. Visits could be arranged to these
sheep and beef cattle farms if interested.*

*John does wood turning as a hobby and I enjoy knitting, jigsaw puzzles, and
gardening.*

*We are 9 km from well known "Cross Hills" Gardens, also Kimbolton Rhododendron
Park. Twenty minutes north of Feilding, 2 hours to Wellington and less than 2
hours to Ohakune.*

Directions: *23 km north of Feilding PO on Kimbolton Road (used to be SH54).
At Cheltenham travel towards Kimbolton. We are 9 km north of Cheltenham.*

Colyton, Feilding

Farmstay
Address: "Hiamoe", Waiata,
Colyton, Feilding
Name: John & Toos Cousins
Telephone: (06) 328-7713 (anytime)
Beds: 1 Double, 2 Single (2 bedrooms) **Bathroom:** 1 Ensuite, 1 Guests share
Tariff: B&B (full) Double $60, Single $35, pre school children free, school age
half price, Dinner $15, Campervans $20, Credit cards accepted. Vouchers
accepted

*Our colonial style home is set in a large garden with views of the Ruahine Ranges
to the East and we are the third generation on our sheep, beef and deer farm.*

*We have many interests and as Holland is Toos recent homeland we are very
accustomed to travel and hosting visitors of all nationalities in our home.*

*We look forward to giving you a warm welcome at "Hiamoe" (Maori for "sleepy
hollow") and during your stay, it is our aim to make you feel part of a "home away
from home".*

*Our location near Feilding places us about half way between Wellington (2 1/2
hours to the south) and Taupo (3 hours to the north)*

Directions: *25 minutes drive from Palmerston North and 15 minutes drive from
Feilding via Colyton but please phone.*

Feilding
Homestay
Address: 5 Wellington Street, Feilding
Name: Beryl Walker
Telephone: (06) 323-4409
Beds: 4 Single (2 bedrooms) **Bathroom:** 1 Guests share
Tariff: B&B (full) Double $55, Single $35, Children half price, Campervans welcome. Vouchers accepted.

A comfortable and sunny family home with open fires in winter. Guests should feel free to use all family rooms and facilities as family members. A chance to catch up with your laundry. A choice of breakfast timed to suit your travel arrangements. Cot and highchair available.

Feilding, only 15 minutes from Highway 1 from Sanson if travelling south or through Rongatea is the centre of a prosperous farming area with many places of natural beauty within reach. It has easy access to the East Coast and is only 15 minutes from the city of Palmerston North. Manfield Racecourse is situated at Feilding.

Feilding has an interesting shopping area and several good restaurants, licensed and unlicensed.

For further directions please ring.

Newbury, Palmerston North
Farmstay
Address: Rangitikei Line, Palmerston North, SH 3.
Name: Keith and Margaret Morriss
Telephone & Fax: (06) 354-8961
Beds: 1 Double, 2 Single (2 bedrooms) **Bathroom:** 1 Family share
Tariff: B&B (full) Double $60, Single $35; Dinner $20; Children half price, Vouchers accepted
Nearest Town: 8 km north of Palmerston North on State Highway 3, 5km south of Awahuri

We enjoy country living, - a short distance from Palmerston North.
A friendly welcome awaits you at "Grinton", our 100-year-old home with family connections, its namesake in Yorkshire, England.
We offer guests a comfortable stay in pleasant garden and country surroundings. Continental or cooked breakfast.
Farming operations consist mainly of beef fattening and calf rearing. Large scale dairying, deer farming, equestrian centre are also in the area.
We both enjoy travel and welcome the stimulation of overseas guests, ensuring them a sampling of some of New Zealand's fine food and complimentary wine. We make time to provide enjoyment for our guests. Local scenic drives include Massey University, the Esplanade Gardens and recently opened Pacific Japanese College. A pleasant day trip in Oct / Nov to the world-renowned Cross-Hills Rhododendron Gardens at Kimbolton, visit Palmerston North's National Rugby Museum or a newly opened Vintage Motorcycle Museum. Our interests include travel, tramping, trout fishing, golf, the Lions Club, music, floral art and dried flowers.

We rely on your comments about our B&Bs.
Please complete and send us the comment form supplied by your host.

Palmerston North

Homestay
Address: "Kilkenn Down",
143 Victoria Ave, Palmerston North
Name: Keay & Ken McCormack
Telephone: (06) 357-3491
Beds: 3 Single (2 bedrooms)
Bathroom: 1 Guests share, 1 Family share
Tariff: B&B (full) Double $55, Single $35, Children 1/2 price, Dinner $15,
Campervans $20, Vouchers accepted

We are a retired couple who enjoy welcoming visitors to our 64 year old character home with modern facilities in pleasant surroundings, close to Palmerston North city (10 mins walk). We have a spacious twin bedroom with comfortable beds, electric blankets, wool underlays and free tea and coffee making facilities. Also a small bedroom with single bed.

Our interests are wide and varied - travel, music, theatre and sport. An evening meal is available (prior notice please). Palmerston North is a University and educational city with many cultural activities as well as museums, live theatre, lovely gardens and walkways.

We have ample off-street parking at rear of house (gates are locked at night). Campervans are welcome - electric hook-up available. We are happy to meet public transport.

Directions: *Take Broadway Ave from The Square in easterly direction. Turn right at first roundabout (Victoria Ave). Look for palm tree in front garden.*

When you stay at B&Bs you are staying with "dinkum Kiwis"

If you love touring New Zealand B&B style...

...check out what is available in Australia

The Australian Bed & Breakfast Book is the perfect accommodation guide for those who want to see the real Australia.

For ordering details, turn to the back of this book

Grey's Inn

Palmerston North
Bed & Breakfast Hotel
Address: 123 Grey Street, Palmerston North
Name: Don & Liz Robertson
Telephone: (06) 358-6928
Fax: (06) 355-0291
Beds: 2 Double, 5 Single (5 bedrooms)
Bathroom: 5 Ensuite
Tariff: B&B (full) Double $70, Single $49, Dinner $21,
Children under 12 yrs $15, Campervans $20
Credit Cards. Vouchers accepted.

Welcome to Grey's Inn, a colonial style home set in quiet gardens just five minutes from the city centre for shopping; close to swimming pool; sports facilities and within five minutes drive to Massey University and Science Centres.

All rooms have private facilities; electric blankets; clock radios; complimentary tea and coffee. TV sets are available.

Home cooked dinner is available by arrangement; or you may wish to eat out at one of our many and varied restaurants within walking distance.

Our Egmont Room which features paintings of one of New Zealand's largest mountains is where we serve a substantial breakfast. This includes fruits, cereal, toast and marmalade etc. followed by a choice of bacon, eggs, sausages and the like.All this is included in the tariff.

We are only two hours drive from Wellington or take our popular commuter train for a day trip to the capital city. Our river city Wanganui is good for a day trip only 45 minutes drive away. Most guests appreciate "Wooly" and Rupert the family dog and cat. We prefer you not to smoke inside.

Palmerston North
Homestay
Address: 19 Phoenix Ave Hokowhitu Palmerston North
Name: Faye & Lindsay Quennell
Telephone: (06) 358 5803
Beds: 1 Double, convertible to singles (1 Bedroom) **Bathroom:** 1 Private
Tariff: B&B (full) Double $70, Single $40, Vouchers accepted
Nearest Town: Palmerston North

Welcome to our comfortable home situated in a quiet, tree-lined cul-de-sac, close to city centre, within easy reach of Polytech / College of Education and Massey University. Our older style home, nestled in a cottage garden has been recently modernized. The guest bedroom has double bed, walk-in wardrobe, tea and coffee making facilities.

The spacious guest bathroom includes shower, toilet ad spa bath. Guests can use adjacent second lounge or join us in main living area. (Cassie, our Burmese cat, will also welcome you.)

Our interests include gardening, trout fishing, golf (Manawatu Golf Course nearby) reading and of course meeting people.

We regularly use NZ homestays so appreciate the importance of privacy, home comforts and a warm welcome.

We are happy to meet plane, bus or train.

Directions: *From the Square, take Fitzherbert Av, turn left into College St. Phoenix Av is the last street on the right before Victoria Ave.*

Smoke free environment.

Levin

Homestay
Address: "Annandale",
Arapaepae Rd., Levin (SH 57)
Name: Cheryl and Wayne Strong
Telephone: (06) 368 5476
Beds: 2 Double, 1 Single (3 bedrooms)
Bathroom: 1 guests share
Tariff: B&B (full) Double $65, Single $37, Dinner $20, Children welcome.
Vouchers accepted.

We will make you most welcome for a restful stay at "Annandale".
Our two storeyed old English style home, built in 1917, is set in an acre of trees and gardens with a further 4 acres of feijoas, marketed locally and internationally from April to July.
We offer our guests a peaceful retreat - whether you are just passing through - or wish to get away from it all for a few days. Levin and the surrounding area have a number of attractions, such as good beaches, golf links and bush walks; or you may choose just to potter around our orchard and talk to our pets which include two dogs, a cat, kunekune pigs, a sulphur crested cockatoo and a number of aviary birds.
Directions: *We are on State Highway 57, 1km north of the Queen St, Arapaepae Rd (SH57) intersection, on the right hand (eastern) side of the road, (sign at gate). Non-smokers preferred.*

Levin

Farmstay
Address: "Norden Green" Ohau, Arapaepae Rd Levin
Name: Alex and Sybil Robinson
Telephone: (06) 368 6374
Beds: 3 Single (2 bedrooms)
Bathroom: 1 Ensuite, 1 Family share
Tariff: B&B (special) Double $55, Single $35, Dinner $15, Children half price, Campervans $15. Vouchers accepted.
Nearest Town: Levin 7 km

We are an active semi-retired couple running a 10 acre block, part orchard and part grazing.
Our home is modern and comfortable with great views of the Tararuas. We have a relaxed easy going lifestyle and enjoy meeting people. We will do our best to make your stay a pleasant one.
"Norden Green" has its namesake in Sussex, England from where we came some 30 years ago. Our four offspring are now settled in Wellington or thereabouts. Our current "family" consists of Cindy, a friendly old labrador and Smokey, a stray that turned up one morning some eight years ago complete with kittens.
Levin offers good shopping and recreational facilities and the district has many tourist attractions. It is in easy reach of Wellington (1h 15mins) and Palmerston North (40mins).
Directions: *We are located 7km south east of Levin on the southern stretch of Arapaepae Rd and 1km south from the junction of Kimberley Rd and Arapaepae Rd (Route 57).*
Please ring for directions.

Levin

Homestay
Address: 44 Queen Street West, Levin
Name: "The Fantails"
Telephone & Fax: (06) 368 9279
Beds: 1 Double, 3 Single, (3 bedrooms)
Bathroom: 1 Ensuite, 1 Guests share
Tariff: B&B (special) Double $60, Single $35, Dinner $20, Children negotiable,
Campervans welcome. Credit Cards. Vouchers accepted.

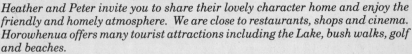

*Heather and Peter invite you to share their lovely character home and enjoy the
friendly and homely atmosphere. We are close to restaurants, shops and cinema.
Horowhenua offers many tourist attractions including the Lake, bush walks, golf
and beaches.*
*Our bedrooms are quiet and comfortable. Beds have woollen underlays and
electric blankets.*
*Our guests' lounge offers great relaxation. We provide refreshments on arrival and
supper. Our breakfasts are delicious.*
*Heather and myself enjoy meeting people and making new
friends. Our interests include music, antiques and
community activities.*
*From our "Fantails Gallery" we offer you an exciting and
special range of New Zealand made arts and crafts.*
*As we are non smokers we request you do not smoke
indoors.*

*We are happy to collect you from and deliver you back to
public transport. It is 75 minutes drive from "The Fantails"
to "The Ferry".*
Directions: *Turn off State Highway One at the Post Office
onto Queen Street West. We are just past the roundabout
opposite the Aquatic Centre.*

Please let your hosts know if you have to cancel.
They will have spent time preparing for you.

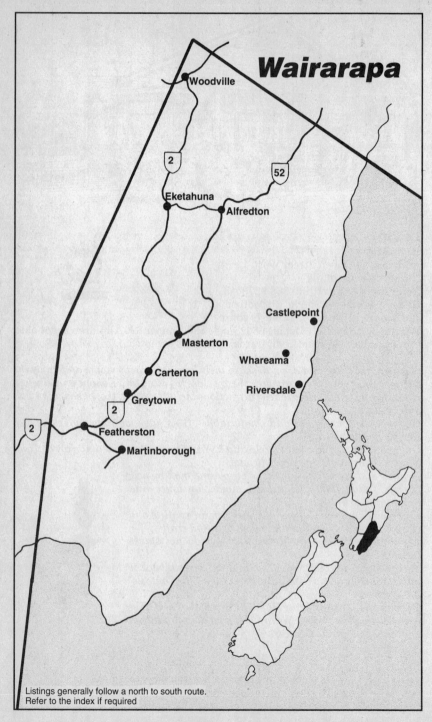

Wairarapa

Woodville

2

52

Eketahuna

Alfredton

Castlepoint

Masterton

Whareama

Carterton

Riversdale

Greytown

2

2

Featherston

Martinborough

Listings generally follow a north to south route.
Refer to the index if required

Woodville
Farmstay/Self-contained accommodation
Address: River Road, Hopelands, Woodville RD1
Name: Chris and Jo Coats
Telephone: (06) 376 4521
Beds: 1 Double, 2 Single (2 bedrooms) **Bathroom**: 1 Family share
Tariff: B&B (full) SCA $60, Single $30 Children half price; Dinner $18, Vouchers accepted between March & December.
Nearest Town: 12 km North East of Woodville off SH 2

We are sheep and cattle farmers on a hill country farm beside the beautiful Manawatu River which is noted for its trout fishing.
The family have fled the nest but return from time to time, seeking quiet from their busy lives.
Depending on the time of year, farming activities of possible interest to tourists may be in progress, i.e. mustering, shearing, etc. and you will be very welcome to participate.
The double bed accommodation is a self-contained unit with it's own toilet and handbasin but no shower facility. Guests share the bathroom facilities if they require a shower.
Directions: *If travelling on Highway 2 between Woodville and Dannevirke - take the Hopelands Road and follow it right to the end. Cross the single way, high bridge over the Manawatu River, turn right, heading towards Pahiatua, and the fourth house (blue) is where 'Welcome' is on the mat.*

Eketahuna
Farmstay
Address: "Tidsfordriv",
RD 3, Eketahuna
Name: Ted and Glenys Hansen
Telephone: (06) 375-8474 evenings
(24 hours notice if possible, please)
Beds: 2 Single (1 bedroom) **Bathroom**: 1 Family share
Tariff: B&B (Full) Double $60, Single $35, Dinner $15, Campervans $20, Credit cards accepted, Vouchers accepted
Nearest Town: Eketahuna 10 km, Masterton 50 km

It will be worth your while to divert off the main highway to visit us on our 700 acre hill country sheep farm. We are the third generation to live on our farm. Black and coloured sheep can also be seen when Ted gives you a tour around the farm in a comfortable 4WD vehicle.
Our home is 70 years old, has recently been modernised and is warm and comfortable. We invite you to join us for dinner. A friendly cat and two labrador dogs are the families pets, though the dogs are not allowed inside.
All the family are active members in a waterfowl conservation group - Ducks Unlimited (NZ) Inc. There are waterfowl on ponds and in aviaries to view.
We recommend a visit to the National Wildlife Centre at Mt Bruce, just 23 km south on State Highway 2. Glenys is involved with the Centre and is more than happy to talk about the work that is being done there.
Directions: *Turn off SH2 south end of Eketahuna and follow road to Alfredton for 10 km. Good sealed road. Farm name on gate.*

Eketahuna

Farmstay
Address: "Mount Donald",
Newman, R.D. 4, Eketahuna
Name: Jim & Lynne Sutherland
Telephone: (06) 375-8315
Beds: 1 Double, 2 Single (2 bedrooms)
Bathroom: 1 Private
Tariff: B&B (full) Double $80, Single $40, Dinner $20, Children
half price, Campervans welcome. Vouchers accepted April to October.
Nearest Town: Eketahuna 5km south, Pahiatua 20km north

You will receive a warm welcome when you stay with us on our 1200 acre sheep and cattle property. Your accommodation is attached to our 90 year old homestead and is spacious, comfortable and private.

You can choose many farm activities plus tramping and shooting, Four wheel drive trips, trout fishing and ponies. Our interests include golf on our local picturesque 18 hole course, gardening with our own cottage garden nursery and dried flowers.

We enjoy hosting guests from all over the world and do our very best to ensure your stay here is enjoyable. Your meals are all home cooked and fresh garden produce used when in season.

A visit to the National Wildlife Centre is a must whilst in our area and is only a 10 minute drive from us.

We are a good stop over point before or after Inter-Island Ferry travel. Wellington City a 2 hour drive, Palmerston North 45 minutes.

We are very easy to find, look for our sign on State Highway 2. The homestead is 600 metres up Central Mangaone Road.

Alfredton

Farmstay
Address: Te Hoe Station, Alfredton, RD 3, Eketahuna
Name: Peter and Venetia Bateman
Telephone: (06) 375 0600
Beds: 1 Double, 2 Single (2 bedrooms) **Bathroom:** 1 Guests share
Tariff: B&B (full) Double $60, Single $35, Dinner $20, Children under 12yrs half price, Vouchers accepted
Nearest Town: 18km East of Eketahuna

We are 40 minutes north of Masterton and 15 minutes east of Eketahuna. Set in lovely, established grounds, the 1924 "Heathcote Hellmore" homestead has its own 'guest wing' with private bathroom, swimming pool and gardens for you to enjoy. For the more energetic, there are 2000 acres of farm land to explore, including a large patch of native bush. Nearby there is golf, tennis and fishing. Please ring us.

Masterton
Small Farmstay + Self-Contained
Accommodation
Address: Harefield, 147 Upper Plain Road,
Masterton
Name: Robert and Marion Ahearn
Telephone: (06) 377-4070
Beds: 1 Double, 1 Single (1 bedroom) **Bathroom**: 1 Private
Detached, fully equipped, self-contained flat, self catering, - 1 Double, 1 Single
(1 bedroom) + 1 Single & 1 fold-down Double in living room. Cot & Highchair
available. **Bathroom:** 1 Private
Tariff: B&B (full) Double $60, Single $35, Children under 12 half price. Dinner
$15-$20, Campervans $20. Vouchers accepted
Self-contained Flat Double $50, $5 each extra person
Nearest Town: Masterton 4kms - 1km from Bypass.

*We are farmers whose family have all left home. Fourteen years ago we built our
cedar house on 13 acres, 5 km from the Post Office, 1 km from Bypass Road.*
*Our guest room is away from the kitchen and our bedroom. A cottage garden
surrounds the house and flat, 200 metres back from the road.*
*We look out on to the beautiful Tararua mountains and paddocks with sheep,
cattle and deer.*
*We have been home hosting for some years and have ourselves been guests in
Europe, Australia and New Zealand.*
*Our interests include travel, reading, arts, tramping, wild life, walking, gardening,
Rose Society, Probus Club, workshop. We are half an hour's drive to Martinborough
vineyards.*
*If you stay in the flat you can choose to be self-catering or arrange dinner and
breakfast with us. Guests in the house may also arrange dinner. Complimentary
tea and coffee at any time. Excellent restaurants 8 minutes away.*
Reductions for longer stays.
*We are half an hour's drive to the National Wildlife Centre and less than two hour's
drive from the Inter-Island Ferry.*
We do not smoke - you may.

Lansdowne, Masterton
Homestay
Address: 65 Titoki Street, Lansdowne, Masterton
Name: Gordon and Doreen McNeilage
Telephone: (06) 377 3817
Beds: 1 Double, 2 Single (2 bedrooms) **Bathroom:** 1 Guests share
Tariff: B&B (continental) Double $55, Single $35, Children $20, Vouchers
accepted.
Nearest Town: Masterton - 2km north Masterton on SH1 turn right.

*We are a family of four, plus one sleepy cat. We are fortunate to live in the beautiful
suburb of Lansdowne, about one mile north of the town of Masterton.*
*Our home is nearly fifty years old and we have altered and improved it to give us
more living space. It is surrounded by gardens and has an outdoor court area.*
You may have family dinner with us or, if you prefer, only bed and breakfast.
*Masterton has a lovely park, attractive shops and restaurants. It is a very
appealing town and we wish to extend warm, friendly hospitality.*

New Zealand's
Federation of Bed &
Breakfast Hotels

Masterton
Bed & Breakfast
Address: 15 Victoria Street, Masterton
Name: Victoria House
Telephone: (06) 377 0186
Beds: 3 Double, 4 Single (6 bedrooms)
Bathroom: 2 Guests share
Tariff: B&B (continental) Double $60, Single $39, Dinner $20, not suitable children under 12. Vouchers accepted.
Nearest Town: 100km north of Wellington on State Highway 2

Welcome to Victoria House. We are forty and have three sons. Our home is a beautiful colonial two storey house built pre 1886. We have renovated the guests' accommodation, keeping the character of the house, while retaining home comforts. (We even stripped light fittings back to the brass and wood).

The guests' bedrooms are like your own room away from home. Furnished colonial style and decorated in soft tonings to create a peaceful atmosphere. All rooms equipped with heaters. Some have handbasins. There are two guests bathrooms, tea, coffee, milo available at all times. There is a comfortable TV lounge where smoking is permitted (No smoking in bedrooms).

Our tariff includes a continental breakfast but cooked can happily be arranged. A home cooked evening meal is available (by prior arrangement). We aim for quality accommodation that's warm and friendly.

Set in a quiet location we are 2 minutes walk from the town centre and many excellent facilities. No pets.

Masterton
Farmstay/Farmlet
Address: "Langtry House", RD 1 Masterton, S.H. 2, Fire No 54
Name: Janet White
Telephone: (06) 378 6085
Beds: 1 King, 1 Queen, 1 Double, 3 Single (4 bedrooms) **Bathroom:** 1 Ensuite (King), 1 Guests share
Tariff: B&B (full) Double with ensuite $40 pp, Other $35pp, Dinner $15-20, Campervans welcome. Vouchers accepted.
Nearest Town: Masterton. 7kms Nth of Masterton on SH2

Langtry House is an original Colonial cottage, shifted, added to, but retaining its' original atmosphere. All guest bedrooms are upstairs. Large lounge and open fire downstairs and the home stands in the middle of an extensive perennial garden, (in demand for weddings!) and surrounded by 15 acres of farmland with various animals therein, except Scarpia the hunter, who seems to get 'thereout' regularly! Guests may try shearing a sheep, milking a cow when in season or wandering down to the nearby Ruamahunga River with our Labrador to find a rabbit.
Local tourist hotspots include the Vintage Farming Museum 5 mins away, (excellent!); Mt. Bruce Wildlife Reserve 10 mins, also easy driving to local open gardens for which Wairarapa is famous.
My interests include opera, horsing around, spinning, sport and listening! Our 4 grown children pop in occasionally otherwise guests have the house to themselves and me. I look forward to meeting you!
Directions: *7 minutes north of Masterton on SH2.*

Whareama, Masterton
Farmstay
Address: "Alderford" RD12 Masterton
Name: Carol & Les Ross
Telephone: (06) 372 3705
Beds: 1 Double (1 Bedroom) **Bathroom:** 1 Ensuite
Tariff: B&B (continental - full $5pp extra) Double $65, Single $40, Dinner $20 (3 course), Vouchers accepted
Nearest Town: Masterton 40km 1/2 hour, Wellington 2 hours

Les and Carol offer you a warm friendly welcome to "Alderford".
Stay in our tastefully decorated warm cottage room with ensuite, away from the main homestead. Cosy double bed, electric blanket, feather duvet, radio, TV, 2 easy chairs. Also tea, coffee, Milo and homemade biscuits on your arrival. Your breakfast served in you room or in the garden. Picnic lunches available. Dinner served in our dining room with open fire. Homemade country meals with our homemade jam, bottled fruit, fresh veges from garden, free range eggs.
Alderford is a 300 acre sheep, cattle and deer farm. You are very welcome to join in the farm activities or enjoy our country garden. We are 10 minutes to the beautiful Riversdale Beach with lovely 9 hole golf course, swimming, fishing etc. We are 10 minutes to the well known Tinui pub, craft shop, open gardens and 25 mins to the beauty of Castlepoint Beach. We also arrange canoe trips for your enjoyment.
Our interests include our garden, fishing, cooking and Lions Club activities.
"Alderford" is a 30 min picturesque drive from Masterton.

Tell other travellers about your favourite B&Bs

Riversdale
Farmstay
Address: "Waikaraka" RD 12, Homewood Road near Riversdale Beach, Masterton, Wairarapa
Name: Simon Burt
Telephone & Fax: (06) 372 3338
Beds: 4 Double, 6 Single (6 Bedrooms) **Bathroom:** 2 Guests share
Tariff: B&B (full) Double $50, Single $25, School Children half price, Dinner $20, Campervans $25, Vouchers accepted
Nearest Town: Riversdale Beach 10km, Masterton 60km

Don't you deserve a real break? A holiday where you swim at your own private beach, play a round of golf at a country course or enjoy a good book in the shade of a tree. Where a group of family or friends can take over the whole place, if they like. But at the same time you are not breaking the bank.

Waikaraka Runaway is located on a 500 acre sheep and cattle farm 63km from Masterton and 10km south of Riversdale in the sunny Wairarapa. Just a delightful walk across the farm (or you can drive) is an extremely private swimming and fishing beach and lagoon. Other nearby beaches include the very safe Uriti Bay (fabulous fishing and safe diving) White Swan beach and the popular seaside resort of Riversdale, all within 15 minutes drive.

The nearest shop is at Riversdale Beach. Riversdale also offers an excellent golf course and all weather tennis courts.

The comfortable old Waikaraka Homestead hosts up to 14 people. The spacious kitchen features a rayburn stove where guests may prepare their own meals if they wish. Horses are available for riding.

Carterton
Small Farmstay
Address: "Longmeadow" Park Road RD2 Carterton
Name: John & Viv Stokes
Telephone: (06) 379 7897
Beds: 1 Double, 2 Single (2 Bedrooms) **Bathroom:** 1 Guests share
Tariff: B&B (full) Double $60, Single $35, Children half price, Dinner $15-$20, Vouchers accepted
Nearest Town: Carterton

Welcome to "Longmeadow", which is situated in a quiet rural setting surrounded by picturesque views of the Tararua Ranges and rolling farmland.

Our 25 acre farmlet with sheep, cattle, donkey and fowls is just the place to relax yet only 2km from the town of Carterton.

Come and stay one night or two on your journey through the Wairarapa as Carterton is central to the region's attractions from the Martinborough vineyards to the Mount Bruce Bird Reserve, tramping in the ranges, jetboating etc, etc.

We are a (very young!) middle aged couple with our youngest son 13 still at home and we enjoy meeting people, gardening and just pottering around our place. Our aim is to provide a friendly relaxed atmosphere to make you stay in the area as enjoyable as possible. Evening meal by arrangement.

We request no smoking in the house.

Directions: *Please write or phone. Arrangements can be made to collect from public transport.*

Greytown
Homestay
Address: 40 Kuratawhiti Street, Greytown
Name: Dinah and Max Edridge
Telephone: (06) 304 9942
Beds: 2 Double, 1 Single (2 bedrooms)
Bathroom: 1 Ensuite, 1 Family share
Tariff: B&B (full) Double with ensuite $80, Double $70, Single $55, School children $15, under 5 free, Vouchers accepted only from Monday to Thursday of each week

... A touch of country ...
... A place of peace ...
Set in 1.6 h amongst historic trees, our pre-1900 brick homestead fully restored, with sunny verandahs complements the generous welcome and care enjoyed by our guests.
Facilities have been specially designed for elderly or disabled.
Our five elder children are now mostly away from home. Our thirteen year old son shares the delights of our property with his dog and cat, some sheep, a trampoline and hot spa.
Every season brings its special delights as you enjoy the picturesque beauty of the southern Wairarapa. Within short distances you can enjoy gentle bush and river walks or serious tramping, canoeing, tennis, cycling (bikes available), swimming, orchards, berry picking, craft and wine making areas, beautiful gardens, surfing, fishing.
We will enjoy sharing your company but will respect your desire for privacy if you wish to 'just be' and relax.
Directions: *please write or phone.*

Featherston
Farmstay + Self-Contained Cottage
Address: "Waituna", East West Access Road,
R.D. 3 Featherston.
Name: Irwin & Kay Luttrell
Telephone: (06) 307-7743
Beds: Homestead: 1 Double, 1 Queen, 2 Single
(3 bedrooms)
Bathroom: 1 Guests share, 1 Ensuite
Cottage: 1 Queen, 1 Double, 1 set of Bunks + 1 single.
Bedsettee (in lounge) (3 bedrooms) Sleeps 6-8.
Tariff: B&B (special) Double from $80, Single from $60, children 1/2 price,
Dinner: Gourmet 3 course with wine. Packed lunch a specialty. Vouchers
accepted Monday to Thursday.
Nearest Town: Featherston or Martinborough (approx 26 km from either)

*We, Irwin and Kay, offer you a warm friendly welcome and invite you to stay with
us at 'Waituna Homestead'. Luxurious accommodation with tea, coffee, milo,
homemade biscuits in your room for late night or early morning snacks. Breakfast,
continental or special at anytime you choose. Lazy morning or afternoon teas while
you relax by the fire or enjoy the parklike gardens. Picnic lunches on the farm, by
the river or at the beach. Visits to vineyards, museums, seal colony, canoeing,
fishing, bush walks, golf, tennis, gliding, craft shops, open gardens all within easy
reach. At the end of the day relax with pre-dinner drinks and share the days
experiences. Enjoy a sumptuous three course dinner with wine. Homemade sweets
to follow.*

*'Waituna Cottage'. Your cottage in the country! Enjoy the peace and tranquillity
with warm fires in winter, lazy BBQs in summer. Fresh flowers and homemade
biscuits to welcome you. Self catering or homestead meals. Relax in the picturesque
homestead gardens.*

Directions: *Please phone us anytime for more information.*

Martinborough

**Country Homestay &
Self-contained Accommodation**
Address: Oldham House,
108 Regent St, Martinborough
Name: Ineke & David Kershaw
Telephone: (06) 306 9805 **Fax:** (06) 306 9237
Beds: Homestead: 1 Double, 1 Single (1 bedroom) **Bathrooms:** 1 Private
Separate Self contained unit: 1 Queen, **Brick House:** 1 Queen, 4 Single (3 bedrooms)
Tariff: B&B (full) Double $70-$100, Single $60-$80, Children negotiable. Credit cards. Vouchers accepted.
Nearest Town: Featherston or Greytown 15 min, Wellington 1 1/4 hrs

If you enjoy old character homes with wood panelling and leadlight, set in large established gardens with country atmosphere and welcoming, friendly hosts, then you will enjoy a stay with us.

Our comfortable, attractive guest accommodation incorporates former staff quarters so facilities are private and separate, yet the rooms are sunny and spacious with lovely rural and/or garden views.

Also available nearby, is a newly decorated three bedroomed brick house.

A hearty breakfast is served at leisure in our wood panelled dining room, which has an open fire and verandah.

Set on 10 acres of farmland, opposite the tennis club, our home is with in walking distance of restaurants, vineyards and golf course.

David is a third generation Martinborough retailer and I (Ineke) work at home looking after the house, garden, our 4 children (three at boarding school) and of course, our guests, who to us, are all VIP's.

TV, private pool, bikes and sports gear available.

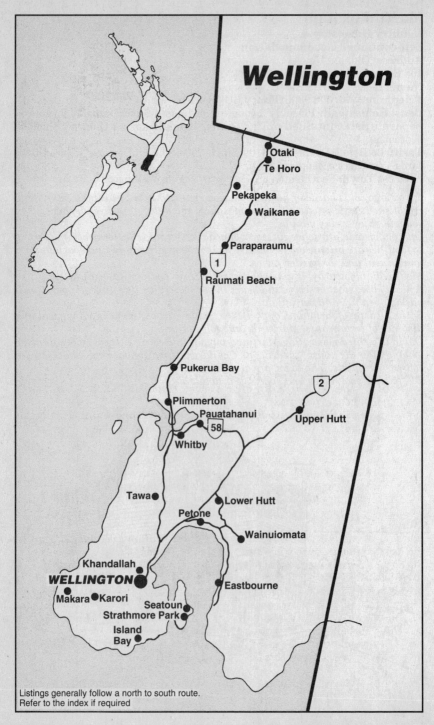

Wellington

Otaki
Te Horo
Pekapeka
Waikanae
Paraparaumu
1
Raumati Beach
Pukerua Bay
Plimmerton
Pauatahanui
2
58
Whitby
Upper Hutt
Tawa
Lower Hutt
Petone
Wainuiomata
Khandallah
WELLINGTON
Makara Karori
Seatoun
Strathmore Park
Eastbourne
Island
Bay

Listings generally follow a north to south route.
Refer to the index if required

Otaki

Homestay
Address: Waitohu Lodge,
294 State Highway 1 North, Otaki
Name: Keith & Mary Oldham
Telephone: (06) 364 5389
Beds: 1 Queen, 3 Single (3 bedrooms), Guest lounge
Bathroom: 1 Guests share
Tariff: B&B (continental with cooked course on request at $5 extra pp) Double/twin $65, Single $40, Dinner by arrangement $20pp, Child $20. Credit cards accepted, Vouchers accepted
Nearest Town: Equidistant 50mins north of Wellington and south of Palmerston North

Kiaora, welcome to sunny Otaki, the first country town north of Wellington and gateway to the Wellington region and the Kapiti Coast.

At Waitohu Lodge we offer you warm hospitality, quality accommodation and the many comforts of our spacious, modern, well appointed home.

Guests appreciate their warm comfortable beds, luxury bathroom with spa bath and shower and guest lounge with opportunity for 'time out' to relax in peace and privacy.

Meals are generous and in season feature fresh fruit and vegetables from our garden with home made muesli and preserves at breakfast.

Ideally located as an interisland ferry stopover we are only 50 minutes drive from Wellington and the Picton ferry. Easy to find we are set back from the highway in 3/4 acre of attractive gardens with secure onsite parking for guests.

We enjoy the natural beauty of the bush and rivers of the Tararua Forest Park, Heritage Trails, garden visits, local wines, art, craft, and restaurants.

Excellent golfing and year round swimming also ensure an enjoyable stay for tired city dwellers and travellers alike. Special weekend packages available.

We and our two character cats look forward to meeting you..

Non smokers preferred.

Directions: *State Highway 1, 100 metres south of the 50k sign as you enter Otaki from the North. 100 metres south of the 100k sign before you leave Otaki from the South.*

Otaki
Country Homestay
Address: "Glenmore"
Rahui Road Otaki
Name: Jack & Heather Bellaney
Telephone: (06) 364 7319
Fax: (06) 364 7797
Beds: 1 King, 2 Single (2 Bedrooms)
Bathroom: 1 Guests share
Tariff: B&B (full) Double $60/$65, Single $40, Dinner $20, Vouchers accepted
Nearest Town: Levin/Paraparaumu 15 mins, Wellington/Palmerston North 55 mins

We invite you to enjoy 'small town hospitality' in our modern home overlooking Otaki Racecourse and Kapiti Island. Our 5 acre property has been developed to create a peaceful rural setting incorporating extensive gardens, small farmlet, bush and lagoon. Views are superb from all rooms.

We offer a courtesy car to and from local transport and scenic tours can be arranged as well as help with ongoing travel.

Being in our mid-fifties we enjoy the outdoors and travel and Jack is a keen fisherman. We are both members of the Lions International service club.

Our guests bathroom has a spa bath, and a guests lounge is available. We do request that guests don't smoke inside.

Situated in the country we are only a few minutes from the main highway, shops, restaurants, beach, river and forest park, so everything is at our 'back door'.

OUR AIM IS TO MAKE YOUR STAY IN OTAKI BOTH MEMORABLE AND ENJOYABLE.

Directions: *Please telephone or write.*

Te Horo, Otaki
Homestay

Address: "Wairakau"
Sims Road, Te Horo
Name: Ray and Irene Mackle
Telephone: (06) 364 3367
Beds: 1 Double, 1 Twin, 1 Single, (3 bedrooms)
Bathroom: 2 Guests share, 1 Family share
Tariff: B&B (full) Double $60, Single $35, Dinner $15, Vouchers accepted
Nearest Town: Otaki 10 km

Our large home is on 10 acres of bush and farmland. A half minute walk through the trees takes you to our secluded beach where we gather shellfish in the summer and swim. The views take in the South Island mountains, Kapiti Island, and Mt Taranaki in the north. We are 5km west of State Highway One and bus services, and 10km from Otaki and the nearest Railway Station, and one hour from Palmerston North and also from Wellington and the Inter-Island Ferries.

Some of our local attractions are: fishing - surf and trout, Kapiti Island trips, Southwards Car Museum, white water rafting, excellent local restaurants, famous Rangiatea Church, tramping , bush walks, hunting, horse riding, and some world renowned potters.

If you wish, we can arrange to escort you on any of these ventures.

We have raised a large family, who have now left home, and are used to cooking wholesome farm meals.

We are able to meet you at the bus or train, and by agreement, provide local transport. Kia Ora.

Te Horo, Otaki

Homestay
Address: 'Stone Pine Creek', Settlement Road, Te Horo
Name: Lorraine and Kerry Hoggard
Telephone: (06) 364 3140
Beds: 1 Double, 1 Single (1 bedroom + Guests sitting area) Bathroom: 1 Private
Tariff: B&B (special) Double $80, Single $50, Dinner $25, Vouchers accepted
Nearest Town: Otaki 8km away, 1hr drive from Wellington

Our home is an Italian style farmhouse set in 12 acres of farmland with a backdrop of rolling hills and panoramic sea views. You'll wake in the gatehouse to views of Kapiti Island. Your separate accommodation contains a mezzanine sleeping area, sitting area and your own bathroom. Tea and coffee facilities provided. This all sits within a walled courtyard along with a swimming pool for summer use and a lawn to laze on.

You are welcome to join us for delicious homecooked meals, breakfast or dinner (wine included).

We have lived in Te Horo for approximately 3 years and are still creating our country garden - lavender being a speciality. Our interests include people, books, gardening, music, art, theatre and travel. We are small farmers with a few sheep, (black and white) cows, ducks and 2 friendly dogs.

Within short distances you may walk in the bush or by the sea, investigate craft places, pick berries, play tennis and golf or just enjoy the peace. We can assure you of a warm welcome and an interesting stay.

One hours drive from Wellington. Non smokers please.
Directions: *Please write or phone.*

Tariffs are constant for this year. However some
may have had to change slightly. Always check.

Te Horo, Otaki

Homestay
Address: 101 School Road, Te Horo
Telephone: (06) 364 2063
Beds: 1 Double (1 Bedroom)
Bathroom: 1 Private
Tariff: B&B (Special) Double $80,
Single $45, Dinner $25, Vouchers accepted
Nearest Town: Wellington 50km on SH1

Lois McKewen and Robin Clulee moved - with children aged 13 and 10 plus cat and dog - to Te Horo from Wellington in 1992. Lois does community work and garden things. Robin divides his time as a communications consultant between an office in Wellington and home. The house has the look of a Cape Dutch farm barn - white plastered walls and exposed timber beams and ceilings. The house and a solar-heated swimming pool sit in a large garden under development. The property is 5ha and being developed as a pear and apple orchard. Guests have exclusive use of a bathroom next to the bedroom and may have privacy, if desired, in an adjacent snug sitting room. Rafting and kayaking in the Otaki River Gorge, tramping in the Tararua ranges, golf at two courses, a winery and restaurant, nurseries and gardens are all available within a 15 minute radius. Lois is a first-class cook and will endeavour to satisfy any special dietary needs.

Peka Peka

**Farmstay (due to alterations we
will be opening February 1995)**
Address: Te Hapua Rd, R.D. 1, Otaki
Telephone: (06) 364 2130
Beds: 1 Double, 3 Single (2 Bedrooms/1 Bedroom
includes 1 double + 1 single) **Bathroom:** 1 Guests share
Tariff: B&B (continental) Double $65, Single $40, Dinner by arrangement,
Vouchers accepted
Nearest Town: Waikanae

Our 20 acre farmlet is 6.5km north of Waikanae and just off State Highway 1. We have a herd of Angora goats, black sheep and cattle. Our home is spacious, sunny and peaceful.
We are 45 mins drive from the InterIsland Ferry and provide an ideal base to explore both the Kapiti Coast and the Wellington Region. We can provide information on the many places of interest in the area - Southwards Car Museum, Lindale Tourist and Agricultural Centre and Ngamanu Bird and Wildlife Sanctuary. We enjoy the relaxation of the country lifestyle but are close to the excitement of the Capital City.
A good selection of restaurants are available or dinner can be provided given reasonable notice. A continental breakfast is provided and special meals also on request. Transport is available if required. As we are non smokers guests are requested not to smoke indoors.
We enjoy travelling, have many interests and enjoy meeting people. We look forward to making your stay with us an enjoyable one.
Due to alterations we will be opening February 1995. Please phone to confirm.
Directions: *Please phone.*

Waikanae

Homestay
Address: "Waimoana", 63 Kakariki Grove, Waikanae
Name: Ian & Phyllis Stewart
Telephone: (04) 293-7158
Beds: 2 Double, 2 Single (2 bedrooms)
Bathroom: 2 Ensuite
Tariff: B&B (special) Double $100, Single $60,
Dinner by arrangement: 4 courses with complimentary sherry and wine $30.
Credit Cards. Vouchers accepted.
Nearest Town: 58km north of Wellington on State Highway 1

We are a recently retired couple. We have two adult daughters who visit home when they can. Our centrally heated home is new and spacious, with every modern facility.

We have two guest rooms. Each offers deluxe accommodation, with both a queen-size and a single bed and ensuite facilities. They share a spacious balcony for admiring the fantastic views of Kapiti Island.

In the centre of the house is an internal swimming pool, with a waterfall set about with rocks and garden. We use fresh local produce. Dine with us by lamplight or select one of the excellent restaurants nearby.

And when you feel ready to explore a little, beach and river, bird sanctuary, bush walks and pottery and craft shops are all nearby. Visit Southward's Car Museum or take a scenic helicopter flight.

We have no pets and our home is smoke-free.

45 mins to inter-island ferry.

Directions: *Please telephone.*

Would you like three weeks free B&B for two people?
Complete the page at the front of the book.

Waikanae

Self-contained Accommodation
Address: "Allenby",
12 Te Maku Grove, Waikanae
Name: Quintin & Meg Hogg
Telephone: (04) 293 2428
Beds: 2 Single (1 bedroom)
Bathroom: 1Ensuite
Tariff: B&B (full) Double $65, Single $40,
Dinner $20-25, Vouchers accepted

*We offer a warm comfortable twin bed unit which opens onto a sunny terrace and
conservatory. Ensuite, private shower, basin and toilet. Laundry facilities also
available.*
*Guests will be provided with continental or cooked breakfast as desired. Tea and
coffee making facilities in room. Dinner can be provided given reasonable notice
or we can recommend excellent restaurants in Waikanae or nearby Paraparaumu
Waikanae has a temperate climate, good beaches, wildlife sanctuaries, bush
walks, golf course, arts and crafts, and is close to world famous Southwards
Vintage Car Museum and Lindale Farm complex. We are handy to Wellington and
the Interisland Ferry Terminal (45 minutes by car).*
*We are keen gardeners and have travelled widely in New Zealand and overseas in
Australia, U.S.A., U.K. and Europe. Interests include music, embroidery, trout
fishing, and meeting people. We welcome non smokers.*
*Please phone for directions (1km off SH1) or will meet travellers arriving by train
or bus.*

Waikanae Beach

Homestay
Address: 115 Tutere St, Waikanae
Name: Jeanette & Bryce Jones
Telephone: (04) 293-6532
Beds: 2 Double, 3 Single (3 bedrooms)
Bathroom: 1 Guests share, 1 Private toilet
Tariff: B&B (special) Double $65, Single $45
Dinner $18, Children $20, under 5 free, Vouchers accepted
Nearest Town: Waikanae, 4km

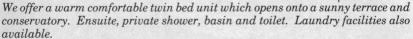

*With direct access to the beach 30 metres away, our home is ideal if you want beach
walks, safe swimming and going to sleep with the sound of the sea. Two guest
rooms have sea viewsThe double room has tea and coffee making facilities. Our
special breakfast is served upstairs with panoramic views of the ocean and Kapiti
Island, a renowned Native Bird Santuary. On a good day Bryce may be able to
take you across to the Island on his boat (a DOC permit to land is required) or try
a spot of fishing.*
*Our home is warm and sunny and we greatly appreciate sharing it with friends
and family. We have lived here practically all our lives, having farmed in the
district many years. Bryce was an R.A.F. Pathfinder pilot in WWII.*
We have both travelled extensively and enjoy exchanging experiences.
*You may share an evening meal with us. Children welcome. Non smokers
preferred. Our only pet is a bright Cairn terrier called Ben.*
Directions: *Please telephone*

Paraparaumu Beach

Homestay
Address: 65 Eatwell Ave,
Paraparaumu Beach
Name: John and Alethea Sargent
Telephone & Fax: (04) 297 0052
Beds: 1 Double, 2 Single (2 bedrooms)
Bathroom: 1 Guests share
Tariff: B&B (continental) Double $60, Single $35,
Dinner $20, Campervans welcome. Vouchers accepted.
Nearest Town: Paraparaumu, 55km north of Wellington on State Highway 1

Our modern Mediterranean style home has all rooms opening onto a swimming pool, spa pool and BBQ area, offering a unique style of indoor / outdoor living. We enjoy our garden and a relaxed lifestyle. Our home is comfortable and warm with electric blankets and duvets on the beds.

We are a few minutes walking distance from the Paraparaumu Beach shopping area, a safe swimming beach and an international golf course. There are a wide variety of interesting attractions on the Kapiti Coast - shopping malls, restaurants, museums, bird sanctuaries, bush walks, craft and pottery, artist galleries, golf driving range, covered swimming pool etc.

We have travelled extensively, both in New Zealand and overseas and now that our 3 children - 1 son and 2 daughters have left home, we would like to return some 'Kiwi' hospitality to other travelling guests.

Our varied interests include our garden, music and handcrafts.

There is off-street parking for campervans if you wish.

Directions: *Please phone.*

Raumati Beach

Homestay
Address: "Woodbury" 1 Kohutuhutu Road,
Raumati Beach
Name: Nancy & David Anderson
Telephone: (04) 297 3003
Beds: 1 Queen (1 Bedroom)
Bathroom: 1 Private
Tariff: B&B (full) Double $70, Single $45,
Dinner $25, Vouchers accepted
Nearest Town: Paraparaumu - 5 minutes away

A warm welcome awaits you at Woodbury - a picturesque Devon cottage set amidst mature trees, just yards from Raumati Beach.

Your private guest house, with a charm of its own, has ensuite facilities, is sunny and warm. A tiled swimming pool is adjacent to the house with your own private patio.

Join us for continental and full breakfast - al fresco or in our dining room.

A world class vintage car museum, Lindale farm - famous for its exquisite cheeses and icecream; and a New Zealand artists gallery are but a few of the many highlights of the Kapiti Coast (and very close to Woodbury) that you can visit.

We're just 40 minutes from Wellington city. We love meeting people - join us for a pre-dinner drink. If you prefer to eat out there are good local restaurants nearby.

I am interested in water colour painting, gardening and cooking, and we both love old things; and theatre, travel and restoring homes.

Directions: *Please phone or write.*

Plimmerton
Homestay
Address: 12 Roys Road, Plimmerton, Wellington
Name: Cren & Rae Collins
Telephone: (04) 2331-367
Beds: 2 Single (1 bedroom) **Bathroom:** 1 Ensuite
Tariff: B&B (full) Double $50, Single $30, Dinner $15
Nearest Town: Porirua, (10 mins drive South)

We are retired sheepfarmers with a grown up family of three. We enjoy reading, watching TV, tramping, croquet and bridge.
Our house is homely and is set on the hill overlooking Karehana Bay, half an hour's drive from Wellington. We have a great view out to Mana Island and Cook Strait. It is a fifteen minute walk down to Plimmerton Village whose shops provide food and essentials. There is good swimming on the safe beaches and rocks to explore.
Directions: *Please phone*

Plimmerton
Homestay
Address: 131 Pope Street,
Plimmerton, Wellington
Name: Joan and Denis Sawkins
Telephone: (04) 233 9444
Beds: 1 Queen (1 bedroom)
Bathroom: Private
Tariff: B&B (full) Double $70, Single $40, Dinner $20. Vouchers accepted.
Nearest Town: Wellington 20 mins, Porirua 5 mins

If you are heading to the South Island, we are 200 metres from State Highway 1, just 20 minutes north of Wellington, so a convenient stopover before the inter-island ferry terminal or airport.
The view from our sunny home is a sea view, looking west to the sunset, Cook Strait and the South Island. We are close to a railway station and Plimmerton beach, which is safe for swimming.
Our spacious home is modern, comfortable and relaxing. Our guest bedroom and bathroom are private, upstairs away from the living area.
As a couple we have travelled extensively, enjoying the hospitality of others, and would enjoy welcoming travellers such as yourself to our home. We both work partially from home, and our interests include gardening, travel, wine and food. Our extended grown-up family are in many parts of New Zealand and overseas.
Directions: *Please telephone ahead of your arrival.*

Private bathroom is for your use exclusively,
Guests share means you may be sharing with other guests,
Family share means you will be sharing with the family.

Plimmerton

Homestay
Address: 57 Pope St, Plimmerton, Wellington
Name: Jill & Ned Pattle
Telephone: (04) 233 8329
Beds: 2 Single (1 Bedroom) **Bathroom:** 1 Family share
Tariff: B&B (special) Double $50, Single $30, Children half price (not suitable for children under 5), Dinner $20, Vouchers accepted
Nearest Town: Wellington, Porirua, Lower Hutt

We enjoy meeting people and welcoming them to our home. Our street runs directly off State Highway 1 and our house has widespread views of the beautiful Pauatahanui Inlet from every room.

The large, sunny guest room is up six steps away from the living area with easy chairs, tea, coffee making facilities and lots of books - many of them about New Zealand. Our area has good walking tracks to safe swimming beaches, shopping in Plimmerton Village by the sea and several restaurants and cafés close by.

Our interests include skiing, tramping, geology, music and botany. We have travelled in Europe and know New Zealand well.

If guests enjoy walking we can take them to our hut (cabin) in the bush (forest). There is a small charge for transport.

Low-fat diets and allergies can be catered for and our home is smoke free. Guests may use our laundry.

We are happy to meet trains or buses in Porirua or Plimmerton.

Directions: *Please telephone.*

Whitby

Homestay
Address: 4 The Companionway, Whitby
Name: Nola and Vance Russell
Telephone: (04) 234-8851
Beds: 1 Double, 2 Single (2 bedrooms)

Bathroom: 1 Guests share
Tariff: B&B (continental) Double $60, Single $35, Not suitable for young children, Dinner $18, Campervans $15 for 2, $5 each extra. Vouchers accepted.
Nearest Town: 8kms from Porirua, 25km from Wellington

Whitby village is situated 3 kms east of the Paremata bridge, on the Pauatahanui Inlet, set in rolling countryside with a network of interesting walkways.

Our home offers a quiet, comfortable sunny stopover featuring a sheltered private patio and an interesting studio wing.

Centrally located for sightseeing, being equally 25 km from Wellington City, Hutt Valley and Paraparaumu, also well placed for travellers joining or leaving the Cook Strait Ferry. Several Golf Courses are within easy distance. For bird lovers a sanctuary with hides 5 km from our home has a wide range of species.

Vance is a full-time artist, a realist working mainly in watercolour and he welcomes visitors into the studio.

Your hosts are ardent travellers and we enjoy sharing our home with fellow travellers and meeting people from different countries.

Our home is suitable for 2 couples travelling together but otherwise our normal practice is to accept one couple or family at a time. Ours is a smokefree house.

Directions: *Please telephone.*

325

Pauatahanui
Homestay
Address: 'Braebyre'
Flightys Road, Pauatahanui
Name: Randall & Jenny Shaw
Telephone: (04) 235 9311
Fax: (04) 235 9345
Beds: 1 Double, 4 Single (3 bedrooms)
Bathroom: 2 Guests share
Tariff: B&B (special) Double $75, Single $40, Dinner $25, Children $20, Campervans $20. Vouchers accepted.
Nearest Town: Lower Hutt 15km, Porirua 15km

Our spacious architecturally designed home is situated on a quiet rural lifestyle block, just off State Highway 58, and 15 minutes from the cities of Upper Hutt, Lower Hutt and Porirua. The Pauatahanui Inlet is nearby, with its unique Wetlands Reserve and the water activities of wind surfing, yachting, and water skiing. We overlook a popular golf course.

Our private guest wing comprises three bedrooms, two bathrooms and a spa pool. There is ample secure parking and provision for campervans.

We are in our late-forties with a grown-up family who have left home. We enjoy maintaining our picturesque gardens and our special interest is farming eighty mohair goats. Randall is a builder and is actively involved in Rotary. Jenny's hobbies include spinning, embroidery, dress-making and cooking. We enjoy travel and sharing experiences with fellow travellers.

Our guests are welcome to share a three-course meal of home-grown produce and quality New Zealand wines.

Directions: *Please phone.*

Tawa
Homestay
Address: 7 Park Ave.,
Tawa, Wellington.
Name: Colleen & Graham Hooper
Telephone: (04) 232-6731
Beds: 4 Single (2 bedrooms)
Bathrooms: 1 Family share
Tariff: B&B (continental) Double $55, Single $30, Dinner $20, Children half price

Tawa is just off the Motorway, 16km north of Wellington, 10 minutes from the Interisland Ferry.

Our home is in a quiet location with sunny, sheltered private patio and garden area. Nearby are safe beaches, and many sports are catered for locally, several golf courses within 20 minutes drive.

Dinner is available if required or alternatively there is a selection of good restaurants within 5 minutes drive.

We are keen travellers ourselves, both in New Zealand and overseas and interested in all sports, particularly golf, and enjoy walking, gardening and music.

Our Harbour Capital and its environs offer much in scenic beauty and other items of interest to reward those who can spare a brief pause to enjoy it.

Tawa

Homestay
Address: 17 Mascot Street,
Tawa, Wellington
Name: Alf and Jeannette Levick
Telephone: (04) 232 5989
Beds: 1 Queen, 1 Single (two bedrooms)
Bathroom: Family share
Tariff: B&B (full) Double $55, Single $30, Dinner $20pp. Vouchers accepted.
Nearest Town: Wellington

Our home is in a quiet street in the suburb of Tawa.
15 kilometres (10 minutes drive) from the central city. We are nestled on the side of the valley with views over farmland. There are two bedrooms available for guests, one with a queen sized bed and the other with a single bed, both with electric blankets, a writing desk and electric heater in each room. We live in a comfortable family home with a wood burner fire, separate bath and shower and two toilets. You are welcome to use our laundry facilities and swimming pool.
We know New Zealand well and enjoy having people share our home. Freshly ground coffee a specialty, gourmet dinner available, breakfast of your choice, continental or full cooked meal.
Jeannette's interests are: Ikebana, embroidery, knitting, dressmaking and Japanese language.
Alf's interests are: Lions Club, amateur radio, woodwork, Scouts and Toastmasters.

Tawa - Wellington

Homestay
Address: 8 Bishops Glen,
Tawa, Wellington
Name: Christine & Tony Van Rijssel
Telephone: (04) 232 8501,
Fax: (04) 237 4559
Beds: 1 Double, 2 Single (2 bedrooms)
Bathroom: 1 Guests share
Tariff: B&B (continental) Double $60, Single $30, Dinner $15
Nearest Town: Wellington

We offer you a warm welcome to our home, situated in a quiet cul-de-sac with a delightful view over the valley. This is a home away from home.
We speak German, Dutch and English.
Now that our children have left the nest we would enjoy sharing our vast experience of travel with others and also enjoy meeting new people. We enjoy tramping, walking and good food, but most of all we would enjoy meeting you.
We are situated only 15 minutes north of Wellington just off State Highway 1 by car or rail.
We are happy to provide transport from trains and InterIsland Ferries prior to arrangement.
Our guest accommodation is down stairs and therefore very private with underfloor heating. The double bed room has its own tea and coffee making facilities. Feel free to use our laundry.

Wellington - Ohariu Valley
Farmstay
Address: Mill Cottage, Papanui Station,
Boom Rock Road, Ohariu Valley, Wellington
Name: Cliff & Bev Inglis
Telephone: (04) 478 8926
Beds: 1 Double, 1 Twin (2 Bedrooms) **Bathroom:** 1 Guests share
Tariff: B&B (full) Double $76, Single $38, Children under 12 half price, Dinner
$28. Campervans welcome. Vouchers accepted
Nearest Town: Wellington City/Johnsonville 10 minutes/25 minutes

*Bev and Cliff invite you to experience a stay on a coastal high country sheep and
cattle station Wellington's only farm stay only 25 minutes drive from central
Wellington.*
*Arrangements can be made for pick-up and drop off. Entering the Ohariu Valley
opens the gateway to some of the most rugged coastline in the North Island and
the ever-changing waters of Cook Strait with mountain views of the North and
South Islands Wellington's highest point, Colonial Knob, 1500ft is at the north
end of Papanui and at the south end is Boom Rock with its vast collection of sealife,
great fishing, seals during winter months and bird life all year around. A tour of
Papanui with us at no charge is to experience the magic viewed daily will make
your stay with us unforgettable. Available to our guests, walks, cycling, camping
out, horse riding, BBQ on our private beach, during your stay our home is your
home. Phone for directions.*

Lower Hutt
Homestay
Address: 22 Pomare Road, Lower Hutt
Name: Sheridan & Warwick Bishop
Telephone: (04) 566 1735 **or Fax:** (04) 566 40
Beds: 1 Double, 1 Single (2 bedrooms)
Bathroom: 1 Private (one party only taken at a time).
Tariff: B&B (full) Double $75, Single $50, Dinner $25, Vouchers accepted
Nearest Town: Lower Hutt 2km, Wellington 17 km

*Our home is situated on a large gently sloping bush clad section overlooking the
Hutt Valley and Wellington Harbour. The sunny garden is spacious and well
established.*
*With only one teenage son still at home we have room to spare in our 75 year old,
fully redecorated house. The guest rooms are spacious with a queen sized bed in
one and tea / coffee making facilities available. Our home is centrally heated and
you are very welcome to make use of our laundry.*
*Pomare Road is accessed straight off State Highway 2 only 15 minutes or 17
kilometres north of Wellington.*
*We know New Zealand well and have travelled overseas extensively. Sherry enjoys
gardening, cooking and sewing and Warwick is interested in art, photography and
music. We both enjoy travel, films and shows.*
We request that our guests not smoke in the house.
Directions: *Please phone, fax or write.*

Lower Hutt - Korokoro
Homestay
Address: "Western Rise" 10 Stanhope Grove, Korokoro, Lower Hutt
Name: Virginia and Maurice Gibbens
Telephone: (04) 589 1872
Beds: 1 Double, 2 Single (2 bedrooms) **Bathroom:** 1 Guests share
Tariff: B&B (special) $35pp, Dinner $25, Luncheon and vegetarian cuisine by arrangement, Vouchers accepted
Nearest Town: Petone 1km, Lower Hutt 5km, Wellington 12km

Want a restful setting and still in the centre of things?
Just off State Highway 2 (highway to the Wairarapa) you can view Wellington's magnificent Harbour. Watch the planes and boats as you relax over a meal either indoors or out.
We have a large family home which we share with a corgi / fox terrier, Prince and Camelot the cat.
We are in our early 50's and do not smoke, therefore request our guests not to smoke indoors.
Our interests include travel, boating and crafts. Maurice works for the New Zealand Police as a finger print expert and Virginia has always wanted to be involved with home stay so looks forward to sharing time with you.
Laundry facility available at small fee. Service free for persons staying 2 consecutive nights.
We are very handy to all that you wish to see and do. A special feature, being the many native bush walks in the area.
10-15 mins to Picton Ferry. Restaurants, many.
Directions: *Please telephone.*

Lower Hutt
Homestay
Address: 131 Woburn Road, Lower Hutt
Name: Margaret Hamilton
Telephone: (04) 569 9338
Beds: 1 Double (1 bedroom) **Bathroom:** 1 Private
Tariff: B&B (continental) Double $60, Single $45. Vouchers accepted.
Nearest Town: Lower Hutt

Welcome to my warm, comfortable home set in a large garden overlooking the Hutt Recreation Ground. Your big room enjoys morning sun and a lovely view of the garden. The queen bed is very comfortable and has an electric blanket and fluffy duvet. I am only minutes from the Lower Hutt shopping centre and there is a good variety of restaurants for you to enjoy.
Should you be coming from Wellington or the ferry, the journey takes about 20 minutes - and I am easy to find.
Our son and his family live in America and our daughter and her family live locally. I very much enjoy music and reading - the garden takes a fair bit of my time and energy but well worth the effort to have fresh flowers in the house.
I look forward to meeting you and will do my utmost to ensure your stay is happy. I prefer non-smokers. Not suitable for children.
Directions: *Please phone.*

Some hosts are away from home during the day.

Lower Hutt

Homestay
Address: 11 Ngaio Crescent, Woburn, Lower Hutt
Name: Judy & Bob Vine
Telephone & Fax: (04) 566 1192
Beds: 1 Double, 2 Single (2 Bedrooms) **Bathroom:** 1 Guests share
Tariff: B&B (special) Double $60, Single $35, Children $20, Dinner $20 by arrangement. Vouchers accepted
Nearest Town: Lower Hutt 1km, Wellington 15km

Our home is situated plumb in the centre of Woburn, a picturesque central city suburb of Lower Hutt, known for its generous sized houses and beautiful gardens. We offer a warm welcome to our home, based on many enjoyable experiences with bed and breakfast hosts in the United Kingdom, Europe and USA and delight in the opportunity to reciprocate some of the hospitality we have been afforded on our own overseas jaunts.

We are within walking distance of the Lower Hutt downtown; only 15 minutes' drive from central Wellington and the Railway Station and Ferry Terminal; airport 25 minutes.

Our facilities include a separate lounge with TV for the comfort and enjoyment of our guests should they wish to take some time out to themselves. Alternatively, we love to entertain and would be delighted to have our guests join us for some hearty Kiwi style cooking with good New Zealand wine.

Laundry facilities.
Directions: *Please phone, fax or write. Transfer transport available.*

Normandale, Lower Hutt

Homestay
Address: 175 Stratton Street, Normandale, Lower Hutt
Name: "Black Fir Lodge"
Telephone: (04) 586 6466 (Answering machine if noone's handy)
Beds: 1 Double, 2 Single (2 Bedrooms) **Bathroom:** 1 Guests share
Tariff: B&B (full) Double $60, Single $35, Dinner $20, Vouchers accepted
Nearest Town: 18km north of Wellington, via SH2

Within half an hour's drive of central Wellington, our modern comfortable home is surrounded by green and pleasant countryside and hills.

On our 30 acre property we have sheep, sociable black chooks and many wild birds. We share our single-storey house with two very friendly dogs (Woodstock the newfy and Lucy the lab) and Splotch the cat.

The rolling hills and bush clad valleys of neighbouring Belmont Regional Park provide an ideal place for walking, mountain biking and horse riding (bring your own bike or horse!). For the culturally-minded, Wellington and Lower Hutt offer art galleries, museums and theatres, plus a great selection of restaurants!

In the evenings, you can relax in the lounge and enjoy the tranquil rural view, or you are welcome to "muck in" with "the gang" in the family room. Tasty, home-cooked dinners are available by arrangement.

Our interests include dogs, genealogy, travel and natural history. Non-smokers only please.
Directions: *Please phone for directions.*

When you stay at B&Bs you are staying with "dinkum Kiwis"

Petone

Homestay
Address: 23 Patrick Street, Petone
Name: Gary & Tui
Telephone: (04) 568 5159
Beds: 1 Queen, 1 Single (2 Bedrooms)
Bathroom: 1 Private, 1 Family share
Tariff: B&B (special) Double $60, Single $30, Dinner $20, Vouchers accepted
Nearest Town: Wellington 8km, Lower Hutt 5km

"Kia Ora" Gary and Tui believe there can't many places in the world where you can stroll along the beach looking over a beautiful harbour to a city humming with activity. Wellington, a magnificent city.
Only 10 mins away our warm and inviting two storey cottage is snuggled in an historic street.
The nearby olde worlde shops are ideal for fossicking. Excellent restaurants add to the character of our multicultural village of Petone.
We have travelled extensively and well know the requirements of the local and international traveller. Good company, food and wine, travel and sport make up some of the things we enjoy.
Your stay at our place will enrich you travelling experiences.
As Maori hosts Gary and Tui along with "Jess" our 14 yr old cat look forward to meeting you.Non smokers preferred.
Directions: *Please phone or write. We will meet and collect you if required.*
Note: Building was not completed at the time of inspection, phone to confirm.

Petone

Homestay
Address: 1 Bolton Street, Petone
Name: Anne and Reg Cotter
Telephone: (04) 568 6960
Beds: 1 Double, 2 Single (2 bedrooms) **Bathroom:** 1 Family share
Tariff: B&B (full) Double $50, Single $25, Children half price, Dinner $15 per person
Nearest Town: Lower Hutt 5 km, Wellington 8 km

We have an older type home by the beach which we have modernised. It has three bedrooms, a large lounge, diningroom, kitchen, bathroom with shower and bath. We are two minutes from the museum on the beach, two minutes from the shops and the bus route into the city. A restaurant is nearby.
We offer one double bed in one room, two single beds in another room with room for an extra bed or a child's cot which is available. Children are very welcome. Laundry facilities available.
We are ten minutes by road to the Picton ferry. Off street parking available.
Reg is a keen amateur ornithologist and he goes to the Chatham Islands with an expedition trying to find the nesting place of the Taiko _ a rare sea bird which is on the endangered list. We are keen to show any folk interested in birds the local places of interest. He is also a member of the genealogy society.

331

Eastbourne

Homestay
Address: 27 Marine Drive,
Mahina Bay, Eastbourne
Name: Janete and Jim Thomas
Telephone: (04) 562 8990
Fax: (04) 562 7667
Beds: 1 Queen, (1 bedroom)
Bathroom: Private
Tariff: B&B (special) Double $80, Single $50.
Credit cards accepted. Vouchers accepted.
Nearest Town: Wellington City 20 minutes

If you like crisp linen and lace, vases of fresh flowers, a lovely comfortable queen bed with woollen underlay, electric blanket and fluffy duvet, then I think you will enjoy staying with us.

We live right beside the ocean so all the rooms have beautiful views of Wellington Harbour with the city beyond.

Breakfast can be as healthy or as wicked as you fancy, from muesli, fresh fruit and herb tea to croissants and lots of freshly brewed coffee.

We would love you to join us for a pre-dinner drink - and four good local restaurants are only two minutes away.

Jim and I enjoy music, books, theatre, anything old and our city. Jim has a small publishing business and we restore old houses.

Our two sons have left home but we still have the charming company of our daughter Elizabeth. We have a quiet and gentle dog called Molly.

Eastbourne is a pretty seaside village 20-30 minutes from the city and Inter-Island Ferry.

We will have achieved our aim if you leave us feeling refreshed and 'special'.
We are strictly non-smoking.
Directions. *Please phone or write.*

There are some good tips for easier travel on page 4

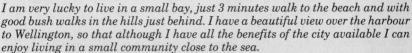

Eastbourne

Homestay
Address: Bush House,
12 Waitohu Road,
York Bay, Eastbourne
Name: Belinda Cattermole
Telephone: (04) 568 5250 after 5pm
Beds: 1 Double, 1 Single (2 bedrooms)
Bathroom: 1 Private, 1 Family share
Tariff: B&B (full) Double $80, Single $50, Dinner $30, Vouchers accepted
Nearest Town: Wellington City 20 minutes

I am very lucky to live in a small bay, just 3 minutes walk to the beach and with good bush walks in the hills just behind. I have a beautiful view over the harbour to Wellington, so that although I have all the benefits of the city available I can enjoy living in a small community close to the sea.

My home is a two storey converted settler cottage set among native bush. The house includes a big country kitchen and dining room which allows me to enjoy my passion for cooking and entertaining; while I still have time to enjoy music, dressmaking and aerobics.

I have lived in Wellington for two years and am now a New Zealand citizen so have a keen interest in exploring the local area and amenities.

Eastbourne is the nearest village, five minutes drive, and includes several good restaurants and crafts shops.

Non-smokers preferred.

Directions: *Please phone or write.*

Eastbourne

Homestay
Address: 15 Marine Dr, York Bay. Eastbourne
Name: Barry & Bev
Telephone: (04) 568 7104
Beds: 2 Single (1 Bedroom) **Bathroom:** 1 Private
Tariff: B&B (continental) Double $60, Single $45, 1 adult + 1 child $55, Dinner $25, Vouchers accepted
Nearest Town: Lower Hutt 10 mins

A breath of fresh air, 20 mins from Wellington City. Quiet and relaxed, nestled between native bush and the beach. Wake to the dawn chorus.

Steps up to the house allow a spectacular panorama of Hutt Valley, Wellington City and harbour. The Kaikouras can be admired from the front windows or the deck. Cosy woodburner for the winter.

Garage parking for 1 car. Laundry and drying facilities available.

Tourist attractions: Harbour ferry from Days Bay to City centre. Bus transport to Lower Hutt and Wellington leaves from our front gate. Golf course, indoor & outdoor swimming pools. Restaurants. All within a few minutes drive.

Interests: Dog Obedience & Agility (especially German Shepherds but we have none living with us now) Jogging, aquarobics, swimming, Theatre, NZ wines, gardening, our children and Grandchildren. Barry is a Sales consultant and Bev formerly a School Dental Nurse, is now a counsellor.

Specials: vegetarian food only, special diets catered for (vegan, dairy free)
Transport can be arranged
Non smokers essential

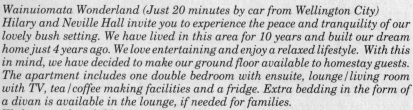

Wainuiomata

Homestay
Address: 22 Kaponga St, Wainuiomata
Name: Kaponga House
Telephone: (04) 564 3495
Beds: 1 Double (1 Bedroom/1 Double
divan in living room for families)
Bathroom: 1 Ensuite, 1 Family share
Tariff: B&B (continental) Double $60,
Single $45, School Children half price, Vouchers accepted
Nearest Town: Lower Hutt

Wainuiomata Wonderland (Just 20 minutes by car from Wellington City)
Hilary and Neville Hall invite you to experience the peace and tranquility of our
lovely bush setting. We have lived in this area for 10 years and built our dream
home just 4 years ago. We love entertaining and enjoy a relaxed lifestyle. With this
in mind, we have decided to make our ground floor available to homestay guests.
The apartment includes one double bedroom with ensuite, lounge/living room
with TV, tea/coffee making facilities and a fridge. Extra bedding in the form of
a divan is available in the lounge, if needed for families.
We have neither children nor pets at home, and we are smokefree.
Attractions close by include the Rimutaka Forest Park, seal colony and an 18 hole
golf course.
We enjoy gardening, golf, tennis and making new friends and look forward to
welcoming you to our home.

Khandallah, Wellington

Homestay
Address: 10A Izard Road,Khandallah, Wellington
Name: Genevieve and Peter Young
Telephone: (04) 4795-036 Home, (04) 4774-444 Peter (work)
Beds: 5 Single, (3 bedrooms) **Bathroom:** 1 Guests share. Pool table
Tariff: B&B (full) Double $60, Single $30; Dinner by arrangement $20. Vouchers
accepted.

We are a couple who enjoy relaxing and meeting people and our particular
interests are travel, sport, food, wine, and the Arts. We have a small tabby cat
called Amy. Our family of 3 girls have left home, and while we both work, we are
able to take time off to show guests our beautiful harbour city. Khandallah is a
hillside suburb handy to all the attractions of the capital, with a village atmosphere
and a ten minute bus or train ride to town. Very close to the ferry terminal.
We look forward to making your stay an enjoyable one.
Directions: *please phone and we will arrange to pick you up.*

New Zealand is known as the friendliest country in the world
and our hosts will live up to that reputation.

Ngaio, Wellington

Homestay
Address: 56 Fox Street, Ngaio, Wellington
Name: Brian and Jennifer Timmings
Telephone & Fax: (04) 479 5325
Beds: 2 Double, 1 Single (3 bedrooms) **Bathroom:** 1 Ensuite, 1 Family share
Tariff: B&B (continental) Double $65 with ensuite, $55 share bathroom, Single $50, Dinner $20, Children by arrangement. Vouchers accepted.
Nearest Town: Wellington

We love our city of Wellington with its beautiful harbour, dramatic hills and spectacular scenery, and we would enjoy having you as our guests and sharing your "Wellington Experience" with us. We live 10 minutes from Wellington Railway Station and Ferry Terminal, in the suburb of Ngaio, surrounded by bush and hills. (We could meet / deliver guests from any central point.)
We have an open plan home, but guests using the ensuite double room would have their own privacy with French doors opening onto a deck and sunny quiet garden. The alternative double room is upstairs, also quiet, comfortable and sunny with extensive views over the local area.
Dinner is optional. In the evening guests may like to relax in our music room as we are a music oriented family. We also enjoy art and the outdoors.
Off-street parking is available (also handy to good train service to city). No pets please and non drinking and non smokers only, thank you.
Hospitality guaranteed.
Directions: *Please phone, fax or write.*

Mt Victoria,
Wellington City

Homestay
Address: 58 Pirie Street, Mt Victoria, **Wellington**
Name: Robert and Elizabeth McGuigan
Telephone: (04) 385 8512
Beds: 1 Queen (en-suite), 3 Single (3 bedrooms)
Bathrooms: 1 Ensuite, 1 Guests share
Tariff: B&B (full) Double $60, Single $40, Children half price. Vouchers accepted.

Our 100-year-old Victorian home is situated in Mount Victoria, an historic and quiet suburb, just a few minutes easy walk from the city. We have a harmless little King Charles spaniel who lives upstairs with us.
We have our own facilities while downstairs is for guests. Downstairs has a TV lounge, dining room with tea and coffee making facilities. three bedrooms and two bathrooms.Please do not smoke in the house.
Wellington area has a lot to offer _ good restaurants and shopping and a good public transport system. A beautiful coastline with wonderful views, Parliament buildings, museums, art galleries and live theatre.
Directions: *Off motorway into Ghuznee Street. Turn right at Taranaki Street, left Vivian Street - straight to Pirie Street.*
From Ferry Terminal: Aotea Quay, Jervois Quay, Cable Street right into Kent Terrace - left at Pirie Street.
From Railway Station; airport and ferry terminal take Super Shuttle.

Mt Cook, Wellington City
Homestay
Address: Please phone
Name: Miss Jamie Bull
Telephone: (04) 384-6505
Beds: 1 Double (1 bedroom)
Tariff: B&B Double $60, Single $40; Dinner by arrangement.
Vouchers accepted.
Nearest Town: Wellington inner city

I am a self-employed choreographer, performer and tutor of dance. Consequently my work takes me around the country (which I love and know well) but when I'm at home I really enjoy sharing my home and my energy with others.
I live in an ninety-year-old inner-city cottage which I am gradually restoring. I think it has character as well as comfort.
It is a 15–20 minute walk to the heart of the city, there are buses nearby and the National Art Gallery and Museum is virtually on the doorstep.
Directions: Please phone.

Wellington City
Homestay / Self-contained Accom
Address: 33 Mortimer Tce, Mitchelltown,Brooklyn, Wellington
Name: Elfi & Nelson Wattie
Telephone: (04) 385 3667
Beds: Home: 1 Double (1 bedroom) **Bathroom:** 1 Family share.
Self-cont. Accom: 1 Double (1 bedroom) + 1 sofa-bed in lounge **Bathroom:** 1 Private. Kitchen
Tariff: B&B (special) $60 Double, $45 Single, Surcharge $5 for 1 night only. Flat $85 Double. Vouchers accepted Doubles only.

For many years we lived in Austria and Germany and travelled to other countries but for "later" we always planned to live in one of the old timber houses sparkling on the hillsides around Wellington Harbour.
Our "house with a view", built in 1925, is in walking distance of the city centre, the National Museum and Art Gallery and the University. There is a big choice of restaurants with a very special one close by.
You will be welcomed by Elfi, Nelson and Lola the Weimaraner dog, and can decide whether to sleep in our charming little double room with ferns and flowers at the window and wake to breakfast that includes home-made bread, or else to be your own boss in the self-contained flat with its large deck overlooking a peaceful garden and the harbour. Elfi has made many quilts and quilted garments but recently she has spent more time shaping our hillside garden.
We both enjoy the natural beauty and lively culture of our city, as well as its fresh air - we are non-smokers.

Continental breakfast consist of fruit, toast, tea/coffee,
Full breakfast is the same with a cooked course,
Special breakfast has something special.

Wellingon City
Bed & Breakfast Hotel

New Zealand's
Federation of Bed &
Breakfast Hotels

Address: 182 Tinakori Road,
Thorndon, Wellington
Name: 'Tinakori Lodge Bed & Breakfast'
Telephone: (04) 473 3478
Fax: (04) 472 5554
Beds: Queen 2, Super King 4, Single 7 (10 bedrooms)
Bathroom: 2 Ensuite, 3 Guests share
Tariff: B&B (special) Double $85, Single $66, Ensuite Double $95, Single $76.
Prices include GST, Credit cards accepted. Vouchers accepted for standard rooms
May to August.

*Tinakori Lodge is a two storeyed, one hundred year old house, conveniently
situated in historic Thorndon within walking distance of restaurants, central
shopping and commercial areas, transport services, botanical gardens and
government centre. We recommend a two night stay to explore our "Absolutely
Positively Wellington".*

*Whether you are in Wellington on holiday or business we endeavour to provide a
warm, comfortable atmosphere with the emphasis on relaxation.*

*In our conservatory (overlooking the bushland reserve) our guests can relax and
chat with your fellow travellers and enjoy complimentary, serve yourself tea,
coffee, hot chocolate, soup, cookies, morning and evening newspapers.*

*Start the day with a scrumptious breakfast buffet selection in our dining room off
the conservatory.*

*Our bedrooms are decorated with warmth and individuality, providing the
comforts of home including Television.*

*To retain the natural freshness in our establishment, we request no smoking.
Laundry service available.*

We recommend advance bookings.

Host: Mel & John Ainsworth.

Seatoun, Wellington

Homestay
Address: 10 Monro Street,
Seatoun, Wellington 6003
Name: Frances Drewell
Telephone: (04) 388 6719
Beds: 1 Double, 2 Single (2 bedrooms)
Bathroom: 1 Guests share
Tariff: B&B (full) Double $70, Single $40,
Children $20, Dinner $20, Vouchers accepted all year.

Handy to Wellington Airport our modern home is located in a quiet village atmosphere with the beach close by.
Guest beds have electric blankets or woollen underlays. Extra comfortable double foldout bed is available if necessary.
Guests share the bathroom and separate toilet.
If you wish to enjoy a NZ style dinner it is available on request. A warm welcome awaits those who want a home away from home atmosphere. Interests are mainly in travel and sport and I play golf regularly.
Laundry facilities available.
Directions: *Entering Wellington from the North or off the Interisland Ferry follow the Airport signs. When the Airport runway is on your right take the left-hand lane and follow the signs to Seatoun. Following the main road through the short tunnel bear right and Monro Street is the third street on the left. Coming from the Airport take the first turn right and then as above. One minute walk to bus stop.*

Strathmore Park, Wellington

Self-contained Accommodation
Address: Please phone for easy directions
Postal Address: P.O. Box 15-148, Wellington
Name: "Treetops"
Telephone: (04) 388 6923
Beds: 1 Double-Kingsize (private cabin)
Bathroom: 1 Ensuite. Electric Blanket, Lambswool Underlay
Tariff: B&B (full) $70 for cabin Double or Single, (includes pickup from arrival point) Dinner (by arrangement before 3pm) $20 - with drinks $25 per person, Credit cards accepted, Vouchers accepted
Nearest Town: Wellington City 9km.

'Treetops' - as the name suggests - is above road level. We drive up to our two carports but always leave one carport empty for our guests' use. We have a lift from the drive to the house - which is greatly appreciated for luggage.
The bus stop to the City is opposite and the Airport is a few minutes drive; noise is not a problem as we are well away from the flight path.
Although only one room - with bathroom - our comfortable cabin is spacious and well equipped to cater for every need including TV, fridge, microwave and electic frypan.
Breakfast? Make it yourself at your own convenience. Juice, fruit, cereals, bacon and eggs, toast etc. in cabin on arrival. (If preferred breakfast in house by arrangement the night before.)
Dinner? As in 'Tariff' above or local restaurants 5 minutes drive.
Although your accommodation is self-contained we (Alison, Sandy and our friendly dog) love getting to know our guests so do come down to the house for a chat whenever you like. 'There are no strangers here - only friends we haven't met'.

Karori, Wellington

Homestay
Address: 83 Campbell Street,
Karori, Wellington
Name: Murray and Elaine Campbell
Telephone: (04) 476 6110
Beds: 1 Double, 4 Single (3 bedrooms)
Bathroom: 2 Private, 1 Guests share
Tariff: B&B (continental) Double $60, Single $40, Dinner $20, Children half price, Vouchers accepted
Nearest Town: Wellington

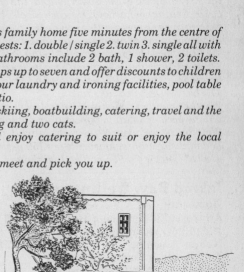

We welcome you to share our spacious family home five minutes from the centre of Wellington. We have 3 bedrooms for guests: 1. double / single 2. twin 3. single all with electric blankets and duvets. Guest bathrooms include 2 bath, 1 shower, 2 toilets. We can accommodate families or groups up to seven and offer discounts to children or longer stay guests. Feel free to use our laundry and ironing facilities, pool table or table tennis, large garden and patio.
Our family interests include sailing, skiing, boatbuilding, catering, travel and the outdoors. We have three pets, one dog and two cats.
Have dinner at home with us and enjoy catering to suit or enjoy the local restaurants in the village.
Directions: *Telephone and we will meet and pick you up.*

Makara, Wellington

Homestay
Address: 134 South Makara Road,
RD, Karori, Wellington
Name: David and Julie Grace
Telephone: (04) 476 7563
Fax: (04) 476 9403
Beds: 1 Double, 2 Single (2 bedrooms)
Bathroom: 1 Guests share
Tariff: B&B (continental) Double $65, Single $40, Children half price, Dinner $25 per person, Full breakfast on request.
Vouchers accepted

Makara is one of Wellington's best-kept secrets. Only 20 minutes by car from the city centre, we live in a peaceful valley surrounded by hills and farmland. We have a spacious house with generous-sized guest rooms looking out over the view. The house is set in a large and interesting garden with a great variety of perennials and shrubs. We are both ex-jounalists with experience in agriculture and gardening. We have three amiable cats. Almost next door are two golf courses, while the Makara Beach and Southern Walkway over the hills are 10 minutes away. We are also 10 minutes from Karori, the largest suburb with all facilities and frequent buses. Please phone for directions. We can transport guests by arrangement Children welcome; half price if school age.

Island Bay, Wellington

Self-Contained Accommodation
Address: 326 The Esplanade, Island Bay, Wellington
Name: The Lighthouse
Telephone: (04) 472 4177 **Mobile:** 025 425 555
Beds: 2 Double (1-2 Bedrooms) **Bathroom:** 1 Private
Tariff: B&B (special) Double $150.
Nearest Town: Wellington

The Lighthouse.
Nestled in Island Bay 10 minutes from the airport or from Wellington City the recently constructed lighthouse has already achieved landmark status. The fishing boats in the bay, the view of the South Island, the ships steaming out of Wellington harbour, the rocky coast, and the Island with its wheeling seagulls provide the perfect setting for a day or two away.
Just a few hundred metres around the corner from buses, shops and a top restaurant the Lighthouse balances modern living with a splendid coastal outlook.
There are three floors comprising: Kitchen and bathroom; bedroom / sitting room; top floor of studio with bed-settee and balcony.
The bed settees each take two.
Whether winter or summer, on holiday, business or passing through, this is a unique accommodation opportunity not to be missed.
Walk the beach, explore the rocks or walk to the seal colony.
Bed and special breakfast rate is $150 per night for two people. Bookings to (04) 4724177, (025) 425555 or The Lighthouse, PO Box 11-275 Wellington.

Island Bay, Wellington

Homestay
Address: 122 Derwent Street, Island Bay, Wellington
Name: "Arohaina"
Telephone & Fax: (04) 383 6952
Beds: 4 Single (2 Twin Bedrooms)
Bathroom: 1 Ensuite, 1 Private

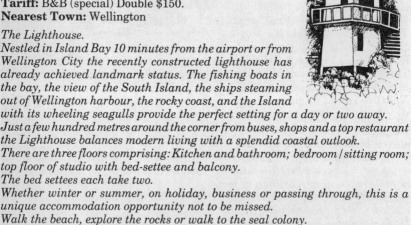
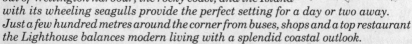

Tariff: B&B (continental) Double $55, Single $40, Children half price, Dinner $15, Lunch $8, Campervans $25 (two people) $5 each extra person. Credit cards: Visa, M/C, B/C.
Nearest Town: Wellington

Our lovely home, which recently celebrated its ninetieth birthday, has been in our family since 1948; when we completed renovations we kept to the spirit of the house; welcoming, with a sense of history and permanence.
We both grew up in Island Bay and the area has a special attraction for us, there is something magical about the rugged outline of Taputeranga Island. Our interests are meeting people, walking along the coastline (Wellington's best!) gardening and photography. Trish likes to write when she has the time.
We are five minutes walk from the beach; two minutes from the bus stop. We are happy to collect and deliver guests free of charge from airport, railway station, ferry. We have travelled extensively in New Zealand and have been to Asia.
Our two children have grown up and left home; we live with a friendly German Shepherd and a streetfighter cat. Trish is training to be a primary teacher; I run the household! Smokefree; centrally heated.
Directions: *Please phone.*

Island Bay, Wellington

Homestay
Address: 52 High Street,
Island Bay, Wellington 6002
Name: Theresa and Jack Stokes
Telephone & Fax: (04) 383 5169
Beds: 2 Double, 2 Single (3 bedrooms)
Bathroom: 1 Private (with double), 1 Guests share (with double and twin)
Tariff: B&B (full) Double/Twin $60, Single $40, Dinner $15. Vouchers accepted.

A modern, seven year old Lockwood house standing in a very private three acre section with probably the finest view in Wellington. Overlooking Island Bay harbour with its fishing boats - the entrance to Port Nicholson (Wellington's harbour) - the Cook Strait with its ferries and cargo vessels on the move day and night.

Ten minutes drive to town centre. Ten minutes walk to the bus terminus. Transport available on request. Not suitable for children under 14. We have a small dog and a Moggy.

Directions: *From State Road 1 or 2 take the Aotea Quay turnoff. (From the ferry take city exit). Follow the main road which bears slightly to the left to T junction (Oriental Parade). Turn right and into Kent Terrace. Move to right lane - round the Basin Reserve (cricket ground) and into Adelaide Road - up the hill leaving Athletic Park rugby ground (large stand) on your left and the road becomes The Parade. On reaching the sea turn SHARP right (Beach Street) and left and left again into High Street and up the private road at the end. Plenty of parking. Only ten minutes from Airport via the Coast Road.*

We rely on your comments about our B&Bs.
Please send us a comment form from the back of the book.

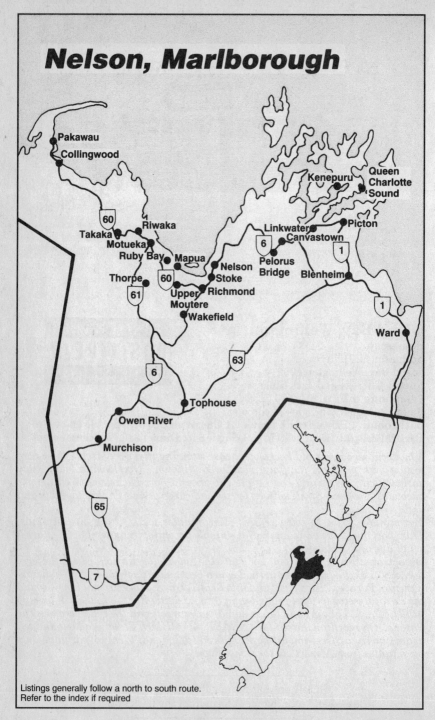

Nelson, Marlborough

Listings generally follow a north to south route.
Refer to the index if required

Bay of Many Coves, Queen Charlotte Sounds

Homestay
Address: "Craglee", Bay of Many Coves,
Private Bag 407, Picton
Name: Anne & Robin Perret
Telephone & Fax: (03) 579 9223
Beds: 1 King, 1 Super King, 1 Double, 4 Single (4 bedrooms)
Bathrooms: 1 Ensuite, 1 Private, 1 Guests share
Tariff: (full) 24hr stay meals inclusive, King with ensuite $85 per person, Double $70 per person, Single $75, Children under 12 half price, Credit cards accepted, Vouchers accepted for B&B only, other meals extra
Nearest Town: Picton

Robin and Anne's home in a secluded bay in the Marlborough Sounds, is warm, comfortable and spacious, with breathtaking views over the bay and surrounding native bush. Awake to the chorus of bellbirds.

Bay of Many Coves is a 30 minute water taxi cruise from Picton, or 30 minute Float Plane flight from Wellington, a great weekend getaway.

While at Craglee you may wish to see bird life, glowworms in our dell, go on bush or beach walks, tramping the Queen Charlotte Walkway with its magnificent views, diving, fishing, swimming, dinghies are available. You may meet a dolphin.

A large deck overlooking the bay has a heated spa for you to enjoy, especially on a starry moonlit night when you can enjoy the beautiful southern sky.

Our menu has variety with fresh fruit and vegetables from our garden and food and wine from Marlborough's gourmet province, you may wish to sample Robin's home brewed ale.

Our guest rooms have ensuite bathrooms, lounge with television and radio. Tea and coffee facilities. Cot and Laundry available.

We share our home with our 12 year old son John who is educated at home, and Toby our Fox Terrier. Children are most welcome.

Directions: *Please phone and we can help you with water taxi or Float Plane bookings which depart twice daily.*

Kenepuru Sound, Marlborough
Guest House
Address: St Omer House,
Kenepuru Sound, RD2, Picton,
Name: Flora, George and Melva Robb
Telephone: (03) 573 4086 **Fax:** 03 573 4586
Beds: 6 Double, 7 Twin or Single, 2 Bunk rooms, (15 bedrooms)
Bathrooms: Guests share
Tariff: B&B (special) Double $72, Single $36, Dinner $25 (4 course) Children under 12 half price, under 2 no charge, Campervans $12, Tent sites available. Credit cards. Vouchers accepted.
Nearest Town: Picton or Havelock, 2 hours by road

A peaceful bay, a fifty-year-old, family-run guest house with plenty of historic interest is where my husband and I and two adult daughters welcome you. Our family are the fifth generation in the area.

The Marlborough Sounds are a maze of waterways – you can cruise, yacht, canoe, row, dive, swim, fish, water ski or explore beaches and wrecks, climb bush-clad hills, tramp walkways, see farmland.

Nearby are mussel and salmon farms, bird sanctuaries, shag colonies and glowworm walks. A nine hole country golf course $5 a day, clubs for hire $5 a day. Horse trekking and pony riding.

Our dining room has a BYO licence, we cater for all meals and tastes – venison, wild pork, shellfish, fish, fresh eggs, vegetables and fruit locally grown are on our menu. The games room is large enough for dancing – has piano, table tennis, TV, etc. mini golf on lawn and tennis court.

Travel: By car – part-metalled road, 2 hrs from Havelock or Picton. Fly float plane from Picton or Porirua or small plane from Wellington, 20 minutes. Watertaxi from Picton or Havelock.

Picton
Homestay, Self-contained Accommodation
Address: Anakiwa Road, Queen Charlotte Sound, RD 1, Picton
Name: Ross and Leslie Close
Telephone & Fax: (03) 574 2547
Beds: 2 Single (1 bedroom) **Bathroom:** Private
Tariff: B&B (continental) Double $70, Single $40, Dinner $20, Vouchers accepted
Nearest Town: Picton

Our home at the head of Queen Charlotte Sound has a magnificent 25 mile long sea view and is in a tranquil and peaceful area noted for its bush walks and variety of bird life. It is only a short walk to New Zealand's Cobham Outward Bound School where visitors are welcome. Just beyond the school is the start of the Queen Charlotte Walkway, a wonderful scenic route from Anakiwa to Ship Cove.

We have a warm and comfortable self-contained apartment downstairs with bathroom, separate bedroom, lounge and fully equipped kitchen. Extra beds available.

Ross is a woodturner and Leslie is a potter and both are happy to demonstrate their skills. Other interests we enjoy are seafishing in our motor launch and walking our Jack Russell terrier. Transport to and from local departure points may be provided by arrangement.
Directions: *Please phone.*

When you stay at B&Bs you are staying with "dinkum Kiwis"

Picton

Homestay, Baystay
Address: Moenui Bay, Queen Charlotte Drive, RD1, Picton
Name: "Ribbonwood"
Telephone: (03) 5742 217
Beds: 1 Double 2 Single (2 bedrooms)
Bathroom: 1 Ensuite, 1 Private
Tariff: B&B (full) Double $65, Ensuite with spa bath $70, Single $40; Dinner $20
Nearest Town: 32 kms from Picton on Queen Charlotte Drive to Nelson

This is a resting site, bush sheltered. Cross the Queen's Chain to swimming beach. Fishing rods available.

Breakfast cooked or as preferred. Ensuite bathroom has spa bath with shower. Guests are welcome to stay for more than one night.

An ideal base for tripping about the Marlborough Scene. An overnight stop from Nelson to Picton Ferry.

My interests are very wide. I have both travelled and worked overseas for the past twenty years. This was my beach house, now doubled in size to become my retirement home.

Sorry, no smoking or animals.

My home is available for the summer season, beginning November and ending April. Please phone for directions to Bay.

Many homes have facilities for campervans. The ideal camping spot with electricity, bathroom, laundry and friendly hospitality.
Tell campervanners about this when you see them.

Picton
Homestay + Self-Contained Accommodation
Address: PO Box 256, Picton
Name: Ron and Wendy Gabites
Telephone: (03) 573 6491
Beds: 1 Double, 1 Single (2 bedrooms) **Bathroom:** 1 Private
Tariff: B&B (full) Double $75, Single $40, Children under 12 half price; Dinner $20, Vouchers accepted

Picton is the main centre for the beautiful Marlborough Sounds, with its lovely bays and scenic views of water and bush-clad hills.
Our new home is situated by the sea in Waikawa Bay (three minutes from Picton). The property has an expansive view over the Bay and Queen Charlotte Sound where we can watch the inter-island ferries, pleasure yachts and launches.
A safe swimming beach, children's playground, boat launching ramp and general store are close by.
We have a fully self-contained and separate apartment downstairs which sleeps four with all facilities. It is very suitable for longer holidays.
Our family of four sons are all away from home and we now have time to pursue our own interests which include sailing, fishing, golfing, leathercraft, gardening and meeting people.
Relax for a few days with us in the beautiful Marlborough Sounds, enjoy sailing, sightseeing, bushwalking, fishing, picnics or a game of golf.
We are happy to meet and provide transport from buses, train or inter-island ferries.

Whatamango Bay, Picton
Homestay, Self-contained Apartment
Address: 424 Port Underwood Rd,
Whatamango Bay, Queen Charlotte Sound,
PO Box 261, Picton
Name: "Seaview", Pam and John Anders
Telephone: (03) 573-7783
Apartment Beds: 2 Double **Bathroom:** 2 Private
Homestay Beds: 2 Single (1 bedrooms) **Bathroom:** 1 Private
Tariff: B&B (full) Double $55, Single $30, Dinner $20, Self-contained apartment: Double $45, $10 each extra person
Nearest Town: Picton 9km

Located in peaceful surroundings only 9km from Picton Ferry Terminal with extensive views of Queen Charlotte Sound and bush clad hills. The fully self contained apartment has one bedroom with double bed, lounge / dining / kitchen with fridge, colour TV, etc. and bathroom with shower, toilet and handbasin.
Wake to the sound of native birds, take a leisurely stroll through the acre of garden. Relax and watch the shipping pass by, the sea birds diving for fish and from time to time the dolphins coming into the bay. A two minute walk will take you to the beach where you have the use of a dinghy or five minutes to historic Karaka Point to view the Maori kumera storage pits.
Directions: *Follow the Port Underwood Road from Waikawa for 4km. We are on the top side of the road. Sign at bottom of drive.*
To avoid disappointment, if possible please phone the evening prior.
Our aim is to make your stay a memorable and enjoyable part of your holiday.

Picton

Homestay Bed & Breakfast
Address: "The Gables", 20 Waikawa Road, Picton
Name: Richard & Ann Smith
Telephone: (03) 573 6772
Beds: 2 Queen, 3 Single (4 bedrooms) All with private facilities
Tariff: B&B (special) Triple $90, Double $75, Single $40, Children $10. Credit cards.

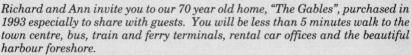

Richard and Ann invite you to our 70 year old home, "The Gables", purchased in 1993 especially to share with guests. You will be less than 5 minutes walk to the town centre, bus, train and ferry terminals, rental car offices and the beautiful harbour foreshore.

Your guest rooms are large, warm and comfortable; all with private facilities. The large lounge has an open fire and tea and coffee making facilities. Our cat visits occasionally.

Delicious breakfasts include fresh fruits, fresh fish, pancakes and hot muffins with brewed coffee and a variety of teas.

Restaurants for your evening meal are close at hand and you will enjoy the walkways, sailing, scenic flights, kayaking and many other ways to relax in this magnificent area.

We will happily provide transport to and from the Interislander ferries, bus and train terminals. Laundry facilities available. Credit cards acceptable. Off street parking.

Come as guests and leave as friends!

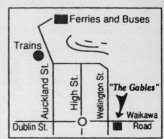

347

Picton

Self-Contained Accommodation
Address: 'Bridgend Cottage', 36 York Street, Picton
Name: Bevan & Lurleen Fowler
Telephone: (03) 573 6734
Beds: 1 Double, 2 Single (2 bedrooms)
Bathroom: 2 Ensuite. All beds with 'Slumbertime' mattresses
Tariff: B&B (special) Double $60, Single $40,
Four people $110, 4 course Dinner $20, Credit cards accepted, Vouchers accepted

We welcome you to Picton at the top of the Queen Charlotte Sound. The most beautiful waterway in the world for boating, fishing and walks.

Our property is situated within easy walking distance of all activities in Picton. The accommodation is self contained including colour TV, tea/coffee making facilities, full cooked breakfast that caters for all tastes. Breakfast arranged for early inter-island ferry passengers.

Dinner is a four course gourmet meal with wine featuring specialities of our region.

Safe and secure off street parking, sun deck, transport provided from buses, train or inter-island ferry by prior arrangement.

Our hobbies are gardening, gourmet cooking, sea fishing and cruising in the Queen Charlotte Sounds. We have our own launch. When time and weather permits, we offer to take our guests fishing or cruising with us.

Laundry facilities available. Paraplegic Unit.

"We know no strangers, only friends we haven't met"

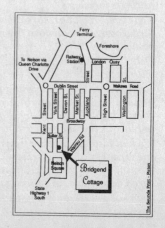

Picton
Self-Contained Accommodation
Address: 11 Dorset St, Picton
Name: Val & Geoff Brannan
Telephone: (03) 573 7177 preferably evenings
Beds: 1 Double (1 bedroom), extra bed in lounge
Bathroom: 1 Ensuite
Tariff: B&B (Special) Double $55, Single $35, Family rates available, Dinner $20. Vouchers accepted

Welcome to our home with views over Picton's lovely harbour, bushclad hills and farmland. Your home here will be a comfortably furnished ground floor apartment where you can relax on a sun deck overlooking gardens, small swimming pool and barbecue area. The living room has a small kitchen area, dining corner, bed settees and TV. The bathroom has a shower, toilet and handbasin.

Our family has varied interests but in particular we enjoy sailing, vintage car restoration and rallying, travel, folk music and meeting people.

We provide a comprehensive continental style breakfast. This is usually prepared and placed in your apartment so you can breakfast at your leisure. If you prefer you may do your own catering (discount tariff).

We enjoy assisting travellers with their itineraries and will meet most ferry, train and bus services on request. We are near Terminals and town.

Don't just pass through Picton - STOP - relax and enjoy the marvellous Marlborough Province with its wineries, scenery, waterways and walks!!

Waikawa Bay, Picton
Homestay
Address: Please Telephone
Name: Yvonne & Gary Roberts
Telephone: (03) 573 8965
Beds: 4 Single (2 Bedrooms)
Bathroom: 1 Guests share
Tariff: B&B (full) Double $65, Single $45, Dinner $25, Vouchers accepted
Nearest Town: Picton

Our home is a newish sort of colonial cottage in a quiet, leafy back street at Waikawa Bay, Picton. We try to provide a warm, tasteful and comfortable environment for visitors.

We are a young middle aged couple firmly bonded to a middle aged dog. We are all rather fond of fine food and good conversation. We also have affection (the dog less so) for, reading, music, the outdoors and a classic wooden motor launch.

Yvonne is intermittently obsessed by patchwork followed closely by golf, gardening and tramping (the undemanding sort). Gary cooks, follows cricket from an armchair, is interested in all things nautical and one day might write a book.

We prefer to receive reservations in advance so we may plan for some style in the feeding and care of our guests.

We enjoy introducing like minded people to our version of Marlborough. Within easy reach are sheltered waterways, a skifield, vineyards (some with boutique restaurants) and a special kind of back country.

Whatamango Bay, Picton
Lodge/Self-contained Accommodation
with cooking facilities

Address: 418 Port Underwood Road,
Whatamango Bay, Picton
Name: Waipuna Lodge: Bill & Esther Phillips
Telephone: (03) 573 8071
Beds: 2 Double, 2 Single, (3 bedrooms)
Bathroom: 1 Guests share
Tariff: B&B (special) Double $70, Single $50, Children under 12 half price,
Dinner $25 by arrangement. Credit cards accepted, Vouchers accepted March -
September.
Nearest Town: Picton 9kms Blenheim 40kms

*We would like to welcome you to our modern comfortable home, 9kms from Picton
which commands a million dollar view of the fabulous 'Queen Charlotte Sounds'.
From your balcony take in the breathtaking view of scenery and bushclad hills or
listen for the sounds of the bellbirds and tuis.*
*Watch for schools of dolphins that frequent our bay or watch yachts and ships that
glide into and out of the Sounds. Take a minute stroll through the bush, to the
beach, where you have the use of a dingy or canoe.*
*A short walk to Historic Site, (Kai Pit's) used by early Maori to store their food. Minutes
away from bushwalks, fishing, diving, sightseeing and the world renown Queen
Charlotte Walkway, which commands some of this country's most spectacular scenery.
Fishing trips can be arranged or bring your boat and hook onto our mooring,
which you can see from the balcony.*
Directions: *Please phone evening prior if possible. Bookings essential.*

Linkwater, Picton
Country Lodge
Address: Queen Charlotte Scenic Drive RD1 Picton
Name: John E Smart
Telephone: (03) 574 2507
Beds: 2 Double, 2 Single (3 Bedrooms) **Bathroom:** 1 Guests share
Tariff: B&B (full) Double $75, Single $52, Children welcome.
Vouchers accepted
Nearest Town: Havelock 11km, Picton 25km

*Linkwater Lodge - an historic homestead set in two acres on Marlborough's
picturesque Queen Charlotte Scenic Drive. Relaxing country environment close to
the Queen Charlotte Walkway and a short distance to both Pelorus and Queen
Charlotte Sound.*
*The lodge offers the comforts of orthopaedic beds, electric blankets, fluffy duvets,
electric heaters in every bedroom and open fires.*
*A full breakfast is provided and other meals are available in the restaurant
attached to the lodge.*
*Enjoy a tranquil, restful holiday or take advantage of the many exciting activities
available in the area. Sailing, kayaking, fishing, bushwalking, mail boat cruise
or a trip around the famous Marlborough Wine Trail.*
Directions: *From Picton 25km along Queen Charlotte Drive, opposite the service
station. From Blenheim turn off Nelson Highway before Havelock at Queen
Charlotte Drive sign - 11km to Linkwater.*

Blenheim

Homestay
Address: Please phone
Name: Adrienne & Rex Handley
Telephone: (03) 578-9562
Beds: 1 Double, 2 Twin (1 converts Kingsize), 1 Single (4 bedrooms)
Bathrooms: 2 Private
Tariff: B&B (Full) Kingsize $70, Double/Twin $65, Single $40, (Tariff less 10% if prebooked by night before) Dinner by arrangement, Vouchers accepted
Nearest Town: Blenheim 3km from Town Centre

Welcome to our warm and spacious 1970's era home situated in a quiet southern suburb with its mature trees, flowering shrubs, sundeck, outdoor pool, ample off road parking and no pets.

Two renovated private bathrooms (one per party) serve the four heated guest rooms. All beds have quality mattresses, electric blankets and wool overlays.

Your hosts are a non smoking married couple with a grown up family and enjoy sharing mutual travel experiences. Rex, a retired airline pilot, has interests in all aspects of aviation from models to home builts and gliding - also builds miniature steam locomotives. Adrienne enjoys cooking, spinning and woolcraft hobbies. We offer our vintage model A Ford soft top tourer for hood down rides or be photographed in, and sightseeing flights around Marlborough can also be arranged.

Comments from our guest book suggest our home has a warm and friendly atmosphere. We invite you to sample this along with our caring personal attention and complimentary beverages.

Blenheim

Homestay
Address: 'Rowallan', 191 Redwood Street, Blenheim
Name: Alan and Mary Stevenson
Telephone: (03) 578 9091
Beds: 1 Double, 5 Single, (3 bedrooms) **Bathroom:** 1 Guests share (another toilet & shower available)
Tariff: B&B (special) Double $65, Single $40, Children $5, Dinner $17, Campervans $5 per person. Vouchers accepted at all times.

We have a lovely warm brick home on the rise at the southern end of Redwood Street (opp. Safe Street). We were farming at Seddon until our son's marriage (early 1984) and we are still very interested in everything pertaining to farming and community work.

As the house is built back from the street, ours is a very quiet, restful home.

We really enjoy meeting people from overseas. We have travelled a little and are members of the Marlborough Travel Club.

Our guest area has its own bathroom with bath, separate shower and separate toilet. There is a small swimming pool and a pool table available. Ample off-street parking. On request early morning tea or coffee provided.

We are happy to provide transport to and from coaches, train or plane; and if desired can take guests on a short tour of our area.

Directions: *Travel to railway crossing on Main Street (State Highway 1), turn between siding and main line into Redwood Street and travel approximately 2.7 km.*

Blenheim

Farmstay
Address: "Rhododendron Lodge", State Highway 1,
St Andrews, Blenheim
Name: Charlie and Audrey Chambers (previously "Weld Cone", Ward)
Telephone: (03) 578 1145
Beds: 4 Single (2 bedrooms, woolrest sleepers & electric blankets)
Bathroom: 1 Ensuite, 1 Private
Tariff: B&B (full) Double $70, Single $40, Vouchers accepted

Welcome to previous guests and new ones. We have retired from lovely "Weld Cone" to an attractive small farm in Blenheim with our much loved rhododendrons - some cattle and sheep.

Our home is very spacious with a large swimming pool in a private courtyard with lovely pungas (tree ferns) and gardens. Our front garden is a feast of rhododendrons; roses; azaleas and trees.

We are very close to Blenheim's many gourmet restaurants and will have available a selection of their menus.

Marlborough has much to offer - Pollard Park; The Wine Trail; Gardens at Seymour Square; Brayshaw Historic Park and the beautiful Marlborough Sounds.

We are 20 minutes from the Picton Ferry. Visitors travelling by train or bus will be collected in Blenheim. Air travellers will be met at Airport. - Happy Holidays.
Directions: *South of Blenheim Town, SH 1 Rural Fireplate No 858*

Continental breakfast consist of fruit, toast, tea/coffee,
Full breakfast is the same with a cooked course,
Special breakfast has something special.

Blenheim
Homestay
Address: "Mirfield",
722 Severne Street, Blenheim
Name: Pam & Charles Hamilton
Telephone: (03) 578-8220
Beds: 2 Double, 2 Single (3 bedrooms)
Bathroom: 1 Guests share, 2 Family share
Tariff: B&B (continental, cooked breakfast $5 extra pp) Double $55, Single $30, children under 12 1/2 price, Dinner $17.50, campervans $5 per person, Vouchers accepted

Welcome to Marlborough and our home. We enjoy meeting people. Our home is spacious, catering for 3 generations. A private TV lounge is available.
Our gardening interests help us to offer organically grown produce for your enjoyment, and having hosted B7B's for 6 years we're flexible and sensitive to your needs.
As well as our sporting interests - especially tennis - we have embarked on an export flower growing venture. There may also be the opportunity to purchase homespun knitwear created by Pam.
"Mirfield" is a convenient stopping place for those using the Ferries, the Airport, or travelling beyond Blenheim. By arrangement, transport can be provided to and from departure points. Make Marlborough a highlight - stay with us.
Directions: *Highway 6 from Blenheim to Nelson. Turn first left after the Shell Service Station.*

Blenheim
Farmstay
Address: Maxwell Pass,
PO Box 269, Blenheim
Name: Jean and John Leslie
Telephone: (03) 578 1941
Beds: 1 Double, 3 Single (3 bedrooms)
Bathroom: 1 Private, 1 Family share
Tariff: B&B (full) Double $60, Single $35,
Children half price, Dinner $20, Vouchers accepted
Nearest Town: Blenheim 8 km

We live 8 km from Blenheim on a 1500 acre hill country property (ranch) running sheep and cattle.
Our home is a modern two-storeyed house set in spacious grounds with a swimming pool.
All beds have electric blankets and guests have own bathroom.
Now that our family have left home we enjoy spending time with guests. Marlborough is a major grape growing area with several wineries plus horticulture, agriculture and livestock farming from high country to the coast. Marlborough Sounds is nearby either by sea or road. Trout fishing is also close at hand and there is a ski field 1 1/2 hours drive. Blenheim has a golf course, croquet green and hard and grass tennis court.
Directions: *Please phone.*

Blenheim
Homestay
Address: 30 Glenroy Crescent,
Blenheim
Name: Barbara and Nicolaas Mels
Telephone: (03) 578 2704
Beds: 2 Single (1 bedroom)
Bathroom: 1 Private
Tariff: B&B (Continental) Double $55, Single $30,
Dinner $15, Children free, Vouchers accepted

Sleepout (garden cottage) with shower and toilet. Situated in a semi-rural neighbourhood. You can park the car alongside and 20 mtrs to lounge and dining room. TV, tea and coffee making facilities are also there but guests are most welcome to spend their evenings in conversation in the lounge. We are close to "pick your own fruit" when in season. Have travelled ourselves and know what a warm welcome and hospitality means to holiday memories. If guests are travelling by road, rail, or air we are happy to fetch and carry. To get to the centre of town via parks is an easy and pleasant walk.
Directions: *Off the Old Renwick Road, near the racecourse.*

Blenheim
Homestay
Address: "Tantallon",
84 McLauchlan St, Blenheim
Name: Ian & Rosemary Douglas
Telephone: (03) 578-8238
Beds: 1 Double, 2 Single (2 bedrooms)
Bathroom: 1 Guests share
Tariff: B&B (full) Double $65, Single $40, Dinner $20, Vouchers accepted

We are a married couple whose 2 daughters have now left home. Our large cat, Boswell, and Corgi dog Emma, share our lives.
Our home is a warm, comfortable Kauri villa, approx 90 years old and situated 2 kms from the town centre and only a few minutes walk to Waterlea Racecourse, Pollard Park and a 9-hole golf course.
We offer quiet, friendly hospitality with your choice of breakfast. We can provide dinner by arrangement or, if you prefer, Blenheim offers a wide choice of excellent restaurants.
Our guest rooms are spacious and are provided with electric blankets and bedside lamps. The double room has a sun-room annexe for your enjoyment.
Tea and coffee, magazines and a daily newspaper are freely available. We respectfully request that you do not smoke indoors.
We look forward to welcoming you.
Directions: *We are located directly off Nelson St. (State Highway 6) but please phone before arrival if possible.*

Blenheim
Country Homestay
Address: "Green Gables"
St. Andrews, R.D. 4, Blenheim
Name: Raelene & Bill Rainbird
Telephone: (03) 578 1869
Beds: 4 Double (2 bedrooms)
Bathroom: 2 Ensuite
Tariff: B&B (full) Double $70, Single $40, Dinner $20, Campervans welcome,
Vouchers accepted
Nearest Town: Blenheim 1 1/2 km

*We live in an exceptionally spacious two storey home with guest accommodation
comprising of two double bedrooms, each with two double beds, ensuite bathrooms,
TVs, heating, radios and electric blankets with glass doors opening onto a terrace
with panoramic views of Blenheim and our landscaped gardens.*

Breakfast is of your choice with cooked or continental.

*We are market gardeners with greenhouses set in the countryside, selling fresh
produce but situated only 1.5 km from town.*

*Our property backs onto the Opawa River offering ample opportunity for trout
fishing, eeling and whitebaiting. We provide a rowboat free.*

*Situated on State Highway 1 gate number 859A, the Main North South Road easy
access and only 20 minutes from Picton ferry terminal.*

Dinner by arrangement. Traditional New Zealand cuisine our speciality.

The standard of accommodation in *The New Zealand Bed and Breakfast Book*
ranges from homely to luxurious,
but you can always be sure of superior hospitality.

Blenheim
Vineyard Homestay/
Self-contained Accommodation
Address: Thainstone, Giffords Rd,
R.D. 3, Blenheim
Name: Jim & Vivienne Murray
Telephone & Fax: (03) 5728823
Beds: 2 Double, 2 Single (3 bedrooms) **Bathroom:** 1 Guests share
+ self contained house: 1 Double, 2 Single (2 bedrooms) 1 Private bathroom
Tariff: B&B (special) Double $80, Single $45, Dinner $25, School Children half
price. Self-contained Accommodation $90 (3 or 4 people)
Nearest Town: 12km north west of Blenheim off Rapaura Rd, a Picton - Nelson/
West Coast through route

We have a very large comfortable home set in our own vineyard and surrounded
by neighbouring vineyards and orchards.
We are central to most Marlborough wineries, only a few minutes from the airport,
and 30 minutes from the ferry.
Our home has a guest wing that includes three spacious bedrooms, a lounge,
dining room, bathroom and also tea / coffee making facilities.
Our cottage, set back from our home with its own driveway, is fully equipped with
a modern kitchen, bathroom, two bedrooms and lounge.
We have a grass tennis court and swimming pool in our BBQ area. We are widely
travelled and have many interests including woodturning, tramping, card playing
and trout fishing. In fact, Jim would be quite happy to throw a line in the rivers
with you. We have no pets, but enjoy bird watching.
Our three course dinners are served with Marlborough wines.

Blenheim
Homestay
Address: 16 Monro Street, Blenheim
Name: Philip and Jennifer Jellyman
Telephone: (03) 578 3148 or 578 0612 (Bus)
Beds: 1 Double, 2 Single (2 bedrooms)
Bathroom: 1 Family share
Tariff: B&B (full) Double $95, Single $50,
Credit cards accepted. Vouchers accepted.
Nearest Town: 300m from town centre

We have a lovely 80 year old home situated within 3-4 minutes walk to shopping
centre. The house is built back from the street surrounded by trees, shrubs and
colourful gardens and offers peaceful solitude to weary travellers. We offer quiet
friendly hospitality and complimentary pre-dinner drinks are available with your
hosts prior to dining out at one of Blenheim's many excellent restaurants.
Our guest rooms are spacious and are provided with electric blankets and bedside
lamps. A large separate guest lounge is provided along with tea / coffee, magazines
and a daily newspaper.
Blenheim is ideally suited for the sportsman. Good skiing in season, excellent
boating facilities in Marlborough Sounds, trout fishing, six good golf courses close
to town and all weather / grass tennis courts.
Should you wish to make use of the above facilities or make a trip around the "wine
trail" we would be happy to make necessary reservations or act as a tour guide.

Blenheim
Homestay + Self-contained Accommodation
Address: Chardonnay Lodge, Rapaura Road RD3, Blenheim
Name: Allan & Jan Graham
Telephone: (03) 570 5194
Mobile: 025 440 372
Beds: 1 Double, 2 Single (2 bedrooms)
Bathroom: 2 Ensuite.
Two Self-contained units with 1 Double + 2 Single in each
Bathroom: 2 Ensuite
Tariff: B&B (continental) Double $70, Single $50, Self contained unit $80, Credit cards accepted, Vouchers accepted
Nearest Town: Blenheim 5 mins

Come and share our parklike grounds with swimming pool, spa pool, and tennis court situated in a country locality. Close to Marlboroughs famous wineries, vineyards and orchards.

Our accommodation comprises "in house" and "detached units" complete with the privacy of your own ensuites. Each bed has a electric blanket and our courtesy van is available for your convenience.

We are an non smoking couple who have travelled extensivelly.

"Ruffy" our very friendly corgi dog shares our home. We are ex orchardists with interests in yachting and vintage cars (for our guests to enjoy). Allan is a retired airline pilot who is now operating a charter/scenic aircraft company called Straits Air.

We are situated on Rapaura Road (turn off at Spring Creek) 5 minutes from Blenheim and 20 minutes from Picton. We are happy to provide our courtesy van for airport and ferry pickups. Close by are two restaurants which provide high standard meals.

Please let your hosts know if you have to cancel.
They will have spent time preparing for you.

Blenheim
Country Retreat
Address: "The Sentinel"
Wrekin Road RD 2 Blenheim
Name: Neil & Lyn Berry
Telephone: (03) 572 9143
Beds: 2 Double, 2 Single (2 Bedrooms)
Bathroom: 2 Ensuite
Tariff: B&B (special) Double $120, Single $95, Dinner $30pp,
Nearest Town: Blenheim 15km

Your hosts Neil and Lyn welcome you to "The Sentinel", a 55 acre (22h) property specialising in beef calf rearing, situated 15km west of Blenheim, in the Brancott Valley beside Marlborough's famous wine trail. We overlook vineyards in the area and the Lower Wairau Valley to the sea.
Our two upstairs guest bedrooms, each containing a double and a single bed, have their own private ensuites. A continental or full breakfast is provided. A special platter or dinner is additional by arrangement. Meals may be taken on the terrace, with the hosts or in the guest lounge. A gas BBQ is also available. We have a grass tennis court and a small swimming pool.
Our interests are winemaking, pottery, sports, fishing, painting.
We can help you plan, wine trail visit, golf, skiing, tours of Marlborough, boat trips of the Sounds, horseriding, white water rafting, gliding, scenic flights, to name just a few.
Transport can be provided to and from Blenheim and the airport.
Directions: *Please phone.*

Blenheim
Homestay
Address: 10 Brooklyn Drive,
Blenheim.
Name: Royston Lodge
Telephone & Fax: (03) 578 6706
Beds: 2 Double, 3 Single (4 Bedrooms)
Bathroom: 1 Private, 1 Guests share
Tariff: B&B (special) Double $75, Single $45, Dinner by arrangement. Vouchers accepted.

Stuart and Robyn offer you a warm and friendly welcome and invite you to stay with us at Royston Lodge. We offer superior quality accommodation for the discerning traveller in our large modern home situated in a quiet residential area minutes from Blenheim's town centre. Relax in our formal lounge and chat with us or if you prefer you can watch TV in our separate TV lounge.
Stuart is an International chef who has travelled widely throughout the world. Naturally all meals are prepared by him. Aperitifs served before dinner.
Marlborough offers a wide variety of leisure activities - fishing, hunting, tramping, boating, diving, water skiing to mention a few; or spend a day visiting wine and / or food producers. We can arrange tours for you. Having lived locally for many years we both have a good knowledge of Blenheim and the Marlborough Sounds and would like to share this delightful area with you.
Pick up from ferry, train, bus or airport by arrangement.

Blenheim

Homestay+Self-contained Accommodation
Address: 60 Beaver Road Blenheim
Name: "Beaver Bed & Breakfast"
Telephone: (03) 578 8401
Beds: 1 Double (1 Bedroom) **Bathroom:** 1 Private
Tariff: B&B (continental) Double $60, Vouchers accepted
Nearest Town: Blenheim

With its own entrance, our self-contained unit consists of a queen sized bed, mini-kitchen, bathroom and toilet and is a modern addition to our 90 year old home. You will find us in a quiet side street only 10 minutes walk from town.
We invite you to stay with us as well as our ageing cat and cockatiel. We are a non-smoking family and work during the day, so please phone after 4.30pm or write beforehand.

Blenheim

Homestay+Self-contained
              Accommodation
Address: "Cranbrook Cottage"
Giffords Rd
Rapaura RD3 Blenheim
Name: "Cranbrook Cottage"
Telephone: (03) 572 8606
Beds: 2 Double, 2 Single (2 Bedrooms + 1 Double in S. room)
Bathroom: 1 Private
Tariff: B&B (special) Double $90, Single $15, The Cottage is a 1 group situation.
Children welcome. Campervans welcome.
Nearest Town: Blenheim

Cranbrook Cottage is our charming historic cottage which we have tastefully prepared for your stay in the heart of the vineyards of Marlborough.
We are a family of five (itinerate student daughters included!) and live in our rammed earth homestead set in an apricot and apple orchard.
The cottage furnishings befit its historical past. It is quaint warm and with excellent bedding, heated towel rails and electric blankets, your stay with us will be memorable.
We are only 25 mins from Picton and 5 mins from the airport. The Wairau River is a short walk where trout can be caught, within 15 mins of us you could explore eleven wineries (six with restaurants) two potterys, a silk painter, a small brewery, country gardens, an apiary, cherry orchards, an olive grove and much more.
We enjoy meeting people and our white linen breakfast can be enjoyed in the cottage or in our farm kitchen. Please phone if possible.

Blenheim
Homestay
Address: "Braeside" 27 Nelson St Blenheim
Name: Phyl & Brian Paul
Telephone: (03) 578 6643
Beds: 1 Double, 3 Single (2 Bedrooms) **Bathroom:** 1 Guests share
Tariff: B&B (special) Double $55, Single $38, Dinner on request, Vouchers accepted
Nearest Town: Blenheim - 1/2km to town centre

Our home is warm and comfortable situated on State Highway 6, 1/2km from town centre. Two minutes walk to beautiful Pollard Park, tennis courts, croquet club, bowling greens, golf course and Waterlea Racecourse.
We are a married couple, whose family have left home. Brian who is a retired professional photographer and has a wealth of knowledge of the district, and Phyl a registered nurse offer quiet and friendly hospitality. Two Burmese cats and a black cocker spaniel share our lives.
Our guest rooms offer - 1 double + 1 single; twin beds; 2 bedrooms; with electric blankets and wool underlays. Each room has a handbasin with hot and cold water. Guests share bathroom, shower and separate toilet.
Dinner available on request or advice on local restaurants.
We are happy to pick you up and deliver to wherever you wish to go.
"Your home away from home".

Ward, Blenheim
Farmstay/Self-contained Accommodation
Address: Mirza Downs, P O Box 24, Ward, Marlborough
Name: Sarah Beerbohm-Waddy & Michael Waddy
Telephone: (03) 575 6871
Beds: 2 Double, 1 Single (3 bedrooms) **Bathrooms:** 1 Private, 1 Guests share
Tariff: B&B (full) Double $95, Single $50, Dinner by arrangement, Children half price, Credit cards accepted, Vouchers accepted
Nearest Town: Blenheim

Mirza Downs is a 1500 acre sheep and cattle farm 50 kms south of Blenheim on the Kaikoura coast. The farm is in rolling Marlborough hill country with 2 kms of private beach (accessible by appointment and 4 x 4 only) with seal colony and magnificent views of the Kaikoura and Marlborough ranges. Guest accommodation is in the main homestead whilst we live in the neighbouring house with our two small children. The homestead has three bedrooms, two bathrooms, kitchen, dining room and sitting room opening onto the verandah and swimming pool. The pool, tennis court and piano are available for guests and there are numerous walks through farm and bush. Lunch and dinner, "farm safari's", and trips to the seal colony by arrangement. The homestead can sometimes be rented as a self-contained unit for longer periods.
Directions: *Please phone for directions.*

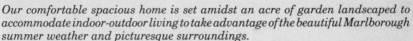

Canvastown
Homestay
Address: "Woodchester",
SH6, Canvastown
(Box 28 Canvastown, Marlborough)
Name: Irene & Graham
Telephone: (03) 574 2240
Beds: 2 Double, 2 Single (3 bedrooms)
Bathroom: 1 Guests share
Tariff: B&B (full) Double $70,
Single $40, Dinner $25. Vouchers accepted April - December inclusive.
Nearest Town: Havelock

Our comfortable spacious home is set amidst an acre of garden landscaped to accommodate indoor-outdoor living to take advantage of the beautiful Marlborough summer weather and picturesque surroundings.

Guest bedrooms and bathroom (bath & shower) are all refreshingly decorated and in a separate wing of the house for your privacy. We are ideally situated for travellers on the Picton-Nelson-West Coast route being right on the main highway approx 1 hour from Picton or Nelson.

We enjoy wholesome nutritious food and will happily cater for your meal requirements with reasonable notice. We are non smokers.

Admidst interesting scenic Marlborough we have in our immediate vicinity the lovely Pelorus Bridge area with its public walkways in beautiful native bush, trout fishing, gold panning and historic Havelock. From Havelock, day trips by launch can be arranged within the Pelorus Sound.

There is the glorious scenic Queen Charlotte drive and we are just 40 minutes from Marlborough's wine trail.

Pelorus Bridge
Self-contained Guest House
Address: Lord Lionel RD2 Rai Valley Marlborough (Please phone for directions)
Name: Lionel & Monika Neilands
Telephone & Fax: (03) 574 2770
Beds: 4 Double, 2 Single (6 Bedrooms) **Bathroom:** Guests share
Tariff: B&B (full) Double $70, Single $35. Credit cards. Vouchers accepted all year round
Nearest Town: Blenheim or Nelson 45 mins away

We wish to invite you to our beautiful Fraemos home. It is the ultimate in peace and tranquillity. A hunting and fishing paradise in the heart of the Pelorus River Country. We are situated 45 minutes from Nelson and Blenheim on State Highway 6 in the midst of 1 1/2 acre of untouched natural South Island native forest with prolific birdlife. We are 25 metres from Pelorus Bridge Scenic Reserve, which is one of the finest reserves in New Zealand. We have plenty of nearby options such as excellent walking tacks, picnic areas, tearooms, gold panning at Canvasstown and French pass is nearby. The guests have the run of the home with a self-contained kitchen with excellent cooking facilities. Major credit cards accepted. Also budget accommodation available.

Lionel has travelled extensively and Monika spricht Deutsch.

Overseas visitors please phone / fax 64 3 574 2770.

Pelorus Bridge

Homestay
Address: "Pelorus Grange" Maungatapu Rd
Pelorus Bridge RD2 Rai Valley Marlborough
Telephone & Fax: (03) 571 6082
Beds: 1 Double, 2 Single (2 Bedrooms)
Bathroom: 1 Ensuite, 1 Private, 1 Family share
Tariff: B&B (full) Double/Twin with ensuite $120, Single $90, Children half price, Dinner $30pp.
Nearest Town: Halfway between Blenheim and Nelson

Pelorus Grange sits in a beautiful valley amidst native forest overlooking the crystal clear Pelorus River. This affords trout fishing, literally from our doorstep. Deer farms surround our property that guests are welcome to visit. The Grange is a spacious modern building built in period style using native timbers throughout the house. It is situated 1.5km upstream of the Pelorus Bridge on SH6.

We have several amenities to offer the interested guests. You can go trout fishing, tramp or stroll in the forest in the adjacent Pelorus Scenic reserve, or you can just relax away from the maddening crowd soaking in the tranquil scenery listening to the quiet river and birds. Other options are sea kayaking, scenic boat tours, gold panning, or an exhilarating day with the mail launch in the Marlborough Sounds.

Start your day in our sunny dining room with either a continental or cooked breakfast. Dinners can be served and the cuisine includes local specialities venison, wild pork, lamb or seafood. Our guests will have the opportunity of tasting our fine Marlborough wines.

Vegetarians can be catered for. Facilities have been designed for elderly or disabled people. (Wheelchairs) No smoking.

Bookings not essential but appreciated.

Private bathroom is for your use exclusively,
Guests share means you may be sharing with other guests,
Family share means you will be sharing with the family.

Nelson

Homestay
Address: 15 Riverside, Nelson
Name: Hunts Home Hosts
- David & Edith Hunt
Telephone: (03) 548-0123
Beds: 1 Double, 2 Single (2 bedrooms)
Bathroom: 1 Private, 1 Family share, 1 Guests share
Tariff: B&B (special) Double $65, Single $40, children
1/2 price, Dinner $20, Campervans welcome, Vouchers
accepted

*Take a break in sunny Nelson - the geographical centre of
New Zealand - with your Home Hosts, David & Edith Hunt at
their beautiful home by the crystal clear River Maitai in the centre of the city.
Sightseeing, excursions, picnics, barbecues, fishing, gold panning, visits to local
potteries and weavers, museums, theatres - all within easy reach.
Bed and cooked breakfast and meals as required including packed lunches.
Guest suite with one twin, one double bedroom. Guest lounge with colour TV,
private facilities including bath, shower and toilet, kitchenette, lock-up garage.
Our service car is available to pick up guests from the Airport or Bus Depot or for
sightseeing trips, etc. My wife speaks English, German & Czech.
Our upstairs quarters always have a warm welcome for those who want our
company. Our brochure with city plan shows the way to our sunny home.
We want our guests to feel comfortable and at home - and a little spoilt. We are looking
back over 15 years of happy home-hosting with an ever increasing circle of friends.*

Nelson

Homestay
Address: Please phone
Name: Dorothy and Bob Brown
Telephone: (03) 548-4751
Beds: 2 Single (1 bedroom)
Bathroom: 1 Private
Tariff: B&B (continental) Double $55, Single $40
Nearest Town: Nelson (5 minute walk)

*We are retired and would like to welcome you to our comfortable, modern home
which is in a garden setting on the banks of the Maitai River and opposite the
Queens Gardens, just five minutes' walk to the city centre, shops and restaurants,
art gallery, cinema and covered heated swimming pool and spa. Central yet quiet.
Off-street parking.
The guest accommodation is spacious and sunny, consisting of a large bedroom
with twin beds, your own sitting room to relax in, with colour TV, fridge, tea and
coffee making facilities, and of course your own bathroom. Or, you are welcome to
join us in the lounge, maybe share a common interest, travel, etc.
Why not spend a few days exploring the wonderful scenic Nelson region? We will
pick you up (and deliver!) to airport or bus.
We just love meeting people and making new friends. We are non smokers. And to our good
friends in NZ and all over the world, we say Hi! and thank you for staying with us.*
Directions: *Please phone*

Collingwood House, Nelson

Nelson
Bed & Breakfast Inn
Address: Collingwood House,
174 Collingwood Street, Nelson
Name: Cecile and Alan Strang
Telephone: (03) 548 4481
Beds: 1 King, 1 Double, 3 Single (3 bedrooms)
Bathroom: 1 Ensuite, 1 Guests share
Tariff: B&B (special) Double $70, Single $50, Children 1/2 price; Dinner $20.
Credit Cards. Vouchers accepted.
Nearest Town: Nelson: 3 blocks from town centre.

This is Bed & Breakfast in the best British tradition. "Collingwood House" is three blocks from the town centre yet quiet. Spacious double guestrooms include comfortable beds, duvets and woolrests, fresh flowers and pretty linen. Upstairs' views feature the city's spires and steeples, trees and surrounding hills.

Start your day with a lavish breakfast: Fruit, cereals and homemade meusli. Our free-range eggs and farm bacon are not to be missed! Juice, fine teas and plenty of fresh filter or cappucino coffee.

On arrival, we'll welcome you with refreshments and any help you may need to discover local attractions including excellent restaurants. We have travelled extensively and after many years offering bed and breakfast we find guests are returning - frequently from overseas - to stay again.

Our family holiday home at Parapara Beach in Golden Bay (2 hours drive) is also available for a quiet holiday.

One of the differences between staying at a hotel and a B&B
is that you don't hug the hotel staff when you leave.

Nelson

Boutique Accommodation
Address: 7 Cambria Street, Nelson
Name: Cambria House
Telephone: (03) 548-4681,
Fax: (03) 546-6649
Beds: 6 Double, 2 Single (7 bedrooms)
Bathroom: 7 Ensuite
Tariff: B&B (special) Double $165, Single $125. Credit Cards.
Nearest Town: Nelson 5 mins to city centre.

Cambria House is a 130 year old Nelson homestead that has been tastefully extended and restored to provide superb accommodation for today's discerning traveller. The highly respected Australian Gourmet Traveller Magazine cited Cambria House as being at the "top end of the Bed & Breakfast Market".

The owners, Bill and Catherine Vincent have sought to create a warm, friendly atmosphere in this lovely old homestead located just 5 minutes from the city centre, yet offering real peace and tranquillity. The building has a wealth of features such as beautiful fireplaces, slate roof, panelling and original doors in rimu and kauri. For winter, all rooms have the comfort of heating and electric blankets. A comfortable guest lounge with log fire opens on to a delightful courtyard garden.

Breakfast at Cambria House is a real feature. Enjoy a healthy continental style breakfast of cereals, yoghurt, bottled preserves and fresh fruit from the region. Alternatively, choose a more traditional breakfast from our a la carte selection featuring farm fresh eggs, venison, bacon, ham, tomatoes and mushrooms or superb local smoked salmon. Home made muffins, jams and marmalades, a fine selection of teas or freshly ground coffee will further complement your meal. Advance booking is highly recommended.

Always telephone ahead to enquire about a B&B. It is a nuisance for you if
you simply arrive to find someone already staying there.
And besides hosts need a little time to prepare.

Nelson

Bed & Breakfast Inn
Address: 29 Collingwood Street, Nelson
Name: California House
Telephone: & Fax (03) 548-4173
Beds: 2 Queen, 2 Double, 1 Twin, 1 Triple (4 bedrooms)
Bathroom: 4 Ensuite
Tariff: B&B (Special) Double $125-$150, Single $95. Credit cards accepted.
Nearest Town: Nelson - 3 blocks from town centre.

Your hosts Neil & Shelley Johnstone invite you to discover a unique bed and breakfast experience in their beautifully preserved Victorian home. Built in 1893 and classified by the New Zealand Historic Places Trust for its historical and architectural significance, California House features English oak panelling, 24 stained glass windows, open fires and spacious rooms. The house is set back from the street in a quiet residential area just 5 minutes walk from the centre of town.

After a warm and friendly welcome you will be shown through the house which is yours to enjoy. Relax in the peaceful sitting room with its Persian rugs, fireplace for those brisk winter nights and numerous books, or on the wide sunny verandahs overlooking lawns and garden. The guest rooms are furnished with colonial oak furniture, comfortable antique beds, memorabilia, fresh flowers and private bathrooms to enhance your comfort and relaxation.

In the morning enjoy leisurely Californian homebaked breakfasts in the sunny kitchen. These may include freshly squeezed orange juice, fresh fruits and cream, muffins, ham and sour cream omelettes, Finnish pancakes topped with strawberries, cream and pure Canadian maple syrup and freshly ground coffee..

Courtesy transport is available to and from bus depots. An airport shuttle bus will deliver you to our door.

Tariffs include breakfast, wine, beer or fruit juice on arrival and tea, coffee, sherry and biscuits available at any time. No smoking in the house. Advance bookings recommended.

Our B&Bs are mostly private homes.
Most do not accept credit cards.

Nelson
Guest House
Address: "Sussex House", 238 Bridge St, Nelson
Name: Mrs. I.C. Hunt
Telephone: (03) 548 9972
Beds: 2 Double, 3 Single (4 bedrooms)
Bathroom: 1 Ensuite, 1 Guests share
Tariff: B&B (full) Double $75, with ensuite $85, Single $50, Children half price, Credit cards accepted, Vouchers accepted
Nearest Town: Nelson

A fine character home that is cheerful, cosy and centrally situated on the banks of the peaceful Maitai River. That's "Sussex House", our charming guest house, 2 / 3 minutes from Nelson's Information Office. Also close to the Suter Art Gallery, the beautiful Queen's Gardens and Botanical Hill (the centre of New Zealand).

The house features four sunny bedrooms that have access to the verandahs overlooking the river. One bedroom has ensuite bathroom.

There is a swimming pool and the secluded garden area allows you to relax and enjoy the tranquil surroundings.

Breakfast includes a selection of seasonal fruit and berries, puffy fruit omelettes, pancakes, savoury mushrooms and homemade jams and marmalades.

Vegetarians and / or guests on special diets are catered for individually. Children are welcome.

No smoking in the house.

Your host, Ida Hunt, comes from Sussex, England.

Please let your hosts know if you have to cancel.
They will have spent time preparing for you.

Nelson

Homestay
Address: Please Phone
Name: Elaine & Peter Cooke
Telephone: (03) 548 1261
Beds: 2 Single (1 bedroom) **Bathroom:** 1 Private
Tariff: B&B (full) Double $65, Single $35, Children $10,
Dinner $20, Campervans $20
Nearest Town: Nelson

Situated on Britania Heights overlooking the entrance to Nelson harbour with extensive views of Tasman Bay, from the Airport to Separation Point.
From our modern home you are within 5 minutes of Nelson City, interesting port area and the renowned Tahuna Beach.
We are an active retired couple with interests in golf, yachting, sea fishing and travel. Our swimming pool reaches pleasant temperatures in summer months while underfloor heating ensures cosy living in winter.
Nelson has much to offer within the district and we recommend a trip over the marble mountain to explore Golden Bay. Spend a night there, make the fabulous trip to Farewell Spit. Return to our home for dinner if you wish, a comfortable night's rest and a good breakfast to continue your travels on.
Directions: *We will pick you up from the Airport or town. Please phone.*

Tahunanui, Nelson

Homestay
Address: "Bagust Retreat"
201 Annesbrook Drive Nelson
Name: Henry & Junie Bagust
Telephone: (03) 548 5868 Please phone first
Beds: 1 Queen, 1 Queen Postupaedic, 1 Single (2 bedrooms)
Bathroom: 2 Ensuite
Tariff: B&B (continental) $55 Double, $40 Single,
Children $12, Dinner $10 (2 course)

Drive up our private drive from Highway 6 to our peaceful home in a quiet sunny bush setting with mountain and sea views. Each delightful new bedsit has its own seperate entrance with covered parking, ensuite, TV, fridge, electric blankets, hair dryer, heating, table and chairs, tea and toast facilities, microwave, also homemade extras. Telephone available.
Our ancestors came to Nelson in 1842 and we feel very proud of our city and district with its many tourist attractions. We have toured extensively throughout N.Z. Also overseas and we delight to return the hospitality we have received from both our overseas and NZ friends. We extend a warm welcome to anyone visiting our city.

Near Tahuna beach, golf course and airport we are only 4 kilometres to the city centre on a main bus route. Our nicest compliment is that all our guests want to return.
Meals by arrangement.

368

Nelson

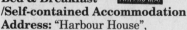

**Bed & Breakfast
/Self-contained Accommodation**
Address: "Harbour House",
371 Wakefield Quay, Nelson
Name: Jeanette & Ian Phillips
Telephone: (03) 548 7430
Beds: 2 Double, 1 Single (2 Bedrooms), Ensuite facility & exclusive use of ground floor - rate on application **Bathroom:** 1 Guests share
Tariff: B&B (special) Double $70, Single $50, Children $30, Dinner priced from menu
Nearest Town: Nelson City 5 mins

Our welcoming old world seaside home is situated overlooking Nelsons Harbour Entrance, with views across Tasman Bay and the mountains beyond.
The ever changing moods of the sea are a constant source of entertainment and fascination, that's why everybody enjoys our sunny garden terrace where you'll find yourself drawn for breakfast, dinner or just to relax.
If activity is something you are after, we have house bicycles for guests use, you could swim in the bay, or rent our hire kayaks, and paddle out to Haulashore Island and the Lighthouse with one of our packed lunches or perhaps you'd rather fish with Ian.
Spacious guest rooms and self contained living areas feature antique furniture which complement our homes wealth of history.
The inside of the house is a smoke free area.
Please phone or write for any further information.
Ian, Jeanette and Seymour the cat look forward to welcoming you to Harbour House.
Directions: *Highway 6 south of Port Nelson.*

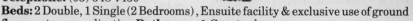

Monaco, Nelson

Homestay
Address: 20 Martin Street, Monaco, Nelson
Name: Jean and Jack Anderson
Telephone: (03) 547-6739
Beds: 1 Double, 2 Single (2 bedrooms) **Bathroom:** 1 Family share
Tariff: B&B (full) Double $48, Single $25, Children half price; Dinner $12.50, Vouchers accepted.

We are a couple who like meeting people. We live beside the sea where it is lovely to walk or put your boat in for a leisurely cruise. Waterskiing is prominent here in the summertime.
Shopping is close at Nelson, Stoke or Richmond. Also very near to historic houses, museum, gardens and craft habitat. In the winter time it is only about an hour's drive to the skifields.
Guests are very welcome on Christmas Day. Enjoy Kiwi hospitality in this "little corner of the world".
We are near the airport and will meet planes or buses at depots. A phone call or a letter would be appreciated before arrival.
Directions: *Take the road from Nelson to Stoke. Turn right at the lights into Songer Street. Travel right to the bottom of Songer Street around the bay into Monaco turning in front of the Monaco Boat Club into Martin Street.*

Stoke, Nelson
Homestay
Address: "Treeview",
7 Titoki Street,
Stoke, Nelson
Name: Kathy & Laurence Carr
Telephone: (03) 547-6307
Beds: 1 Double, 2 Single (2 bedrooms)
Bathroom: 1 Guests share
Tariff: B&B (continental) Double $55,
Single $35, Children half price, Vouchers accepted

Our comfortable home is ideally situated with rural views.
Our breakfast room gets the morning sun. Relaxed atmosphere. We welcome you to this attractive area, within walking distance to Stoke Centre on Highway 6 with all facilities. Isel Park and Broadgreen Rose Gardens, historic homes, Museums. Short distance to restaurants, beaches and tourist attractions. Guests love the walks through the park, up the valleys. Views of mountains, sea and sunsets. We are both New Zealand born with English ancestors. Kathy a country girl at heart, Laurence likes a game of golf and is a retired Tugmaster of Port Nelson. We are non-smokers but you are free to use the "smokers seat" on the terrace. Off street parking. Pets welcome. We have a cocker spaniel.
Directions: *From Nelson to Stoke on Highway 6, turn left at Stoke traffic lights into Songer Street. Titoki Street is last street on right before the hill. From Richmond on Highway 6 turn right at traffic lights into Songer Street.*

Stoke, Nelson
Homestay
Address: 28 Devon St,
Stoke, Nelson
Name: Ralph and Reigl
Telephone: (03) 547 744z
Beds: 4 Single (2 bedrooms)
Bathroom: 1 Private
Tariff: B&B (continental) Double $70 Single $40,
Dinner by arrangement, Vouchers accepted.
Nearest Town: Stoke Shopping Centre 1 km, Nelson and/or Richmond 8 km

We are a retired couple who have been entertaining local and overseas visitors for some years. It is our policy to host one party of up to 4 guests at a time so we can give undivided attention to our visitors. All are assured of a warm welcome, good food, comfortable beds and superior toilet facilities. Off street parking is supplied. Comments in our visitor's book encourage us to believe we fulfil our aim of providing "A Home away from Home".
The property is adjacent to the famed Broadgreen Historic Home with its floodlit rose gardens and the Nayland heated swimming pool complex is a 5 minutes walk with a 10 minute walk to the Stoke Shopping Centre which boasts a post office, a choice of banking facilities and full shopping. Tahuna Beach, halfway to Nelson is a 10 minute drive.
Pick up from bus stops and airport available and special interest tours arranged.

Stoke, Nelson
Homestay
Address: 585 Waimea Road, Nelson
Name: Maureen & Ramon Box
Telephone: (03) 547-3622
Beds: 2 Double, 2 Single (3 bedrooms)
Bathroom: 1 Family share, 1 Double brm has own toilet
Tariff: B&B (continental) Double $60, Single $30, Children $10, Dinner $20, Vouchers accepted

We live 5 minutes from Nelson City, 2 minutes from the airport and beach. We have a large home with wide views of Tasman Bay and panoramic mountain range. Sunsets are breathtaking to watch when relaxing with us.
We are real outdoor people with many interests, Ramon has built his own yacht and is happy to take guests sailing, he also has a mussel farm in Pelorus Sound which our guest can sample. We also have house pets. We look forward to meeting you with a warm welcome to Nelson
Directions: *Please phone.*

Stoke, Nelson
Homestay
Address: Holland House, 'Aldinga', 14 Aldinga Avenue, Stoke, Nelson
Name: Mike and Glenda Gepp
Telephone & Fax: (03) 547 9853
Beds: 2 Double, 2 Single, (3 bedrooms) **Bathroom:** 2 Ensuite, 1 Guests share
Tariff: B&B (full) Double $85, Single $60, Dinner by arrangement, Children by arrangement, Vouchers accepted all year except February

Holland House is an historic homestead and is believed to be the oldest house in New Zealand still inhabited. George Holland and his family arrived in New Zealand aboard the 'Bolton' in March 1842, loosing two of his children on the journey. The house was built around 1845 of cob under a wooden shingle roof, now slate, and has an Historic Places Trust classification.
The house retains all its early character but with the comforts of modern plumbing. Meals are cooked on the rayburn which also supplies hot water to the radiators throughout the house.
Guests have the run of the house and are welcome to make themselves comfortable in either of the lounges or enjoy the garden.
We enjoy having visitors and are happy to assist with touring plans in the area such as the wine trail, rafting, fishing and the potteries.
Waimea estuary and its varied bird life is ten minutes walk.

Nelson

Quality Homestay
Address: Harbour View Homestay,
11 Fifeshire Crescent, Nelson
Name: Judy and Rob
Telephone: (03) 548 8567
Beds: 2 Double, 2 Single (3 bedrooms)
Bathroom: 2 Ensuite, 1 Private
Tariff: B&B (special) Double $110, Single $80, Dinner $30 by arrangement.
Some Credit cards accepted. Vouchers accepted May to August with continental
breakfast.
Nearest Town: Midway between Tahunanui Beach and Nelson City via the
waterfront.

*Our home is above the harbour entrance with huge windows and decks to capture
the spectacular views of beautiful Tasman Bay, Haulashore Island, Tahunanui
Beach, and across the sea to Abel Tasman National Park and mountains. You can
observe from the decks, dining-room, BBQ or spa, ships and pleasure craft
cruising by as they enter and leave the harbour.*

*We are within minutes of the airport, beach, city centre, shopping and eating
establishments including our family-owned restaurant. We can assist with
arranging wine trails, gold panning, trout fishing, river rafting, harbour excursions
etc. if you can tear yourself away from our magnificent view.*

*We want our guests to completely relax therefore all our bedrooms have private
bathrooms and central heating in winter. We thank you for not smoking inside,
outside is fine. For your convenience some credit cards are accepted. We would be
happy to meet you at the airport or bus or if directions are required please phone.*

Nelson

Homestay
Address: 4 Seaton Street, Atawhai, Nelson
Name: Mike Cooper and Lennane Kent
Telephone & Fax: (03) 5451671
Beds: 1 Double, 2 Single (2 bedrooms)
Bathroom: 1 Guests share
Tariff: B&B (full) Double $55 first night ($50 subsequent nights), Single $30 first
night ($27.50 subsequent nights), Dinner $17.50. Vouchers accepted.
Nearest Town: 6km from Nelson close to main Picton & Blenheim Road.

*Our home is in a quiet suburb overlooking the Nelson Haven, the Boulder Bank,
Tasman Bay and out to the mountains beyond. We spend many an idle moment
watching the changing moods of the Bay. Breakfast with this view is an ideal way
to start any day of your holiday.*

*Our interests include distance running (veterans class), sea fishing, pre school
and special education and our ageing and very friendly airedale terrier. We are
happy to accommodate families with children or adults with disabilities on the
understanding that the house has not been adapted for this purpose. We are also
accepting of the peculiarities of boaties, joggers and dog owners.*

*While you may like to join us in the evenings there is a small guest lounge space
with TV and coffee and tea making facilities for your use.*

*Guests have their own entrance to the house. Ours is a non-smoking household.
We can give you simple directions to the house or will be happy to meet you in town
or at the Airport.*

Nelson
Guest House
Address: 19 Beach Road Tahunanui Nelson
Name: Aloha Lodge
Telephone: (03) 546 4000
Fax: (03) 546 4420
Beds: 25 Double or Twin (25 Bedrooms)
Bathroom: 8 Ensuite, 8 Private, 2 Guests share
Tariff: B&B (full) Summer/Winter Double $70/$54, Single $60/$50, Children $10 extra, Campervans 2 sites. Credit cards. Vouchers accepted between May 31st - Sept 30
Nearest Town: Nelson City

A warm welcome greets you at the Aloha Lodge.
John and Linda invite you to share the luxury and comforts of Aloha, while you enjoy the delights of Nelson City.
After a day on the Tahunanui beach opposite the Lodge you can relax in our picturesque award winning garden and enjoy a family BBQ.
You may then wish to treat yourself to an extra night in one of our executive suites with sauna and spa bath and spectacular views over the Tasman Bay.
Each morning enjoy a cooked breakfast in the guest dining room where many lasting friendship is made.
The Aloha Lodge is a luxury Bed & Breakfast at budget price.
(3) Executive suites
(5) Rooms with private ensuite
(17) Rooms with shared facilities

Always have a phone card with you. Most public phones do not take coins

---

Nelson

Guest House
Address: 'Northbrook Villa' 174 Tasman Street Nelson
Name: Michael & Lynette Hislop
Telephone: (03) 548 3021
Beds: 4 Queen, 2 Single (4 Bedrooms)
Bathroom: 2 Ensuite, 1 Guests share
Tariff: B&B (Special) Double $80-115, Single $45-60, Children under 12 $25.
Credit cards accepted. Vouchers accepted
Nearest Town: Nelson

A warm and friendly WELCOME awaits you at NORTHBROOK VILLA, our home is yours to enjoy. We have a beautiful Victorian villa with large living areas. The guest bedrooms are attractively decorated with comfortable beds and pleasant outlooks, they are being extended to provide ensuites to each without compromising the character of the house and its original ambience.

Northbrook Villa resides within a secluded sunny garden with swimming pool and spa for you to enjoy. The house verandahs provide for relaxation in the sun or shade. Accessible facilities for the disabled are available on the ground floor. All carparking is provided on-site under security lighting.

Breakfast features homemade muffins, cereals, home preserves and a variety of cooked breakfasts, finishing off with a selection of teas or coffee ensuring a great start to the day ahead whether you are travelling to a new destination or staying on to enjoy the many activities that Nelson has to offer.

The City Centre, Queens Gardens, Suter Art Galley and Nelson Polytechnic are all within 10 minutes walking distance.

Missie is resident cat.

Monaco, Nelson

Homestay
Address: 67 Martin St Monaco Nelson
Name: Bryan Keane
Telephone: (03) 547 7530
Beds: 2 Double, 1 Single (2 Bedrooms)
Bathroom: 1 Ensuite, 1 Family share
Tariff: B&B (special) Double $95-110, Single $75, Children half price, Dinner $15-30. Credit cards accepted. Vouchers accepted (special conditions apply)
Nearest Town: Nelson 8km

A warm welcome awaits you at Anchor Down. We are ideally situated just 10km from Nelson at Monaco. Our seaside home offers you comfort and relaxation, your stay will be one to remember.

We have two spacious guest rooms, one with ensuite, both have TV, stereo and telephone for your convenience. Relax in our private spa and swimming pool or play a game of snooker in the billiard room after an evening walk in the setting sun.

Being right on the water edge boating is a major part of our life. We offer our boat for fishing, skiing or just a zip around the harbour.

We take pride in serving quality food, prepared with creative flair using fresh local produce, this guarantees you satisfaction from our wide menu.

Many of our guests have vowed to return so we look forward to sharing our home with you.

Anchor Down - A truly unique place to stay -

Nelson
Bed & Breakfast

Address: "Kemp House"
80 Tahunanui Dr, Nelson
Name: Trish & Peter Kemp
Telephone: (03) 548 6881
Beds: 2 Double, 3 Single (4 Bedrooms)
Bathroom: 1 Guests share, 1 Family share
Tariff: B&B (full) Double $65, Single $45, No children under 12. Also available a B&B Cabin own continental breakfast facilities, TV and fridge $40 per night (twin beds). Credit cards. Vouchers accepted.
Nearest Town: Nelson 4km south on Highway 6

With 14 years experience in tramping and cycling, Trish and Peter look forward to sharing the Nelson area with you. We encourge people to experience all that Nelson has to offer and we are happy to arrange transport to and from tramping tracks and also help with any booking arrangement where possible.

We are only a phone call away from pick up from airport or bus depot.

Our sunny, comfortable home is only 4km from Nelson City, 3km from the airport, 800 metres from lovely Tahuna Beach and local restaurants with a small shopping centre nearby.

Our bedrooms are sunny and pleasant to relax in after a busy day, one with its own sundeck. There is also a deck and outdoor area off the dining room for our guests use.

We also have a guest telephone and a laundry service available. We like to get to know you, so our guests are encouraged to make themselves at home in our lounge.

Non smoking inside please.

We accept major credet cards.

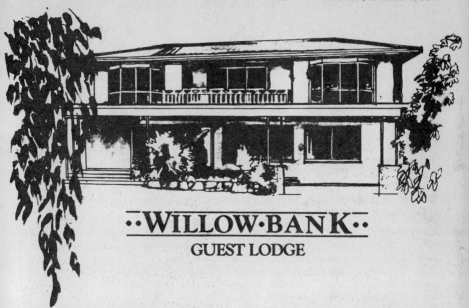

··WILLOW·BANK··
GUEST LODGE

Nelson
Bed & Breakfast Lodge
Address: 71 Golf Road, Tahunanui, Nelson
Name: Willowbank Guest Lodge
Telephone: (03) 548 5041
Fax: (03) 548 5078
Beds: 4 Double, 6 Single (6 Bedrooms)
Bathroom: 3 Guests share
Tariff: B&B (full) Double $67, Single $49, Children under 15 $15 (Pre-school free). Credit cards. Vouchers accepted full year
Nearest Town: Nelson 4km to city centre

Although in a delightfully quiet setting, Willowbank Guest Lodge is just a few minutes walk from Nelson's beautiful Tahunanui Beach. We pride ourselves on our warmth and friendliness, and are committed to ensuring that you get the most from your stay in Nelson, be it for a restful stopover or for making the most of enjoying the scenic variety and wonderful experiences available in the area.

We provide a courtesy car to and from bus depots and the airport. Phone us on arrival in Nelson. Willowbank is also on the shuttle bus route to and from the city centre.

Facilities include: large comfortable guest lounge, in-ground swimming pool, off-street parking, coffee & tea making, pool table, laundry, barbecue area. Rooms are fully serviced daily.

For guests' comfort, Willowbank is smoke-free inside, but sheltered and comfortable outside areas are available.

A very good variety of restaurants are within walking distance.

Abel Tasman National Park Tours and Nelson Day Tours pick up from gate.

Visa/Mastercard/Bankcard accepted.

Willowbank is a member of New Zealand's Federation of B&B's.

Your hosts: Cecily & Ron Mayes.

Nelson
International
   Bed & Breakfast
Address: Borogove
27 Grove St Nelson
Name: Borogove
Telephone: (03) 548 9442
Beds: 2 Double, 1 Twin (3 Bedrooms)
Bathroom: 2 Ensuite, 1 Private
Tariff: B&B (full) Double $70, Single $40. Credit Cards: Visa, M/C. Vouchers accepted April to September

Borogove is an Edwardian villa of authentic New Zealand design. Built in 1907 it has the characteristic high ceilings and spaciousness of that time; period furnishings retain the atmosphere of a gracious past.
Each bedroom is charmingly decorated and has an ensuite bathroom or adjacent private facilities. Arm-chairs, tea / coffee, heaters, electric blankets, TV and well-stocked book shelves add to your comfort.
Set in a fragrant and peaceful garden, deck-chairs invite you to relax.
After a restful night's sleep you will be offered a delicious full breakfast including fresh fruit salad, local honey and preserves, freshly ground coffee and a choice of teas.
Your hosts are Wilhelm and Judy Hiener, travellers, writers, restaurateurs to mention some of their activities.
Borogove is a non-smoking house and is less than 5 minutes walk to the Visitors Information Centre, Post office and bus stations and the varied shops and restaurants of Nelson City.

Tahunanui, Nelson
Homestay
Address: "Treetops" 156 Moana Avenue, Tahunanui, Nelson
Name: Jim & Jill Mills
Telephone: (03) 548 5831
Beds: 1 Double, 2 Single (2 Bedrooms) **Bathroom:** 1 Guests share
Tariff: B&B (full) Double $75, Single $45, Dinner by arrangement $15-20, Vouchers accepted March to November
Nearest Town: Nelson

We welcome visitors to our smoke free home situated on the hillside above Tahunanui Beach. Panoramic views from the house and deck of Tasman Bay and the Mount Arthur Range are part of our life, as are the frequent magnificent sunsets. As an alternative we have a secluded patio with herb garden for sitting and relaxing.
Between the modern, comfortable guest rooms, which are down stairs, is a sitting room with its own deck if you wish to be on your own, and a writing area is available. The house is a few minutes drive from the airport, beach, city centre, restaurants and golf course.
Having travelled extensively ourselves we like to meet visitors from all parts. Our interests include sailing, gardening, walking, cooking, fly and sea fishing, and we can often arrange these or other activities for our guests.
Please ring for directions or we can pick you up from the city or airport.

Richmond

Homestay
Address: "Bayview", 37 Kihilla Road,
Richmond, Nelson
Name: Ray & Janice O'Loughlin
Telephone: (03) 544 6541 (afternoon or evening)
Beds: 1 Queen, 1 Super King (2 bedrooms)
Bathroom: 1 Guests share
Tariff: B&B (continental) Double $85, Single $50,
Dinner $20, Vouchers accepted from April to October
Nearest Town: Richmond 1 km. Nelson 12 kms.

"Bayview" is a large, modern, spacious home in the Richmond foothills. Our property borders a green area planted with large trees and we enjoy the tranquillity of this rural scene and the spectacular views of the bay and mountains. Built on three levels, all rooms in our home are warm, sunny, light and airy, with exposed beam ceilings and large windows. Guests may enjoy afternoon tea, a quiet drink, or even breakfast on the sunny deck overlooking the bay.

Guest bedrooms are private, immaculate and furnished with your complete comfort in mind. From the Queen bedroom on the upper level you can watch the stars, while the King room has views over the garden and bay. The guest bathroom is extra large with shower, marble vanity and large spabath, from which you may also watch the starts twinkle through two skylights as you soak in the tub. Toilet is separate. Laundry facilities also available.

We are a middle-aged working couple who enjoy meeting people and have a friendly Cocker spaniel, cat and many birds in a large aviary. In our spare time we love to read, relax at nearby beaches, maintain our prize-winning garden, capture moments to remember on film and play squash. Janice loves to cook and guests may choose to join their hosts for either a three course dinner or a lighter meal.

We look forward to meeting you and will do our best to make your stay enjoyable.

Richmond
Bed & Breakfast
Address: "Mapledurham",
8 Edward St, Richmond, Nelson
Name: Deborah & Giles Grigg
Telephone: (03) 544-4210
Beds: 2 Queen, 1 Twin (3 bedrooms)
Bathroom: 2 Ensuite, 1 Private
Tariff: B&B (special) Double $135-$140, Single $95, Dinner $30, Long stay discounts, Visa/MC accepted.
Nearest Town: Nelson City 13km, Nelson airport 7km (SH6)

Luxury and a warm welcome await you at Mapledurham, a carefully restored colonial villa, only minutes walk from Richmond centre.

Trees and shrubs surround the old garden making a haven for birds and guests alike.

On warm evenings you may like to relax in the vine covered pergola or on one of the verandahs.

Inside, panelled ceilings and spaciousness from a bygone era, plus magnificent beds and sumptuous lounge furniture, combine with log fires in winter to produce comfort of a very high order.

Good food and drink is a feature of Mapledurham hospitality, a welcoming drink and bowl of fruit are just the beginning.

Dinner, cooked with creative flair is offered by arrangement. A leisurely breakfast may be selected from the wide choice available and tea, fresh-ground coffee and fruit juice are available all day.

Guests leave feeling relaxed and refreshed, so come and enjoy the Mapledurham experience for yourself. We look forward to your company too.

Smoking outside please.

Directions: *Please phone for details*

Richmond

Country Homestay
Address: "Sunview Country Homestay"
Hill Street, Hope, Nelson (off White Road, Hope) on H 6.
Name: Noeline & Carl Arnold
Telephone & Fax: (03) 544 7286 or (03) 544 7584
Beds: 2 Double, 1 King + 1 Single, 2 Twin (5 bedrooms)
Bathrooms: 1 Private, 2 Guests share.
Tariff: B&B (full) Double $80-$90, Single $50-$55, Dinner $25, Children half price, Vouchers accepted from March to October.
Nearest Town: Richmond; 5km south of Richmond on State Highway 6, turn up Whites Rd to Hill St.

Enjoy a stay at our orchard property situated on the foothills 5 minutes south of Richmond with fabulous views of Tasman Bay, the Waimea Plains and Moutain Range beyond.

At "Sunview" we grow:-

Boysenberries, Tayberries, Tamarillos, Avocados and Citrus. Fresh fruits from our orchard are served when in season or home preserved fruits and juices.

Guests may enjoy an orchard walk or use our large swimming pool or just relax on our patios overlooking the breathtaking views.

We are 5-25 minutes from Beaches, Rivers, Richmond shopping centre and Nelson city plus "Sunview" is a good starting point to enjoy the district's scenic trips, walkways, wine and pottery trails, or Abel Tasman National Park.

Carl is a builder and our orchard started as a hobby for him and now has developed to a very busy horticultural farm unit. Noeline is a very capable cook, having many years experience cooking for Carl and a large family.

We enjoy the privilege of meeting people from different countries now that our family has left home. Guests will love a relaxing holiday in our very spacious home.

Some hosts are away from home during the day.

Richmond

Rural Homestay
Address: Seachange Farm,
Appleby, Richmond R.D. 1, Nelson
Name: Dot & Dave Wills
Telephone: (03) 544-2702
Beds: 1 Double, 2 Single (2 bedrooms)
Bathroom: 1 Private, Family share toilet
Tariff: B&B (full) Double $50, Single $30, Children half price, Dinner $15.
Vouchers accepted.
Nearest Town: Richmond (7 km), Nelson (22 km)

*Welcome to Seachange Farm. We have abandoned the city and invite you to join
us for the good life under the Appleby sunshine on our small farmlet, with its
garden vineyard and winery. We also have our own sheep, hens and two cats, Biff
and Esmo.*
*We are well situated for day trips to Golden Bay, Nelson Lakes, Rabbit Island and
Nelson city and its environs. We take only one party at a time and you really will
enjoy your stay in our comfortable home.*
Directions: *State Highway 60 from Richmond, cross the Waimea River (Appleby
Bridge), take second turning on the left at Peaviner Corner. We are 200 metres on left.*

Richmond

Homestay
Address: 3 George Kidd St,
Richmond, Nelson
Name: Lesley and Tony Marshall
Telephone: (03) 544 7741
Beds: 1 Double, 1 Single (2 bedrooms)
Bathroom: 1 Guests share
Tariff: B&B (special) Double $70, Single $45, Dinner $20, Vouchers accepted
March to October

*Our large modern home is located in a quiet area on the Richmond foothills with
views across to the mountains.*
*We offer guests a friendly relaxed atmosphere, enjoy meeting fellow travellers and
have an extensive knowledge of the attractions of the region.*
Complimentary tea and coffee available to you at any time of the day.
*Breakfast is provided at a time to suit. Please join us for a family dinner any
evening by arrangement, and feel free to relax with us in the lounge over coffee.*
*Our sunny bedrooms open onto a deck area, and have quality furnishings to make
your stay comfortable. We like to feel our guests leave us feeling their stay has been
a home away from home.*
Laundry facilities available if required.
We prefer a phone call prior to arrival. A non smoking house.
Directions: *Please phone.*

Richmond
Bed & Breakfast Inn
Address: 10 Wensley Road, Richmond, Nelson
Name: Kirshaw House
Telephone: (03) 544 0957
Beds: 1 Queen, 1 Twin, 1 Single, 1 Executive suite (4 Bedrooms)
Bathroom: 1 Ensuite (executive suite), 1 Ensuite (Queen),1 Private
Tariff: B&B (full) Queen/Twin $80, Single $55, Executive Suite $120.
Nearest Town: Richmond

Your hosts Bernie and Louis invite you to join them for a taste of traditional English Bed and Breakfast.

Kirshaw House has recently been restored to a very high standard, offering the grace and elegance of yesteryear. Many interesting features include a unique leadlight window which along with the house has a New Zealand Historic Places Trust classification.

Guest rooms with ensuite and luxury private bathroom, are beautifully furnished with antiques and fresh flowers, and the sitting room and sunroom offer comfort and warmth after a day of sightseeing.

Full English breakfasts are cooked to your choice, along with homemade muffins and peserves. Continental breakfasts are also available with fresh local juices, tea and coffee.

Bernie and Louis are well travelled and have extensive knowledge of hunting, tramping and wine trails in the region.

Situated 12 minutes from Nelson City, Kirshaw House is noted for its peace and tranquillity and is an easy walk from local restaurants, shops and Washbourne Gardens. Spend a few night soaking up the old world charm and hospitality of this charming guest house and resume your travels relaxed and refreshed.

There's quite a tale about Kirshaw House ... we'd love to tell you about it.

Kirshaw House is a non-smoking household and does not cater for children under 12 years of age.

Centrally placed to visit Abel Tasman National Park, wine and craft trails, lakes, golf course.

Directions: *Please phone for details.*

Richmond
Country Homestay
Address: 87 Main Rd, Hope, Nelson
Name: Alison and Murray Nicholls
Telephone: (03) 544 8026
Beds: 2 Double, 2 Single (3 Bedrooms)
Bathroom: 1 Guests share, 1 Family share
Tariff: B&B (full) Double $60, Single $35, Dinner by arrangement $12pp, Vouchers accepted
Nearest Town: Richmond 2km Nelson 17km

Our home is situated on a kiwifruit and apple orchard, on State Highway 6 2km south of Richmond. A lengthy driveway ensures quiet surroundings in a lovely garden setting.
Guests may enjoy a stroll through the orchard, or swim in our pool.
We are centrally situated placing Nelson's many attractions within easy reach. We will happily provide information about these and make arrangements as required. Complimentary tea or coffee is available to guests upon arrival.
Full or continental breakfast is included, and dinner is provided by arrangement. A phone call before arrival would be appreciated.
Ours is a non smoking home.

Richmond
Homestay
Address: Althorpe, 13 Dorset St,
Richmond, Nelson
Name: Bob & Jenny
Telephone: (03) 544 8117
Beds: 1 Double, 3 Single (2 Bedrooms)
Bathroom: 1 Guests share
Tariff: B&B (special) Double $80, Single $45,
Dinner $25. Credit cards. Vouchers accepted
Nearest Town: Richmond, 2 blocks from town centre

Althorpe, built in 1887, is a large comfortable family home. We retain half of the original acre section which gives ample off street parking. The garden is private with many trees so there is always a sunny or sheltered spot in which to relax. Inside you will find spacious rooms, all tastefully restored and comfortably furnished featuring beautiful Rimu panelling and large fire places, but for that extra feeling of luxury the house is also centrally heated.
Dinner is available by arrangement and as cooking is a special interest of your hostess you will not be disappointed. A wide choice of exciting food is served for breakfast and a selection of fruit juice, tea or coffee is always available either in your room or any of the living rooms.
We have enjoyed our travels and wonderful hospitality whilst overseas and would like the opportunity to share our home and area with you. We would however prefer no smoking in the house.
Directions: *Phone for details.*

Brightwater

Farmstay
Address: Millrace Farm, River Terrace, RD 1, Brightwater, Nelson
Name: Lesley and David Gilchrist
Telephone: (03) 542 3376
Beds: 1 Double, 2 Single (2 bedrooms) **Bathroom:** 1 Guests share
Tariff: B&B (full) Double $60, Single $35, Dinner $20, Vouchers accepted
Nearest Town: Nelson

Our small farm is situated 1km off SH6 at Brightwater, which is 22km south of Nelson.
We offer a relaxed rural environment within easy reach of the well-known Nelson beaches, rivers and walks, including Abel Tasman and Nelson Lakes National Parks. We have cattle, sheep, turkeys, hens, two dogs and a cat on our 10 hectares.
Guest bedrooms and bathroom are upstairs, also a lounge where guests can relax and make tea or coffee if they wish.
A choice of continental or cooked breakfast includes home-made marmalade or jam, or our own honey. Dinner by arrangement - this may be a barbecue in the summer.
We prefer our guests to be non-smokers.
Directions: *Please phone.*

Brightwater

Homestay
Address: 'Pepper Tree Place',
126 Lord Rutherford Road,
Brightwater, Nelson
Name: Andrew and Charlotte
Telephone: (03) 542 3280
Beds: 1 Double, 2 Single (2 bedrooms)
Bathroom: 1 Guests share
Tariff: B&B (special) Double $60, Single $35, Dinner $20pp, Vouchers accepted
Nearest Town: Richmond 10 km

Come and share the congenial, relaxed, peaceful environment of our comfortable home and garden. We live just off SH6, close to Lord Rutherford's Memorial in about 1/2 acre of cultivated garden. We grow a large variety of vegetables, have our own hens - in fact we are almost self sufficient.
We extend a warm welcome to our guests who have the privacy of their own TV lounge with tea and coffee making facilities. You are welcome to share our evening meal, chat afterwards over a locally produced liqueur and then curl up in bed with the latest edition of NZ Geographic.
We serve home baked bread, freshly cooked muffins, fresh berryfruit in season, yoghurt and home made jams for breakfast, which may be cooked or continental as required.
Directions: *Travel about 9kms south of Richmond on SH6 to crossroads with the Brightwater Inn on your left hand side. Continue on SH6, turn first left into Lord Rutherford Road South, Pepper Tree Place is 80m from the corner.*

Thorpe
Farmstay +
Self-Contained Accommodation
Address: Rerenga Farm, Thorpe, RD 2 Wakefield, Dovedale-Woodstock Road, Nelson
Name: Robert and Joan Panzer
Telephone: (03) 543 3825 **Fax:** (03) 543 3640
Beds: 1 Double (1 bedroom) **Bathroom**: 1 Family share
Self-contained: 1 Double, 1 Single **Bathroom**: 1 Private
Tariff: B&B (special) Double $60, Single $35, Dinner $18
For longer stay and self-contained accommodation, please enquire.

Thorpe is halfway between Nelson and Motueka, with plenty of nearby options for tramping (Abel Tasman, Northwest Nelson and Mt Arthur); fishing (Motueka River 3 minutes away); or the local crafts and vineyards.
We offer a peaceful, rural retreat with the sunny Nelson climate, view of Mt Arthur, good food, and international Kiwi hosts. Our 80 year old farmhouse surrounded by rolling hills, forests and rivers, is in the middle of 20 acres planted in timber, fruit, and nut trees, plus sheep, pigs, chooks, geese, cats and a dog. Situated along the Dove River, guests arrive at our door by foot crossing over our own swing bridge or by driving over a vehicle bridge.
Robert is from Holland and involved in tourism, and along with Joan from the United States, are happy to advise, assist or even guide you in your travel plans. Our two small children are lovable and enjoy our guests.

Wakefield
Homestay
Address: Whitby Lodge,
212 Whitby Road, Wakefield, Nelson
Name: Marion and Buster Stringer
Telephone: (03) 541 8117
Beds: 1 Double, 2 Single (2 bedrooms)
Bathroom: 1 Guests share
Tariff: B&B (full) Double $60, Single $40, Dinner $20. Vouchers accepted.

Our home is very easy to find just 1 km north of Wakefield Village on SH 6. We are in the centre of Nelson Province, an ideal base for visiting lakes, mountains, and beaches, or following wine and pottery trails. Take a day trip to visit the largest and purest spring in the world in Golden Bay, see the Rutherford Memorial, the local historic church and the Steam Museum.
We are a well-travelled couple with a very comfortable home, complete with open fire in winter and swimming pool in summer. Our interests include trail-bike riding, spinning and embroidery and writing. References excellent.
We serve substantial home-cooked meals and invite you to enjoy our hospitality (non-smokers please).
Directions - *please phone.*

Wakefield
Homestay
Address: 6 Anslow Place, Wakefield, Nelson
Name: Ngaire and Norman Lochhead
Telephone: (03) 541 8321
Beds: 4 Single (2 bedrooms) **Bathrooms**: 1 Guests share
Tariff: B&B (continental) Double $55, Single $35, Children half price; Dinner $15; Campervans welcome. Vouchers accepted.
Nearest Town: Nelson 32 km, Richmond 16 km

Our house is in a country like setting situated in a quiet cul-de-sac. 1 Minute off Highway 6 - 5 minutes walk to village shops. With oldest church and school in New Zealand, steam museum. golf course, one hour away from ski fields and lakes, also 1/2 hour to fishing, rivers and beaches. Being retired farmers we like to make you very welcome.
Directions: *Keeping on Highway 6 from Nelson, through Richmond, then just as you near Wakefield, turn right into Martin Ave, then right into Harcourt Place, then left into Anslow Place, on left of our home is a children's park.*

Wakefield
Bed & Breakfast
Address: Wai-iti, R.D.1 Wakefield
Name: "Glendora"
Telephone: (03) 541 8813
Fax: (03) 548 1373
Beds: 1 Queen
Bathroom: 1 Private in S.C. cottage
2 Single beds, 1 family share bathroom in homestead
Tariff: B&B (special) Double $85-$105, Dinner $25 with wine, Children by arrangement, Vouchers accepted
Nearest Town: Richmond 18kms, Nelson 33 kms.

"Glendora" offers quality accommodation, comfort and ambience in a "smoke-free" and thoroughly rural atmosphere. 3 donkeys, 2 cows, chickens, 2 small dogs, Molly the cat, no resident children and space to be as sociable as you please.
Built in the 1860's "The School Teacher's House" has been tastefully refurbished whilst retaining its original charm.
Convenient situation for day trips around the scenic Nelson Province. Lakes and Skiing are just an hour away. We feature our own free-range eggs, home grown and local produce. We serve "good" fresh ground coffee.
Accommodation: In-house twin bedroom and share bathroom. Or "Wisteria Cottage": Private and self-contained. Open plan living; sleeping alcove; Queen size bed; ensuite bathroom. Early colonial furnishings & original NZ artists works. All food provided; Dinner, breakfast, lunch, morning/afternoon teas or join us for any one or all of these.
We are located on State Highway No.6, 3kms south of Wakefield Village.
Your Hosts: Shona Moon (NZ born)
Hugh Gordon (ex-patriate American)

Tell other travellers about your favourite B&Bs

Bronte, (near Mapua, Nelson)

Fine Accommodation
Address: Bronte Rd East, off Coastal Highway 60, near Mapua.
Postal: "Bronte Fine Accommodation", RD 1, Upper Moutere, Nelson
Hosts: Chris Edmonds & Christine Gillespie, Margaret & Bruce Fraser
Telephone: (03) 540 2422 **Fax:** (03) 540 2432
Beds: Bronte House: 2 Queen, 1 Single (2 rooms) Hopkirk & Hamilton suites:
1 King, 1 King/Twin (2 suites)
Stafford Place: 1 King/Twin (1 room) **Bathrooms:** 4 ensuite, 1 Private
Tariff: B&B (Special) Double $120-$145, Single $105-$130, Dinner $30pp,
Lunch $8pp. Tariffs apply 1 November 1994 - 31 October 1995. Credit Cards:
Visa & M/C.
Nearest Town: Richmond (12 mins), Nelson (25 mins)

Bronte Fine Accommodation has been described as an estuary paradise. Two homesteads and two suites nestle in three and a half acres of secluded gardens sweeping down to the Waimea Inlet: Stafford Place is a traditionally elegant home of gracious comfort; the contemporary beauty of Bronte House is complemented by fine furnishings and original artworks.

They share the exquisite, historic setting, and a welcoming and relaxed atmosphere. Generous, warm hospitality preserves privacy or provides company, as you wish.

Bronte House has two guest rooms with stunning views and en suite bathrooms. A private sitting/dining room has decks overlooking gardens, mountains and estuary. Another spacious decked lounge enjoys similar views. A hot spa pool is set on yet another deck.

Stafford Place has a private guest lounge with large open fire, comfortable living room and wide decks.

A guest room combines warmth, comfort and old world charm, with its high timber ceiling and fireplace. A private bathroom has spa bath and shower.

Garden pathways lead to two suites on the estuary shore. Each spacious brand new suite has a deck, comfortable beds, cosy sofas, writing desk and tea and coffee facilities. A dressing room leads to the bathroom with spa bath and shower.

All accommodations have quality linens, comfortable beds with woolen underlays and electric blankets, heaters, hairdryers, luxurious bathrobes and fresh flowers.

Delicious breakfasts served at each homestead, on the decks when weather allows, include fresh fruit juice, home-made toasted muesli, pancakes or waffles with fruit and pure maple syrup, smoked salmon omelettes, croissants..... Fresh fruit, freshly ground coffee, Indian and herbal teas are always available.

A courtesy car is available to transport you to your evening meal at one of the excellent restaurants a few minutes away at Richmond. Occasionally dinner may be offered at Bronte.

Bronte House specialises in seafood and fresh pasta; home grown meats might be enjoyed at Stafford Place. We use fresh local produce - sun ripened and organically grown whenever possible.

At Bronte you can hide away in the gardens with a book, soak in the spa, laze on the decks, indulge in a massage. Enjoy the windsurfer, Canadian canoe and sailing dinghy, or take a cruise on our 25 ft yacht. Swim in the pool, play tennis or croquet, borrow the bikes, or stroll in the orchard - all eighty five acres! You may well find a host keen to join you at golf on the nearby links - we enjoy spending time with guests! We have travelled and take a keen interest in current events and world affairs.

Bronte is an environment of peaceful luxury. We regret our facilities are unsuitable for children under 16 years. We are smoke-free. Bronte House has an elegant black cat, Stafford place a yard dog and standard poodle.

Bronte is ideally placed in the centre of the Nelson Province, midway between Nelson city and Kaiteriteri beach; within easy reach are great trout fisheries (we can arrange a professional fishing/hunting guide), Nelson Lakes, ski fields, swimming at Rabbit Island; bush walks, boat trips and sea kayaking in Abel Tasman National Park; and much more... 5 award winning wineries are close by; the craft trail starts right here at the Bronte Road studio of internationally renowned potters Darryl and Lesley Robertson.

Transport is available to Nelson Airport.

Upper Moutere (Harakeke)
Bed & Breakfast
Address: "Harakeke Lodge"
Harley Road RD2 Upper Moutere Nelson
Name: Joan Roesch
Telephone: (03) 543 2799
Beds: 1 Double (1 Bedroom)
Bathroom: 1 Ensuite
Tariff: B&B (special) Double $60, Single $35, Vouchers accepted
Nearest Town: Motueka (15km on Moutere Highway)

Set on a rise in the Moutere Valley on a secluded two acres, encompassed by mature trees with a spectacular view of Mt Arthur and surrounding countryside, the house is modelled on an English style country farm house and adapted to New Zealand living, using native timber extensively throughout, with cosy cottage style accommodation.

The area is popular for its pottery and craft shops especially wood-turning. Also in the immediate location are 5 wineries of international renown.

Only 20 minutes drive brings you to the beautiful golden beaches of Kaiteriteri with coastal cruises, or if you are feeling energetic, tramping in the Abel Tasman National Park.

We are a family of four with our pet dog Ebby who is a Schnauzer and two cats. Our main interest at present is re-establishing the garden. We enjoy meeting people and making new friends.

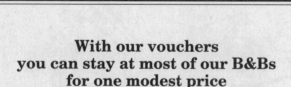

Ruby Bay
Private Hotel
Address: Holton House, Coastal Highway SH 60, Ruby Bay, Nelson
Name: Lynda & Hilary Blundell
Telephone & Fax: (03) 540-2269
Beds: 2 Double (2 bedrooms) **Bathroom:** 2 Ensuite
Tariff: B&B (special) Double $135, Single $120,
Dinner $30 pp, Visa & Mastercard accepted,
Nearest Town: Motueka (10 mins), Richmond (15 mins)

Holton has been a landmark in Nelson for 125 years. With it's unusual red and white facade, high-pitched gables and slate roof, this historic house sits tranquilly amid majestic trees on the hillside overlooking Ruby Bay.

The house has been recently restored, with due respect paid to it's original character, warmth and charm. Antique furniture, polished wood, open fires and tapestries enhance the sense of timelessness and romance which is part of this gracious old home. The garden has many interesting and rare plants, old-fashioned roses, specimen trees, and giant eucalypts.

There are two double attic bedrooms (with ensuite bathrooms), tastefully and comfortably furnished. Downstairs, your private sitting / dining room opens onto a conservatory and secluded side garden. The covered verandah, framed by an ancient wisteria, offers a vista down to the sea.

Breakfast is a la carte and dinner is available by arrangement. All meals feature imaginative use of fresh local produce, organic vegetables, fruit and herbs from our garden, and free-range eggs from our hens. Local wines are available with dinner.

On the Coastal Highway, 30 minutes from Nelson, Holton is a convenient base from which to visit Abel Tasman Park, beaches, wineries and the craft trail. No TV disturbs the peaceful atmosphere and we cater for non-smokers only.

Because we have only two guest rooms, we have time to spend with our visitors, and can assure you of friendly, personal attention. We look forward to meeting you and sharing our little piece of paradise.

Directions: *On the Coastal Highway at Ruby Bay between Richmond and Motueka.*

Motueka Valley

Country Homestay
Address: Doone Cottage,
Motueka Valley Highway, R.D. 1, Motueka
Name: Stan & Glen Davenport
Telephone & Fax: (03) 5268 740
Beds: 2 Double, 2 Single (2 Bedrooms); Garden Chalet 1 Double, 1 Single
Bathroom: 1 Private, 1 Family share
Tariff: B&B (special) Double $90, Single $50, Dinner $25, Not suitable for
children, Vouchers accepted May to October (inclusive)
Nearest Town: Motueka (28 km), Nelson (64 km)

Doone
Cottage

New Zealand
Association
FARM & HOME
HOSTS

*Homely hospitality, peace and tranquillity, trout fishing, beautiful garden and
bush setting, native birds, goats, sheep, chickens, ducks, donkeys and pigs,
weaving studio - all abound at Doone Cottage. A lovely 100 year old home,
comfortably furnished cottage style in an attractive 4 acre setting of garden, native
trees and ferns, lawns and shrubs, which have a beautiful outlook across the
Motueka Valley to the Mt Arthur range. Double and twin accommodation available
with private bathroom facilities for guests and own private verandah. Home cooked
meals, home made bread, fresh garden vegetables, free range eggs etc.*

*Your hostess spins wool from the raw fleece and has her own weaving studio where
you can see the finished garments, blankets, wallhangings, rugs etc.*

*There is much to interest the tourist and fisherman. The Motueka River is at the
gate, with several others closeby, providing the opportunity to fish some of the best
brown trout rivers in the South Island. Fishing licences and a local guide are
available. Wilderness trips can be arranged. Excellent day trips include the
Nelson Lakes and Abel Tasman National Parks, Kaiteriteri beaches, Northwest
Nelson Forest Park, Golden Bay and Nelson.*

*This is one of New Zealand's main fruit producing regions where the sun shines
over 2,400 hours annually. The region is rich in crafts of all descriptions.*

*We are very fortunate to live in this beautiful corner of New Zealand and we enjoy
sharing our home and surroundings with visitors from all over the world.*

Directions: *From Motueka we are 28K on Motueka Valley H'way (old SH 61)
heading south. From the south turn left off H'way 6 at Kohatu Hotel Motupiko, we
are 28K from this junction on Motueka Valley H'way (old SH 61).*

Motueka

Private Hotel/Homestay
Address: 430 High Street, Motueka
(just south of junction HW 60 & 61)
Name: Bea and Dion Grooten
Telephone & Fax: (03) 528-7318
Beds: 7 Double, 3 Single (7 bedrooms)
Bathroom: 4 Ensuite, 2 Guests share
Tariff: B&B (continental) Double $72, Single $48, Ensuite Double $89, Single $79, Triple $104,(Not suitable for children under 10 years) Dinner $22.50-$24.50, Vouchers accepted

Our aim is to please you
Unser Ziel ist Ihr wohlbefinden
Notre objectif est Votre bien-etre
Il Nostro scupo e il Vostro benessere
Uit en toch een beetje Thuis.
"The Troubadour" used to be a nunnery! Be our guest and visit the three National Parks (Abel Tasman, Nelson Lakes and New Zealands second largest, Kahurangi National park). We can arrange a "bush and beyond" guided tramp through high country wilderness. Bea and Dion both have overseas experience in hotel and catering industry.
"The Troubadour" is as clean as the water in Pupu Springs. For dinner we offer a choice of at least two set menus in a small and cosy restaurants or outdoors on the sun terrace. Personal service in smoke free atmosphere. All vegetables and herbs are from own garden and we use fresh local quality produce.
Bus services will set you down near "The Troubadour" on request. Off street parking is available and should you be walking in one of the National Parks we can store your car or belongings.
Golf lovers! just minutes to a 18 hole beachfront golf course.

The standard of accommodation in *The New Zealand Bed and Breakfast Book*
ranges from homely to luxurious,
but you can always be sure of superior hospitality.

Motueka
Farmstay Retreat
Address: Mariri, RD 2,
Upper Moutere, Nelson
Name: Joyanne and Richard Easton
Telephone: (03) 526 6865 **Fax:** (03) 526 6011
Beds: 1 Super King, 1 Queen, 1 Twin (3 bedrooms)
Bathroom: Ensuites + Private
Tariff: B&B (a la carte) Double $130, Single $110, Dinner $30, Children under 12yrs half price.
Nearest Town: Motueka 6km

Set in one acre of intimate gardens, our large family home "Wairepo" offers you a warm welcome. Our home is furnished most comfortably with country charm, native timbers, a touch of luxury and many personal home made products.

There are two bedrooms upstairs, one super-king and one twin, with private ensuite, including double spa which overlooks in privacy the native fernery. Also upstairs for guests personal use is private lounge, open fire-place, kitchen and verandahs with all rooms having magnificent views over the garden and Tasman Bay mountain ranges. Downstairs bedroom has a large queen bed with own private marble tiled bathroom. All of our beds are most comfortable with quality linen.

We encourage guests to have the freedom of our home, walking through the rambling garden of mixed borders, roses, trees and cobbled paths leading them to the swimming pool and tennis court for their own use. Surrounding the garden is 40 hectares of apples and pears which we harvest in our packhouse from February to May plus 3,000 paeony tubers which are grown for flower production. Breakfast is "a la carte" featuring our fresh local fruit and produce including home made muffins, fruit leathers, bacon & eggs, omelettes and croissants with home made spreads. Dinner is by arrangement with seafoods, venison and lamb etc., barbecued by the pool if desired. Local wine is complimentary. Coffee, teas and eats always available.

Our home is only minutes away from some of Nelson's beautiful beaches for swimming, walking and windsurfing. We are centrally placed to visit Abel Tasman National Park, wine and craft trails, mountains, lakes, golf courses and trout fishing rivers - guides available. We enjoy spending time with our visitors and can assure you of personal friendly attention

Directions: *On State Highway 60 Coastal Route to Motueka 40kms from Nelson, Weka Rd, 3kms from Tasman Township.*

Motueka
Self-contained Accommodation
Address: Waiwhero Road,
R D 1, Motueka
Name: Veronica and Alan Hall
Telephone: (03) 526 8857
Beds: 1 Double (1 bedroom)
Bathroom: Private
Tariff: B&B (special) Double $50,
Single $30, Dinner $15, Vouchers accepted
Nearest Town: Motueka

We own a 14.2 hectare property, 16km from Motueka off Highway 61. An ideal base for sightseeing, tramping, fishing, horse-trekking or just plain relaxing. The area is renown for the Arts & Craft Trail and ideally situated for anglers to fish the Motueka and Baton Rivers and their tributaries.

We are building a new homestead on the property where we run a small herd of cattle, 2 dogs and have a large organic garden. We are happy to share vegetarian and non-vegetarian cuisine, using a variety of local produce.

Your accommodation will be a one bedroom farm cottage - a completely refurbished, self-contained unit with its own driveway, flower and vegetable gardens and barbecue. We supply everything from cooking facilities and utensils; washing machine and colour TV to pillows, mattress and bedding.

We really enjoy meeting people, have travelled extensively and our interests range from all outdoor pursuits to trivial pursuit and cards.

Riwaka, Motueka
Homestay
Address: "Sea Haven",
Green Tree Road, Riwaka,
RD3, Motueka
Name: Dennis & Maureen Farrer
Telephone: (03) 528-6219
Beds: 1 Double, 4 Single (2 bedroom) **Bathroom:** 1 Private, 1 Family share
Tariff: B&B (full) Own suite Double $70, each extra $22, Family share Double $60, Single $35, Dinner $20, Children under 12 $15, Vouchers accepted
Nearest Town: Motueka 5 km, Nelson 55 km

Our two storey home overlooks the tidal estuary at Riwaka Wharf with sea views across Tasman Bay to D'Urville Island. Close by is the Abel Tasman National Park, the North West Nelson Forest Park, the beaches of Stephens Bay, Marahau and Kaiteriteri and the Motueka River. The attractions of this area are many and varied from walking and boating to craft and wine trails, be prepared to stay awhile.

Our guest accomodation on the ground floor is a separate suite with twin bedroom, private bathroom, sitting room with double bed settee, TV, fridge, tea / coffee making. We also offer a twin bedroom upstairs sharing family living accommodation and facilities.

Directions: *From Motueka take the Takaka Road (SH60), after crossing Motueka River Bridge turn right into Lodder Lane. At the end of Lodder Lane, turn left into School Road, then right into Green Tree Road. Arriving by bus or air at Motueka please phone for assistance.*

Riwaka, Motueka

Bed & Breakfast
Address: Main Rd
Riwaka Motueka
Name: Hillview
Telephone: (03) 528 6042
Beds: 1 Double, 2 Single (2 Bedrooms) **Bathroom:** 1 Guests share
Tariff: B&B (continental) Double $70, Single $50.
Cooked breakfast extra. Vouchers accepted October November.
Nearest Town: Motueka 5 mins

Relaxing in country scenery from your upstairs hideaway, your hosts Chris and Margaret are prepared to spoil you with service.

The rooms open into a viewing area where your breakfast is served at your table, also provided fridge, tea / coffee making facilities.

Margaret has spent several years in the motel industry which has taught her the importance of cleanliness and giving the homely touch to your rooms.

Chris has spent most of her life in the area and has a great love and knowledge of our lovely countryside and can guide you to all the beauty spots, plus mins away from brown trout fishing.

Twenty five minutes will take you to the gateway to Abel Tasman National Park for walking, kayaking, launch cruise or just laze around on the golden sands, 2hrs drive will take you to the pleasures of Golden Bay and if you dare a bungy jump.

Good licenced restaurants close by including takeaways. Menu's available.

Directions: *From Motueka, take the road to Takaka (SH 60) reaching Riwaka approx 5 mins where you will see our sign on your left.*

Riwaka Valley

Farmstay +
Self-contained Accommodation
Address: Riwaka Valley RD 3, Motueka
Name: Lois and Kim Woods
Telephone: (03) 528 9267
Beds: 2 Double, 2 Single (4 bedrooms)
Bathroom: 1 Private, 1 Guests share
Tariff: B&B (full) Double $70, Single $35, Dinner $20,
Children special family rates, Campervans welcome
Nearest Town: Motueka 15km

New Zealand Association
FARM & HOME HOSTS

We offer accommodation in a modern self-contained fully serviced flat and in our own home where we have set aside the upstairs area as semi-private for guests. Kaiweka Farm is situated in the north branch of the Riwaka Valley adjacent to the scenic reserve at the Riwaka River source. We are close to the Abel Tasman National Park, Kaiteriteri Beach and beautiful walks.

The homestead and flat are situated in a large garden with tennis court and BBQ area overlooking farmland and native bush. We run sheep, goats, and cattle and run an engineering business from the farm. Hobbies include weaving, spinning, gardening, yachting, boating, camping and walking. Our flat contains 2 rooms, sleeps 4, fully equipped with fridge, TV, microwave oven, electric blankets; - linen and towels supplied. $60 two people. Meals by prior notice. A gas BBQ available.

Directions: *From Motueka follow Highway 60 to bottom of the Takaka Hill. Turn left at sign "Riwaka Valley" and continue on "North branch" towards "source of the Riwaka River". Kaiweka Farm is 7 km from Highway 60. Our sign is on the right.*

Marahau - adjacent to Abel Tasman National Park

Homestay
Address: 'Abel Tasman Stables'
Marahau Valley Road, R.D. 2, Motueka
Name: George Bloomfield
Telephone: (03) 527 8181
Beds: 1 Double, 2 Single (2 Bedrooms)
Bathroom: 1 Ensuite, 1 Family share
Tariff: B&B (continental) Double $55, Single $30, Dinner $15, Vouchers accepted
Nearest Town: Motueka

Abel Tasman Stables homestay situated alongside the very popular Abel Tasman National Park offers friendly Kiwi hospitality in quiet relaxed surroundings only five minutes walk to Marahau beach and Abel Tasman coastal track.

The house, situated on an elevated site gives magnificent views of Tasman Bay and Abel Tasman National Park. Activities available in Marahau include sea kayaking, powered canoeing, boat trips, swimming with seals, tramping, fishing, fresh and salt water swimming, visit to farm park and of course horse riding or trekking from our own stable. Meals available at the licensed Park Cafe' at the start of the Abel Tasman track or by arrangement with host.

Directions: *From Motueka travel north following signs to Abel Tasman National Park. Marahau Valley Road is well signposted. The homestay property is up the first drive on the left.*

Takaka Hill

Farmstay + Self-Contained Accommodation
Address: Kairuru, State Highway 60, Takaka Hill, Motueka
Name: David and Wendy Henderson
Telephone & Fax: (03) 528 8091,
Mobile: 025 337 457
Beds: Homestead: 1 Double, 2 Single (2 bedrooms) **Bathroom:** 1 Private.
Cottages: Each has 1 Double, 2 Single (2 bedrooms) **Bathroom:** 1 Private
Tariff: B&B (Full) Double $100, Single $60, Triple $120, Quad $140, Dinner $25. Cottage alone (full linen) $80 for 2 people, $10 each extra person. Children, longer stays, and off season rates negotiable, Credit Cards: Visa/MC. Vouchers accepted May-October
Nearest Town: 17 km North West of Motueka.

We are a farming family with two girls aged 15 and 7, farming sheep and cattle on our 4000 acre hill country farm. The cottages, exclusively yours, are modern, fully equipped with two bedrooms; open plan living; dining; sittingroom; bathroom and laundry. Both cottages have wonderful seaviews overlooking the Abel Tasman National Park. A good selection for breakfast is supplied at the cottages but made by yourselves. Your accommodation is private but handy to our home for dinner and socialising. Our home is large and comfortable set in an established attractive garden with swimming pool, games court and lots of native birds. Farming activities of possible interest, that you are most welcome to join in on, could include mustering, docking, dipping, shearing and feeding pet animals. On a short interesting walk to our Historic Marble Quarry you will discover where Parliament Buildings originated; amazing marble formations, native bush, caves and streams.

Directions: *From Motueka take the road to Takaka (State Highway 60). Kairuru is 17km from Motueka on the right hand side.*

Takaka Hill, Motueka

Country Homestay
Address: Marble Park, SH 60,
Takaka Hill, Motueka.
Postal: Box 6008, Riwaka
Name: John & Zelma Stanley
Telephone: (03) 528 8061
Beds: 2 Double, 4 Single (4 bedrooms)
Bathroom: 2 Ensuite, 1 Guests share
Tariff: B&B (full) Double $75-95, Single $55, Dinner $25,
Children under 12yrs $25. Credit Cards.
Nearest Town: Motueka 18km on SH60

Marble Park Homestay is easily located by a large sign at the gate.
We are situated midway between Motueka and Golden Bay on Highway 60 among
unique karst limestone formations, with extensive views of Tasman Bay, east to
Nelson at an elevation of 600 metres. Zelma and I have backgrounds in
rockhounding, vintage touring, amateur theatre and are active trampers, with
personal experience of local walks. We have comfortable areas for reading, writing
or relaxing while enjoying the views, also maps and reference materials both
geological and botanical on hand. We can arrange transport for the many
activities in our area, such as tramping, fishing and boating. Abel Tasman and
Kahurangi National Parks, Kaiteriteri Beach Resort, Harwood Hole, Ngarua
Cave and Cobb Power Station are close by. We are central to the activities and
attractions of both Tasman and Golden Bays. Breakfast is served at your
convenience from a varied selection and we offer a three course evening meal
enhanced with local wine. Please phone or write for further information.
Directions: *From Motueka take the road to Takaka on State Highway 60. Travel*
up the Takaka Hill for 18km. Marble Park sign at gateway on your right.

Tukurua, Takaka

Homestay+Self-contained
Accommodation
Address: "Elliotts Gardens"
Tukurua R.D. 2, Takaka
Name: Bette & Murray Elliott
Telephone: (03) 525 9275
Beds: 1 Double, 2 Single (2 Bedrooms)
Bathroom: 1 Private
Tariff: B&B (continental) Double $85, Single $65, Children $20. S.C. $75.
Nearest Town: Takaka 18km

My husband and I are a retired couple and we would like to invite you to visit our
comfortable architecturally designed home situated in 10 acres of developing
garden on the seafront at Tukurua Beach. The property offers panoramic views of
Golden Bay extending from Farewell Spit to D'urville Island with lovely clean
sandy beaches to walk on.
We have been establishing our garden on Pakahi soil for the past 10 years. There
are large plantings of rhododendrons, azaleas, camellias, magnolias, iris, proteas
and many other trees and shrubs. Large area of lawn, Rock Garden and
Herbaceous Borders and an area put aside for future water garden.
The accommodation consists of spacious living area with dining facilities TV and
video - Non smokers preferred. Service with serenity.
Directions: *18km north of Takaka on Seaward side of SHW 60.*

Patons Rock, Takaka
Farmstay
Address: Patons Rock Rd,
Takaka
Name: Patondale
Telephone & Fax: (03) 525 8262
Beds: 1 Double, 2 Single (2 Bedrooms)
Bathroom: 1 Guests share
Tariff: B&B (full) Double $90, Single $70,
Children $20, Dinner $20, Vouchers accepted
Nearest Town: Takaka 10km, Collingwood 17km

*We David, Vicki and Hayden James (aged 13 years) welcome you to our little piece
of paradise.*

*Nestled high above Patons Rock beach our architecturally designed home has
superb sea, mountain and rural views and is well appointed for your comfort.*

*Our dairyfarm of 200 acres will give you the opportunity to observe or participate in
the daily task of milking our dairyherd or maybe the chance to feed a calf in the season.
Our interests include travel, gardening and local government. We are non-
smokers who have a family cat called "Lucky".*

*Golden Bay has lots to offer the tourist with its vast expanse of secluded beaches,
scenic walk tracks, sea and river fishing plus the world famous "Pupu Springs".
Join us and relax in our beautiful surroundings of Golden Bay. Reservation is
necessary to avoid disappointment.*

Directions: *Turnoff at sign on SH60, 10km from Takaka township enroute to
Collingwood.*

Takaka
Homestay
Address: 9 Waitapu, St
Takaka, Golden Bay
Name: Catie's Bed & Breakfast
Telephone: (03) 525 8888
Beds: 2 Queen (2 Bedrooms)
Bathroom: 2 Ensuite
Tariff: B&B (special) Double $120,
Single $80, Children half price,
Dinner $20pp upon request
Nearest Town: Takaka

*After spending eleven years travelling, and enjoying such wonderful hospitality,
I would like to share with you, our New Zealand hospitality and have you enjoy
my home at yours leisure.*

*An old character home, originally built as a Parsonage in 1912, has recently been
renovated, with open fireplaces throughout the house (including the bedrooms).
Come relax on the verandahs, and enjoy the sun and gardens.*

*The Golden Bay area has much to offer in the way of outdoor activities; scenic
flights and tours, day walks, craft trails and horse trekking to name a few.*

*Upon arrival you may relax on the verandah, with a choice of New Zealand made
cheeses and pate with crackers, served with locally made wines, or enjoy my
homemade treats with tea or freshly ground coffee.*

*A healthy breakfast is served consisting of freshly made muffins, or pancakes,
omelets, hash browns, fresh fruit, granola and juice. The choice is yours.*

Picnic baskets are available on request.

Note: Building was not completed at the time of inspection, phone to confirm,

TUKURUA LODGE

**GOLDEN BAY
NELSON**

Tukurua, Takaka

Intimate Seaside Lodge
Address: "Tukurua Lodge"
Tukurua Beach Golden Bay
Name: Diana & Wayne Johnson
Telephone: (03) 525 8644
Beds: 2 Double, 1 Single (2 Bedrooms)
Bathroom: 2 Ensuite
Tariff: B&B (full) Double $95, Single $75, Dinner $25. Credit cards. Vouchers accepted Easter to Labour Weekend
Nearest Town: Takaka 18km, Collingwood 10km

We welcome you to our piece of paradise in this untouched corner of NZ and invite you to share it with us.

Tukurua Lodge, set on 10 acres overlooking expansive lawns, gardens and seascapes, is the ideal place to unwind and explore all the natural and artistic delights this wonderful region has to offer.

Your sunny rooms have their own entrance and ensuites for your convenience.

We both have spent many years in the hospitality industry and take pride in our healthy country style breakfast and dinners using fresh home grown and local produce.

Peaceful grounds, a safe sandy beach and our pool, all help to make this a magical spot to take time out in.

We offer free pick up from the Takaka Aerodrome and bus station. Heaphy Track and Tarakohe Whalf by arrangement. We do look forward to meeting you.

Directions: *18km from Takaka on SH 60 to Collingwood turn off at Tukurua Lodge sign.*

Collingwood

Bed & Breakfast

Address: Hakea Hill House, Parapara, Golden Bay
Postal: P O Box 35, Collingwood
Name: Hakea Hill House
Telephone & Fax: (03) 524-8487, from overseas: 64-3-524-8487
Beds: Double or two singles in each of the three bedrooms
Bathroom: 2 Guests share
Tariff: B&B (special) Double $100, Single $75, children $35 (under 16 years) (incl GST), breakfast; menu includes European, American, and Australasian cuisine, ordered in the evening, served at any time, Credit cards accepted.
Nearest Town: Takaka 20 km and Collingwood 10 km

Hakea Hill House, built above the estuary behind Para Para Beach, has views that encompass Para Para Peak to the Wakamarama Ranges to the South, Farewell Spit to D'Urville Island beyond Separation Point over Golden Bay, and to Mount Taranaki on the North Island.

The house is modern and spacious with a hint of Southwest and New Mexico style. Two guest rooms have large balconies. Both American and New Zealand electric outlets are installed. Television and tea or coffee in guest rooms and telephone and Fax are available at all times.

Vic is a practising physician specialising in Family Practice and Emergency Medicine. His hobbies include astronomy; guests are welcome to explore the magnificent Southern skies with Questar 3.5 and Odyssey 17.5 inch telescopes. Liza, besides homemaker, community activist, and expert cook, is interested in sailing, horse riding, machine quilting and wearable art.

We have three teenage children, five computers, two outdoor dogs, and thirty five hectares of hills and trails.

Golden Bay is well worth the effort of a visit. The best weather is late summer and autumn. One may fly from Wellington for the weekend with Takaka Valley Air Services (Telephone 0800 501 901) or drive from Nelson (two hours) to explore Farewell Spit, Kaihoka Lakes, Aorere gold fields, limestone caves, Waikoropupu Springs, Settlers' Museums, pottery and craft outlets, wild West Coast beaches and serene Bay-side beaches, mudflats and estuaries, scenic light plane flights, pony trekking, golf, safe Bay and estuary sailing, canoeing, river rafting, fishing, scalloping and whitebaiting in season, bush walks, and bungy jumping.

Directions: *Reservations are necessary. Please phone in person for reservations and detailed directions.*

Collingwood
Award Winning Seaside Lodge
Address: "Northwest Lodge",
Totara Avenue, Beachfront,
RD1, Pakawau, Collingwood
Name: Philip & Angela England
Telephone: (03) 524 8108
Beds: 2 Queen, 4 Single (4 bedrooms)
Bathroom: 2 Ensuite, 1 Family share
Tariff: B&B (special) Double $80-$120, Single $60-$80, Dinner $35 with wine.
Credit cards accepted
Nearest Town: Collingwood 10 kms, Takaka 30 kms

Northwest Lodge is your tranquil seaside haven uniquely nestled on a native tree covered sandspit.
Awaken to the chorus of bellbirds and tuis. Walk shell covered quartz sand beaches with blue-green waves lapping the shore.
Golden Bay is an ideal four season holiday destination. Stay 2 to 3 days or more. We can help you plan your activities.
The Lodge was awarded an environmental award in 1993. It's been artistically created to take advantage of extensive estuarine/wildfowl habitat, rural and mountain views. The interior is warm, open and glows with natural timber.
Executive rooms feature timber panelled private en-suites, local artwork, individual decks, cedar seating and flowering vine covered pergolas overhead.
Graceful wading and migratory seabirds glide overhead and settle to feed before your eyes.
Dine at a superbly crafted heart rimu elliptically shaped table and enjoy cheerful company, NZ wines and selected local seafood and fresh produce. Angela's cooking is superb. The Lodge is a pick up point for local tour companies - Farewell Spit safaris and mail run.
Directions: *10kms past Collingwood on main coastal road towards Farewell Spit (Lodge clearly signposted).*

Collingwood
Homestay
Address: Elizabeth Street, Collingwood
Name: Collingwood Homestay
Telephone: (03) 524 8079
Beds: 1 King, 1 Queen, 2 Single (3 bedrooms)
Bathroom: 1 Ensuite, 1 guests share
Tariff: B&B (special) Double $95, Single $65, Dinner $25, Children half price.
Credit Cards. Vouchers accepted from April to October + GST

Welcome to Collingwood. Our beautifully renovated colonial style home, situated on the hill, has magnificent views of the Aorere River Estuary and Mountain Range. We are in walking distance from the township and beautiful beach. Our guestrooms are very comfortable, awake to a fantastic view and the sound of bellbirds, tuis and our rooster. Our hens lay the eggs for your superb breakfast. We have been working in the hospitality industry for many years in Europe and New Zealand. We also speak Dutch and German. We share our home with Teddy and Tina, our Beagles and Paki, our gentle old cat. Some of Adrian's hobbies are: tramping, fishing and windsurfing and he would be delighted to take you with him.

Maggie likes home decorating and renovating old furniture and is an excellent cook. Because we have only three guestrooms we have time to spend with our guests. We look forward to meeting you.

Avoid disappointment. Booking is essential.

Pakawau Beach, Collingwood
Homestay + Self-contained Accommodation
Address: Pakawau Beach, Collingwood R.D. Golden Bay
Name: Val and Graham Williams
Telephone: (03) 524 8168
Beds: 1 Double, 1 Single (1 bedroom) **Bathroom:** 1 Family share, Spa available.
Tariff: B&B (full) Double $60, Single $40, Dinner $12.50. Vouchers accepted anytime of year.
Nearest Town: Collingwood 12km

We are the northern most bed and breakfast accommodation in the South Island, 9km from Farewell Spit. We are on the beachfront with views from Separation Point to Farewell Spit with a safe swimming beach only metres from our front door. We offer a range of self contained accommodation with a base rate of $50 per night. We are keen gardeners and grow most of our vegetables. Local seafoods available eg. whitebait, scallops, cockles. A sailing dinghy, canoe, fishing gear and bicycles are available. We have lived here for ten years and can advise or guide you to the 'Beauties of the Bay'. The Farewell Spit Safari and Westhaven Mail Scenic Run will pick you up from our gate. We are handy to Wharariki Beach, Kaihoke Lakes, Te Anaroa Caves, Heaphy Track and Pupu Springs.

We are non smokers who enjoy walking, biking and swimming. Our two children have left home but not our three cats. We look forward to meeting people and sharing our lifestyle.

Tophouse

Historic, Basic Farmstay
Address: Tophouse, RD2, Nelson
Name: Melody and Mike Nicholls
Telephone: (03) 521 1848
Beds: 2 Double, 8 Single (5 bedrooms)
Bathrooms: 3 guests share
Tariff: B&B (continental) Double $70, Single $35, Dinner $15;
Children negotiable, Credit cards accepted
Nearest Town: Blenheim 98 km, Murchison 57 km, Nelson 72 km, St Arnaud
9km

We, Melody and Mike Nicholls, with our two young sons, invite you to share our unique home with its huge open fires, lovely setting and homely atmosphere.

Tophouse, a cob (mud) building, dating from the 1880's when it was a hotel, and reopened in 1989 as a Farm Guest House, has that 'good old days' feel about it.

Situated on 300 ha (730 acres) of picturesque high country farm running cattle, with much native bush and an abundance of bird life, Tophouse is only 9 km from St Arnaud.

St Arnaud, gateway to Nelson Lakes National Park, is nestled on the shore of Lake Rotoiti, a popular holiday spot for its peace and beauty, bush walks, fishing etc and in the winter becomes a ski village serving the two local fields, Rainbow and Mt Robert.

A typical farmhouse dinner is taken with the family and since the fire's going, 'real' toast for breakfast.

Directions: *Just off State Highway 63 between Blenheim and Murchison and 9 km from St Arnaud is Tophouse, that's us! The area took its name from the building. If travelling from Nelson, leave State Highway 6 at Belgrove and travel towards St Arnaud, we're signposted from the main road and looking forward to your visit.*

Tariffs are constant for this year. However some
may have had to change slightly. Always check.

Lake Rotoroa
Self-contained Homestay

Address: Braeburn House,
Lake Rotoroa, Nelson Lakes
National Park, RD3, Murchison
Name: Yvonne & Landa McMahon
Telephone : (03) 523 9065
Beds: 1 Double, 2 Single (2 bedrooms)
Bathroom: 1 Private
Tariff: B&B (special) Double $90, Single $70, Dinner $30, Picnic lunch $7.50, Children negotiable. Credit cards: Visa/MC.
Nearest Town: Murchison

Braeburn House is situated over the Rotoroa Bridge at beautiful Lake Rotoroa. Relax and enjoy the magnificent wilderness surroundings in your own quality 2 bedroom private suite which features extensive use of native timbers. The suite has a private entrance, bathroom, lounge / dining area, double and twin bedrooms. There are coffee / tea making facilities, TV, hairdryer, and lots of little extras including original paintings, pottery, hand woven rugs and quality furnishings. The cuisine is excellent with a 3 course evening meal, full breakfast and a picnic lunch provided. Yvonne is an award winning artist and takes great care in the preparation and presentation of the food.

The area provides a wealth of outdoor activities including fishing, hunting, tramping, skiing, horse trekking, and white water rafting. Landa has extensive knowledge of the area and its recreational pursuits. Yvonne, Landa and Kimberley extend a warm welcome to all visitors.

Murchison
Farmstay

Address: "Awapiriti",
Highway 65, Maruia Valley,
Private Bag, Murchison
Name: David & Irene Free
Telephone & Fax: (03) 523-9466
Beds: 1 Double, 2 Single (2 bedrooms)
Bathroom: 1 Guests share
Tariff: B&B (continental) Double $70, Single $45, Dinner $20 pp. Vouchers accepted.

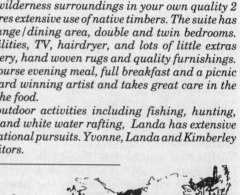

We invite you to spend some time with us at Awapiriti, our secluded hideaway in its spcaious garden setting. Enjoy our beautiful valley scenery and sample our farming lifestyle. Our farm is bounded by the Maruia River with a swing foot bridge and a private road bridge entrance. We are centrally placed for travellers, just 18 kms south of Murchison on Highway 65 (approx 3 hrs from the Cook Strait Ferry). We are within close proximity to many local rivers with excellent fishing and all the outdoor pursuits this area offers. You are most welcome to view N.Z. Red Deer and imported Canadian Elk which we farm. The farm has large areas of native bush with lots of places to walk and observe the native birds - one of our special interests.

We provide a complimentary pre-dinner drink and wine with the meal with a selection of our organically grown vegetables and farm raised lamb, venison or wild pork. A cheerful wood fire will await you on wet or cold days. We enjoy meeting people and promise you a friendly interesting stay.

Directions: *Please telephone*

Murchison
Farmstay/Self-contained Accommodation

Address: "Green-Hills",
Mangles Valley, Murchison
Name: Margaret & Henry Rouse
Telephone: (03) 523 9067
Beds: 4 Single (2 bedrooms)
Bathroom: 1 Family share
Tariff: B&B (continental) Double $60, Single $35,
Dinner $15 pp. Vouchers accepted.
Nearest Town: Murchison

*We welcome you to our hill country sheep and beef farm set in the beautiful
Mangles Valley. We have hosted overseas and New Zealand visitors for several
years and all have appreciated the beauty and relaxed atmosphere.*
*There is excellent trout fishing, feeding eels and gold-panning in the Mangles
River below the house. We are within close proximity of a nine-hole golf course
(clubs available), horse trekking, white water rafting, kayaking and glow worms.
We are surrounded by native bush, beautiful rivers and peaceful bush walks.*
*We are in our 60s, have travelled overseas several times, love meeting people and
welcoming them to our home and lovely garden. We are involved in community
affairs - Lions, W.D.F.F. and S.P.E.L.D. teaching.*
*Breakfast includes home-made muesli, fresh fruits from the garden, local honey,
home-made marmalade and farm eggs if wanted.. All vegetables home grown.
A very comfortable self-contained cottage sleeps 4 is also available - includes
colour TV, wood-burner. This is ideal for a longer stay.*
Directions: *Please phone.*

Owen River, Murchison
Country Stay

Address: 'Strathowen'
Owen River, Murchison
Name: Dianne & David Moate
Telephone: (03) 523 9075
Beds: 1 Double, 2 Single (2 bedrooms)
Bathroom: 2 Ensuite
Tariff: B&B (continental) Double $90,
Single $60, Dinner $30, Children (welcome) negotiable. Credit cards.
Nearest Town: 1Murchison 18 km, 1 1/2 hrs Nelson, 2 1/2 hrs Picton.

*Strathowen is situated in the beautiful Owen Valley. We are surrounded by rivers,
lakes and National Parks. Strathowen is ideally situated for those interested in
the many activities and scenery that the Murchison area provides.*
*The travel-weary may like to rest in our garden beneath silver birches and weeping
willows overlooking the river below, or take a walk along the path beside the Owen
River as it weaves around the boundary of our 15 acre property.*
*Our dining area features a view of the Owen River through a large bay window
and we offer a tastefully prepared dinner with a selection of wine from Nelson and
Marlborough. We provide a separate spacious sitting room for guests and our two
comfortable guest bedrooms each have ensuite bathrooms.*
*We are a younger couple with one child and a Welsh Springer Spaniel named Scott.
David is a fulltime Professional Trout Fishing Guide.*
We look forward to welcoming you to strathowen.
Directions: *Please phone ahead.*

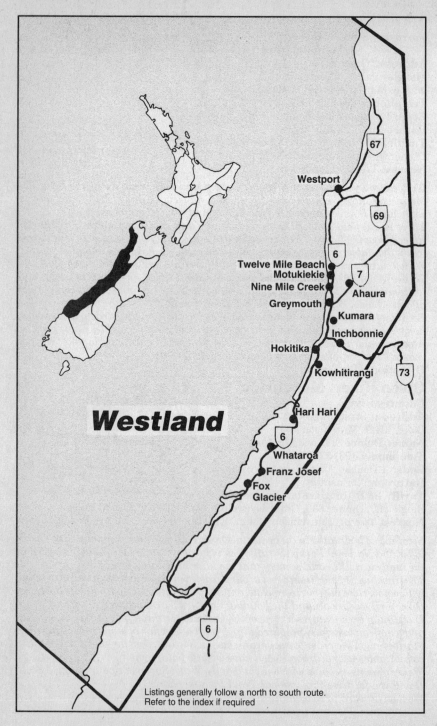

Westland

Westport

67

69

6

Twelve Mile Beach
Motukiekie

7

Nine Mile Creek

Ahaura

Greymouth

Kumara

Inchbonnie

Hokitika

Kowhitirangi

73

Hari Hari

6

Whataroa

Franz Josef

Fox
Glacier

Listings generally follow a north to south route.
Refer to the index if required

Westport

Homestay
Address: "Wynyard"
Fairdown Beach,
PO Box 127, Westport
Name: Dinty Stephens
Telephone: (03) 789 9860 before 9 am or after 5 pm
Beds: 1 Double, 2 Single (2 bedrooms)
Bathroom: 1 Guests share, 1 separate shower room.
Tariff: B&B (continental) Double $65, Single $40; Dinner $20; Children welcome.
Vouchers accepted.

Forget pollution and noise. Watch the breakers roll, enjoy the peace of native bush - or how about just lazing? Come and enjoy the hospitality and scenery of the West Coast. Westport, where friendly people live, has much to offer - jet boating, caving, white and black water rafting. You tell us where your interest lies and we will try to help.

"Wynyard" is designed so that those with disabilities, paraplegics or simply needing a quiet rest can enjoy this peaceful environment. Should you need a special diet, need transport from airport, we at "Wynyard" can help – comfortable, warm, and friendly hospitality assured.

It is advisable to make a reservation. Please phone before 9 am or in the evening.

Twelve Mile Beach

Homestay
Address: 12 Mile Beach, Bed & Breakfast
1RD Runanga Westland
Name: Jill Cotton
Telephone: (03) 7311 886
Beds: 1 Queen, 1 Single (2 Bedrooms)
Bathroom: 1 Guests share
Tariff: B&B (continental) Double $60,
Single $35, Dinner $20, Vouchers accepted

My newly designed beachfront cottage, in the small 12 Mile settlement beside the sea, features native rimu timber in the interior and furniture. Guests beds, with woolrest sleepers and electric blankets, and guests bathroom, are peaceful and private. You will fall asleep to the soothing rhythm of the Tasman Sea.

Step out onto the beach and try your luck panning for gold, fossicking for greenstone, or simply walking and enjoying the beautiful sunsets. Good books - good music or TV for evening.

Your hostess is well travelled and has exceptional knowledge of the art and craft industry in the South Island.

Dinner includes freshly picked organic garden vegetables, NZ wines are available! Tourist information and booking facility, especially for National Park activities, 15 mins away.

Laundry facilities available.

Directions: *24km south of Punakaiki on Highway 6, 9km south of All Nations Tavern. 21km north of Greymouth on Highway 6. Bottom of big hill, 2nd house down drive beside sea with B&B sign.*

Motukiekie, Coast Road
Homestay
Address: Tigger's House, Motukiekie Rocks,
12 Mile Bluff, R.D. 1, Runanga, Westland
Name: Jenny Greene
Telephone: (03) 731 1654
Beds: 2 Double, 1 Single (2 bedrooms - 1 cot + extra 2 singles if req'd)
Bathroom: 1 Family share
Tariff: B&B (continental) Double $65, Single $35,
Children $15-$5 (under 12 years), Dinner $25, Vouchers accepted
Nearest Town: 20 km North of Greymouth,
25 km South of Punakaiki (Pancake Rocks)

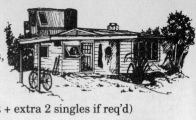

"Tigger's House" is a quaint historic miner's cottage on State Highway Six near the Paparoa National Park. A cosy, comfortable, wooden home with a new extension that blends into the beautiful bush surroundings.
My small cottage has unique rustic charm and is a peaceful retreat on a spectacular headland with superb views of mountains and the rugged coastline. There are fascinating cliff, beach and river walks and old coal-mines to explore nearby.
I have a young child and a cat called Agapanther. We enjoy having people to stay and provide warm, friendly hospitality. I have travelled extensively and have an interesting library. I also offer lots of tourist information and prepare delicious food. Facilities are shared.
I also earn my living weaving, tutoring creative drama and movement, teaching English to foreigners and writing.
Transport can be arranged from Greymouth or Punakaiki on request. Please telephone first to make a booking. I am closed for B&B in winter.
Directions: *25 km south of Punakaiki on State Highway 6, 2.3 km after 13 Mile Creek on top of hill, Motukiekie B&B sign on right. Last house at end of drive. 20 km north of Greymouth on State Highway 6, 1.5 km after 10 Mile Creek on top of hill, B&B sign on left.*

Ahaura
Homestay
Address: "The Academy",
Main Road, Ahaura
Name: Felix & Glenda Pickering
Telephone: (03) 732 3731
Beds: 1 Double, 4 Single (3 bedrooms)
Bathroom: 1 Guests share
Tariff: B&B (full) $35 per person, Children (under 12) 1/2 price, $15 Dinner,
Campervans welcome, Vouchers accepted March to October
Nearest Town: Greymouth - 34 km South

Your hosts Felix and Glenda welcome you to our modern two storey home, nestled on 14 acres beside the Ahaura River.
We have raised a family of three and are now alone, and are keen to welcome you with genuine West Coast hospitality. We have two cats in our household.
Enjoy the peace and quiet of a rural life-style, but with all the amenities of the local village within walking distance, eg. squash, tennis, gun-club. To this can be added great trout fishing, bush walking, gold panning.
If less than inclined to physical pursuits, quietly explore numerous small valleys, hidden lakes, and historical sites.
We are centrally situated and within a few hours travel of all major tourist attractions the "Coast" has to offer.

Nine Mile Creek, Greymouth

Homestay
Address: "The Breakers", Nine Mile Creek,
Highway 6, Coast Road, Westland
Name: Tony & Ib Pupich
Telephone: (03) 762-7743
Beds: 2 Double, 2 Single (3 bedrooms)
Bathroom: 1 Ensuite, 1Guests share
Tariff: B&B (full) Double $70, Single $40, Children 1/2 price,
Dinner $20, Vouchers accepted from April to September
Nearest Town: Greymouth

*We are retired farmers in our fifties who offer warm hospitality in our lovely home
set in two acres of garden and native bush overlooking the Tasman Sea and
adjoining the Paparoa National Park.*
*We have three guest bedrooms, two double, one with ensuite and one twin. All have
fantastic views. The sunsets are unbelievably beautiful.*
*A full breakfast is served at your convenience. A three course dinner is served with
New Zealand wines.*
*There is a lot for you to do in the area. Punakaiki Blowholes and Pancake Rocks,
Helicopter hikes, caves, rafting, and many bush walks. We are one hundred
metres from the beach where you can fossick for green stone, go shellfishing or
surfcasting.*
Directions: *9 miles North of Greymouth on Highway 6 at 9 Mile Creek, Coast
Road. Our house is signposted with our name.*

Greymouth

Homestay
Address: "Ardwyn House",
48 Chapel Street, Greymouth
Name: Alun and Mary Owen
Telephone: (03) 768-6107
Beds: 1 Double, 4 Single (3 bedrooms) **Bathroom:** 1 Guests share
Tariff: B&B (continental) Double $60 or $65 with cooked breakfast. Single $40,
Credit cards: Visa/BC.
Nearest Town: Greymouth

*Ardwyn House is three minutes walk from the town centre in a quiet garden setting
of two acres offering sea, river and town views.*
*The house was built in the 1920s and is a fine example of an imposing residence
with fine woodwork and leadlight windows, whilst being a comfortable and
friendly home.*
*We are ideally situated for travellers touring the west coast as Greymouth is
central and a popular stopover.*
*We offer a courtesy car service to and from local travel centres and also provide off-
street parking.*

Greymouth

Homestay
Address: "Oak Lodge", Coal Creek, Greymouth
Name: Roy and Zelda Anderson
Telephone: (03) 768 6832
Fax: (03) 768 4362
Beds: 2 Double, 2 Single (3 bedrooms)
Bathroom: 3 Ensuite
Tariff: B&B (special) Double $130, Single $90, Dinner $25,
Credit cards accepted

Our home is set in rural surroundings "Coal Creek", 3km North from Greymouth, State highway 6. Antique furniture and many interesting curio's will fascinate you in what was an old farmhouse built in 1901. While the gardens are an outdoor treat, especially in early spring when the rhoddendrons, azaleas and bulbs are in full bloom.

We are centrally situated to visit Shantytown, Punakiki, the Paparoa National Park and good fishing rivers.

Having lived in Greymouth for much of our lives we have an intimate knowledge of some of the most interesting walks in New Zealand. Our 20 acre hobby farm supports sheep and the famous Scottish Belted Galloway cows.

Traditional home cooked meals are served, complimentary wines and local beer.

On the premises are a spa, sauna, swimming pool, and tennis court available for our guests.

We have travelled extensively and appreciate you may like time out in our lounge or join us in our living room. Zelda enjoys gardening, while Roy is an active Rotarian and has a very interesting collection of early Greymouth photos, and stamp collection.

Many homes have facilities for campervans. The ideal camping spot with electricity, bathroom, laundry and friendly hospitality.
Tell campervanners about this when you see them.

Greymouth
Guest House
Address: Golden Coast Guest House,
10 Smith Street, Greymouth
Name: Gladys Roche
Telephone: (03) 768 7839
Beds: 1 Double, 2 Queen, 1 Twin (4 bedrooms) **Bathroom:** Guests share
Tariff: B&B (full) Double $66, Single $45, Children $14. No pets. Motel unit
sleeps 2 $60. A.A. Approved.
Credit Card: Visa. Vouchers accepted.

*Gladys Roche is the hostess at the Golden Coast Guest House and has been for the
last 28 years. It is two minutes from town Railway Station and buses but there is
no noise from trains. It is built on a slight rise with lovely gardens and barbecue
area. There is a TV lounge and tea and coffee making facilities and laundry. There
is also off-street parking. Electric blankets and heaters in all rooms. Your comfort
is my business.*
Directions: *Main highway 6 to South Road opposite Railway Station and Buses.*

Greymouth
Homestay
Address: 20 Stanton Crescent Greymouth
Name: Bev & Graham Piner
Telephone: (03) 768 5397
Beds: 4 Single (2 Bedrooms) **Bathroom:** 1 Guests share
Tariff: B&B (full) Double $60, Single $35, Children half price, Dinner $20,
Vouchers accepted
Nearest Town: Greymouth

Guests no smoking in our home please.
One family consists ourselves plus adult son at home and a very friendly cat.
*We offer a very comfortable home complete with swimming pool in lovely bush
surroundings with wonderful view of sea and mountains.*
*Our interests are travelling, meeting people, gardening, antiques and curious,
decorating, cooking. Graham is a gold miner who loves fishing in his spare time.
We can include visits to a working gold mine. Local sightseeing if no transport.
Good home-made food - picnic lunches. We will transport anyone using bus, plane
or train.*
We look forward to showing you our lovely district.
Directions: *Please phone.*

Kumara, Hokitika

Farmstay
Address: "Gold and Green" Awatuna RD2 Kumara Westland
Name: Helen & John Hadland
Telephone: (03) 755 7070
Beds: 1 Double, 2 Single (2 Bedrooms) **Bathroom:** 1 Family share
Tariff: B&B (full) Double $60, Single $35, Children half price, Dinner $18,
Campervans facilities available, Vouchers accepted
Nearest Town: Hokitika SH 6 (15km south), Greymouth SH6 (25km north)

Welcome to our comfortable, modern, rural, family home situated 15 mins north of Hokitika on a rugged bushclad terrace overlooking the driftwood strewn coast of the Tasman Sea.
Explore the native bush of our 200 acre farm, feed the goats and cattle, milk the house-cow, make friends with Nip the dog and Piggy, or stroll on the beach.
John and I have opened our home to foster children in recent years and we welcome the opportunity to share genuine West Coast hospitality with our guests.
Johns work is in conservation and enjoys fishing, deer-stalking and gold-panning while my interests are centred around maintaining the family home.
We also offer guided trips to nearby glowworm dells, historic abandoned mines, gold panning, trout-fishing and surfcasting. Or relax in our swimming pool.
Children welcome (cot / highchair available). Also space for campervans.
Located 15km north of Hokitika on SH6 or 7km south of Kumara Junction roundabout. Look for the Gold and Green sign.

Inchbonnie

Self-Contained Accommodation
Address: "Whispering Pines", Inchbonnie,
RD1, Kumara, Westland 7871
Name: Russell and Jean Adams
Telephone: (03) 738-0153
Beds: 1 Double, 4 Single (2 bedrooms)
Bathroom: 1 Private
Tariff: B&B (full) Double $60, Single $40, Children $10,
Dinner by arrangement $20, Children $10 Campervan facilities $20.
Credit cards: Visa & M/C. Vouchers accepted
Nearest Town: Arthurs Pass apprx 30 km (East) Hokitika or Greymouth apprx 70 km (West)

Inchbonnie is a rural farming community. We offer a fully furnished historic mill cottage in a quiet scenic area - a great place to relax and "catch up".The cottage is on our property and we farm sheep, beef and deer. We are situated in the midst of some of the best trout fishing in the South Island - Lake Brunner and Lake Poerua and rivers within 10 minutes travel. Abundant bird life and good scenic walks nearby.
Our home was built about 1916 and is set in a large English style garden. Russell is the farmer, Jean handspins, handknits and sells her work and also gardens. Our adult family live away but come home weekends. Craig is a keen fisherman and also shoots, Janine loves riding and enjoys needlepoint.
Directions: *Turn over Taramakau River at Stillwater-Greymouth sign near Jacksons (S.H. 73) onto Lake Brunner Road, continue* **straight** *on to Mitchells Road. We are on the* **left***. "Whispering Pines" at gate. Approx. 8.5 km from S.H. 73.*

Hokitika

Homestay
Address: 31 Whitcombe Tce, Hokitika
Name: Audrey and Norris Sweney
Telephone: (03) 755 7948
Beds: 1 Queen, 1 Single (2 bedrooms) **Bathroom:** 1 Guests share
Tariff: B&B (special) Double $60, Single $35. Vouchers accepted.

Welcome to our comfortable home which is situated on a terrace with a magnificent view of the Southern Alps including Mt Cook and Tasman, town and sea. We are retired farmers with many interests.
Norris belongs to the local Lions Club, he is also a keen fisherman and rugby man. I enjoy lawn bowls in which I play for a month in Australia each winter, also a keen gardener and tramper. We have both travelled widely in New Zealand and overseas. I can speak and understand a little German.
When travelling from Greymouth take first turn on left into Tudor St turn left again at next intersection, Bonar Drive, left again onto Whitcombe Tce. We are the 2nd house on the next left turn. Travelling from South turn right into Tudor St and take 3 left turns.

Hokitika

Guest House
Address: 20 Hamilton Street, Hokitika
Name: Central Guest House – Julie Collier & Russell Wenn
Telephone & Fax: (03) 755 8232

Central Guest House

Beds: 6 Double/Twin, 1 Single, 1 Quad (8 bedrooms, ample guest share bathroom and shower facilities).
Tariff: B&B (continental) Double/Twin $59, Single $39; Full English breakfast available $5 extra per person. Credit Cards. Vouchers accepted.

Our 1920s character guest house is centrally located, offering the convenience of adjacent restaurant and close proximity to all town services.
Cross the road to the Museum to learn more about Hokitika's historical significance to the West Coast gold rush. A minute's walk from the beach (the sunsets can be spectacular).
We offer our guests informal personal service, whilst respecting their privacy. Our guests lounge provides a warm and comfortable atmosphere where guests may choose to relax in the company of others.
Also provided: tea and coffee making facilities, electric blankets, activities information. Laundry facilities available. Major credit cards accepted.
No resident pets. For the comfort and safety of all guests smoking is not permitted indoors.
Local activities inclide many walkways, gold panning, hunting, fishing, whitebaiting (in season), kayaking and rafting.
Travelling times: Lake Kaniere 20 minutes, Shantytown 30 minutes, Punakaiki Blowholes 1 hour, Greymouth 30 minutes, Glaciers 2 hours, Christchurch 4 hours, Nelson 5 hours, Queenstown 7 hours.
We will be pleased to collect anyone arriving by bus or plane.
Directions: *turn left at town clock and take first street to right.*

Hokitika

Homestay
Address: "Rossendale", 234 Gibson Quay, Hokitika
Name: Vi and Arthur Haworth
Telephone & Fax: (03) 755 6620
Beds:1 Double, 2 Single (2 bedrooms) **Bathroom:** 1 Guest share.
Tariff: B&B (Full) Double $60, Single $35, Dinner $15, Children half price,
Vouchers accepted

*We are a semi retired couple with a grown up family who are now married. We
have travelled extensively both within NZ and overseas and enjoy meeting people
from other countries, also fellow New Zealanders.*
*We offer hospitality in a spacious home situated at the edge of town on the banks
of the Hokitika River. We are 1 km from the centre of town with full view of the
Southern Alps and with off street parking. We have two guest bedrooms, one
double with H & C, and one twin. All beds have electric blankets. Guests have
their own bathroom.*
*We offer a full cooked breakfast or a continental, whichever you prefer. Dinner by
arrangement.*
*Our hobbies are gardening, fishing, bush walks, gold panning and meeting people.
Hokitika is within easy reach of all 'West Coast' main attractions, from the beaches
to the Alps, together with pleasant bush walks, and scenic drives.*
We will meet the plane or bus. Assisted sightseeing if required.

Hokitika

Homestay
Address: 70 Tudor Street, Hokitika
Name: Brian and Berna McCarthy
Telephone: (03) 755 7599
Beds: 4 Single (2 bedrooms) **Bathroom:** 1 Guests share
Tariff: B&B (continental, or full on request) Double $60, Single $35, Children
under 12 $15, Vouchers accepted

*We are both fourth generation West Coasters who have retired to Hokitika from
South Westland and have been home hosting for 9 years. We enjoy meeting people,
are proud of our region and are only too keen to tell you of it's attractions. Our
interests are Rugby, Lions, gold prospecting, West Coast history, we both play golf
and lawn bowls as well as fishing for whitebait in season. Guest's comments
returned all say "Hospitality excellent".*
The glow worm dell is only 5 minutes walk away.
*Hokitika has three green stone shops where you can watch the artifacts being
made, a paua jewellery, a gold room, museum, excellent craft shops, and a glass
blowing studio.*
Directions: *When travelling from North take the first turn on your left. Our two
storied brick home is the third house on the left. Travelling from South take the
last turn on your right (Tudor Street) third house on your left. Turn off SH6 at
airport sign from either direction.*

Kowhitirangi, Hokitika

Homestay/Country Living
Address: "Harris Creek",
Kowhitirangi RD I, Hokitika
Name: Carol & Sid Singer
Telephone: (03) 755 7935
Beds: 2 Double, 2 Single (2 bedrooms)
Bathroom: 1 Guests share
Tariff: B&B (continental) Double $65, Single $35,
Nearest Town: Hokitika 18km (15 mins)

Welcome to Kokatahi and Kowhitirangi Valley surrounded by snow capped mountains and lush green farmland. Handy to Lake Kaniere, walkways, Dorothy Falls or a tramp to Toaroha Hot Springs. A base north, to Pancake Rocks south, to the Glaciers. Ten minutes drive to our spectacular Hokitika Gorge with its blue, green deep water viewed from a swing bridge. Those who enjoy fly fishing we have a stream at our front gate also a river nearby. Arranged on request, jet boating, shooting, scenic drives.

Our four girls have travelled overseas, two now reside in America. We live alone with our obedient apricot poodle, in our peaceful, warm, comfortable family home, enjoying the company of interesting delightful people from all walks of life. Sid is a builder, enjoys woodturning, whitebaiting and outside activities. Carol enjoys being home, crafts, voluntary community work.

Offering home packed lunches, homemade bread, fresh homemade yoghurt and jams. All beds have electric blankets and woolrests.

Appreciate smoking outside, please. Laundry available.

Directions: *Please phone. Thank you.*

Hokitika

Farmstay
Address: Riley's Roost,
Golf Links Road, Southside, Hokitika
Postal: Box 87, Hokitika
Name: Mike and Cheryl Riley   RILEYS ROOST
Telephone: (03) 755 6018
Beds: 1 Double, 4 Single (3 bedrooms)   **Bathroom:** 1 Ensuite, 1 Family share
Tariff: B&B (continental) Double $75, Single $65, Dinner $25
Nearest Town: Hokitika 3km

Riley's Roost is near the golf course on the right heading South from Hokitika. A large grey and purple complex back off the road built for the sea views and the sun. The entire complex was designed and built by Mike in 1987. The ongoing project includes a squash court, mini shearing shed, large glasshouses and vegetable garden. Mutton and beef are reared on the rural property.

The couple lead a busy, active life and enjoy people. The family home is a unique and interesting design. An open fireplace is framed by two walls of local stone, one with an arch and bush mural behind. Finished in native rimu the house is clean but not always tidy. A gentle sloped rimu stairway leads to the bedrooms. Mike built a lot of the furniture.

Mike and Cheryl sold a motel complex at Fox Glacier and moved to Hokitika when the eldest of their four children reached high school age. Mike is a semi retired builder and athlete. Cheryl paints, writes and makes driftwood sculptures.

Directions: *Turn right off State Highway 6 after the Hokitika Bridge onto Golf Links Road. The second house on the right. An artistic piece of driftwood stands beside the white gates. The dog barks but doesn't bite!*

417

Hari Hari

Country Lodge/Farmstay
Address: State Highway 6,
Hari Hari, South Westland
Name: Wapiti Park Homestead
Telephone & Fax: (03) 753-3074
International: 64-3-753-3074
Beds: 2 King, 2 Queen, 4 Single (5 bedrooms)
Bathrooms: 2 Ensuite, 1 Private, 1 Guest share
Tariff: B&B (full) Double $100 Guest share, $120 Ensuite/Private, Single $70-$80, Dinner $25. Credit cards: Visa/MC.
Nearest Town: Hari Hari 1/2km SH6. Hokitika 75km north on SH6.

Set in tranquil surroundings, our modern colonial style homestead overlooks the deer farm which specialises in breeding wapiti (elk). The farm tour at 6pm is informative and enables guests to handfeed the wapiti and view red, white and fallow deer, sheep and goats.

Our superior, accommodation features large spacious rooms with attractive individual decor and firm beds, two lounges and a trophy/games room.

Delicious meals promote traditional country fare, cater for a wide variety of tastes and dinners include 3 courses with complimentary wine.

Being located on SH6 makes us an ideal stopover between Picton/Christchurch and Wanaka/Queenstown, or spoil yourself with an extended stay and relax in the warm, friendly, informal atmosphere that allows you to enjoy as much peace and quiet as you wish. You can then explore the region and glaciers at leisure.

South Westland is renowned for its scenic beauty. Close by are historical goldfields, National Parks, White Heron Sanctuary and delightful bush walks.

We offer guided fishing trips for brown trout and salmon and hunting safaris. *We also arrange horse treks and nature tours. Other interests include travel, gardening, the outdoors, photography and ornithology.*

Your hosts are two enthusiastic Kiwis who will endeavour to make your stay at Wapiti Park a holiday highlight.

Reservations are advisable. No smoking in the house please.

Whataroa, South Westland

Farmhouse
Address: "Matai Lodge", Whataroa, South Westland
Name: Jim and Glenice Purcell
Telephone or Fax: (03) 753 4156
Beds: 2 Queensize, 2 Single (3 bedrooms) **Bathroom:** 2 Private
Tariff: B&B (full) Double $100, Single $60 person, Dinner $25
Nearest Town: Hokitika SH6 (north), Franz Joseph S.H.6 (south)

*We are situated 20 mins from the **Franz Josef Glacier** and live on a 400 acre farm of sheep, cattle and horses, surrounded by World Heritage Park.*

Our modern home has been designed to give our farmstay guests their own suite of two bedrooms, lounge and private bathroom upstairs or double room with ensuite downstairs.

There is a backdrop of native bush and you look out to the Southern Alps.

We offer a warm friendly, relaxed atmosphere with plentiful home cooked meals including complimentary NZ wine. Now our family has left home we enjoy entertaining guests from all over the world. You can see sheep close up and watch wool from sheep being spun into yarn or have a go!

I speak Japanese and have taught spinning, weaving and felting in Japan. My husband and I play golf and tennis, there is a very picturesque 9 hole golf course nearby.

Other activities such as horse riding, fishing, kayaking can be arranged and a highlight from November to February is a visit to the White Heron Bird Sanctuary. There are many bush and beach walks close by.

We look forward to sharing our home and knowledge of this scenic area with our guests.

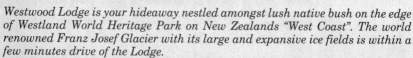

Franz Josef
Superior Country Lodge
Address: State Highway 6 Franz Josef
Name: Annette & Peter Gardiner
Telephone: (03) 752 0111
Beds: 4 Double, 4 Single (6 Bedrooms)
Bathroom: 6 Ensuite
Tariff: B&B (continental) Double $130, Single $130. Credit cards.
Nearest Town: Franz Josef Glacier

Westwood Lodge is your hideaway nestled amongst lush native bush on the edge of Westland World Heritage Park on New Zealands "West Coast". The world renowned Franz Josef Glacier with its large and expansive ice fields is within a few minutes drive of the Lodge.

Westwood Lodge is located 1km, on State Highway 6, north of the township in a quiet and relaxed atmosphere of 2 acres.

There are many activities and services to suit all tastes. The National Park Museum and Visitor Centre, guided walks on the glacier, scenic flights of the glacier by helicopters or ski planes, rain forest walks all of which are available year round.

After the days adventure is over relax in the warmth and comfort of the large guest lounge and talk with new friends in this perfect haven.

Fox Glacier
Homestay
Address: "Cook Flat Cottage" PO Box 42, Fox Glacier
Name: Jan and John Scott
Telephone: (03) 751 0834
Beds: 1 Double, 1 Single (1 bedroom) **Bathroom:** 1 Ensuite
Tariff: B&B (full) Double $70, Single $50, Children under 12 $5-10. Vouchers accepted April to September.
Nearest Town: Hokitika (north)

Our modern colonial home has a rural outlook and is situated off SH6 on the road to Lake Matheson just a few 100 metres from the Fox Glacier township.

We are a young couple with two small boys and a cat. We enjoy welcoming visitors to our area and making them feel comfortable in our home. Our guest bedroom is cosy and warm with an ensuite bathroom. We offer a double bed and have a stretcher bed and cot available for children.

From the guest room is a picturesque view of Mt Cook and the surrounding mountains. The Fox Glacier itself is a mere 6 km away and we are also the same distance away from the world famous Lake Matheson with its unique reflections of New Zealand's highest peaks, Mt Cook and Mt Tasman. Gillespie's Beach is 16 km away which is renowned for its rugged West Coast beach line and is steeped in gold mining history.

Evening dining can be enjoyed at either of the local hotels or restaurants which are within walking distance.

We do request visitors not to smoke in our home.

We can help you with any arrangements of the various sightseeing activities you may wish to do and can help with transport if necessary.

Fox Glacier
Farm Accommodation
Address: "The Homestead", P.O. Box 25, Fox Glacier
Name: Noeleen & Kevin Williams
Telephone: (03) 7510 835 Fox Glacier
Beds: 1 Queen, 1 Double, 2 Single (3 bedrooms) **Bathroom:** 2 Ensuite, 1 Private
Tariff: B&B (special) Double $80 , Single $50. Travellers cheques accepted.
Vouchers accepted April to September.
Nearest Town: Fox Glacier 1/2km, Hokitika SH6 (North) 160km.

*We are a married couple with a grown family and a corgi. We own a large beef
cattle/sheep farm. (Guests are welcome to stroll through the house paddocks).
Beautiful bush-clad mountains surround on three sides and we enjoy a view of Mt
Cook.*
*Our spacious home, built by Kevin's Grandparents in the mid 1890's has lovely
examples of leadlight windows. There is a private lounge, tea/coffee facilities
provided.*
*Being close to the Fox township (1km) evening dining can be taken at the tourist
hotels and restaurants.*
*We feel our home has the best of both worlds; having no immediate neighbours yet
within walking distance of Village tourist facilities (helicopters, ski-planes,
glacier walks, hunting and fishing guides,), 6km to glacier, 4km to world famous
Lake Matheson with its mirror reflection.*
Directions: *On private road opp. Motor Camp entrance, on Cook Flat Rd (road
to Lake Matheson), just before Catholic Church.*

Fox Glacier
Homestay
Address: Cook Flat Rd, Fox Glacier
Name: Reflection Lodge
Telephone: (03) 751 0707
Beds: 1 Double, 2 Single (2 bedrooms) **Bathroom:** 1 Guests share
Tariff: B&B (continental) Double $80, Single $65, Children $20
Nearest Town: Hokitika

*Welcome to Fox Glacier. We are a young family who enjoy welcoming people into
our home.*
*Our modern house is surrounded by lovely gardens with NZ two highest peaks
reflecting into our own private lake directly outside the family room.*
*I offer two rooms. One double and one twin room with share facilities. I have a
spacious lounge for my guests to relax and enjoy the ever changing moods of the
mountains.*
*Our home is situated on the Cook Flat Rd 1km from the township and is handy
to Fox Glaciers many attractions.*
Evening dining can be enjoyed at either of the local hotels or restaurants.
We look forward to meeting you, and sharing our little piece of paradise.
For more information please phone Raelene Tuck.

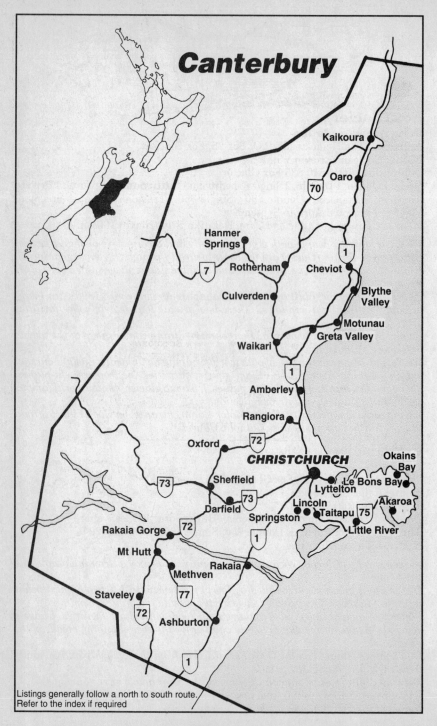

Canterbury

Kaikoura

Oaro

70

Hanmer Springs

Rotherham

Cheviot

7

1

Culverden

Blythe Valley

Motunau

Greta Valley

Waikari

1

Amberley

Rangiora

Oxford

72

CHRISTCHURCH

Okains Bay

Sheffield

Le Bons Bay

73

Lyttelton

73

Lincoln

Akaroa

Darfield

Springston

Taitapu

75

Rakaia Gorge

72

Little River

Mt Hutt

1

Methven

Rakaia

Staveley

77

72

Ashburton

1

Listings generally follow a north to south route.
Refer to the index if required

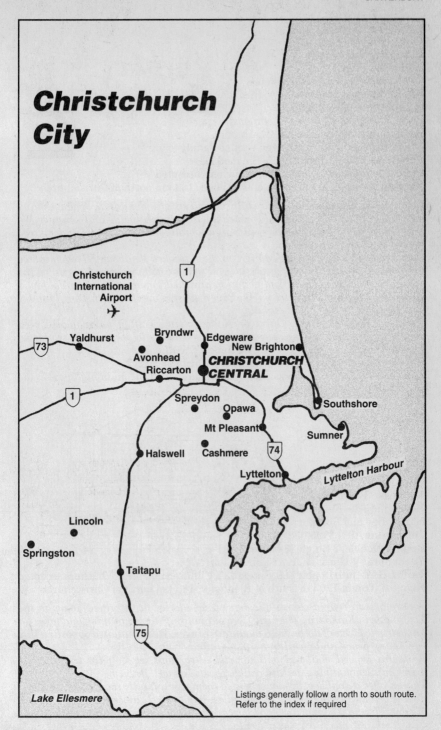

Christchurch City

Christchurch
International
Airport ✈

Yaldhurst

73

Bryndwr

Edgeware

New Brighton

CHRISTCHURCH CENTRAL

1

Avonhead

Riccarton

1

Spreydon

Opawa

Southshore

Mt Pleasant

Sumner

Halswell

Cashmere

74

Lyttelton

Lyttelton Harbour

Lincoln

Springston

Taitapu

75

Lake Ellesmere

Listings generally follow a north to south route.
Refer to the index if required

Kaikoura

Homestay
Address: "Bayview",
296 Scarborough Street, Kaikoura
Name: Bob and Margaret Woodill
Telephone: (03) 319-5480
Beds: 2 Double, 1 Single (3 bedrooms)
Bathroom: 1 shower room, 1 bathroom,
1 toilet Guests share. 1 shower + toilet Family share.
Tariff: B&B (full) Double $55, Single $35,
Children half price, Dinner $20. Vouchers accepted.
Nearest Town: 130 km south of Blenheim, 183 km north of Christchurch

We are a retired couple with four children and six grandchildren. We have many interests, golf, lawn bowls, woodwork, cake icing, stretch sewing and ceramics. We are keen gardeners and for many years grew tomatoes and cucumbers under glass. We also make our own bread.

Our home on an acre of garden high on the Kaikoura Peninsula, a few minutes from the town centre, very peaceful and private with splendid views of the mountains and sea. The accommodation attached to our home has a double, a small double and a twin bedroom. We have a guest lounge and bathroom, laundry and facilities for tea / coffee making.

We have a swimming pool. District activities include golfing, nature walks, bird watching, museum, fishing, sea trips to view whales, dolphins, seals, sea birds, limestone caves and many more. We have a friendly Burmese cat.

We offer transport for visitors travelling by train or bus.

Scarborough Street, the access to the Peninsula, is off the main highway on the south side of the town. _____

Kaikoura

Homestay
Address: "Bevron",
196 Esplanade, Kaikoura
Name: Bev and Ron Barr
Telephone: (03) 3195-432
Beds: 2 Double, 3 Single (3 bedrooms)
Bathroom: 1 Guest share, 1 Family share
Tariff: B&B (full) Double $60, Single $35, Children half price, Vouchers accepted
Nearest Town: 130 km south of Blenheim, 183 km north of Christchurch

We are a semi-retired couple and have a wonderful two storeyed home on the Esplanade in Kaikoura. The view from our balcony is breathtaking and gives an unobstructed view of the bay and mountain ranges. We are situated opposite a safe swimming beach and a children's playground.

Kaikoura is well endowed with tourist attractions, eg dolphin trips, whale watching, scuba diving, nature walks, coastal as well as bush.

We can offer a double bedroom or single rooms, or a family room consisting of a double bed and 2 single beds. Also a guest lounge and games room.

We are a friendly couple and look forward to extending our hospitality to you.

Kaikoura
Bed & Breakfast Inn
Address: The Old Convent ,
Cnr Mt Fyffe & Mill Road, Kaikoura
Name: Steve, Liz & Peter
Telephone: (03) 319-6603
Beds: 4 Double, 4 Single (6 bedrooms)
Bathroom: 3 Ensuite, 2 Guests share
Tariff: B&B (continental) Double/Twin $50-$60, ensuite $70-$80, Single $35.
Credit Cards.
Nearest Town: Kaikoura town centre - 3.6km.

Get in the habit, stay at the Old Convent, nun can compare. Experience the atmosphere under the vaulted ceiling of the converted chapel, it's heavenly. I must confess however the occasional nocturnal creak punctures the tranquillity with thoughts of the supernatural.

Our conversion is nearly completed with each bedroom individually styled. We are now concentrating on the exterior of the Convent and the adjoining schoolrooms where the Sisters of Our Lady of the Missions once ruled.

The Convent is a sanctuary offering informal personal service whilst respecting needs for privacy. Set in farmland amid the majestic scenery of Kaikoura's mountainous coastline, it is the ideal place to linger an extra day to experience the many marine and land based activities, or just relax and contemplate things spiritual. Perked coffee, tea, juice, biscuits, laundry facilities, vintage bicycles and courtesy car are complimentary. You will enjoy our lavish continental breakfast and in bumpy seas may even share it with the whales and dolphins.

Directions: *At north edge of town turn west off SH 1 up Mill Road 2 km.*

We rely on your comments about our B&Bs.
Please send us a comment form from the back of the book.

Kaikoura

Bed and Breakfast
Address: "Beachfront",
78 Esplanade, Kaikoura
Name: Pat and Maurie Bradshaw
Telephone: (03) 319 5890
Beds: 4 Double, 4 Single (5 bedrooms) **Bathrooms:** 3 ensuite, 1 guests share
Tariff: B&B (full) Double with ensuite $65, Double $55, Single $30, Children (on request), Visa & Mastercard accepted, Vouchers accepted
Nearest Town: 130km south of Blenheim, 183km north of Christchurch

We are a semi-retired couple who have lived in Kaikoura for 33 years and we are fully involved in community activities. Our home is situated on the seafront five minutes walk from Village shops. Our two upstairs bedrooms with balcony have a magnificent view of sea, bush and mountains, as does our lounge and dining area. We serve a full English Breakfast using local fresh products. We are happy to share our wide knowledge of the area and its attractions to help you to make full use of your time with us. We are happy to meet train and buses and also to make reservations for local tours and restaurants. We ask guests not to smoke inside our home.

Kaikoura

Homestay Accommodation
Address: "The Gums"
Schoolhouse Road, Kaikoura
Name: Ian & Alison Boyd
Telephone: (03) 319 5736
Beds: 2 Double, 4 Single (3 Bedrooms)
Bathroom: 1 Guests share, 1 Family share
Tariff: B&B (continental) Double $55, Single $35, Children $15, Campervans welcome. Vouchers accepted (June to September Double $50).
Nearest Town: Kaikoura 5km

Ian is a retired technical teacher and Alison a part time librarian. We have a new home on eleven acres. The land has a meandering stream flowing through it with gum trees along the banks. We have a panoramic view of the mountains and sea. A beautiful, peaceful setting.
Courtesy car, two bicycles and a farm visit are complementary.
District activities include golf, tennis, fishing, nature walks, whale and dolphin trips, seals and limestone caves.
Continental breakfast - Cereal, fruits, yoghurt, fruit juice, muesli, tea, coffee, toast and spreads.
We look forward to your company.
Directions: *Driving north 3.5km from Kaikoura on SH 1, turn left, 1.5km along Schoolhouse Road. We are a non smoking household.*

Kaikoura

Guest House
Address: R.D. 2,
Kaikoura
Name: Fyffe Gallery & Restaurant
Telephone: (03) 319 6869
Beds: 2 Double, 1 Twin (3 bedrooms)
Bathroom: 3 Ensuite
Tariff: B&B (full) $95 per room.   Credit Cards accepted.
Nearest Town: 6kms South of Kaikoura on SH 1.

Fyffe Gallery is a new building that includes an art gallery and gift shop, a restaurant and 3 accommodation rooms all with ensuites and own TV.
It is also the home of Jan & Graeme Rasmussen. Jan is a proffesional artist and sells her own work and other selected artists in her gallery.
The unique earth block house with its hand split cedar shake roof is based on an early 1860 colonial design. The earth blocks were made on site and recycled timber and fittings have been used extensively.
The exterior is coated with natural materials and the interior walls with a traditional lime wash. Very environmentally friendly.
All bedrooms have magnificent views of the mountains across farm land.
We also have a lovely large brick paved courtyard with tables and sun umbrellas set in a country garden. Here we can serve meals, Devonshire style teas and cappuccino coffee. Large off road car park.
Directions: *6 Kms South of Kaikoura Township on SH 1.*

Kaikoura

Farmstay+Self-contained
                    Accommodation
Address: "The Kahutara"
Dairy Farm Road, Kaikoura
Name: John & Nikki Smith
Telephone & Fax: (03) 319 5580
Beds: 1 Twin, 1 Single (2 Bedrooms), Self-contained Bunkhouse accommodates 4, Linen supplied **Bathroom:** 1 Family share
Tariff: B&B (full) Double $60, Single $35, Children half price, Dinner $25, Vouchers accepted
Nearest Town: 25km from Kaikoura township on inland Waiau route - 183km north of Christchurch

"The Kahutara" is a haven in the hills. Our comfortable country home is nestled among the hills in a tranquil garden setting. We operate a 2000 acre beef cattle and sheep farm with a small thoroughbred stud.
Our guest rooms have electric blankets, heater and private guest lounge.
A choice of continental or cooked breakfast with home-made jams, while the evening meals for those who choose to join us would be a traditional New Zealand farm meal.
We have excellent paragliding facilities, a pleasant river walk to protected bird sanctuary lake, or guests can participate in seasonal farm duties. We are only 45 minutes to the popular Mt Lyford Skifield or we can book you on a whale watch.
Directions: *Please phone or fax.*

Oaro, Kaikoura

Farmhouse
Address: Oaro, R.D. 2, Kaikoura
Name: Kathleen and Peter King
Telephone: (03) 319 5494
Beds: 2 Single (1 bedroom)
Bathroom: 1 Private
Tariff: B&B (full) Double $55, Single $28,
Children half price; Dinner $15, Vouchers accepted
Nearest Town: 22 km south of Kaikoura

We are semi-retired living on 48 acres having sold our hill-country property ten years ago. We have three daughters - all live away from home - and six grandchildren. Two cats share our home with us.
This is a mild climate and we are experimenting in a small way growing citrus and subtropical fruits, predominantly feijoas.
Oaro is close to the sea and we have a fine view north along the Kaikoura coast. A walk south along the coast is always popular. The 20 minute drive to Kaikoura takes you alongside our scenic rocky coast.
We enjoy sharing our home with visitors and assure you of a warm welcome.
We are happy for you to join us for dinner but if you prefer there is a restaurant 2 km north where they have takeaways as well as meals.
Directions: *We are 22 km south of Kaikoura just a short distance off the main north-south highway.*

Rotherham

Farmstay
Address: Mount Palm,
Rotherham, North Canterbury
Name: Helen Robinson
Telephone: (03) 315 6358
Beds: 1 Double, 4 Single (3 bedrooms)
Bathrooms: 1 Guests share
Tariff: B&B (full) Double $90, Single $50, Dinner $20, School children half price.
Nearest Town: Rotherham 8kms.

You will receive a warm welcome when you visit our home which is an attractive, spacious 100 year old wooden homestead, set among beautiful cedars and oregans on a hill country farm, running cattle and sheep, two black cats and a young labrador.
Situated on the Lowry Range in North Canterbury, it is only 110 km to Christchurch, being the nearest International Airport. It is an hours drive to Kaikoura where the world famous whales can be experienced; half an hour to Hanmer Springs where you will find thermal pools, bungy jumping, jet boat rides, forest walks, skiing and other outdoor activities. Other attractions nearby are the Amuri Salmon Farm, golf course and the Mt Lyford ski area.
You may just prefer the relaxing atmosphere of the house and garden, or an informative tour of the farm can easily be arranged.
The large bedrooms have their own washbasins and electric blankets. A bathroom, separate shower and toilet are available solely for guests.
Please telephone for reservations mornings or evenings.

428

Hanmer Springs
Farm Bed and Breakfast + Farm Cabin
Address: 'Percival Bed and Breakfast',
Rural Bag 55027 Christchurch
Name: June and Michael Manion
Telephone and Fax: (03) 315 7062
Beds: 1 Double, 1 Twin, 1 Triple (3 bedrooms)
Bathroom: 1 Private, 1 Family share
Tariff: B&B (continental) Double $80, Single $45: Campervans welcome, Farm Cabin: Adult $15, Children $5, Credit cards accepted, Vouchers accepted
Nearest Town: 4 kms before Hanmer Springs township on the main road. Sign opposite the gate

Percival is centrally situated within the Hanmer Basin and has panoramic views of the surrounding hills, mountains and forest. It was originally part of the historic 'St Helens' station, a well known early run in Canterbury, before becoming incorporated into Molesworth.

"Percival" consists of mainly heavy river flats with some light wintering country. A beef cow herd is run in conjunction with a Romney ewe flock, some red deer and several thoroughbred brood mares.

Having previously owned and operated our own hotel for 16 years, we appreciate our environment and enjoy sharing our lifestyle with others. The homestead kitchen, where breakfast is served is the hub of the property. We are 4th generation farmers and enjoy fishing, shooting, tramping, and skiing. Our accommodation is adjacent to the homestead and with private facilities. There is a solar heated swimming pool and grass tennis court in our grounds and Farm Tours are available on request as an extra.

Hanmer Springs is a unique alpine thermal resort which is famous for its forest walks and tranquil environment as much as the "Hot Springs".

A warm welcome awaits guests at "Percival".

Always telephone ahead to enquire about a B&B. It is a nuisance for you if you simply arrive to find someone already staying there.
And besides hosts need a little time to prepare.

Hanmer Springs
Homestay
Address: Champagne Flat Hanmer Springs
Name: Chris & Virginia Parsons
Telephone & Fax: (03) 315 7413
Beds: 2 Double, 1 Single (3 Bedrooms) **Bathroom:** 1 Guests share
Tariff: B&B (full) Double $45pp, Single $50pp, Children half price, Dinner $20pp. Credit cards. Vouchers accepted
Nearest Town: Hanmer Springs 6km

Champagne Flat is a small farmlet situated just 6 kilometres from the tiny township of Hanmer Springs. Its history is closely tied in with the building of the Ferry Bridge in 1887 and we are only 2 minutes from this historic construction which is now used for bungy jumping.
Our home is a modern two-storeyed farm house with its own facilities for guests. Each guest room has its own outstanding views - wake up to a spectacular view of the snow-capped mountains and the braided Waiau River. You will have warm, spacious surroundings and share our enjoyment of the peace and tranquillity of the Hanmer Valley.
We are a friendly, outgoing couple - husband a high school teacher, wife a 'retired' social worker dabbling in real estate, gardening and Red Cross.
We specialise in scrumptious full English breakfasts and you may join us for dinner if you wish.
Participate in local activities - thermal pools, trout fishing, forest walks, golf, skiing, jet-boating.
Directions: *1 1/2 hours easy drive north from Christchurch. SH 7 Hanmer turn off. 4 hours south from the Picton Ferry via Kaikoura inland.*

Hanmer Springs
Bed & Breakfast
Address: "Meadow Song"
177 Jacks Pass Road
Hanmer Springs
Name: Ngaire Shields
Telephone: (03) 315 7577
Beds: 2 Queen, 1 Twin (3 Bedrooms)
Bathroom: 1 Ensuite, 1 Guests share
Tariff: B&B (full) Double $90, $100 with Ensuite, Single $60. Credit cards accepted.

Hanmer Springs is a truly magnificent alpine resort in keeping with the recreational diversity of the area we offer an alternative to the traditional form of accommodation the customary quality service combined with the warm friendly atmosphere of a privately owned home.
A short walk from the township our home will become your private retreat. By day enjoy the peace and tranquillity of our beautiful scenic surrounding, play golf, soak in the thermal pool, horse trekking, fishing, magnificent forest walks, bungy jumping, jet boating, rafting. By night enjoy the fine cuisine available in our local restaurants, then relax in the comfort of your home away from home Meadow Song. We are a non smoking household but a cigarette can be enjoyed whilst walking round our garden. Electric duel blankets feather duvets colour TV comfortable beds in all guests rooms. Booking please ring.

Culverden
Homestay+Farmstay
Address: "Coldstream" SH 7
Culverden North Canterbury
Name: Noeline & Evan Millar
Telephone & Fax: (03) 315 8277
Beds: 4 Single (2 Twin Bedrooms)
Bathroom: 1 Ensuite, 1 Family share
Tariff: B&B (full) Double $100, Single $50, Children $25, Dinner $20, Campervans facilities available, Vouchers accepted
Nearest Town: 2km east of Culverden, 1 hour north of Christchurch on SH 7

"Coldstream" has been owned by Noeline and Evan Millar since 1990. It is a border dyke irrigation property that runs beef cattle and Romney sheep. The homestead is a superb modern 2 storey home set in spacious grounds with lawn sweeping down to a stream and small lake which is home to waterfowl and two white swans. Panoramic views of the Southern Alps, Lowery Range, and the Kaikouras from every room. Activities available in the Amuri area are hot thermal pools, trout and salmon fishing, skiing, white water rafting, jet boating, mountain biking, bushwalks, bungy jumping, horse trekking, golf and tennis.
"Coldstream" is just over the Pahau River if travelling north on State Highway 7, the Hanmer Tourist Resort is a further 20 minutes drive northwest of "Coldstream".

Gore Bay, Cheviot
Homestay
Address: "Saltburn", Gore Bay, Cheviot RD3, Canterbury
Name: Dorothy and Les Jefferson
Telephone: (03) 319 8686
Beds: 1 Double, 2 Single (2 bedrooms, electric blankets)
Bathroom: 1 Private, 1 Family share
Tariff: B&B (full) Double $60, Single $35, Children half price; Dinner by arrangement $20, Vouchers accepted
Nearest Town: Cheviot 9 km

Originally from England, my husband and I have retired to the house we have built overlooking the bay in this attractive area.
We have travelled extensively, both in New Zealand and overseas, and thoroughly enjoy meeting people from other countries.
At home we are keen gardeners and appreciate the mild climate we experience here. We also enjoy tramping and there are many walking tracks, delightful views and a safe surfing and swimming beach. We have a small dog.
Native birds abound and a seal colony lies along the coast to the north, while a walkway follows the coastline southward through natural bush to the Hurunui River mouth, an excellent fishing spot.
Cheviot, the nearest shopping area is 1 hour 30 mins drive north of Christchurch on State Highway One and 1 hours drive south from Kaikoura.

Motunau, North Canterbury

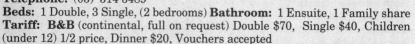

Farmstay
Address: "Seaward Downs", Greta Valley R.D., North Canterbury
Name: Julie & Jonathan Douglas
Telephone: (03) 314 3489
Beds: 1 Double, 3 Single, (2 bedrooms) **Bathroom:** 1 Ensuite, 1 Family share
Tariff: B&B (continental, full on request) Double $70, Single $40, Children (under 12) 1/2 price, Dinner $20, Vouchers accepted
Nearest Town: Greta Valley 20 km HW1, 1 1/4 hour drive from Christchurch

We welcome you to our 1200 acre sheep and beef farm on the sea coast of North Canterbury, 20 kms from Greta Valley (Highway 1), 1 hour 30 mins from the popular Hamner Springs resort or the Whales at Kaikoura.
We are a family of 4 with 2 schoolchildren who enjoy meeting people from all over the world. We welcome you to join us in farming activities and hobbies such as gardening, craft, golf and horse-riding. Fishing available close by (sea or river). Our house is nestled in a large landscaped garden with un-interrupted views of the mountains to the West and the sea to the East, Motunau Beach only minutes away. We offer a guest room with double and single beds, own bathroom and private entrance or twin room by request. All beds have electric blankets. Transport can be arranged for a small charge from Greta Valley bus stop. We welcome you to relax with us and enjoy wonderful farm style cooking.
Directions: *Please phone*

Greta Valley & Waikari

Farmstay
Address: Foxdown, Greta Valley.
Postal: Amberley, R.D.3.
Name: Alison and Peter Fox
Telephone: (03) 314 3704
Fax: (03) 314 3401
Beds: 2 Double (1 queen), 3 Single beds (3 bedrooms)
Bathrooms: 2 Guests share
Tariff: B&B (full) Double $68, Single $42, unsuitable for children, Dinner $20, Vouchers accepted
Nearest Town: Farm is situated 1 1/4 hours drive north of Christchurch (90 km) on a valley road between Highway 1 at Greta Valley and Highway 7 at Waikari. 4 hours drive from Picton or West Coast. 2 hours drive from Kaikoura.

Foxdown is a farm of 1400 hectares (3500 acres) carrying 5500 sheep and 250 cattle on the rolling to steep North Canterbury hills. It has been in the Fox family for 117 years, and we have enjoyed hosting for 17 years.
Our home is a large, modern, sunny, two-storeyed homestead with own facilities for guests and wonderful views from all rooms. There is a swimming pool, trampoline, tennis court, and small paperback book exchange. We have 2 quiet part siamese cats and a small Corgi dog. Foxdown is now managed by son Andrew, with help from Peter and casual workers. If farm work permits, you can be taken on a farm tour by Peter and see farm activities and more beautiful views. Our interests include contract bridge, farm forestry, wool, machine knitting, travelling, meeting Overseas people and fellow New Zealanders.
Nearby (10kms) is Scargill Golf Course (9holes), also 2 walkways. Motunau Beach is 33kms, and Hamner Springs hot pools are 84kms.
Directions: *The Homestead drive is opposite cattle yards at the end of Foxdown Road. Foxdown Road is 16 km from Waikari and 11 km from Greta Valley.*

Greta Valley

Farmstay
Address: "Gorrie Downs",
Greta Valley, RD, North Canterbury
Name: Janette and Rod McKenzie
Telephone: (03) 314 3475.
Fax: (03) 314 8291
Beds: 1 Queen, 3 Single (2 bedrooms)
Bathroom: 1 Ensuite, 1 Family share
Tariff: B&B (continental, full on request) Double $85, Single $50, Children under 12 half price, Dinner $20,
Nearest Town: Greta Valley 7km, Cheviot 30 mins north, Amberley 30 mins south, Christchurch 1 hr south, Picton 4 hrs north

Our home is a very comfortable 45-year-old house, with established garden and trees, in a peaceful valley with magnificent views of the countryside.

One guest room has a separate entrance, a queen size and a single bed, with own bathroom. A second room with two single beds is available, share bathroom. Furnishings are designed with your comfort in mind, with electric blankets and good heating in all rooms.

Having travelled extensively overseas, we enjoy meeting people. We are involved in numerous business activities which we run from our 1000 acre farm. These include the farming of bulls, raising coloured sheep for handcraft wool exports, farm information services, and international consultancy.

We are ideally situated for those travelling the Picton-Kaikoura-Christchurch route, only five minutes off the highway. Five minutes away is a safe swimming beach.

You are guaranteed a memorable stay when you break the journey with us. We are a non-smoking household.

Would you like a weeks free B&B for two people?
Please complete and send us the comment form supplied by your host.

Waikari
Farmstay
Address: "Waituna"
Waikari North Canterbury
Name: David & Joanna Cameron
Telephone & Fax: (03) 314 4575
Beds: 5 Single (3 Bedrooms)
Bathroom: 1 Guests share plus extra loo and handbasin
Tariff: B&B (continental) Double $90, Single $50, Dinner $25pp by arrangement, Vouchers accepted
Nearest Town: Waikari 5km, 76km north of Christchurch

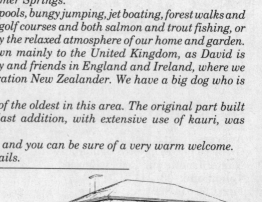

Waituna is a sheep and cattle farm situated 2.5km off Highway 7, halfway between Christchurch and Hanmer Springs.
In Hanmer you will find thermal pools, bungy jumping, jet boating, forest walks and skiing. Nearer to home there are golf courses and both salmon and trout fishing, or perhaps you would prefer to enjoy the relaxed atmosphere of our home and garden. We enjoy travelling, being drawn mainly to the United Kingdom, as David is English and we still have family and friends in England and Ireland, where we lived until 1972. Jo is 5th generation New Zealander. We have a big dog who is almost part of the family!
The Waituna homestead is one of the oldest in this area. The original part built of limestone in 1879 and the last addition, with extensive use of kauri, was completed in 1905.
We look forward to meeting you and you can be sure of a very warm welcome.
Directions: *Please ring for details.*

Amberley
Guest House
Address: RD1, Amberley
Name: Harleston Guest House
Telephone: (03) 312 9806
Beds: 3 Double, 1 Single (4 bedrooms)
Bathroom: 2 Private, 1 Guests share
Tariff: B&B (full) Double $80, Single $40; Dinner $26 (4 courses); Children half price, under 5 free.

Hosts: Kathy Anderson & David Richardson.
Harleston, a North Canterbury landmark protected by the N.Z. Historic Places Trust, is one of the first farmhouses to be built in Canterbury. Constructed with limestone block 133 years ago, it is an elegantly simple home with a great deal of character.
Harleston is ideally situated for travellers wishing to use the inter-island ferries. Going north you can enjoy a half-hour start on city dwellers and for southbound travellers, instead of wearily trying to find accommodation in a strange city late in the day, you can stay with us and after a hearty breakfast drive to Christchurch with the advantages a new day brings.
Guests can enjoy acclaimed cuisine, the nearby (usually deserted) beach or perhaps visit a local vineyard, catch a fish, explore the varying countryside or simply relax in our garden. We take pride in offering warm hospitality to all our guests and thoroughly enjoy caring for them.
Directions: *State Highway 1, 40 km north of Christchurch, 10 km south of Amberley, sign at gate.*

434

C.R-BULL '93.

Ashley, Rangiora

Farmstay
Address: "Woolly Meadows Farmyard",
242 Cones Road, Ashley, Rangiora R.D. 2,
Name: John & Lynda van Beek
Telephone: (03) 313-5387 or Mobile (025) 332 597
Fax: (03) 313-6724
Beds: 1 Double, 3 Single (3 bedrooms) **Bathroom:** 1 Guests share
Tariff: B&B (full) Double $60, Single $40, Dinner $20, Campervans $20 per night (own toilet & shower). Vouchers accepted.
Nearest Town: Rangiora (5 mins) Christchurch (25 mins)

Our modern 4 bedroomed home is situated 25km from Christchurch City & Airport, 12 km from State Highway 1. Turn at Woodend onto Highway 72 to Rangiora. Take the road to Ashley, we are 1.3 km over the Ashley River Bridge, 5 km from Rangiora town.
Our farm is 40 acres with 150 breeding sheep plus their lambs, 20 head of cattle, including our house cow we milk. Our farm is open to tourists for visits & BBQ lunches - we have a variety of small animals, our speciality is our pet sheep - they eat food from your hand. Many schools visit here for farm education. We developed Woolly Meadows Farmyard in 1986, home hosting overseas guests in 1983. We have a large garden and lawn area with roses, native trees - you can relax and view the sheep.
Dinner always available - use our answerphone or fax if necessary.
We have lived in this area for many years and are happy to share it with you while you travel our beautiful country.

Rangiora

Homestay
Address: 29 Victoria Street, Rangiora
Name: Chris & Wendy Carmody
Telephone: (03) 313-8378
Beds: 1 Double, 2 Single (3 bedrooms) **Bathroom:** 1 Guests share
Tariff: B&B (full) Double $60, Single $30, family discount available on request.
Dinner upon request.

"Glowing sky at sunset", "fine weather after bad", "place of peace" these translations for the Maori 'Rangiora' reflect the quintessence character of accommodation we seek to provide.
Guests have their own space which includes a comfortable lounge which may be used to entertain one's own visitors if one wishes. Or guests are most welcome to share and mingle in our family life in the family side of our large and spacious home. Recent landscaping and renovation has improved wheelchair access should it be necessary.
Directions: *20 minutes motorway driving north of Christchurch.*

Oxford
Homestay + Self-Contained Accommodation
Address: 37 High Street, Oxford
Name: Norton and Helen Dunn
Telephone: (03) 312 4167
Beds: 3 Double bedrooms, (one brm has guest shower, toilet, sitting room, kitchen facilities, verandah entrance) others bathroom is handy
Tariff: B&B (full) Self-contained unit Double $60, Single $30, Homestay B&B (full) Double $50, Single $25, Dinner $15 by arrangement, Children 5-13yrs $12, under 5 no charge. Vouchers accepted.
Nearest Town: Walking distance to the shops, 55 km from Christchurch

Our house is 60 years old and has a spacious garden - warm and sunny.
We are a contented married couple with a family of three grown-up sons. We retired from Dunedin to live in Oxford - a charming, restful town and a friendly community. Oxford offers scenic walks, horse treks, homecrafts, pottery, herbs, basket making and home spun hand-knitted garments, bowls, tennis, squash, restaurant, golf and bridge club handy.
Directions: *High Street is off the Main Road - left- sign outside the gate.*

Sheffield
Homestay
Address: Pine House,
Waddington & Waimakariri
Gorge Roads corner, Waddington, Sheffield
Name: Chris and Quilliam Collister
Telephone: (03) 318 3762
Beds: 1 Double, 2 Single (2 bedrooms) **Bathroom:** 1 Guests share
Tariff: B&B (full) Double $60, Single $35, Dinner $15, Children half price, Vouchers accepted
Nearest Town: Darfield 12km

Pine House is a 2 storeyed character home (circa 1875), in a large country garden setting with grand old trees. Our guest bedrooms are warm and comfortable, and the beds have wollen underlays and electric blankets. Breakfast is served in the guest sitting room, which is bright and sunny and overlooks the garden. T.V, and tea\coffee making facilities are always available here.
We are conveniently situated close by the intersection of Highway 72, the scenic southern inland road, and Highway 73, the main road to the West Coast. The Tranz Alpine Express passes Waddington, and can be boarded nearby. Central Christchurch is a pleasant 45 minute drive from here, while the airport can be reached in 30 minutes. We are 5 kilometres from the Waimakariri River gorge bridge, and close to jet boating, salmon fishing, and spectacular scenery.
Our family of 4 is: Quilliam, a teacher, Chris, part-time library assistant, and 2 teenage sons, both students. All keen travellers, we enjoy welcoming guests from many countries to our house.
Directions: *Pine House is on Highway 72, just north of the intersection with Highway 73 to the West Coast, and 12km west of Darfield. If phoning, please call before 8.45am or after 4pm, as Chris may be working.*

Bryndwr, Christchurch
Homestay
Address: "Allisford", 1/61 Aorangi Road,
Bryndwr, Christchurch
Name: Allison Crawford
Telephone: (03) 351 7742
Beds: 2 Single (1 bedroom) **Bathroom:** share with Allison
Tariff: B&B (full) Double $55, Single $35; Dinner $12

*"Allisford" is a private residence in a choice area where warm friendly hospitality
is offered in comfortable surroundings.*
*A large twin bedroom is available for guests, also a comfortable lounge opening
onto lawn and garden.*
There is also off-street parking.
*The nearest No. 17B Wairakei Rd bus stop is only three minutes walk away and
this bus passes the Arts Centre, the Museum, the Botanical Gardens and the
McDougall Art Gallery on the way into the city centre.*
*Allisford is situated about halfway between the Airport and the city centre and is
also easily reached from north, south and west main highways, or drive down
Memorial Avenue from the airport, turn left into Ilam Rd, past aqualand and you
are in Aorangi Rd.*
*You may have the breakfast of your choice and are welcome to have dinner by
arrangement.*
Directions: *Please phone. I am seldom far away for long in the daytime and
rarely out at night.*

Bryndwr, Christchurch
Homestay
Address: Please Phone
Name: Doreen and Ruth
Telephone: (03) 351 6858
 Beds: 2 Single (1 bedroom) **Bathroom:** 1 Private
Tariff: B&B (full) Double $55, Single $35
Nearest Town: 10 minutes from Christchurch City.

*Our comfortable red brick home is situated in a quiet street and we offer a double
room with two single beds. Also for your use is a large sunny lounge with open fire
in winter. This room has colour TV and tea making facilities. We are 7 minutes
from Christchurch International Airport, 2 minutes from the main highway north
and approximately 15 minutes from the main highway south.*
*Within close proximity to us are shopping malls and restaurants. The bus stop
to the city centre is a 5 minute walk. Your hosts - two ladies who enjoy meeting
people. Also living here are a shy cat and a young friendly Jack Russell terrier.
We have both travelled throughout New Zealand and overseas. Our interests
include gardening and tramping.*
We look forward to meeting you.

Continental breakfast consist of fruit, toast, tea/coffee,
Full breakfast is the same with a cooked course,
Special breakfast has something special.

437

New Brighton, Christchurch

Homestay
Address: 'Rose of Light',
558 New Brighton Road, Christchurch 9
Name: Shirley May
Telephone: (03) 388 5804
Beds: 1 Double, 1 Single (2 bedrooms)
Bathroom: 1 Guests share
Tariff: B&B (full) Double $60, Single $40, Candle-lit Dinner $22, also Vegetarian , Vegan by arrangement, Children half price. Credit Cards. Vouchers accepted.

'Rose of Light' is a gracious, much-loved family home with the visiting 5th generation climbing the walnut tree planted by their great-great-grandfather. It has always been a haven for guests.

A speciality of Shirley's is the therapeutic massage she offers with her 20 years' expertise. Many guests with travel weariness or aches or pains avail themselves of this relaxation before retiring.

Wander around our garden; browse in our extensive library; feed the ducks on the Avon River opposite; stroll down to wonderful Brighton surfing beach. There is a mountain view and river walk at the gate. We're a minute's walk from the bus stop for town, 2 minutes walk to Brighton Mall's all hours' shopping and variety of eateries. Olympic pool complex and 5 golf courses are in close proximity.

The guest room has a winter's open fire, queen size bed, couch, TV, supper facilities and outside access with garaged parking. Shirley has travelled widely and looks forward to meeting you.

New Brighton, Christchurch

B&B Inn & Guesthouse
Address: 97 Lonsdale Street,
New Brighton,
Christchurch 8007
Name: Convent Lodge
Telephone & Fax: (03) 388 3388
Beds: 2 Double, 2 Twin, 2 Single (6 bedrooms)
Bathroom: Guests share 3 toilets, 3 showers, 2 baths
Tariff: B&B (continental) Double $58, Single $38, Dinner $15, Credit cards: Visa/MC/Diners. Vouchers accepted.

Rob and Christine welcome you to a warm and friendly atmosphere where old fashion service and smiles can still be found.

We have placed importance on home comforts with ducted central heating and a log fire in lower lounge. Our complex has 2 lounges, 3 showers, 2 baths, 3 toilets, separate kitchen and dining room for guests use entirely.

Our guests enjoy the peace and tranquillity which can not always be found in the inner city. Adjacent to Convent Lodge is a golf course and tennis court (rackets and balls supplied). We are only a moments walk to the village mall, bus stop and beach (pack swimming costumes). Heated swimming complex and leisure park close by. (See management for 10 speed bicycles)

Fresh sea air, soft sound of surf, extra comfy beds, electric blankets and heaters will ensure you a great nights sleep.

Our courtesy van is available to pick you up from point of arrival in Christchurch to the Lodge.

Avonhead, Christchurch
Homestay
Address: 101A Yaldhurst Road
Avonhead Christchurch 4
Name: Peter & Penny Davies
Telephone & Fax: (03) 348 9977
Mobile: 025-320-146
Beds: 2 Double, 2 Single (2 Bedrooms) **Bathroom:** 2 Ensuite
Tariff: B&B (full) Double $75, Single $50, Children half price, Vouchers accepted
Nearest Town: Christchurch

A warm Kiwi welcome awaits you when you arrive at our family home. We are a professional couple in our mid to late 30's who enjoy meeting people from different countries.

Your luxury accommodation has been specifically designed for you the traveller in mind. Each spacious bedroom offers a double and single bed, a full ensuite bathroom, hairdryer, iron, ironing board, electric blankets and heaters.

There is a separate guests lounge and kitchenette for your exclusive use. Laundry facilities are also available.

Directions: We are situated on the main road west, halfway between the airport and the city, (approx 6km each way) and two minutes away from the junction of the northern and southern motorway.

We live in on a quiet rear section with plenty of off street parking. (Please drive in).

We both look forward to your visit and know you will take away happy memories of your time in Christchurch.

439

Avonhead, Christchurch

Homestay
Address: 67 Toorak Avenue, Avonhead, Christchurch 4
Name: Fleur Lodge
Telephone: (03) 342 5473
Beds: 1 Double, 4 Single (3 bedrooms) **Bathroom:** 1 Guests share, 1 Family share
Tariff: B&B (full) Double $80, Single $60, Dinner $25. Vouchers accepted.
Nearest Town: 20 mins Christchurch City, 6 mins Airport

We have a large new home situated in a quiet residential street, built for maximum sun and light. The bedrooms are well lit and very comfortable and the family room has a cosy log burner for winter warmth. A cat shares our home and we prefer non-smoking guests.

City bus stops are handy and depart every thirty minutes. City centre is 9km and Airport 4km. We are able to meet guests at Airport or any other City destination. We will arrange sightseeing tours of city and suburbs that include free pick up and return. Our interests include travel, gardening, lawn bowls and we are members of various clubs. We enjoy good food and invite guests to sample a home cooked three course dinner for a cost of $20 per person.

Please phone for reservation before 9.00am or after 4.00pm.

Avonhead, Christchurch

Homestay
Name: Sally's Homestay
Address: Avonhead, Christchurch 4
Telephone: (03) 342 8172
Beds: 2 Single (1 Bedroom) **Bathroom:** 1 Family share
Tariff: B&B (continental) Double $55, Single $35, Dinner $15
Nearest Town: 5km to centre city

My home is a private residence in a convenient and very pleasant location that offers the very best of NZ hospitality.

A twin bedroom is available for guests. I also have a separate lounge where if you wish you may entertain your friends, or you may join with me in my living room. Situated 1 1/2km from Christchurch International Airport, also close to North South and West highways, also bus stops two houses away. There is also off-street parking.

I have recently retired and enjoy sharing my home with visitors and assure you of warm welcome.

Directions: *Please phone.*

Christchurch City

Private Hotel
Address: 52 Armagh Street, Christchurch
Name: Windsor Private Hotel
Telephone: (03) 366 1503 or 366 2707, Fax (03) 366 9796
Beds: 40 bedrooms **Bathroom:** Guests share
Tariff: B&B (full) Double $84, Single $55, Children under 12 years $15, Credit cards accepted, Vouchers accepted May to October, Quote this book for 10% discount.

"The Windsor", originally named Warwick House, was built at the turn of the century. Located in the quiet northwest situation of Cranmer Square, we are within easy walking distance of the Art Centre, museum, gardens, theatre, town hall and Cathedral Square (our city centre), with its banks, buses, shopping arcades and excellent restaurants.
Guests are greeted on arrival and shown around our charming colonial style home. Our nicely furnished bedrooms, all with a small posie of flowers and an original water colour by local artist Denise McCulloch, lend charm to the warm and cosy bedrooms which are all individually heated. The shared bathroom facilities are all conveniently appointed for guests comfort. The dining room where our generous morning menu includes juice, fresh fruit and cereals, followed by a choice of bacon and eggs, sausages, tomatoes, toast and marmalade. The lounge where we serve tea, coffee and biscuits each evening at 9.00 pm is where everyone gathers to watch television and have a chat. There are 24 hour tea, coffee and laundry facilities along with off-street parking for the motorist. For the comfort and convenience of our guests we encourage non-smoking.

Opawa, Christchurch

Homestay
Address: 41 Opawa Road,
Christchurch 8002
Name: Carolyn and Stephen Mangan
Telephone: (03) 3653-718
Mobile: (025) 335-733
Beds: 1 Double waterbed, 2 Single (2 bedrooms)
Bathroom: 1 Guests share
Tariff: B&B (full) $30 per person, Children under 10 free, Dinner with wine $20,
Vouchers accepted

We are a young couple with two girls aged 1 and 6 and we are in the process of restoring our family home built in 1879. We have been hosting for 4 years now and love meeting people. A warm welcome, a comfortable bed and a good breakfast await our guests.

Rates quoted are for one night. Longer stays are discounted accordingly. We offer a generous three course meal with NZ wines.

We are 3-4 km from the city centre where some of Christchurch's best restaurants are. Full laundry and drying facilities available at a small charge. Tea and coffee making facility available in rooms.

We are both keen skiers and would only be too happy to arrange a day skiing at any of our surrounding ski fields or help with your holiday plans during your stay in Christchurch or perhaps you would like a day fishing. Ask, you never know what we could arrange for you.

Christchurch City

Homestay
Address: Cranmer Lodge 26 Cranmer Square,
Christchurch 1 **Name:** Margaret & Dennis Cottle
Telephone: (03) 379-7864 **Fax:** (03) 377-1976
Cranmer Lodge
Beds: 1 Double, 1 Twin, 1 Single (3 Bedrooms) **Bathroom:** 2 Family share
Tariff: B&B (continental) $70 Double or Twin, $50 Single
Budget accommodation is also available in the Chester House Annex:
Beds: 1 Double 1 Twin, 2 Single (4 Bedrooms) **Bathroom:** 1 Guests share
Tariff: B&B (continental self-service) $60 Double, $55 Twin, $35 Single

Cranmer Lodge is an attractive old home in charming inner city surroundings. It was built in 1889 overlooking Cranmer Square with its tranquil green open space and stately English trees. Cranmer Square is surrounded by the historic inner city residential and cultural area containing the old Provincial Government Buildings, the old Canterbury University buildings, the Museum and the McDougall Art Gallery. Victoria Square, Cathedral Square, shops, restaurants, theatres and banks are within five minutes easy walk, as are the city buses, the Town Hall, the Tourist Information Centre and the Botanic Gardens. Cranmer Lodge is ideal for visitors relying on public transport as city shuttle mini-buses for Airport and Railway Station will call at the door while city facilities and tourist attractions are within easy walking distance. Chester House is a modest city home of the 1920's with wood panelling, leadlight windows and a large lounge. There is a dining room and kitchen which are entirely self service, materials for a continental breakfast are provided, guests are free to help themselves whenever they like and make their own tea and coffee. Chester House and Cranmer Lodge are on the same site and all guests check in at Cranmer Lodge. They are both non-smoking.

Christchurch City

Homestay
Address: "KleynBos",
59 Ngaio Street, Christchurch
Name: Gerda de Kleyne & Hans van den Bos
Telephone: (03) 332 2896
Beds: 1 Double, 2 Single (2 bedrooms)
Bathroom: 1 Private, 1 Guests share
Tariff: B&B (continental) Double $60, Single $35, B&B with private lounge & bathroom $85, Vouchers accepted
Nearest Town: 4km from inner city centre

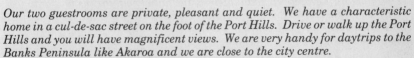

Our two guestrooms are private, pleasant and quiet. We have a characteristic home in a cul-de-sac street on the foot of the Port Hills. Drive or walk up the Port Hills and you will have magnificent views. We are very handy for daytrips to the Banks Peninsula like Akaroa and we are close to the city centre.

The garden is lovely and well established with a barbeque area. We preserve fruit, make jams and bake bread.

For your convenience we have composed a folder about Christchurch which can work as a real timesaver. It also gives you helpful suggestions where to have dinner.

We are around forty, have a son and daughter. Your hostess works as a registered nurse. We do not have family in New Zealand and having guests is to us a little like having family come to stay. We enjoy having guests and look forward to meeting you.

Directions: *By car - follow SH 73 or 74 till they meet on the intersection Brougham and Waltham Road, south of city centre. Head towards St Martins. After 1.5 km turn right into Gamblings Road, then first left.*

From Airport, take super shuttle.

From City Bus 12.

You are welcome to ring for further directions.

Christchurch City

Homestay

Address: 'Wairere', 55 Fendalton Road,
Christchurch 1

Name: Moira & David Penrose

Telephone & Fax: (03) 3555-661

Beds: 2 Double, 1 Twin (3 bedrooms)

Bathrooms: 1 Ensuite, 2 Guests share

Tariff: B&B (full) Double $90, Single $60, Dinner $25 with complimentary wine

Nearest Town: Christchurch City

We have been home hosting for more than eight years and enjoy sharing our home and city with overseas visitors.

Our new home is ideally situated adjacent to some of Christchurch's most beautiful parks.

You may even wish to walk downtown, across the golf course, and past the lake - 25 mins.

Guest comfort is assured by double glazing, central heating and firms beds.

We are in our fifties, retired, with interests including golf, sailing and antiques. We are non smokers, and have five children and five grandchildren.

Our extensive knowledge of the South Island's scenic attractions has often been of assistance to those visitors planning their stay here.

Our location related to all main inlets to the city, makes our home very easy to find. The following map may be of assistance.

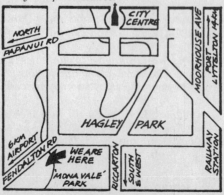

444

Christchurch City

Quality Homestay
Address: "Fendalton Homestay",
50 Clifford Avenue,
Fendalton, Christchurch 1.
Name: Pam Rattray
Telephone: (03) 355-4298
(Please let ring at least 10 times)
Beds: 2 King, 1 Queen, 2 Single (3 bedrooms) **Bathrooms:** 3 Ensuite
Tariff: B&B (special) Double $95-$120, Single $85-$110.
Credit cards. Vouchers accepted May through October
Nearest Town: Airport 10 minutes, City Centre 5 minutes

Enjoy warm relaxed hospitality staying with us right in the middle of one of Christchurch's most beautiful suburbs with large trees and lovely gardens.
Being central it's a pleasant walk into town through Hagley Park or across the road to the lovely public gardens of Mona Vale.
You can sit under the grape vine in the big conservatory that warms the whole house or wander down past the swimming pool to feed the wild ducks in the clear stream at the bottom of the garden.
Eat your large home cooked breakfast in the sunny dining room which has a small New Zealand art collection. Each room has large beds, an ensuite bathroom, colour TV and tea making facilities. The spa (jacuzzi) is usually hot but it's worth ringing 24 hrs in advance if you are really keen. Laundry facilities available. Major credit cards accepted.
We are a non-smoking household with a small friendly cat.

Christchurch City

Guest House
Address: Home-Lea Guest House
195 Bealey Ave, Christchurch
Name: Sylvia and Mervyn Smith
Telephone & Fax: (03) 379 9977
Beds: 2 Double, 7 Single (5 bedrooms)
Bathroom: 2 Guests share
Tariff: B&B (continental) Double $75, Single $45,
Children negotiable. Credit cards. Vouchers accepted.
Nearest Town: 10 minutes walk to city centre

Home-Lea is a charming and comfortable two storyed character home built in the early 1900's and we offer quality Bed & Breakfast to our guests in a quiet homely atmosphere. We have single, double, triple and quad rooms to cater for all types of travellers.
We are very easy to find and are within easy walking distance of the City Centre, Restaurants, Town Hall, Museum, Art Gallery, Botanical Gardens, Arts Centre, Markets etc.
Our bedrooms are all furnished with quality bedding and electric blankets to ensure a comfortable stay. The cosy lounge has an open fire to greet you during the colder winter months. The dining room overlooks and opens onto a pretty secluded garden where guests are welcome to relax.
Tea and coffee are available at all times along with home baked cookies.
Off-street parking for guests. We look forward to meeting you and will do our best to make your stay enjoyable. Inspection welcome.

Riverview Lodge

Christchurch City

Homestay/Bed & Breakfast
Address: "Riverview Lodge" 361 Cambridge Terrace, Christchurch
Name: Ernst Wipperfuerth
Telephone & Fax: (03) 3652860
Beds: 3 Double, 2 Single (3 bedrooms) **Bathroom:** 2 Ensuite, 1 Private
Tariff: B&B (special) Double $95-130, Single $75-90, Children neg. Credit cards.

Listed in FODOR'S 94 as "pick of the B&B accommodation in Christchurch".
If you like quality accommodation in a relaxed and quiet atmosphere, still just minutes walking away from the centre of an exciting city: this is the place to stay.
My house is a restored Edwardian residence that reflects the grace and style of the period with some fine carved Kauri and Rimu features.
It is ideally situated on the banks of the Avon River in a tranquil setting surrounded by an old English garden with mature trees.
Guest rooms are elegant, combining modern facilities with colonial furnishings. All rooms have ensuite/private facilities, colour TV and heating, balconies provide a superb river view.
Tea and coffee making facilities are available at all times. Breakfast is a house speciality with a wide choice of cooked and continental fare.
Kayaks, bicycles and golfclubs are available for guests to use.
As an experienced traveller and tour operator I'll be happy to provide you with all the information that will make your stay in Christchurch and New Zealand unforgettable. German, Spanish, Dutch, French is spoken
Directions: *RIVERVIEW LODGE is located on the corner of Cambridge Terrace and Churchill Street.*

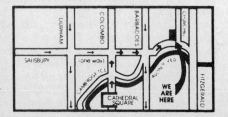

Christchurch City

Bed & Breakfast
Address: Eliza's Manor House,
82 Bealey Av., Christchurch
Name: Roz & John Smith
Telephone: (03) 366 8584 or 366 1073
Fax: (03) 366 4946
Beds: 9 Ensuite bedrooms: King, Queen, Twin,
2 Share facility bedrooms: Queen, Twin
Tariff: B&B (continental buffet) Queen, King, Twin ensuites from $85, Queen, Twin from $75. Cot & highchair available. Special rates in winter from $60. Credit Cards. Vouchers accepted between 1 May - 1 November.

Eliza's is a superb gracious Victorian mansion, built in 1860, and lovingly restored. The original architectural gems including a magnificent entrance foyer, coloured lead light windows and banquet room are complimented with comfortable furnishings, antiques and collectables. The bedrooms, all different, each with their own charm, are decorated in country cottage style with comfortable beds and most with their own en-suite.

The tariff includes continental buffet breakfast. We serve dinner four nights per week and there are many restaurants nearby. Eliza's is a very comfortable and exciting place to stay where you can relax and enjoy the convivial atmosphere.

We are a short pleasant drive from the airport and conveniently situated 10-15 mins level walk to Art centre, Botanical gardens, Art galleries, City centre, golf course, museums.

Eliza's is set well back from the street with magnificent trees, courtyard gardens and off street parking.

We offer complimentary tea, coffee, hot chocolate anytime, a cosy lounge to meet new friends and an olde-English style bar.

We look forward to sharing the delights of Eliza's with you.

Please fax, ring or write your bookings to us.

We extend a warm welcome to you. Roz and John Smith

Christchurch City
Homestay
Address: "Willow Lodge",
71 River Road, Avonside, Christchurch 1
Name: Grania McKenzie
Telephone: (03) 389 9395
Beds: 2 Double, 4 Single (3 bedrooms) **Bathroom:** 2 Guests share, 1 Private
Tariff: B&B (special) Double $85-$95, Single $55, Children negotiable, Credit
cards accepted, Vouchers accepted
Nearest Town: 15 min walk to city centre

*"Willow Lodge" is friendly and warm - a house where you will feel at home. A
rambling natural garden with mature trees surrounds the house above the Avon
River. It is a lovely 20 minute walk along the river into the city centre - or take a
number 19 bus.*
*The house has leadlights and natural wood including Rimu wardrobes in all
guest rooms. It has been decorated to retain a gracious 1930s style, and even
includes an old claw footed bath.*
*As well, there are modern showers, TV in each room, and an upstairs sunroom
with fridge, tea and coffee facilities.*
*There is contemporary NZ art in all rooms. and plenty of books. I have travelled
extensively and love theatre, music, fine arts, fine food - and especially living in
this city and intorducing people to it. Tennis court, rackets, golf clubs and bicycles
available for guests. Breakfast is fresh and generous - country style.*
Directions: *Shuttle services from Airport or phone for directions.*

Christchurch City

Homestay
Address: "Four and Twenty"
420 Manchester St,
Edgeware, Christchurch
Name: Molly & Peter Banks
Telephone & Fax: (03) 365 5704
Beds: 1 Double, 1 Twin, 1 Single (3 bedrooms)
Bathroom: 1 Guests share
Tariff: B&B (full) Double $70, Single $45, Children neg. Credit cards accepted.

"Four and Twenty" is a spacious 2 storey home that has been tastefully rebuilt and redecorated. It is 5 minutes drive (15 minutes walk) from the city centre, close to many interesting restaurants, cafes and shops, the Avon River, Victoria Square, Hagley Park and the Botanical Gardens, Canterbury Museum, and the Arts Centre Weekend Market.

We offer "special" homestyle breakfasts using local seasonal produce. Tea and coffee is always available, along with colour TV if required. We do not smoke, but we don't mind guests smoking in the rear courtyard.

For the past eight years, since our family left home, we have enjoyed the Bed & Breakfast/Homestay experience meeting many interesting people from New Zealand and abroad. We are keen travellers and look forward to sharing our home with you. "There are no strangers in this house, just friends we have yet to meet".

Directions: *Manchester Street runs parallel to and one block east of the city's most central street, Colombo Street. We are at its northern end between Purchas and Canon Streets.*

Ilam, Christchurch

Homestay
Address: 7 Westmont St,
Ilam, Christchurch
Name: Anne & Tony Fogarty
Telephone: (03) 358 2762
Beds: 4 Single (2 Bedrooms)
Bathroom: 1 Guests share, 1 Family share
Tariff: B&B (continental) Double $70, Single $40, Children $15, Dinner by arrangement, Vouchers accepted
Nearest Town: Christchurch

Our home is in the beautiful suburb of Ilam, ideally situated close to Christchurch Airport (7 minutes by car) and the central city area (10 minutes). Adjacent to the city bus route, we are very accessible to Christchurch's many attractions.

We have travelled extensively in Europe and Asia. During our travels we have used the Bed & Breakfast system and appreciated the need for a comfortable bed and a good breakfast.

We look forward to sharing our New Zealand hospitality as well as our local knowledge. We would be happy to collect visitors from the airport, for a small additional charge. We will serve dinner by arrangement (and extra charge).

As parents of four adult children, all of whom have attended nearby Canterbury University, we enjoy a broad understanding of people. We are interested in most sports - gardening, travel, politics, and happy to chat about almost anything!! We look forward to helping make your stay in Christchurch a special time.

449

Christchurch City
Luxury Homestay
Address: 6 Eversleigh Street, Christchurch 1
Name: David & Betty Purdue
Telephone: (03) 355 7174
Fax: (03) 377 2755
Beds: 2 Double, 1 Single (3 Bedrooms)
Bathroom: 1 Ensuite, 1 Guests share
Tariff: B&B (special) Double $90-100, Single $60. Credit cards accepted.
Nearest Town: Christchurch

Fifteen minutes walk from Cathedral Square you will find 'Hadleigh' a unique arts and craft style home built for a wealthy merchant in 1904; and classified by the NZ Historic Places Trust.

Surrounded by trees and a romantic garden, Hadleigh has been our family home for more than twenty years; and is sometimes open for concerts; art exhibitions; and garden and historic home tours.

We welcome you to enjoy the ambience of a gracious age with polished native timbers, leadlight windows, open fires, and antique furniture throughout.

Each luxurious bedroom has electric blankets and heaters; television, tea and coffee; ample towels and private bathroom facilities.

A formal lounge, billiard room, guest lounge, and guest kitchenette and laundry facilities are available.

Our generous breakfast may include freshly squeezed juice, fresh fruit, choice of cereals and yoghurts, home made preserves, breads and pastries; and a traditional cooked English breakfast.

Allergy sufferers please note we have family pets. No smoking indoors.

Advance bookings are strongly recommended.

Phone for directions.

Christchurch City

Bed & Breakfast
Address: "Turret House", 435 Durham Street North, Christchurch
Name: Glenda & Graham Weavers
Telephone: (03) 365 3900, Fax (03) 365 5601
Beds: 5 Double, 6 Single (6 bedrooms incl 2 suites)
Bathroom: 6 Ensuite
Tariff: B&B (continental) Double $85 - $100, Single $65 - $90, extra adult $15, children under 10 yrs $10.
Credit cards accepted.

Turret House is a gracious superior bed and breakfast accommodation located in downtown Christchurch. It is within easy walking distance of Cathedral Square, the Botanical Gardens, museum, art gallery, the arts centre and Hagley Park 18 hole golf course and casino.
Built in 1885 this historic residence is one of only three in the area protected by the New Zealand Historic Places Trust.
It has been extensively restored to capture the original character and charm. Situated within the grounds is one of Christchurch's best examples of our native kauri tree.
Elaborately decorated bedrooms with heaters and electric blankets combine comfort and old world elegance with private bathrooms including bath and shower, all offering a totally relaxed and comfortable environment.
Tea, coffee and biscuits available 24 hrs. Cots and highchairs are also available. There is a licensed restaurant next door.
If you're looking for a place to stay where the accommodation is superior and the atmosphere friendly _ experience Turret House.
Directions: *just 15 minutes from Christchurch Airport. Situated on the corner of Bealey Ave and Durham Street.*

New Zealand is known as the friendliest country in the world
and our hosts will live up to that reputation.

Christchurch City
Guest House
Address: 56 Armagh Street
Christchurch
Name: The Grange
Telephone: (03) 366 2850
Beds: 2 King/Twin, 2 Queen, 2 Double, 1 Single (7 Bedrooms)
Bathroom: 5 Ensuite, 1 Guests share
Tariff: B&B (full) Double $99, Single $79, Dinner $25. Credit cards accepted.
Vouchers accepted March - October
Nearest Town: Christchurch

At The Grange Guesthouse you will enjoy your visit in this tastefully renovated Victorian mansion with wood panelling and a magnificent wooden feature staircase, you can relax in the gracious guest lounge or in the tranquil garden.
The Grange Guesthouse is situated within walking distance to most of Christchurch's favourite spots including; Cathedral Square, the Arts Centre, Art Gallery and Museum also the Botanic Gardens, Hagley Park and Mona Vale.
During your stay at The Grange you will be treated to superior accommodation, complimentary tea and coffee, off-street parking, laundry service and sightseeing tours and onward travel can be arranged.
If you wish to stay indoors there is Sky TV including CNN News and the movie channel. Non-smoking is encouraged.
Banks shops restaurants, night clubs and the Art Centre are all easy walking distance.
Paul and Marie Simpson are a mother and son team whose hospitality will ensure your stay is a pleasurable and pleasant one.

Merivale, Christchurch
Bed and Breakfast Inn
Address: "Villa Victoria", The Lane,
27 Holly Road, Christchurch 1
Name: Kate McNeill
Telephone: (03) 355 7977
Beds: 2 Double (2 bedrooms)
Bathrooms: 2 ensuite
Tariff: B&B (special) Double $120-$135,
Single $65-$70
Nearest Town: Christchurch.
5 minutes from City. 20 minutes walking.

A warm welcome awaits you at "Villa Victoria".
Authentically restored by Kate - the 90 year old villa reflects all the elegance and charm of a world gone by. This tranquil haven has been designed to be a home away from home. Each bedroom is completely private with its own ensuite.
Delectable home style breakfast is served in the elegant dining room or during summer mornings on the verandah overlooking the picturesque, private garden.
Complimentary New Zealand wine and cheese served early evening.
Not suitable for children.
You are welcome to smoke but please do so outdoors.
Directions: *Please phone.*

Merivale, Christchurch
Homestay
Address: 4/40 Ranfurly Street
Name: Joan Shakes
Telephone: (03) 355 2726
Beds: 2 Single (1 Bedroom) **Bathroom:** 1 Ensuite
Tariff: B&B (full) Double $55, Single $35, Dinner $15
Nearest Town: Christchurch

Welcome to my well appointed townhouse - a perfect base for your Christchurch stay - five minutes from the city centre and easy walking distance from some of the finest restaurants and exclusive shopping.
Comfortable accommodation is provided in a twin upstairs bedroom with ensuite, downstairs you can relax in the lounge looking out on to a restful and attractive courtyard.
My interests are music, theatre and travel, but most of all meeting people.
There is off-street parking. Please phone for directions.
Dinner by arrangement.

Southshore, Christchurch
Homestay
Address: Rockinghorse Road, Southshore
Name: Jan & Graham
Telephone: (03) 388 4067
Beds: 1 Double, 2 Single (2 Bedrooms) **Bathroom:** 1 Ensuite, 1 Family share
Tariff: B&B (full) Double $70, Single $45, Dinner $20, Packed lunch $6pp.
Vouchers accepted.
Nearest Town: Christchurch centre 15 mins drive

Share with us one of the best kept secrets of Christchurch - the seaside environment of South Shore.
Known locally as "The Spit" this unique area lies between the ocean and the estuary of the Avon and Heathcote rivers. From the walkways around the estuary you can observe the birdlife and enjoy the open water views where windsurfing and yachting are popular pastimes.
On the ocean side the miles of sandy beach are great for strolling, jogging and swimming. South Shore is handy to Ferrymead Historic Park, Mt Cavandish Gondola, the Summit Road Scenic Drive to Port Lyttleton. Our home is situated down a private driveway with direct access to the beach.
For guests we have a large double bedroom with ensuite and your own access to the garden and beach. Upstairs a cosy twin room with guests toilet and hand-basin. Share host's bathroom. Both rooms overlook the dunes wilderness, are warm and welcoming with every comfort.
Breakfasts range from continental to "hearty".
We are in our fifties, Jan recently retired from her retail picture framing and embroidery business. We also share interests in art, antiques, gardening, music and cooking. Graham is a member of the Vintage Car Club and Jan of the Embroiderers Guild. We are non-smokers - including Sophie the cat.
Directions: *Please phone for reservations and directions. City and Airport pick up service.*

Southshore, Christchurch

Homestay
Address: 33 Rockinghorse Road, Southshore, Christchurch 7
Name: Andrew and Geraldine Doudney
Telephone: (03) 388 8001 - Please phone ahead
Beds: 2 King, 2 Single (2 bedrooms) **Bathroom:** 2 Ensuite
Tariff: B&B (special) Double $65, Single $50, Dinner $20, Campervans welcome, Credit cards accepted, Vouchers accepted

A warm welcome awaits you at our modern beach home nestled in a wilderness sand dune area. We retain privacy with beautiful native trees and ferns.

Walk on the beach at sunrise - relax in the peace and tranquillity of our comfortable garden setting - see the sun set behind the Southern Alps, across the estuary.

A major shopping complex just 5 minutes away.

You will enjoy our speciality breakfasts which includes our own fresh baked bread, fruit of the season, cereals and mueslis. A selection of teas and fresh coffee.

Other meals use our home grown vegetables. Free range eggs used. Speciality vegetarian meals available - advise your preference.

The bedrooms are designed for comfort and luxury. Our guests sleep in King-size beds on New Zealand wool under quilts with wool duvets.

We have grown up in Christchurch and would enjoy assisting you have a memorable, friendly, relaxing, informative, time and look forward to enjoying your company.

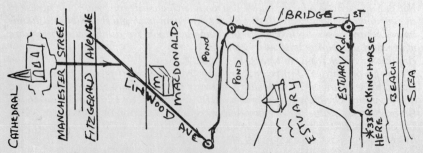

Riccarton, Christchurch

Homestay
Address: 314 Yaldhurst Road, Christchurch
Name: Gladsome Lodge
Telephone: (03) 3427 414 (24 hrs)
Beds: 3 Double, 5 Single (5 bedrooms)
Bathroom: 1 Ensuite, 2 Guests share
Tariff: B&B (continental) Double $75, Single $55, Dinner (2 course) $15, Children negotiable, Vouchers accepted
Nearest Town: Christchurch 8km East, 1km from Highway 1 Junction for South, West and Northbound Traffic.

Ideally located near Christchurch International Airport, en route to all the Canterbury ski fields; close to key tourist attractions - Wigram Air Museum, Arts Centre, Antarctic Centre and Riccarton Racecourse.

A 100ft Landmark Gum Tree makes finding our homestay easy. Once seen, never forgotten.

Hosts Sue and Stuart enjoy entertaining guests in their spacious non-smoking family home. Sue can provide much local information plus transfer service the 2kms to Christchurch International Airport. Stuart is currently on Lions 202E Cabinet, but can usually be persuaded into a game of tennis or squash.

A tennis court, swimming pool, large sauna, along with tea and coffee facilities provide recreation and relaxation for weary travellers. An open fireplace and central heating provide plenty of warmth along with electric blankets on all beds. On site parking is provided and we accept the four major credit cards. We are licensed to accommodate only ten guests, so personal attention is guaranteed. We welcome you to Gladsome Lodge.

Directions: *Turn left off Highway 1, at Russley Road Junction, you will sight the Gum Tree 1km on left.*

Spreydon, Christchurch

Self-contained Accommodation
Address: 105 Lyttelton Street, Christchurch
Name: Bev & Kerry Bloomfield
Telephone: (03) 332-5360 Please phone
Beds: 1 Double, 2 Single (2 bedrooms) **Bathroom:** 1 Private
Tariff: B&B (continental) $60 Double, $10 each extra person. Campervans welcome.

If you wish peace and quiet in the city, we have a modern two bedroom self-contained flat which is situated on a back section.

It is separated from our house by a carport into which you can put your car. It has a private phone, TV, fridge / freezer, stove, washing machine and your own front lawn. We also have a cot and highchair available if needed, and all the beds have electric blankets.

We provide a comprehensive continental style breakfast. This is prepared and placed in your apartment so you can breakfast at leisure. If your prefer you may do your own catering (discount tariff).

We are a 5 minute drive from the centre of the city.

Cashmere, Christchurch
Homestay
Address: 'Burford Manor' , 3 Lucknow Place, Cashmere 2, Christchurch
Name: Kathleen & David Burford
Telephone: (03) 337 1905
Beds: 1 Double, 1 Queen, 1 Single (3 bedrooms)
Bathrooms: 2 private, 1 Ensuite
Tariff: B&B (full) Double $90, Single $55, Dinner $20, Children half price, 10% discount for 2 or more nights, Credit cards accepted, Vouchers accepted from April to October

Our six year old home is the ultimate in luxury, built in Halswell Quarry Stone, it incorporates the charm of yesteryear plus all the conveniences of a modern home, spacious and warm with private and ensuite bathroms.

The prize-winning cottage garden is a wonderful background to the magnificent views of Rural Canterbury and the Southern Alps.

We are five minutes drive from the city centre and conveniently located to excellent public transport.

A very quiet peaceful area with abundant native bird life and walking trails.

Your hosts David and Kathleen have three adult children (Nathan lives at home) and are an informal couple who love meeting people.

We have travelled extensively in New Zealand and overseas and are happy to offer assistance with travel plans.

Third generation Cantabrians our local knowledge and contacts are an asset to guests particular interests.

Our hobbies include Rotary, travel, tramping, jogging, skiing, gardening, stamp collecting, embroidery and patchwork (you are welcome to view the many exhibition quilts).

Breakfast - the choice and time is flexible - try our home-made bread.

Guests are welcome to share in all the facilities of our home.

Complimentary transport within the city.

Directions: *Please telephone anytime.*

Cashmere Hills, Christchurch

Bed and Breakfast
Address: "Cashmere House",
141 Hackthorne Road, Cashmere,
Christchurch 2
Name: Birgit & Monty Claxton
Telephone & Fax: 03) 332 7864, Overseas: 64 3 332 7864
Beds: 2 King, 2 Double, 1 Twin (5 bedrooms incl. 1 suite)
Bathrooms: 3 ensuite, 2 private
Tariff: B&B (special) Double $140-$190, Single $105
Nearest Town: Christchurch City

"Cashmere House" - Come and share our lovingly restored eight and a half thousand square feet historic mansion situated on Cashmere Hills.

It is set in an acre of grounds with established trees and an abundance of old-fashioned roses. It is comfortably furnished with antiques and collectables.

All five generously sized bedrooms have a beautiful view over city, sea and Southern Alps.

In the evening, enjoy a game of billiards, relax and read in the conservatory and well-stocked library, watch television in the living room, or you might prefer to sit and chat in front of the fire.

There are several good restaurants close by. A leisurely breakfast may be selected from the wide choice available, while tea and coffee are on tap all day.

We garage several classic cars and have a friendly Airedale Terrier.

Directions: *Bus at gate. Airport and City pick up arranged. No smoking.*
Swedish, German and limited French and Italian spoken.
Open Sept - June.

One of the differences between staying at a hotel and a B&B
is that you don't hug the hotel staff when you leave.

Cashmere, Christchurch
Homestay
Address: 12A Hackthorne Road,
Cashmere, Christchurch 2
Name: Janet Milne
Telephone: (03) 337 1423
Beds: 1 Kingsize, 6 Single (3 bedrooms)
Bathroom: 1 Ensuite, 1 Family share
Tariff: B&B (continental) Double $70, Single $35,
Dinner $25, Children under 12 years half price, Vouchers accepted
Nearest Town: Christchurch - approx. 10 minutes

I have an attractive two storey home which I designed and then supervised the construction. It is situated in a quiet back section of the Cashmere Hills and the view extends across the city to the mountains. The lower storey is one large room which has one Kingsize bed, two bunks, a television set, a heater, table and chairs, wardrobe, telephone and an ensuite ie. shower, small handbasin and lavatory. The swimming pool is in close proximity to this area.
Guests can choose whether to be accommodated in the lower storey and be independent or be in the upper storey and share facilities. I am a Registered General and Obstetric Nurse working part-time. I teach English as a foreign language - privately.
I study Spanish language and this year I began university study for a B.A. Degree majoring linguistics. I have two adult daughters. One is married and the other is travelling overseas. I have travelled extensively in foreign countries and I enjoy conversing with other 'travellers'! I would appreciate guests not smoking in my home.

Summit Road Christchurch
Homestay
Address: Marleys Hill, P.O. Box 12286, Christchurch
Name: Sue Haley
Telephone: (03) 366 2209
Beds: 2 Single (1 Bedroom)   **Bathroom:** 1 Ensuite
Tariff: B&B (full) Double $70, Single $40, Dinner $20, Vouchers accepted
Nearest Town: Christchurch

Originally built as a retreat house for the Little Company of Mary in 1927/28, this home has a unique atmosphere.
Nestled on 25 acres of land on the summit of the Cashmere Hills, 'Marley' offers the opportunity for quiet and relaxation in a warm, welcoming environment.
Hillside walks and trails lead to the incomparable views of Christchurch, the Canterbury plains, Lyttleton and the harbour bays.
If a visit to Christchurch is wanted you can be there in 15 minutes by car (11kms). Tourist information available and we will enjoy helping you to plan sightseeing trips in Christchurch and Canterbury.
Directions to Marley provided on booking. City and Airport pickup available.

Redcliffs, Christchurch

Homestay
Address: 125 Main Rd.,
Redcliffs, Christchurch 8
Name: Cynthia and Lyndsey Ebert
Telephone: (03) 3849 792
Beds: 4 Single (2 bedrooms)
Bathroom: 1 Private, 1 Family share
Tariff: B&B (continental) $45 pp,
Vouchers accepted

Relax and enjoy our comfortable home by the sea.
Situated approximately 20 minutes by bus from the city centre, our home is on the foreshore of the Christchurch Estuary, with magnificent views of the sea, birds and boating. What more could you wish for?
Nearby is the Sumner beach, Mount Cavendish Gondola and lovely walkways with hills, beaches and cliffs to explore.
We are non-smoking and our guest facilities include a sunny, twin bedroom with its own private bathroom and toilet, plus a twin bedroom with family share toilet and bathroom. Guests are welcome to enjoy the tranquil garden and seaside surroundings.
Cynthia and Lyndsey offer dinner by arrangement or local restaurants offer a wide choice of cuisine. A generous continental breakfast is included in the tariff and laundry facilities are available.
Please phone (03) 384-9792 before calling.

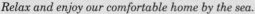

Lyttelton

Homestay
Address: Randolph House,
49 Sumner Road, Lyttelton
Name: Judy & Jonathan Elworthy
Telephone & Fax: (03) 328 8877
Beds: 1 Double, 3 Single (3 bedrooms)
Bathroom: 1 Guests share
Tariff: B&B (special) Double $80, Single $45,
Children half price, Dinner $25pp
by arrangement, Credit cards accepted.

Lyttelton is an attractive and historic harbour town, twenty minutes from the centre of Christchurch.
Judy, an interior decorator and Jonathan an ex-cabinet minister, welcome you to their 19th century villa that is warm and sunny and has been superbly restored. It looks down on the harbour and commands amazing views of the sea and the surrounding hills.
Judy & Jonathan enjoy cooking. Fresh vegetables, fruit, New Zealand wines and cheeses are specialities. No pavlova! Dinner includes plenty of chat about your country and theirs. Breakfast is as major or minor as you wish.
If you like to walk in the hills or sail the sea, they will go with you or arrange things for you. Come and use Randolph House as a base from which to enjoy the many recreational and cultural activities that abound in Christchurch and Banks Peninsular.

459

Sumner, Christchurch
Homestay
Address: 65 Ocean View Terrace
Sumner Christchurch
Name: Ocean View Lodge
Telephone: (03) 326 7527
Fax: (03) 326 5611
Beds: 2 Double, 1 Single (3 Bedrooms)
Bathroom: 1 Guests share
Tariff: B&B (full) Double $75, Single $60, Dinner by arrangement $30 including local wines. Credit cards accepted. Vouchers accepted
Nearest Town: Christchurch

Your hosts, Tony and Marj have been involved with tourism for many years. Tony is a very involved Trout Fishing Guide, and Marj has enjoyed many years of hosting visitors. We both are well travelled, with Tony also being a keen sailor, with many miles of Ocean Racing to his credit. Our near new home is very private and restful with pleasant surroundings and views, not far to the beach. We are non smokers, have a friendly cat and 3 sons, usually one at home. Sumner Village is approx 10 minutes walk, and has a variety of restaurants and wine bars.
We are happy to pick you up from the airport. City bus is very regular.
We are very easy to find. Come though Sumner, head towards Lyttleton, and we are 2nd to last home on the left as you leave Sumner. Phone for directions.

Sumner, Christchurch
Homestay
Address: Panorama Road,
Clifton Hill
Name: Jo & Derek
Telephone: (03) 326 5755
Beds: 1 Double (1 Bedroom)
Bathroom: 1 Private
Tariff: B&B (continental) Double $75, Single $40, Dinner $20,
Nearest Town: Christchurch

There are two of us to welcome you - one working and one semi-retired. We are keen on sport, the outdoors, gardening and music and have both lived and worked overseas.
The house is quiet, warm, and has a relaxed atmosphere. Our three decks and terraced garden make the most of all day sun and breathtaking views. The guest bedroom and lounge have views over the ocean, the estuary, the city and the plains to the Southern Alps. The comfortable guest lounge has TV and stereo. The property is not suitable for young children. You are welcome to smoke but please do so outdoors.
We are about 20 minutes drive east of the city centre, 10 minutes from the Gondola and Ferrymead Historic Park, and 3 minutes from Sumner Village and beach. You can take a quiet scenic country walk on the Port Hills within minutes of the house.

Cass Bay, Lyttelton

Homestay, Self-contained Accommodation
Address: 3 Harbour View Tce., Cass Bay
Banks Peninsula District
Name: Hank and Susi Boots
Telephone: (03) 328 7250 or 384 1819 bus.
Beds: 1 Double, 2 Single (2 bedrooms) **Bathroom:** 1 Guests share
Tariff: B&B (special) Double $85, Twin $95, Single $60, Dinner $25
Nearest Town: Christchurch 10km, Lyttelton 3km

Cass Bay: A semi rural little settlement nestled in the foothills between Lyttelton and Governors Bay. 15km from Christchurch city centre. Lyttelton provides hourly bus connections to Christchurch. The beautiful area around the harbour has walking tracks, nature reserves, several swimming beaches, a golf course, horse track facilities and the harbour provides for sailing, wind-surfing and steamboat trips.

The guest part of the house has a double bedroom with king-size waveless waterbed and another bedroom with two single extra long beds and cot, a modern bathroom with massage shower, fully equipped kitchen, automatic washing machine, separate living to retreat and a dining area. Further features: sundeck and large balcony with breath-taking hill and harbour views, free usage of solar heated swimming pool. Usage of sauna is available at extra cost. The hosts are retired restaurateurs, providing barbecue or in-house dinners at request and sight seeing tours over the peninsula or further afield. Wir sprechen Deutsch und Schweizerdeutsch. Nous parlons Français. Wij spreken Nederlands.

Substantial breakfast is included in our prices and we will be pleased to attend to special wishes of our guests.

Halswell, Christchurch

Farmstay (Orchard)
Address: "Pear Drop Inn",
Christchurch-Akaroa Road,
Christchurch R.D. 2
Name: "Pear Drop Inn"
Telephone: (03) 329 6778 **Fax:** (03) 325 2505
Beds: 2 Double, 4 Single, Cot available (3 bedrooms,
Honeymoon suite) **Bathroom:** 1 Private, 1 Family share
Tariff: B&B (full) Double $60, Single $30, Dinner $25,
Children under 12 half price, Campervans welcome,
Vouchers accepted
Nearest Town: Christchurch 10 mins drive on Highway 75

A rural farmstay close to Christchurch city, with vistas of the Southern Alps, and a pleasant garden. A speciality is delicious home cooking with home grown vegetables and fruits. Join in creative hobbies - spinning and art. Unique sightseeing and many outdoor attractions. Golf and horse riding locally. Akaroa and Christchurch by shuttle bus from the gate. Guests are made welcome in the relaxing well appointed rooms. Feel at home with books, TV, BBQ, conversation - or in the kitchen! A holiday special! By arrangement, drawing and painting holidays. Seven days full board plus five days tuition by Brenda, a qualified art teacher. $500. An invitation is cordially extended to join the Christmas festivities with the family. A minimum of three days - Booking essential.

Having travelled widely there's an appreciation of guests needs, and a desire to please the tourist. This is a home away from home for national, international, group or individual visitors. Si c'est bon (French spoken) Visitors met at terminals.

461

Halswell, Christchurch
Farmstay
Address: 681 Cashmere Road, Halswell, Christchurch 3
Name: Angela and Dan
Telephone: (03) 322 8160
Beds: 1 Double, 2 Single (2 bedrooms) **Bathrooms:** 1 guests share
Tariff: B&B (continental) Double $70, Single $40, Dinner $20

9km from Christchurch, our 70 year old homestead is situated on a 270 hectare sheep, cattle and deer farm on the Port Hills. The house is set amongst mature trees and a large woodland garden full of rhododendrons and camellias. We are a young couple with mainly outdoor interests, including mountainbiking and skiing. We also have housepets. Our character home is spacious, and has a friendly, relaxed atmosphere (non-smoking). Guests have a separate bathroom. Breakfast is in the dining room. Dinner is available by request with NZ wine, or choose from one of Christchurch's many restaurants and cafes. A short walk up the hill gives a magnificent view of the city, Canterbury Plains and Southern Alps. With Christchurch city centre only 14 minutes drive (airport 20 minutes) we offer the best of both worlds - farmstay and city convenience. We look forward to meeting you.
Directions: *Please phone.*

Tai Tapu, Christchurch
Farmstay+Self-contained
           Accommodation
Address: Ballymoney
Wards Road RD2 Christchurch
Name: Merrilies & Peter Rebbeck
Telephone: (03) 329 6706
Beds: 1 Double, 1 Single (1 Bedroom) **Bathroom:** 1 Private
Tariff: B&B (special) Double $40pp, Single $50, Children $20, Dinner $25, Campervans $25, Vouchers accepted
Nearest Town: Christchurch 20km, Lincoln and Tai Tapu 5km

We have a small farm mainly rearing calves. We also have horses cattle coloured sheep goats kuni kuni pigs and hens. A large pond hosts carp many varieties of domestic and wild duck and guinea fowl. There are also two golden retrievers, a fox terrier and a couple of cats.
Our farm is situated on a quiet road and the house is surrounded by a large garden. We have tennis croquet horse riding bikes and a small swimming pool available, no charge. Golf available five minutes away.
Guest accommodation is separated from the house by a brick courtyard. The bedroom has a double and single bed. Wash hand basin tea and coffee making facilities television heaters etc. A separate guest bathroom with laundry facilities. Separate guest lavatory.
Gourmet meals, include lots of home grown meat, vegetables, fruit free range eggs and hot homemade bread.
Directions: *Off the Christchurch Akaroa highway at Tai Tapu. Please phone.*

Yaldhurst, Christchurch
Country Stay
Address: 164 Old West Coast Road, R.D. 6, Christchurch
Name: Dick & Nuie Thomas
Telephone: (03) 3425418
Beds: 2 Double 1 Single (2 bedrooms) **Bathrooms:** 1 Private, 1 Family share
Tariff: B&B (full) Double $30pp, Single $20, Dinner $25pp. Vouchers accepted.
Nearest Town: Christchurch 15 minutes, Airport 5 minutes.

We have 6 acres in a beautiful rural setting with the convenience of Christchurch and the airport so close.
There are many local attractions and activities available nearby - ski fields, vineyards, golf courses, wild life parks, river fishing and jet boating along with the attractions of Christchurch city.
There is an all weather tennis court for guests to enjoy.
Our teenage children have all left home but still come and go and we welcome you to enjoy our family life with us.

Lincoln, Christchurch
Country homestay
Address: "Menteith", Springs Road, R.D. 6, Christchurch
Name: Fay & Stephen Graham
Telephone: (03) 3252395
Beds: 1 King, 2 Single (2 bedrooms) **Bathroom:** 1 Ensuite, 1 Private
Tariff: B&B (full) Double with ensuite $75, Double $70, Single $50, Dinner $25 with complimentary wine, Vouchers accepted
Nearest Town: Christchurch City 20 mins, Airport 15 mins

"Menteith" a 10 acre farmlet supporting sheep and beekeeping, is nestled among mature trees with spectacular mountain views and country tranquillity. Our modern home offers an indoor pool table, outdoor spa and swimming pool while guests bedrooms contain tea/coffee making facilities, electric blankets, heating, clock radios and cosy firm beds. Guests can enjoy the relaxed, rural outlook with easy city and Railway Station access.
We share our non-smoking home with our well travelled adult son and 2 cats, offering warm hospitality and home grown produce. Delightful local restaurants with reasonable prices are within 5 minutes drive or dinner is available here by arrangement. Lincoln 3km away, contains a golf course and University.
We have travelled extensively in NZ and overseas, happily offering help with your travel plans. Interests during our retirement are Rotary, skiing, golf, tramping and genealogy. Fay is a keen spinner - you're welcome to try your hand at spinning. City and airport pickups can be arranged.
Directions: *9 kms along Springs road from SH 1 at Wigram.*

Springston, Christchurch
Country Homestay
Address: "Chigwell", Goulds Road,
Springston, Christchurch R.D. 4
Name: John & Jeannie Campbell
Telephone: (03) 3295-748
Beds: 2 Double, 6 Single (4 bedrooms, all upstairs)
Bathroom: 1 Private, 1 Guests share
Tariff: B&B (full) Double $80, Single $45,
Children half price, Dinner $20, Vouchers accepted
Nearest Town: Lincoln (10 kms) Christchurch (30 kms)

"Chigwell", offering you modern accommodation on a 48 acre farmlet, with spectacular views to the west of the Southern Alps and to the east Banks Peninsular, is a suitable location for those folk preferring a rural atmosphere but with easy (30 minute) access to the City of Christchurch; a 10 minute distance connection with the Trans Alpine rail experience and 8 km East off SH1 at Burnham. From Chigwell, you can enjoy an 1 1/2 hour scenic drive to the early French settlement of Akaroa.

Your hosts John and Jeannie have had several overseas trips and are keen to meet people travelling in New Zealand. They are middle aged with a grown up family and have been farming nearby on a mixed cropping farm. They have a flock of coloured sheep, also graze cattle and make hay. City and Airport pickup, plus day trips with your hosts can be arranged.

Barrys Bay, Akaroa
Farmstay, Chalet with ensuite
Address: Bayview, Main Akaroa
Highway 75, Barrys Bay
Post: Bayview, Private Bag, Little River
Name: Jacqui & Martin
Telephone: (03) 304 5875 **Mobile:** 025 351 549
Beds: 2 Double, 3 Single (3 bedrooms) **Bathroom:** 1 Ensuite, 1 Guests share
Tariff: B&B (full farmstyle) Double $90, Single $45, Dinner $20, Children negotiable. Campervans facilities available, Vouchers accepted May to October
Nearest Town: Akaroa - 20 minute drive

Bayview, situated in the beautiful volcanic hills of Banks Peninsula, is a scenic hours drive from Christchurch and its international airport. Join us on our 500 acre sheep and cattle farm of steep hill-country rising to 2700 feet. The natural beauty offers contrasting landscapes of native bush, woodlands and high open hill country - great for walking. Trek by 4 Wheel drive motorbike around the farm to see breathtaking views of the entire harbour and lush valleys below. Be involved in the daily activities of milking the cow, joining with mustering the sheep, see sheep dogs work and sheep shorn. As a special bonus, sail or fish on our 30 foot yacht - circumstances permitting. Our home is warm and welcoming and has breath-taking views from wide verandas. Guests have their own bathrooms. We serve our own lamb and vegetables, local cheeses and NZ wines, with pre-dinner drinks of your choice. Banks Peninsula has much to offer you. We recommend a stay of several days and promise you a warm welcome.
Directions: *Take the Akaroa Highway 75 to the Hilltop Hotel. Bayview is situated 2kms below the hotel on the Akaroa side. Buses stop at our gate.*

Barrys Bay, Akaroa

Homestay/Farmstay
Address: Oihitu Estate, Barrys Bay, Akaroa
Name: Lynette & Ross Curry
Telephone & Fax: (03) 304-5804
Beds: 2 Queen (2 bedrooms) **Bathroom:** 2 Ensuite
Tariff: B&B (Special) Double $100, Single $70, Dinner $22.50, Children negotiable.
Credit cards: Visa & M/C. Vouchers accepted from 1 May to 31 October
Nearest Town: Akaroa 12 km, Christchurch 70km

We are fortunate to live in one of the larger historic homes in the county, built in the 1860's, set amid the rolling hills of Banks Peninsula with views of the Akaroa Harbour and our three year old daughter, Kirsten who is fourth generation on this farm.

We have a 315 acre dairy farm which also runs deer, pig and the many pets including horses for experienced riders.

We have converted two of the larger rooms to accommodate you in luxury, each with ensuite bathroom, a firm queensized bed and furnished in antiques of the period.

You will receive traditional farm fare from the wood stove. Bacon, egg and toast cooked on the embers, also fruit from our own orchard for breakfast. For dinner a farm style roast with home grown vegetables, preceded by drinks and nibbles. Tea, coffee and home baking are always available.

We have both travelled. We enjoy meeting and socialising with people whether it be relaxing in front of the open fire, on the large verandah or strolling through the informal garden.

Directions: *Our front entrance is conveniently situated on the Akaroa Highway with our sign "Oihitu Estate" behind a white picket fence on the harbours edge.*

Continental breakfast consist of fruit, toast, tea/coffee,
Full breakfast is the same with a cooked course,
Special breakfast has something special.

Akaroa

Homestay
Address: O-Tanga Matua,
R.D.1 Akaroa
Name: Gwen and Murray Manhire
Telephone: (03) 304 7127
Beds: 2 Single (1 bedroom)
Bathroom: 1 Private
Tariff: B&B (full) Double $70, Single $40.

Our modern colonial home stands in the sunshine in an acre of bush and well-established garden, just about two minutes walk from the beach on the shore of the incomparable Akaroa harbour. The view is magnificent. The sea and shoreline are everchanging in colour, always lovely. Birdlife and birdsong are ever-present — wood pigeons, fantails and bellbirds as well as many seabirds nearby will offer their special welcome.
Truly rural, we enjoy sharing the country life. We love our garden, our friendly old dog, and our contented brown chooks.
You will be warm and comfortable and welcome in our home.
Our guest accommodation consists of a twin bedded room and adjacent private bathroom. You are assured of a good breakfast and tea and coffee when you choose. Akaroa township is less than five minutes away where excellent craftshops, exhilarating walkways, superb restaurants, our well-know Herb Farm, and boat and fishing trips offer a wonderful holiday.

Akaroa

Homestay
Address: "Glencarrig",
7 Percy Street, Akaroa,
Banks Peninsula
Name: Mike and Kaye Stokes
Telephone: (03) 304 7008
Beds: 3 Double, 1 Single (3 bedrooms) **Bathroom:** 1 Ensuite, 1 Guests share
Tariff B&B (special) Double $95 - 120, Single $50, Children by arrangement.
Nearest Town: 82 km from Christchurch

We welcome you to share our listed Historic home built in 1851 by Rev. and Mrs Aylmer as the first Anglican vicarage. For a short while it was also used as the church. We are the 6th owners in 143 years. Relax in tranquil surroundings of one and a half acres with pretty stream and garden, water wheel, many native trees and birds. Sleep in spacious rooms featuring hand made quilts, books, antiques and french doors opening onto wide verandahs.
Showers and bath available in ensuite and bathroom. Wheelchair access to house and bathrooms. Three sittingrooms for guests to use. Rooms are centrally heated by modern hot water radiators run from the wood burning Rayburn stove in the kitchen. Breakfast is served in the sunny blue and white kitchen with french doors opening onto country and with herb garden and swimming pool.
Easy three minute walk to shops, galleries and restaurants in the village.

Akaroa

Homestay B&B
Address: "Lavaud House" 83 Rue Lavaud, Akaroa
Name: Francis and Frances Gallagher
Telephone and fax: (03) 304-7121
Beds: 3 Double, 2 Twin (4 bedrooms)
Bathroom: 2 Ensuite, 1 Guests share
Tariff: B&B (continental) Double $70, Single $40, Children negotiable. Vouchers accepted from 1 May to October 31
Nearest Town: Christchurch 80 kms

Our historic French designed 2 storied home overlooks the main beach and harbour and is within 2 mins walk of restaurants and shops.

The spacious bedrooms with ensuite bathrooms have Queen size beds, electric blankets and television. The large twin room has wool mattresses, electric blankets and down duvets.

All rooms have fresh flowers, heaters and a view of the harbour.

The guest sitting room has plenty of books, television, and a piano, plus a superb outlook.

You will enjoy our lovely antique furniture. A full continental breakfast is served in the dining room around our old dining table.

Fresh fruit - tea and coffee are available with home made biscuits.

Spend time in our large and colourful garden, enjoy the birds and harbour views.

Retired farmers, well travelled, we enjoy meeting people.

We are sure you will love this area as much as we do. Plan to stay awhile.

Directions: *We are centrally situated in the main street, opposite the war memorial.*

Paua Bay, Akaroa

Farmstay
Address: Paua Bay
Post: C/o 113 Beach Road, Akaroa
Name: Murray & Sue Johns
Telephone: (03) 304-8511
Beds: 1 Double (1 bedroom)
Bathroom: 1 private
Tariff: B&B (full) Double $60,
Single $30, Dinner $15,
Vouchers accepted during winter
Nearest Town: Akaroa

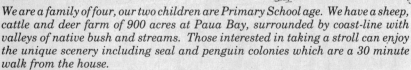

We are a family of four, our two children are Primary School age. We have a sheep, cattle and deer farm of 900 acres at Paua Bay, surrounded by coast-line with valleys of native bush and streams. Those interested in taking a stroll can enjoy the unique scenery including seal and penguin colonies which are a 30 minute walk from the house.

You would be most welcome to participate in any farm activity that occurs during your stay. Qualified riding instruction available.

Our cosy colonial home is nestled against native bush surrounded by a large cottage garden including a swimming pool and spectacular views over the Pacific. The farm is a twenty minute drive from picturesque Akaroa which is a French-style harbour village. You can be sure of a warm welcome here.

Directions: *Please phone. Evening if possible.*

Akaroa

Guest House
Address: Oinako Lodge,
99 Beach Road, Akaroa
Name: John & Susanne Cross
Telephone & fax: (03) 304 8787
Beds: 5 Double, (5 bedrooms)
Twin beds available
Bathroom: 4 Ensuite, 1 Private
Tariff: B&B (special) Double $135-$165,
discount for length of stay,
Single $90, Children negotiable.
Credit cards: Visa & M/C.

Step back in time to a more romantic era when staying with us in this elegantly restored original homestead of a French settler. Enjoy the tranquillity and added attractions of the beautiful harbour township of Akaroa. Our large two-storey Victorian Manor House is surrounded by trees, stream and garden. Only a few minutes walk from the pier,, shops, bakery etc.

The guest rooms are spacious and elegant with fresh flowers and large spa baths. The beds are king or queen size with electric blankets.

A complimentary bottle of wine, cheese and crackers and tea / coffee and homemade biscuits can be taken to your rooms or eaten on the balcony overlooking the harbour or in the guest lounge listening to music or reading by the open fire.

We will happily make bookings for restaurants (some elegant eating within walking distance), boat rides, horse trekking etc. and help you plan your stay or your trip further north or south. - An excellent place to unwind and relax.

Akaroa

Homestay
Address: "Potters Croft" Rue Grehan, Akaroa
Name: Graham & Lee Dunster
Telephone & Fax: (03) 304 7660
Beds: 1 King, 1 Double (2 Bedrooms)
Bathroom: 1 Private, 2 Family share
Tariff: B&B (full) Double $120, Single $80, Children half price, Dinner $25, Vouchers accepted May- September
Nearest Town: Akaroa 1/2km, Christchurch 80km

We have recently moved to Akaroa from a farm in North Canterbury where we have been hosting overseas guests for 10 years. At Potters Croft we are carrying on with this interesting and enjoyable lifestyle.

Potters Croft is on the edge of Akaroa township only a short walking distance to the restaurants, shops and main warf of the village.

It consists of an attractive comfortable well equipped home surrounded by 32 acres of unique native bush. Five hundred year old Totara and Kahikatea trees, many Kowhai trees, bell birds, native wood pigeons and a sparkling stream make it an ideal place to relax and enjoy your own private bush walks.

You are free to do as you wish at Potters Croft.

Lunches (picnic or otherwise) and evening meals with refreshments can be provided.

For those who like fishing we can take you fishing on the harbour. All equipment provided.

Tell other travellers about your favourite B&Bs

Akaroa
Homestay
Address: 21-B Watson Street, Akaroa
Name: Bella-Vista
Telephone & Fax: (03) 304 7137
Beds: 2 Double, 2 Single (3 Bedrooms)
Bathroom: 1 Ensuite, 1 Guests share.
Ensuite room has TV, video, tea making etc.
Tariff: B&B (continental) Double $70, $80, Single $40, Children welcome
Nearest Town: Christchurch

Looking for quality Bed & Breakfast at Akaroa, Joy Luisetti assures you of an especially warm welcome, top hospitality quality home, excellent and convenient facilities.

"Bella-Vista" (Beautiful View) overlooks hills and harbour five minutes to main street and restaurants.
Tariff includes continental breakfast, but cooked is available if required on request where you can sit in peace and quiet overlooking hills and harbours.
Akaroa has a very mild climate and is just the place to get away from it all.

Akaroa
Homestay B & B
Address: "Lavender Hill" 1 Lighthouse Road, Akaroa, Banks Peninsula
Name: Erica & Allister Stewart
Telephone: (03) 304 7082
Beds: 1 Double, 2 Single (2 Bedrooms)
Bathroom: 1 Family share
Tariff: B&B (continental) Double $70, Single $40, Children negotiable, Vouchers accepted
Nearest Town: Christchurch

Our home is on the boundary of village and farmland with wonderful views of harbour, village and hills.
Opposite us is the Garden of Tane with winding paths down through the trees to the waters edge and the old historic lighthouse. For those interested in history it is only a short walk to two old cemeteries.
We do not serve an evening meal but can recommend good restaurants to suit a variety of tastes.
Bathroom and separate toilet which are adjacent to guests bedrooms are shared, but guests take priority.
Beds have electric blankets and woollen underlays and are very comfortable.
We are both interested in art, Erica is an artist working in stained glass and making jewellery using china shards. Allister is a retired teacher.
Being non smokers we appreciate you not smoking indoors.
Directions: *Easy to find but please phone or write ahead. You will be most welcome.*

Okains Bay, Banks Peninsula

Farmstay
Address: 'Kawatea' Okains Bay, Banks Peninsula
Name: Judy and Kerry Thacker
Telephone: (03) 304 8621
Beds: 3 Double, 2 Single (3 bedrooms)
Bathroom: 1 Ensuite, 1 Family share
Tariff: B&B (special) Double $75-80, Single $45, Dinner $20,
Children under 12 half price. Vouchers accepted.
Nearest Town: Akaroa 20km.

'Kawatea' is a large historic homestead set in spacious gardens in one of the beautiful Bays of Banks Peninsula.

Okains Bay's safe sandy beach is a peaceful haven for swimming or relaxing.

Sheep and beef are run on the 530 hectare hill country farm which is bounded by 5km of scenic coastline, with interesting walks, panoramic views and a seal colony. There are many pets, horses for experienced riders and an aviary.

'Kawatea' is large enough to provide privacy but sufficiently informal to enable guests to feel at home.

Extensive use of native timbers and stained glass are a feature of the house.

In summer barbecue on the expansive verandah with freshly gathered seafood, accompanied by excellent NZ wines a speciality. Picnic baskets can be arranged for people on the move. In winter warm by the open fires, with wholesome soups and home made bread .

Nearby attractions include a Maori and Colonial Museum, winery, cheese factory, many scenic reserves, and the township of Akaroa noted for its French settlement, craftshops and harbour cruises.

The family have farmed in Okains Bay for 150 years, so we have a wide knowledge of local history and enjoy conversing with guests.

Guests are invited to join in the family and farm activities as they feel inclined. We promise you a memorable stay.

Directions: *Take Highway 75 from Christchurch. Follow signposts to top of Okains Bay. We are 6km down hill on right hand side.*

Le Bons Bay, Akaroa

Farmstay +
Self-contained Accom
Address: Le Bons Bay,
R.D. 3, Akaroa, Canterbury
Name: Anne & Gerhard ten Hove
Telephone: (03) 304-8529
Beds: 1 King, 2 Single (2 bedrooms) **Bathroom:** 1 Family share
Tariff: B&B (full) Double $60, Single $35, Children half price, Dinner $20pp.
Vouchers accepted.
Tariff for self-contained cottage: $45 1 night for 2 people, $40 more than 1
night, $10 for each extra adult, Children (under 15) 1/2 price.
Nearest Town: Akaroa 20 km

*We are a middle aged couple who enjoy meeting people. Ours is a hilly beef farm
with some sheep and a number of pet animals including an abyssinian cat.*
*Our house, built in 1880, is set in extensive gardens. We have two comfortable
rooms, one with king-size bed and one twin. Electric blankets on beds and heaters
in rooms. One room on ground floor, toilet and shower shared with hosts.*
*Enjoy our home cooking. Most meat, vege, fruit home grown. We have free range
hens and our own honey. Explore the beauty of Banks Peninsula. From Akaroa
take a cruise to view Hectors Dolphins. Bush walks and Okains Maori and
Colonial Museum close by. 3 kms to safe sandy ocean beach.*
*Self-contained cottage: comfortable, 2 bedrooms with panoramic ocean view.
Sleeps 7, cot & high chair available. Linen supplied, dinner by arrangement.
More suitable for summer months.*

Mt Hutt, Methven

Farmhouse
Address: "Tyrone",
No. 12 RD, Rakaia,
Name: Pam and Roger Callaghan
Telephone: (03) 302-8096
Beds: 1 Double, 2 Single (2 bedrooms)
Bathroom: 1 Ensuite, 1 Private
Tariff: B&B (full) Double $70, Single $40, Dinner $25, Vouchers accepted
Nearest Town: Methven 8km

*"Tyrone" Farmstay is centrally situated in the Methven, Mt Hutt, Rakaia Gorge
area, one hour from Christchurch Airport. The farm consists of three hundred
acres running sheep, cattle, deer.*
*Our home is positioned on the farm to take advantage of the mountain views (Mt
Hutt), this forms the back drop for the deer grazing a few metres away.*
*As our family have left home we now have two spare bedrooms which we would like
to share with guests. There are electric blankets on the beds, also available are
games room, BBQ, swimming pool, tea and coffee making facilities.*
*Dinner a 3 course evening meal with pre dinner drinks and New Zealand wine.
Area activities include skiing, jet boating, bush and alpine walks. Golf on one of
New Zealand's best 18 hole country courses.*
Directions: *from Methven travel the alternative Rakaia Gorge route towards
SH72 for 8km, farm is on right hand side, or from Highway 72 turn left at Mt Hutt
Station and travel for 5km.*

Mt Hutt, Methven

Farmstay
Address: Hart Rd, HW 72, Methven
Postal: "Glenview", RD 12, Rakaia
Name: Karen & Andrew Hart
Telephone: (03) 302 8620 **or** (025) 335136
Beds: 2 Double, 4 Single, + Cot (3 bedrooms)
Bathroom: 1Ensuite, 1 Private, 1 Family share
Tariff: B&B (Continental -Full available on request) Double $80, Single $40,
Dinner $20, Children half price, under 2 free, Campervan power point available,
Vouchers accepted
Nearest Town: Methven 10km

We live with our two children on a 1200 acre sheep and beef farm at the top of the Canterbury Plains. Our large modern farmhouse at 1500 ft above sea level is built for views of the Plains, Southern Alps, and especially up into Mt Hutt Skifield. Our farm is on the picturesque inland highway between Christchurch and southern destinations. Come and join in or observe our farming activities. There is always something to see. Walks, skiing, horse riding, parachuting, jet boating, fishing and golf are all in our area.

Our spacious guest rooms have separate access, TV, comfortable beds with electric blankets; and private bathroom and toilet.

Andrew enjoys computing and Karen teaches part time.

Directions: *Christchurch or Timaru - 1 hour. Geraldine, Ashburton - 30 mins. Rakaia Gorge, Methven - 10 mins. Our Accommodation signs are on Highway 72, 5km north of Alford Forest or 3km south of Mt Hutt Skifield Rd.. Our house is 1.5km up Hart Road.*

Tell other travellers about your favourite B&Bs

Staveley - Mt Hutt

Farmstay

Address: "Wairere Downs Deer Farm",
Sawmill Road, Staveley, No 1 RD (Route 72), Ashburton

Name: Roger & Colleen Mehrtens

Telephone & Fax: (03) 303 0804

Beds: 1 Double, 4 Single (3 bedrooms) **Bathroom:** 2 Private

Tariff: B&B (full) Double $80, Single $50, Dinner $25, Children half price. Tariff
includes farm tour. Credit cards accepted. Vouchers accepted May to October.

Nearest Town: Methven 20km, Ashburton 40km

*We extend a warm welcome to you to experience a taste of country living in the
beautiful foothills of Mid-Canterbury, where the Canterbury plains rise towards
the majestic Southern Alps.*

*An area well known for its hospitality, crisp clean air, sparkling water and
fabulous scenery. Add to this a diverse range of recreational activities and you
have the perfect stop over or holiday place.*

*Wairere Downs is situated just 700 metres off the scenic inland Route 72 which
links Christchurch and Queenstown and is the Inter City Bus route.*

*Our 540 acre farm consists of rolling hills with pockets of
native bush and spectacular views of the plains and snow
capped mountains. A farm tour drives through the deer herds
and our black and coloured sheep flock, a must for our guests.
Our separate guest wing is well heated and has private
facilities. NZ cuisine, pre dinner drinks, and NZ wines are
served with your meal.*

Laundry facilities.

Local attractions are:

*Fishing. Lakes, streams and the famous Rakaia
River (Braided River).*

Jet boating.

Skiing Mt Hutt.

Hot air ballooning.

Golf (18 hole course)

Horse riding.

Native bush walks.

Mt Somers sub alpine walkway.

Directions: *Sawmill Road is off Route 72
(40kms Ashburton - 20kms Methven)*

474

Rakaia Gorge - Mt Hutt

Farmstay
Address: Rakaia Gorge Homestead,
No 12 R.D., Rakaia, Mid Canterbury
Name: Birgitte Richards and Steve Gerard
Telephone: (03) 302-8448
Beds: 2 Double, 2 Single (3 bedrooms)
Bathroom: 1 Ensuite, 1 Guests share
Tariff: B&B (full) Double $70, Single $40,
Children $15, Dinner $20, Vouchers accepted
Nearest Town: Methven 15 kms, Christchurch (1hr 10min East)

Set in the depths of rural Mid Canterbury in the very picturesque Rakaia Gorge, this secluded hideaway sits right on the banks of the Rakaia River. Built in times of rural prosperity in the late 1890's our Homestead features extensive wood panelling, formal dining room now a small museum, large hallway and sitting room with an open fire. We have park-like surroundings of mature trees and garden with a tennis court.
Originally part of Mt Hutt Station, the farm is now a 600 acre sheep and beef farm which we're happy to show you around.
We have excellent salmon fishing in the highly regarded Rakaia river, quite literally on our doorstep, and trout fishing in local lakes and streams. We've rods etc. available. Mt Hutt Ski Field is the big attraction during winter (May-Oct) and we're conveniently close. Other attractions nearby include: jet boating, scenic walks, golf, horse riding
The Rakaia Gorge Homestead featured on the front cover of the 1994 B&B book.
Directions: *1 km South of the Rakaia Gorge Bridges on State Highway 72/77.*

Rakaia

Guest House
Address: "St Ita's Guesthouse"
Barrhill/Methven Rd, Rakaia
Name: Ken & Miriam Cutforth
Telephone & Fax: (03) 302 7546
Beds: 2 Double, 6 Single (4 Bedrooms)
2 Double +1 Twin bedroom with ensuites;
1 bedroom with 4 Single beds with shared bathroom)
Bathroom: 3 Ensuite, 1 Family share
Tariff: B&B (full) Double $70, Single $40, School Children $20, Dinner $15,
Hamper lunch $5. Tariff includes complimentary morning or afternoon teas.
Credit Cards. Vouchers accepted.
Nearest Town: Rakaia 2 minutes walking distance

A warm welcome is assured at St Ita's. Built in 1912, this former Convent is full of charm. The spacious home is set in more than an acre of grounds and is located on the western fringe of Rakaia township opposite the Domain.
Rakaia is 50 kilometres south of Christchurch, with its river famous for salmon fishing. Jetboating, horse trekking, golf and visiting the local pubs are popular pastimes in Rakaia. Within 30 minutes you can be at Mt Hutt Skifield, on the Transalpine Railway or a Scenic Walkway. St Ita's meals are based on local produce - fresh vegetables and fruit (mainly from our garden); lamb, beef, venison or salmon. Espresso coffee or tea is complimentary to wash down home baking. Cooked or continental breakfasts are served. Many guests choose St Ita's for its tranquillity - relax in front of an open fire with our cat and golden retriever; watch Sky Television; play tennis or pool.

Ashburton
Homestay
Address: 1 Sudbury Street, Ashburton
Name: Pat and Dave Weir
Telephone: (03) 308 3534
Beds: 1 Double, 2 Single (2 bedrooms) **Bathroom:** 1 Family share
Tariff: B&B (full) Double $50, Single $30, Dinner $15 or $20, Children under 13 half price. Vouchers accepted.
Nearest Town: Ashburton is apprx 80 km south of Christchurch

We are 10-15 minutes walk from town, our comfortable home is situated in a quiet street and we have the added enjoyment of looking out onto a rural scene. The guest accommodation is roomy and comfortable. Your hosts are a middle aged couple with a variety of interests. We welcome the opportunity to meet and greet visitors and wish to make your stay a happy one. We do request visitors not to smoke in our home.

Vegeterian or additional meals to bed and breakfast available on request. We are a few minutes walk away from Ashburton River Walkway and Riding for Disabled grounds. Laundry facilities are available to guests.

Ashburton
Farmstay
Address: "Carradale Farm",
Ferriman's Road, No 8 R.D.,
Mid-Canterbury
Name: Jim & Karen McIntyre
Telephone: (03) 308-6577
Beds: 4 Single (2 bedrooms)
Bathroom: 1 Private, 1 Family share
Tariff: B&B (full) Double $60, Single $35, Dinner $20, Children half price, Campervans & caravan power point $25. Credit Cards. Vouchers accepted.
Nearest Town: Ashburton - 8 km West of Ashburton; 1 hour Christchurch International Airport.

Our modern brick homestead which captures the sun in all rooms is cosy and inviting. It is situated in a sheltered garden where you can enjoy peace, tranquility and fresh country air or indulge in a game of tennis.

Both guest rooms have comfortable twin beds, electric blankets, reading lamps and tea making facilities. Laundry and ironing facilities available.

We offer home grown meat and vegetables.

We have a 225 hectare irrigated sheep and cattle farm. You may like to join in farm activities or be taken for a farm tour; sheep shearing demonstration included.

Our 3 adult children have left home although our son who is married lives and works on the farm.

As we have both travelled extensively in New Zealand, Australia, United Kingdom and Europe we would like to offer hospitality to fellow travellers.

Our hobbies include meeting people, travel, reading, photography, gardening, sewing, cake decorating, rugby, cricket and Jim belongs to Masonic Lodge.

Directions: *Turn off State Highway 1 and cross the railway line at Tinwald Tavern, heading west onto Lagmhor Road driving past Tinwald Golf Course. The road then becomes Frasers Road. Travel 6 km to 5 crossroads. Make a left turn onto Ferrimans Road. Our home is the only house on the right side of the road.*

Ashburton
Farmhouse
Address: "Riverview", Ealing, No 3 R.D., Ashburton
Name: Valmai & Ken McKenzie
Telephone: (03) 303 7040
Beds: 2 Single (1 bedroom) **Bathroom:** 1 Private
Tariff: B&B (full) Double $60, Single $30, Dinner $20, Campervans welcome $20
share hosts bathroom facilities, Vouchers accepted
Nearest Town: Ashburton - 32k South on SH1

Our bull-beef farm is handily situated on the banks of the Rangitata River (noted for salmon fishing) on State Highway 1, halfway between the mountains (with picturesque bush walks) and the sea, about an hour from Mt Hutt Skifield and 1 1/2 hrs from Christchurch International Airport.. Surrounded by a many types of farms, if wished, we can offer the visitor interested in farming much to see.
Ken's interests include Lions and fishing and, when work permits, is available to show visitors around and introduce keen fisherman to favourite fishing holes. Valmai's interests include woolcrafts, C.W.I., cooking and gardening. We invite you to enjoy our 3 course evening meal and hospitality of a high standard in our warm comfortable home in attractive surroundings.
Directions: *Travel 32km south from Ashburton on Highway 1 - at Ealing turn left onto Ealing - Coldstream Rd. House 400m from corner letter-box named. We would appreciate it if you would phone first.*

Ashburton
Guest House
Address: "Tudor House" Windermere, SH1, Ashburton
Name: Graeme & Margaret Thomas
Telephone: (03) 302 6815
Beds: 2 Double, 2 Single (3 Bedrooms) **Bathroom:** Guests share
Tariff: B&B (continental) Double $60, Single $30, Dinner $20, Meals available
if required. Credit cards: Visa. Vouchers accepted.
Nearest Town: 7.5km south of Ashburton on SH1

'Tudor House' is unique in the Southern Hemisphere. This 3 storied Tudor house has been built by an English craftsman exactly to the 16th century Tudor style. Set in a parkland with over two acres of gardens and thirty acres of farmland running beef cattle and sheep, this landmark has matured over the years.
Mount Hutt ski field is within easy distance, as is salmon fishing at either the Ashburton or Rangitata Rivers.
Directions: *On main highway, 7.5km to the south of Ashburton, on left hand side travelling south. Look for our sign.*

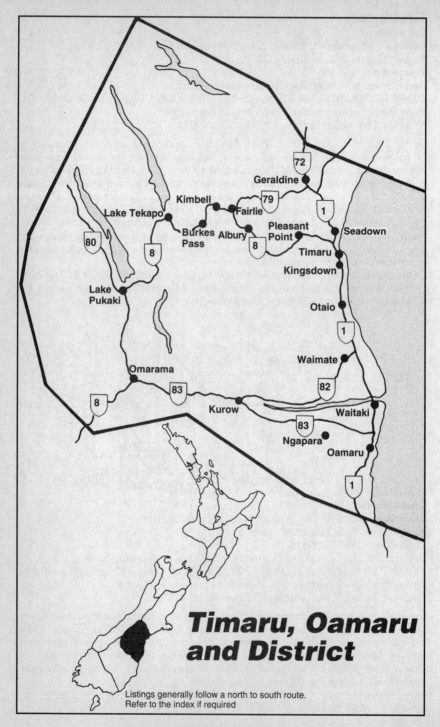

Timaru, Oamaru and District

Listings generally follow a north to south route.
Refer to the index if required

Geraldine

Homestay
Address: "Wharepuke Bed and Breakfast",
Pye Road, The Downs, RD21, Geraldine
Name: Joan & Peter Larsen
Telephone: (03) 693 8982
Beds: 1 Double 2 Single (2 bedrooms)
Bathroom: 1 Guests share
Tariff: B&B (full) Double $80, Single $50; Dinner $20 per person
Nearest Town: Geraldine 1 km

*The name "Wharepuke" means house on the hill in Maori, and our home is situated
in an attractive 1 acre garden setting with magnificent views of mountain and
countryside, and adjacent to Talbot Forest Reserve with its numerous bush walks.
We are a middle-aged couple, who enjoy the opportunity of meeting visitors to New
Zealand and promise you relaxing, comfortable hospitality.*
*Our spacious old home built about the turn of the century has been renovated to
modern standards, with all the atmosphere of the past being retained.*
*A breakfast of your choice is served at your requested time and an evening meal
is available by arrangement if required.*
Directions: *At junction in main street by Mobil garage turn into Pine Street, left
into Jollie Street, right up hill (Totara Street) which runs onto Pye Road.
"Wharepuke" is third on left*

Geraldine

Farmstay +
Self-contained Accommodation
Address: Brenton Road, Hilton.
Postal: RD21, Geraldine
Name: "Hilton Heights" -
Hilary Muir & Rodger Slater
Telephone: 0064 (0) 3 697 4842
Fax: 0064 (0) 3 697 4887
Beds: 1 Double, 1 Single (1 bedroom)
Bathroom: Ensuite

Tariff: B&B (continental) Double $60, Single $30, Dinner $15, Children extra.
Vouchers accepted.
Nearest Town: Geraldine- turn off SH79 into Brenton Road 8km west of
Geraldine.

*Quiet rural farm setting with a wonderful view of mountains and countryside - we
are situated on the very edge of the foothills between the Southern Alps and the
Canterbury Plains.*
*Sunny, well appointed home with garden and lawn surrounds. Separate
accommodation sleeps 3 in one main room, private but attached to house.*
*Barbeque, patio and tennis court in spacious outdoor setting with a native garden
and the musical notes of the NZ Bellbird. We grow Drysdale sheep, cereals, seeds
and offer farm related activities.*
*South Canterburys historic limestone kilns and local pottery 5kms further inland.
Keen interests - golf, tennis, fishing - community. We live 8 minutes pleasant drive
west from Geraldine just off SH79 on route to Mt Cook. Sign at mailbox. 2 hour
drive to Mount Cook and Christchurch, 1/2 hour to Timaru.*

Geraldine
Farmstay
Address: "Scotsdale", Peel Forest &
Coopers Creek Road, 22 R.D., Geraldine
Name: Aylene & Alex Stalker
Telephone: (03) 696 3874 'Collect',
Fax: (03) 696 3881
Beds: 2 Double, 5 Single (4 bedrooms, each room has vanity unit)
Bathroom: 1 Guests share, 2 separate toilets
Tariff: B&B (special) $40 per person Dinner $20 per person Children under
12yrs half price. Credit Cards. Vouchers accepted.
Nearest Town: 7 km North of Geraldine on Highway 72

Aylene and Alex invite you to experience the serenity of the country in our comfortable, antique studded, spacious home. Our friendly and warm atmosphere attracts many visitors. We are farming 350 acres, running 2,500 Merino and Romney sheep and breeding Hackney ponies to drive in our Gigs.
Our home is set in 2 acres of shrubs, flower gardens and lawn where you may enjoy playing Croquet. Bedrooms open onto balcony featuring breath taking panoramic views of the Southern Alps. Enjoy watching sheep dogs working, view the farm animals and amble along Coopers Creek. There are also many deer farms in our area.
Aylene's interests also include patchwork and embroidery.
"Scotsdale" is 5 minutes away from Peel Forest Scenic Park with native bush walks and native birds. 3 kms to Rangitata River for Trout / Salmon fishing and white water rafting. 5 minutes to Geraldine which has many attractions including 2 golf courses and a winery. 1 1/2 hours to Christchurch. Easy to find, makes an excellent stopover between Christchurch - Mt Cook - Queenstown or Christchurch - Dunedin.
A warm welcome awaits overseas and New Zealand visitors alike. We invite you to join us for dinner (home grown meat and vegetables) and share an evening of relaxation and friendship. We look forward to meeting you.
Directions: *"Scotsdale" is situated at Coopers Creek on Highway 72 at the junction of Coopers Creek - Peel Forest Road. Just 7 kms North of Geraldine.*

Geraldine
Guest Lodge
Address: "The Crossing",
Woodbury Road, RD 21, Geraldine
Name: Tom and Norma Francis
Telephone: (03) 693 9689
Beds: 4 Double, 1 Single (4 bedrooms)
Bathroom: 2 Ensuite, 1 Guests share
Tariff: B&B (continental) Honeymoon suite with luxury ensuite $118; Twin room with luxury ensuite $108; Double $86; Single $50; Dinner $25 (3-course).

"The Crossing" is an old English-style country home, elegantly decorated and furnished with antiques throughout.
Downstairs, there are three large reception rooms which open out onto a shady verandah and in summer, guests are welcome to explore the gardens and surrounding thirty-seven acres of land.
There is a glorious view of the mountains and a pond which has a "carpet" of bluebells and daffodils framing it in the Spring.
Two peacocks enjoy strutting on the lawn and you will be able to hear white doves coo-ing from their dove-cote.
In Winter, we light the open fires and there is comfortable leather furniture to recline on.
We are proud of our fully-licensed restaurant and our excellent chef is happy to cater for all tastes and requirements. In-house guests can enjoy a three-course meal with choices or, if preferred, can choose from the A-La-Carte Menu.
We are situated 1 1/2 - 2 hour's drive from Christchurch and half an hour's drive from Timaru: Ashburton and Fairlie.
Directions: *Signposted on SH 72/79 Woodbury Road corner 1 km north of Geraldine.*

Geraldine
Homestay - Country Home + Self-contained Accommodation
Address: Orari Back Rd, Geraldine
Name: Leon & Rosemary O'Sullivan
Telephone: (03) 693 8877
Beds: 2 Double, 2 Single (3 Bedrooms) **Bathroom:** 1 Ensuite, 1 Guests share
Tariff: B&B (continental) Double $60, Single $35, Dinner $20, Campervans welcome. Vouchers accepted
Nearest Town: Geraldine

Our modern family home includes a warm visitors flat with double bed and single day bed, TV, dinette with breakfast making facilities and own bathroom.
Inside we have one visitors bedroom with double bed and one single bed sharing a bathroom.
We have recently shifted from sheep farming in the MacKenzie to this small farm where we run deer and grow calla lilies.
We are a middle-aged couple with five grown-up children. Our interests include all sports, Lions, gardening and all handcrafts.
For the golf enthusiasts the beautiful Denfield Course is right opposite the house and being only 1 1/2 hrs from Christchurch we are handy to all tourist attractions in the South Canterbury region.
We look forward to sharing it with you.
Directions: *Our home is just 4km off State Highway 1. Turn at Orari onto the road to Geraldine. Travel 4km and turn right onto Orari Back Road. Our house is first on left. From Geraldine phone for directions.*

Geraldine
Guest House
Address: "Heron Rose" 29 Cox St Geraldine
Name: Sky & Raewyn Williams
Telephone: (03) 693 8343
Beds: 1 Queen, 4 Single (3 Bedrooms) **Bathroom:** 1 Guests share
Tariff: B&B (full) Double $70, Single $40, Children under 13 $20, Dinner $15 by arrangement. Credit cards.
Nearest Town: Geraldine town centre, an easy 5 minute walk

A warm welcome and cordial hospitality awaits you at "Heron Rose". Our home is a beautiful older style house (circa 1930) with many original features. It is set in the heart of Geraldine which is on the main route to Mount Cook and Queenstown. We will provide you with a comfortable base from which to explore the delights of the area or a pleasant overnight haven on your travels.
We are a creative couple with interests in art, travel, organic gardening and roses. We produce pottery and other crafts which we sell from our gallery on the property. We offer you comfortable beds in tastefully decorated rooms with a choice of delicious breakfasts. If you like to eat out for dinner, good restaurants are only a five minute stroll away. We ask guests to refrain from smoking indoors. Come, be our guests and let us pamper you.
Directions: *500 metres from Geraldine Post Office on SH79 to Mount Cook.*

Seadown, Timaru
Farmstay
Address: Seadown, RD3, Timaru
Name: Margaret and Ross Paterson
Telephone: (03) 688 2468
Beds: 1 Double, 4 Single (3 bedrooms)
Bathroom: 1 Guests share, 1 Family share
Tariff: B&B (full) Double $55, Single $35, Children half price; Dinner $20; Campervans welcome, but no power, Vouchers accepted
Nearest Town: Between Timaru and Temuka

We are a mixed cropping farm situated in South Canterbury between Timaru and Temuka, east of State Highway 1.
We grow grass-seed, clover, grain crops and freezing peas and also have 600 sheep.
Our home is an older type home which has been modernised. Electric blankets on all guests' beds. Laundry facilities are available. A swimming pool can be enjoyed in the warmer weather.
Your hostess is interested in spinning, gardening and breadmaking. You are welcome to have your meals with us.
Day trips can be comfortably taken to Mount Cook, Hydro Lakes and skifields. Fishing and golf course a few minutes away; also a walk to the sea coast.
A warm welcome awaits overseas and New Zealand visitors alike.
Directions: *From north approximately 5 km from Temuka to Dominion Road on left. Turn right if travelling from Timaru approx 11 km. To the end of Dominion Road - turn right then left onto Beach Road, till you come to Hides Road on left - first house on left on Hides Road.*

Timaru
Homestay
Address: 16 Selwyn Street, Timaru
Name: Margaret and Nevis Jones
Telephone: (03) 688 1400
Beds: 2 Double, 1 Single (2 bedrooms)
Bathroom: 1 Guests share
Tariff: B&B (full) Double $60, Single $35, Children half price; Dinner $15, Vouchers accepted

Our home is a spacious, comfortable, two-storeyed brick house with a grass tennis court in use from October until March.
Situated in central Timaru _ 5 minutes walk from the beach and 15 minutes from town, our home is set back from the road in a private garden surrounded by trees.
We have travelled and worked overseas with our four children three and a half years of our married life, and share an enjoyment of meeting people from other countries and feel we have an appreciation of what it is like to be a visitor in a foreign country.
Our main interests centre around music and the theatre in which we are both actively involved. We also play tennis and golf. We enjoy making use of the many walks and opportunities to get into the mountains which are so accessible from Timaru.
Timaru is 2 hours from Christchurch, Dunedin, Mt Cook, and five skifields.
Directions: *Please phone.*

Kingsdown, Timaru

Homestay
Address: Tyree House,
Bristols Rd. R.D.1,
Kingsdown, Timaru
Name: Marie-Louise and Alan Bailey
Telephone: (03) 612 6966
Fax: (03) 612 6247
Beds: 1 Double, 1 Queen, 4 Single (5 bedrooms)
Bathrooms: 1 Ensuite,1 guest share, separate shower
Tariff: B&B (full) Double $96-$107, Single $60, Dinner $25, Children under 13 half price. Campervans welcome. Credit cards accepted, Vouchers accepted from April to June
Nearest Town: Timaru

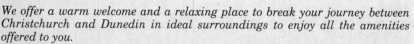

We offer a warm welcome and a relaxing place to break your journey between Christchurch and Dunedin in ideal surroundings to enjoy all the amenities offered to you.

Our home is quite unique in that it is built almost entirely of recycled materials. It is also built around a 100yr old chapel, which is used for weddings. Interesting history surrounds the area, mountains offer a beautiful backdrop.

We not only provide our guests with top quality accommodation and a breakfast of their choice, but also offer the opportunity to enjoy a number of different activities including skiing, golf, fishing, bush walks, scenic tours, farm and garden visits, picnics or just relaxing in our home.

At the end of your day you may choose to relax with us over pre-dinner drinks, then sample a wholesome New Zealand dinner.

We have a 10 seater Mini Bus which we use for our tours, or to meet guests from Airports, Rail and Coach on request.

We welcome guests at Christmas. "Come and Visit Us."

Would you like a weeks free B&B for two people?
Please complete and send us the comment form supplied by your host.

G.R.BULL '93

Kingsdown, Timaru
Rural Homestay
Address: "Mountain View", Talbots Road, Kingsdown, No 1 RD, Timaru
Name: Mary and Graeme Bell
Telephone: (03) 688 1070
Beds: 1 Double, 4 Single (3 bedrooms)
Bathroom: 2 Private, 1 Family share
Tariff: B&B (full) Double $60 Single $30, Children half price; Dinner $20; Campervans $6 per person with power, Vouchers accepted

'Mountain View' is a farmlet on Talbots Road 200 metres from State Highway 1, just 3 kms from the southern boundary of Timaru. A blue and white Bed & Breakfast sign on State Highway 1, 400 metres south of Talbots Road.
Your hosts offer warm Kiwi hospitality and are semi-retired farmers who have hosted on their farm for 10 years. We still have a few deer, sheep and sheep dog. Our home is situated in a tranquil sheltered garden overlooking farm land and a wonderful view of the mountains. Electric blankets on all beds, two private bathrooms for guests and laundry facilities available. Breakfast of your choice is served at your requested time and an evening meal is available with prior notice - Venison a speciality. Our interests include gardening, spinning, engineering and training of sheep dogs.
 Nearby fishing, golf courses, swimming both at beach and heated swimming pools and a walk on the sea coast to the lighthouse. Day trips can be comfortably taken to Mt Cook, Hydro Lakes and Ski Fields.

Fairlie
Farmstay
Address: "Mornview" McLeans Road, No 17, RD, Fairlie
Name: Anne & Norman McConnell
Telephone: (03) 685 8379
Beds: 1 Double, 2 Single (2 Bedrooms) **Bathroom:** 1 Guests share
Tariff: B&B (full) Double $50, Single $25, Children $10, Dinner $15
Nearest Town: Fairlie

Our property is a 600 acre downlands sheep and cattle farm with numerous wildlife. Our home is a large four bedroom house with a welcoming garden and extensive views of the surrounding countryside.
Close to ski fields and walkways.
Phone calls welcome anytime.
Directions: *5km up McLeans Road 3km from Fairlie on Timaru Highway 8.*

Kimbell, Fairlie
Self-contained Accommodation
Address: State Highway 8, Kimbell, Fairlie ~ *Colonial Cottages* ~
Name: Colonial Cottages: Ron & Kay Collyer
Telephone & Fax: (03) 685-8170
Laurel Cottage: 1 Double 1 Single (2 bedrooms).
Walnut Cottage: 2 Double 1 Single (2 bedrooms).
Tariff: B&B (full) Laurel Cottage $75 per person,
Walnut Cottage $65 per person, Children 4-14 half price, Credit cards accepted.
 Nearest Town: Fairlie 7 km, Skifield 6 km to gate.

Around 2 hrs Christchurch, 3 hrs Queenstown, our romantic heritage cottages are a unique holiday experience, especially for honeymooners and those who enjoy the nostalgia of yesteryear.
Your cottage is for your exclusive use. Sleep-in and eat when you're ready, as checkout is 1pm. The kitchen is stocked with farm fresh breakfast fare or ask for a special occasion breakfast.
So warm and cosy with open fires, comfy beds with lovely bedlinen, fresh flowers and special homely touches, antiques and memorabilia plus todays mod-cons for your comfort. Laurel Cottage, in Perambulator Lane, is quieter, on half acre while Walnut Cottage is on 1 acre with a trout stream. Both have cottage gardens.
A serene rural village nestled under the mountains, Kimbell has beuatiful trees and fresh clear air. In nearby Fairle there's a choice of eateries from licensed to fast foods, or eat in by candlelight. Meals by arrangement.
Nearby there's skiing, hiking, fishing, cycling, swimming, golfing, tennis, arts and crafts.
Directions: *Sign at gate.*

Kimbell, Fairlie
Homestay
Address: Rivendell Lodge,
Stanton Rd, Kimbell
Name: Joan Gill
Telephone: (03) 685 8833
Beds: 1 Double, 6 Single (4 Bedrooms/1 attic)
Bathroom: 1 Guests share, 1 Family share
Tariff: B&B (full) Double $70, Single $35,
Children negotiable, Dinner $20, Vouchers accepted
Nearest Town: Fairlie 8km

They stayed long in Rivendell and found it hard to leave. The house was perfect whether you liked food, or sleep, or work, or storytelling, or singing, or just sitting and thinking best, or a pleasant mixture of all them all.
Everyone grew refreshed and strong in a few days there. Merely to be there was a cure for weariness, fear and sadness.
J.R.R. Tolkien - Lord of the Rings
I am a writer with a passion for mountains and have named my home on its treeclad 3/4 acre with stream after the home of the elves.
Discover Kimbell, a peaceful historic village midway between Christchurch and Queenstown, close to Mt Dobson skifield with excellent hunting and fishing nearby. Rest awhile in Rivendell or join me walking or tramping. Guided excursions available. Catering for non-smokers.
Rivendell Lodge is 100 metres off SH 8 at Kimbell up Stanton Rd, past the garage towards Burkes Pass.

Lake Pukaki / Mount Cook

Farmstay
Address: "Tasman Downs Station", Lake Tekapo
Name: Linda & Bruce Hayman
Telephone: (03) 680-6841
Beds: 1 Double, 2 Single (2 bedrooms)
Bathroom: 1 Private, 1 Family share
Tariff: B&B (full) Double $90, Single $50, Dinner $20.
Nearest Town: Lake Tekapo 27kms.

"A place of unsurpassed beauty"
Perfectly located on the shores of Lake Pukaki, behind which are magnificent views of Mount Cook and the Southern Alps.
Our modern, local stone home, blends in with the natural surrounds. We have a 9-hole mini golf course, and peaceful surrounds to relax in.
Your host, who is an ex RAF Pilot, and whose family have farmed this property since 1914, has rich pioneering, and surprisingly wide experiences.
This high-country farm runs sheep and cattle with crops grown for self-sufficiency. Informative farm tours are available by arrangement.
This is your great opportunity to experience true New Zealand farm life, with friendly hosts.

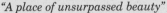

Lake Tekapo

Homestay
Address: 3 Pioneer Drive,
P O Box 99, Lake Tekapo
Name: Elizabeth (Tam) & Brett Shand
Telephone & Fax: (03) 6806-703
Beds: 1 Double, 2 Single (2 bedrooms)
Bathroom: 2 Guests share, separate toilet
Tariff: B&B (full) Double $80, Single $55,
Dinner $20 by arrangement. Credit cards: Visa, BC, M/C
Nearest Town: Lake Tekapo Village 5 minutes walk.
Fairlie (35 minutes drive east) Twizel (35 minutes west)

When we left our farm to live at our favourite place, looking out over the turquoise blue Lake Tekapo and distant mountains, we added to our holiday house a bedroom wing. This we offer to you with its warm, quiet rooms. A non-smoking home. One spacious bedroom with comfortable chairs opens onto a deck and garden. The second large bedroom looks out over our garden. Both see the lake. When required by a group, a third twin bedroom is available. Bathrooms, one with bath and basin, one with shower and basin. Separate toilet.
Our home has an air-conditioned family room with open fireplace, books and maps. A verandah, deck and garden offer a choice of places to read, write and relax with views of the mountains and ever changing lake just 100 metres away. Clear air reveals a night sky to remember.
Enjoy hot or cold cereals, yoghurts and fruits in season, homemade bread, toast or full country breakfast.
Introductions to walks, guides for fishing, hunting, climbing and skiing. Fly over the Southern Alps. Drive 75 minutes to Mount Cook National Park. Lake Tekapo, midway between Christchurch and Queenstown is a great place to stop.

Lake Tekapo

Self-contained Accommodation
Address: "Holbrook", State Highway 8, Lake Tekapo
Name: Lesley & Alister France
Telephone: (03) 685 8535
Beds: 1 Double, 6 Single (3 Bedrooms) **Bathroom:** 1 Private
Tariff: (Accommodation only) Double $70, Single $10*, Children $10*, Dinner by
arrangement, Breakfast: continental $8, cooked $12, Vouchers accepted April to
December, * Per extra person ($70 min. charge)
Nearest Town: Lake Tekapo

*Holbrook is part of a high county sheep station of 14,000 hectares (35,000 acres)
situated on the main tourist route (State Highway 8) between Burkes Pass and
Lake Tekapo.*
*Our cottage is close to our homestead, is fully self contained and is warm, spacious
and comfortable. We provide electric blankets, feather duvets, wood for the log fire,
telephone, TV, automatic washing machine and everything necessary to make
your stay with us an enjoyable experience.*
*You will be most welcome to explore our property and become involved in any
activities that are going on during your visit. Our area is well known for its many
outdoor pursuits including fishing, tramping, shooting and snow skiing.*
*We look forward to sharing our way of life with you over breakfast in the homestead
and if you make a prior arrangement with us, we would be happy to prepare and
share an evening meal with you.*

Lake Pukaki

Homestay
Address: "Rhoborough Downs", Lake Pukaki, P.B. Fairlie
Name: Roberta Preston
Telephone: (03) 435-0509
Beds: 1 Double, 3 Single (3 bedrooms) **Bathroom:** 1 Family share (guests have
first option)
Tariff: B&B (full) Double $70, Single $40, Dinner $25pp.
Nearest Town: Twizel 10 minute drive

*A wonderful quiet place to stop a night or two approximately halfway between
Christchurch and Queenstown.*
It is a 40 minute drive to Mt Cook National Park and Ohau State forest.
*The 18,000 acre property has been in our family since 1919 where merino sheep
graze the high mountains to 6000 feet.*
*Glorious mountain views from the homestead where Roberta serves delicious New
Zealand cuisine, home grown meat in quiet and tranquil surroundings. Roberta
is a Kiwi Host.*
*Twizel is 10 minutes away has a bank, doctor, hairdresser, shops etc, golf tennis,
squash facilities and several restaurants.*
Directions: *Please phone a day before or preferably earlier as bookings are
necessary.*

Omarama
Farmstay
Address: Dunstan Downs, Omarama
Name: Tim and Geva Innes
Telephone: (03) 438-9862 **Fax:** (03) 438-9517
Beds: 1 Double, 3 Single (2 bedrooms)
Bathroom: 1 Guests share, 1 Family share
Tariff: B&B (full) Double $60, Single $30, Dinner $20, Children half price, Vouchers accepted
Nearest Town: Omarama: Dunstan Downs is 17 km west of Omarama on State Highway 8

Dunstan Downs is a sheep and cattle station in the heart of the South Island high country. We have two children, one at boarding school, the other at a Polytechnic, and a cat.
Our home is full of country warmth and you are welcome to join us for dinner or bed and breakfast.
The Ahuriri River is at our back door, also several lakes nearby. A guide can be arranged at extra cost.
Great tramping nearby in the Ohau and Ahuriri areas. Skiing at Ohau in season only an hour away or 15 min by helicopter (at a price).

Omarama
Country Homestay
Address: "The Briars",
Ahuriri Heights, Omarama, SH8
Name: Marylou and Don Blue
Telephone: (03) 438 9615
Beds: 4 Single (2 bedrooms)
Bathroom: 1 Guests share
Tariff: B&B (continental) Double $65, Single $35, Vouchers accepted
Nearest Town: 2km north of Omarama on State Highway 8

Marylou and Don graciously welcome you to "The Briars" as private house guests and we will endeavour to give you warm and kindly service. Enjoy our charming and comfortable home created with lovely colour schemes, antiques, art, embroideries, and formal country gardens, which blend into the countryside.
Afternoon tea / coffee can be served on arrival.
When returning from an evening meal at one of Omarama's quality restaurants you can enjoy a homely supper with us. After a restful night in bedrooms which have electric blankets and heaters, enjoy a leisurely breakfast while viewing the changing lights on unsurpassed panoramic mountain landscapes.
Mt Cook is a pleasant and easy drive away.
The Clay Cliffs are seen from our kitchen window.
Marylou and Don have fond memories of living on Ohau Downs Sheep Station and hosting guests from all over the world. Now we welcome guests to our new home "The Briers".
Conveniently situated approximately halfway between Christchurch and Queenstown. Please ring at a meal time or just arrive.

Omarama
Farmstay
Address: Dunstan Downs Farm House, Omarama
Name: Nicky and Peter Cohen
Telephone: (03) 438 9817
Beds: 1 Double, 2 Single (2 bedrooms) **Bathroom:** Family share
Tariff: B&B (continental, Full if requested) Double $80, Single $40, Dinner $20, Children half price.
Nearest Town: 17km west of Omarama on State Highway 8

We live in the well known and beautfiul high country of the Waitaki Basin, known as "Sportsmans Paradise", in an A-Frame home.
During your stay you are more than welcome to become involved in farm activities with us, permitted there is something happening! Rabbit shooting, fishing, mountain walks or just enjoying the wonderful peace and quiet are all here for you to indulge in.
We have many animals on the property, but the domestic variety are always well behaved around our guests.
We are ideally situated on the main highway between Mount Cook and Queenstown, so stop over for a night, or a week. Picnic lunches can be provided for your day trips.
We extend this invitation to you, to see and share New Zealand high country life with us, as private house guests.
Backpackers also welcome.

Waimate and Lake Wanaka
Homestay+Self-contained Accommodation
Address: Homestay: Point Bush Road, Waimate,
South Canterbury, SC: 17 Aubrey Road, Wanaka (arrange through above)
Name: Norm & Annette Davis
Telephone: (03) 689 7877
Beds: 1 Double, 4 Single (3 Bedrooms) **Bathroom:** 1 Ensuite, 1 Guests share
Tariff: B&B (continental) Double $70, Single $45, Children $15, Dinner $15, Vouchers accepted
Nearest Town: Waimate, South Canterbury 2km west under White Horse

A pleasant, comfortable working farm homestead with gardens and craft shop overlooking Waimate and the Pacific Ocean. Waitaki River jet boating, salmon and trout fishing, bush walks, hunting and camping available by prior arrangement - or just relax!
Aeroclub members: Flight instruction, aerial photography, scenic flights, and introductory flights available.
Lake front 2 bedroom house with spectacular view available also at Lake Wanaka. One double, 2 single beds plus day bed in living room. Heated by in-built woodburner. Within 5 minutes of lake water facilities and 45 minutes of Cardrona and Treble Cone Ski Fields. $85 per night - take sleeping bags or linen.

Waimate

Homestead Lodge
Address: "Wainono Homestead Lodge", State
Highway 1, Studholme, PO Box 93, Waimate.
Name: Wayne & Kathy Manderson
Telephone: (03) 689 9883 or 0800 109 883
Beds: 3 Double, 2 Single (4 Bedrooms)
Bathroom: 1 Guests share
Tariff: B&B (special) Double $100, Single $85,
Children POA, Dinner $40 (3 course). Credit cards: Visa, B/C & D/C.
Nearest Town: Waimate

*Wainono Homestead is a distinctive two storey Edwardian house set in a peaceful
5 acre garden setting on State Highway One midway between Timaru and
Oamaru and approximately 2 hours 30 minutes drive from Christchurch or
Dunedin.*

*The Homestead near Studholme Junction was built in 1910 as a gentleman's
residence for Paul Studholme and features original leadlight windows and wood
panelling. The large drawing room and library with large open fires are ideal for
relaxing in. You are warmly invited to enjoy the tranquillity of the well known
country lodge and garden and the charm of a brief encounter with life as it was
in a more gracious era.*

*We have 2 children and enjoy meeting people. Your breakfast will give you a great
start to the day. Homemade muesli, fresh fruits and juice and special cooked menu
to delight your tastes.*

*Dinner menu of 3 courses changed daily with a complimentary drink. We
endeavour to cater for any special requirements you may have.*

Kurow-Oamaru

Farmstay/Self-contained Accommodation
Address: "Glenmac", 7k R.D., Oamaru
Name: Kaye & Keith Dennison
Telephone & Fax: (03)436 0200 (after 4pm)
Beds: 2 Double, 4 Single (4 bedrooms)
Bathroom: 1 Guests share, 1 Family share
Tariff: B&B (continental, full $5 extra) Double $50,
Single $30, Family discount available, Dinner $20,
Campervans $20 (up to 4 people), Vouchers accepted
Nearest Town: Oamaru 60 km East, Kurow 16 km West

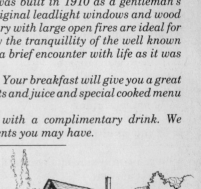

New Zealand
Association
FARM & HOME
HOSTS

*A warm welcome awaits you at "Glenmac" where you will experience the atmosphere
of a hill country sheep and cattle farm and enjoy delicious home cooked meals. You
will be able to join in farm activities, if you wish, or just relax in our peaceful
setting. The house is large, set in spacious grounds with views of the hills and
surrounding farmland. "Glenmac" consists of 4000 acres on which we run merino
sheep and beef cattle. Fishing, jet boating, tennis, squash, golf, skiing, and
walking are some of the activities available nearby.*

*Comments from our visitors' book include: "A Home away from Home", "Great
hospitality", "A warm & friendly family". Please feel free to call into "Glenmac".
Sometimes we are outside and don't hear the phone.*

Directions: *We are 5km off HW 83 which is a direct route to and from Mt Cook.
Watch for our sign at the end of Gards Road which is 4th road on left after
Duntroon or 4th road on right after Kurow.*

TIPS
for easier travel

★ **Ensuite and private bathroom** are for your use exclusively, **Guests share** bathroom means you may be sharing with other guests, **Family share** bathroom means you will be sharing with the family.

★ In the tariff section of each listing **'continental' breakfast** consists of fruit, cereal, toast, tea/coffee; **'full'** breakfast is the same with an additional cooked course; **'special'** breakfast has something special.

★ Do not try to travel too far in one day. Take time to enjoy the company of your hosts and other locals.

★ **Telephone ahead** to enquire about a B&B. It is a nuisance for you if you arrive to find the accommodation has been taken. And besides hosts need a little time to prepare.

★ The most suitable **time to arrive is late afternoon**, and to leave is before 10 in the morning.

★ **If you would like dinner** please give your host sufficient notice to prepare.

★ If you are unsure of anything ask your hosts about it. They will give you a direct answer.

★ Our B&Bs are mostly private homes. **Most do not accept credit cards.**

★ If you have made your reservations from overseas, check that your dates are correct. You might cross the dateline to come to New Zealand.

★ **Please let your hosts know if you have to cancel**. They will have spent time preparing for you.

★ Make your Cook Strait Ferry reservation in advance. e.

★ **If you need to use a public phone,** use the first one you see. It may be hours before you see another.

★ **Carry a phone card.** Most public phones do not take coins. Phone cards can be bought from dairies, bookstores and petrol stations.

★ New Zealand road signs are getting better, but your best directions come from asking a local.

★ Most listings show hosts accept vouchers. The only vouchers accepted are New Zealand Bed & Breakfast Book vouchers.

Oamaru
Farmstay in town
Address: 107 Reservoir Road,
Oamaru
Name: June & Ken McAuley
Telephone: (03) 4371360
Beds: 3 Single + 1 foldaway (2 bedrooms)
Bathroom: 1 Family share plus 2 toilets with handbasins
Tariff: B&B (full) Double $60, Single $35, Dinner $15, Vouchers accepted

Welcome to our home. We are semi-retired farmers. Our home is centrally heated, modern, spacious and very comfortable. Beds all have electric blankets. Bathroom and toilet are next to guest rooms.
You may have a family dinner with us and share an evening of relaxation and friendship or just Bed & Breakfast. No children or house pets here.
On our small farm we rear calves and graze cattle and goats.
Our many interests include square dancing, knitting, sewing, C.W.I., farming activities and developing residential building lots. We enjoy having overseas visitors staying in our home. Non smokers preferred.
Please feel free to call in as sometimes we are outside and don't hear the phone. Visit Oamaru's Penguin Colony, (4 kms) Oct/March - Historic Places and Public Gardens.
Directions: *On SH1 at Waitaki Girls High School (7 blocks north of Main Shopping Centre) turn into Ouse street. Follow white line all the way up Derwent Street and into Reservoir Road (1.5kms from SH1). Name and number on letterbox.*

Ngapara, Oamaru
Farmstay
Address: "Wallfield",
6 C.R.D., Oamaru (postal address only)
Name: Bill & Pat Bews
Telephone: (03) 432-6881
Beds: 1 Double, 2 Single (2 bedrooms) **Bathroom:** 1 Family share
Tariff: B&B (continental) Double $50, Single $25,
Dinner $20, Campervans $20, Vouchers accepted
Nearest Town: Oamaru 31 kms.

We are third generation farmers on a mixed farm (sheep, cattle, cropping). Our modern home is set in spacious gardens (with swimming pool) creating a peaceful atmosphere which we treasure. We have four children all happily married. Our interests include golf, tramping, gardening, commercial lavender growing, travel and meeting people.
Directions: *Our farm is situated approximately 15 km South of the Waitaki River and 30 km West of Oamaru on Conlans Road which is signposted and about half way between the townships of Ngapara and Tokarahi. Our name is on the gate. The major turnoff points are from Highway One just South of Oamaru and Highway 83 just East of Duntroon (both well signposted). It is just 10 minutes drive to the Tokarahi Golf course which is enroute to the Dansey's Pass - a picturesque drive linking North & Central Otago.*

Oamaru
Farmstay
Address: Herbert, 12.O.R.D. Oamaru
Name: Dorothy and Duncan McKenzie
Telephone: (03) 439 5614
Beds: 1 Double, 3 Single (3 bedrooms) **Bathroom:** 1 Guests share
Tariff: B&B (full) Double $60, Single $30, Dinner $20, Children half price, Vouchers accepted
Nearest Town: Oamaru 20km north of Herbert Township

We are a semi-retired couple living on a small sheep and cattle farm set in a beautiful area of rolling downland between SH 1 and the Pacific Ocean.
We have been involved in home hosting for the past 12 years and enjoy meeting guests from all parts of the world.
Our large retirement house set in one acre of garden was built with home hosting in mind.
We are close to rivers, beaches and bush walks with the Moeraki Boulders the chief local attraction. Both yellow-eyed and little blue penguins may be seen at Moeraki or Oamaru.
Oamaru, our nearest shopping centre, is famous for its early white stone buildings. The Oamaru stone quarries may be visited.
Evening meal by arrangement; cooked breakfast.
Please phone.

Oamaru
Homestay
Address: 'Braeview', 21 Tamar Street, Oamaru
Name: Aileen and Roger Wilson
Telephone: (03) 434 6312 (home), phone & fax bus. (03) 434 8874
Beds: 1 Double, 2 Single (2 bedrooms)
Bathroom: 1 Guests share, 1 Family share
Tariff: B&B (full) Double $55, Single $35, Dinner $20, Children half price. Credit Cards. Vouchers accepted.

We enjoy meeting people and a warm welcome awaits you at our home where you can relax and admire the lovely mountain and rural views from our sunny living area. We have travelled overseas and have been hosted in several European and Japanese homes and now we wish to be able to show our hospitality to visitors. We have also hosted International Exchange Students and enjoyed that experience very much.
We are situated only 5 minutes away from golf courses and 10 minutes walk to Penguin Colonies and unique Oamaru Stone Historic Buildings. We can arrange a farm visit for guests.
Directions: *Please phone or fax for details. Transport can be arranged from bus or train terminals.*

Oamaru

Homestay
Address: "Tara" Springhill Road 30RD Oamaru
Name: Baxter & Marianne
Telephone: (03) 434 8187
Beds: 1 Double (1 Bedroom) **Bathroom:** 1 Family share
Tariff: B&B (full) Double $60, Single $30,
Dinner $20 by arrangement, Vouchers accepted
Nearest Town: Oamaru

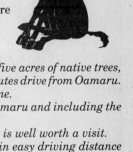

Welcome to "Tara" our secluded stone cottage nestled in five acres of native trees, gardens and with some delightful donkeys. Tara is 8 minutes drive from Oamaru. We have two grown-up children who are away from home.
There are many delightful excursions in and around. Oamaru and including the Harbour-Tyne St precinct and the Oamaru gardens.
Parkside Stone Quarry where Oamaru Stone originates is well worth a visit.
Skiing, boating, fishing, tramping and golf are all within easy driving distance form here.
You are assured of a warm welcome, our cottage is extremely comfortable. The guest room has twin beds with electric blankets.
A home cooked evening meal is available (by arrangement) or you may like to eat out at one of Oamaru's pleasant restaurants.
Directions: *Please phone.*

Oamaru

Homestay - Woodlands
Address: Whiterocks Road
6 D R D Oamaru
Name: Diana Taylor
Telephone: (03) 434 7250
Beds: 1 Double, 3 Single (3 Bedrooms)
Bathroom: 1 Guests share
Tariff: B&B (full) Double $60, Single $30,
Children half price, Dinner $20, Vouchers accepted
Nearest Town: Oamaru

My husband Mark and I have moved from the Dairy farm, (leaving our two married sons in charge) to a beautiful old stone home built 80 years ago set in five acres, bringing a few calves with us, plus two cats and a dog.
The garden of mature trees, shrubs and fruit trees give privacy and seclusion yet we are 3 minutes from Golf course and Herb Garden and 5 minutes from Town Centre. Oamaru has many magnificent Oamaru Stone Buildings which have been restored. Viewing of the Penguins is in the evening and the Public Gardens can be seen by horse drawn wagon.
You will be welcome to stay with us, sit in the garden, take a swim or sauna or just talk. A trip to the Dairy Farm at the mouth of the Waitaki River (famous for salmon and trout) is only a 20 minute drive and easily arranged for anyone wishing to see farming at close quarters.
Come and enjoy a warm North Otago welcome with us.
Directions: *Coming South from Oamaru drive under the "over bridge", past the District County Yard first turning on right into Whiterocks Road.*
Travelling North (from Dunedin) after passing Alma Garage, turn left at Monument onto Whiterocks Road, third mail box on left, approx 250 metres off SH 1.

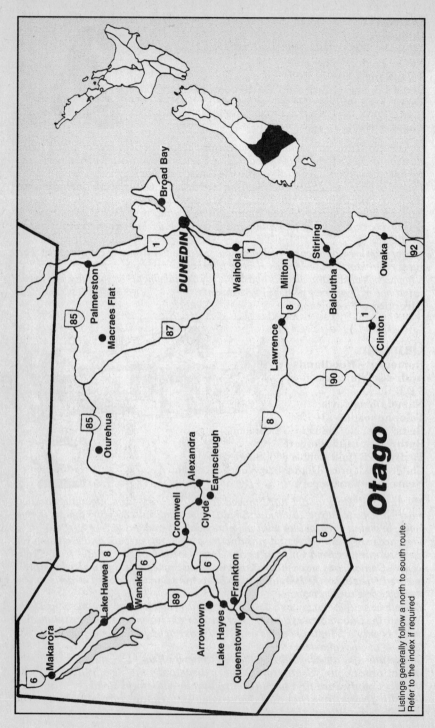

Listings generally follow a north to south route.
Refer to the index if required

Otago

Makarora

Homestay
Address: State Highway 6, Makarora
Postal: Private Bag, Wanaka
Name: Barb & Clint O'Brien
Telephone: (03) 443-8255
Beds: 1 Double, 2 Single (2 bedrooms) **Bathroom**: 1 Guests share
Tariff: B&B (full) Double $70, Single $40,
Dinner $25 by arrangement. Vouchers accepted.
Nearest Town: Wanaka 60 km

*Our new open-plan home constructed of natural timbers has 2 guest bedrooms
with their own bathroom. We have lived in the Makarora Valley for 12 years.
Clinton is a National Park Ranger while I run our small Service Station and
tourist shop, during the day. We are surrounded by farm land and have 3 acres
of our own, with a collection of friendly farm animals which are able to be viewed
and fed by our guests. Makarora is a small rural community found at the head of
Lake Wanaka. The Haast Highway, which is the main tourist route from the West
Coast to Otago, passes right through the Makarora Valley. The world famous
Mount Aspiring National Park is only a 5 minute drive from us. Makarora has
become the short walks capital of New Zealand. The National Park also offers
excellent fishing, hunting, tramping and climbing opportunities using Makarora
as a base. Alpine flights and jet-boating can be arranged.*
Directions: *from Wanaka - travel North along State Highway 6 approx 60 km
where you will find a Shell Service Station on the left hand side. Other travelling
times - Queenstown 130 km (2 hours), Haast 80 km (1hr 15 min), Fox Glacier 186
km (2 hr 30 mins).*

Makarora

Homestay
Address: State Highway 6, Makarora
Name: Andrea Larrivee
Telephone: (03) 443 9177
Beds: 1 Double, 2 Single (2 bedrooms)
Bathroom: 1 Guests share
Tariff: B&B (full) $40 per person,
Dinner $25per person, Children under 13yrs
half price, Vouchers accepted April to September
Nearest Town: Wanaka 65km

*Nestled in native bush, my home is secluded. Only a
short walk down the drive are a Mt Aspiring National
Park Information Centre and a tourist tearooms / shop
where jet boating and scenic flights are available. A ten
minute walk takes you to the Makarora River and some
of the best trout fishing in the country. Two walks in the
National Park begin out my back door with others nearby.*
*Originally from the United States, I have lived in Makarora for nineteen years. My
home is a unique, two storied octagon built mostly with local and recycled
materials. The upper storey contains the open living area with mountain and bush
views out every window making it a bird watcher's delight. The guest rooms are
located on the ground floor and share their own bathroom.*
Laundry facilities and a sauna are available for a small charge.
Directions: *Last house on a private drive next to the National Park Information
Centre.*

Lake Hawea
Homestay
Address: 3 Bodkin Street,
Lake Hawea, Otago
Name: Lyall Campbell
Telephone: (03) 443 1343
Beds: 1 Double, 2 Single (2 bedrooms)
Bathroom: 1 Ensuite, 1 Family share
Tariff: B&B (continental) Double $65,
Single $33, Dinner $16, Children half price, Vouchers accepted
Nearest Town: Wanaka - 15km distance

I am a retired teacher actively involved in craft dyeing of silks. My other interests are tramping, skiing and spinning. I have frequently entertained overseas visitors and always enjoy the chance to meet new people.
My three-storied A frame is set in an extensive sheltered compound with many specimen trees. One guest room opens onto a balcony with a mountain view; the other room has a view of Lake Hawea and an ensuite. Access to both via a circular staircase. Over the fence are tennis courts, a bowling green and a children's playground. I have a cat and a small dog.
Lake Hawea - two minutes walk - is popular for boating, fishing and swimming. Wanaka - ten minutes drive - offers good food, shopping and adventure activities. Three skifields are within easy reach.
Directions: *Turn off the Wanaka - Haast road at Hawea Dam. Drive up past the hotel to the store and you will see 'the A-frame through the Archway'.*
Non-smokers preferred.

Lake Hawea
Homestay
Address: "Hillkirk House",
33 Noema Terrace, Lake Hawea
Name: Mike and Doreen Allen
Telephone: (03) 443-1655
Beds: 4 Single (2 bedrooms), 1 converts King
Bathroom: 1 Ensuite, 1 Family share
Tariff: B&B (special) Double $80, Single $45, Dinner by arrangement,
 Children under 12yrs half price, Vouchers accepted May to September
Nearest Town: Wanaka 15km

We are a congenial retired English couple, well travelled and actively involved in outdoor pursuits, who enjoy sharing our home and lifestyle. Our main interests are fly fishing, tramping and skiing, but the immediate area offers most outdoor sports imaginable. We happily share our local knowledge and contacts to help guests maximise this potential. Strategically located at the eastern foot of Haast Pass, within easy reach of Mt. Aspiring National Park and local ski fields, our comfortable modern home offers a 360 degree ridgecrest panorama of lake and mountains. A pleasant sundeck overlooks secluded garden. Lakeshore, 5 minutes stroll.
Doreen boasts "last all day breakfasts" - fresh fruit and percolated coffee - with dinner and lunch by arrangement, using home made produce.
Mike regularly hosts famous overseas anglers. Quality hire gear, books, videos and fly tying facilities 'in house'.
One twin (or king) with ensuite. Second bathroom, separate toilet and shower.
Directions: *Over Hawea Dam up past hotel, on past store, first right, first left, sign on right before bend.*

Lake Hawea

**Farmstay+Self-contained
Cottage & Fishing Trips**
Address: Nook Road, Lake Hawea,
Central Otago
Name: Harry & Robyn Urquhart
Telephone: (03) 443 1535
Beds: 1 Double, 3 Single (3 Bedrooms)
Bathroom: 1 Private
Tariff: B&B (continental) Double $70, Single $45,
Extra $15, Campervans welcome.   Vouchers accepted.
Nearest Town: Wanaka

*We offer a self-contained modern cottage with all linen provided and a fully-
equipped kitchen, private barbecue area.*
*We prefer our visitors to enjoy their privacy on our farm and so we only accept one
booking at each time. The cottage is set in 2 acres of established garden beside our
homestead. Harry's mother had a nursery here for 30 years and so the garden is
of extensive interest to those who love plants and birdlife. We have a 6 year old son
Luke who delights in the company of visiting children.*
*We run a 300 acre mixed farm of sheep, barley and lucernhay. We happily show
visitors around the farm or merely leave them to explore by themselves. A 20
minute walk over the farm provides extensive mountain and lake views and
includes private lakeside beyond our paddocks. For those who are interested, we
operate a commercially licenced fishing boat for lake trolling or fly-fishing trips.
All fishing gear and meals are included. Price and trip are individually designed
to suit the customer.*

Wanaka

Homestay
Address: 15 Norman Terrace,
Wanaka
Name: Sue & Dick Williman
Telephone: (03) 443-9333
Beds: 1 Double, 2 Single (2 bedrooms)
Bathroom: 1 Guests share
Tariff: B&B (continental) Double $60,
Single $35, Children $15. Vouchers accepted.

*Our modern family home includes a warm visitors flat with twin and double
bedrooms, living room with colour TV, dinette with tea making facilities and your
own bathroom. Our lavish continental breakfast, served for you to eat at your
leisure, has been a point of commendation by many guests.*
*Our home is less than 100m from Lake Wanaka. There is easy access to it and to
pleasant lakeside walks through the trees of Wanaka Station Park.*
*We have travelled extensively overseas ourselves and take a special delight in
welcoming overseas visitors as well as New Zealanders. Wanaka is a holiday
centre with appeal to those who like scenic grandeur. We look forward to advising
you on the many fine summer and winter activities.*
The town offers a variety of good restaurants.
Laundry facilities & garage space available. We request visitors not to smoke in our home.
Directions: *From the town centre follow west around the lake towards Glendhu
Bay. Take the second on the right (Sargood Drive) into Ripponlea. Norman
Terrace is the first road on the right. Follow around the dog leg, ours is a back
section on the left.*

Wanaka

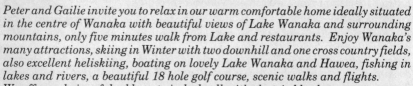

Homestay
Address: 85 Warren St, Wanaka
Name: Peter & Gailie Cooke
Telephone: (03) 443 7995 or
(03) 443 7524. Fax: (03) 443 9076.
Beds: 1 Double, 4 Single (3 bedrooms)
Bathroom: 1 Private, 1 Family share
Tariff: B&B (full) $70 Double, $35 single,
Dinner by arrangement, Vouchers accepted

*Peter and Gailie invite you to relax in our warm comfortable home ideally situated
in the centre of Wanaka with beautiful views of Lake Wanaka and surrounding
mountains, only five minutes walk from Lake and restaurants. Enjoy Wanaka's
many attractions, skiing in Winter with two downhill and one cross country fields,
also excellent heliskiing, boating on lovely Lake Wanaka and Hawea, fishing in
lakes and rivers, a beautiful 18 hole golf course, scenic walks and flights.
We offer a choice of double or twin beds all with electric blankets.
Peter is manager of a Real Estate Company and a keen trout fisherman, happy to
show guests good fishing spots. Gailie manages her gift Gallery as well as enjoying
golf and skiing.
We both enjoy meeting people, we have been home hosting for many years and will
endeavour to make your stay with us a happy one.*
Directions: *Please phone (03) 443 7995 or (03) 443 7524*

Wanaka

Homestay
Address: 75 Tenby Street, Wanaka
Name: Betty & Bill Miller
Telephone: (03) 443-7369
Beds: 1 Double 2 Single (2 bedrooms) **Bathroom:** 1 Private, 1 Family share
Tariff: B&B (continental) Double $60, Single $40, Vouchers accepted

*We invite you to enjoy the magnificent views of our lake and mountains from our
modern 2-level home in central Wanaka.
Our guest accommodation is on the ground floor and the double accommodation
is fully self-contained, private lounge with TV, small kitchen with tea making
facilities, bathroom and toilet. If required there is a double divan in the lounge.
Guests in our twin room share hosts' bathroom and toilet.
We are both retired and have a strong interst in meeting visitors from both N.Z.
and overseas. We have an intimate knowledge of things to do and see around
Wanaka including walks, drives, sight-seeing by launch and hovercraft, trout-
fishing and scenic flights. We are happy to help our guests organise their leisure
time if required.
Our home is close to the town centre, churches, bowling green and Wanaka's
beautiful golf course.
We request visitors not to smoke in our home.
Please phone for directions.*

Wanaka
Country Home Homestay
Address: Riverbank Rd. c/- NZ Post, Wanaka
Name: Patricia & Michael Barnett
Telephone: (03) 443-7295
Beds: 1 Double, 4 Single (3 bedrooms) **Bathroom:** 1 Ensuite, 1 Guest share
Tariff: B&B (full) Double $90, Single $45, Dinner by arrangement, School children half price, Vouchers accepted

We enjoy the lifestyle of the Southern Lakes district and look forward to sharing it with you. Our comfortable home is situated in a peaceful, rural setting 3 kms from Wanaka and has panoramic views of the mountains and surrounding countryside.
We grow our own vegetables. Freshly ground coffee or tea is available whenever you want it.
There are many outdoor activities available including splendid walks, suitable for all levels of fitness: golf, bowls, boating, fishing - river or lake and guided if required. We have several of New Zealand's finest ski fields within easy reach, and the best heliskiing in the country.
Having travelled overseas ourselves, we understand how important friendly, comfortable accommodation is when you are far from home, and along with Sam cat and Meg dog we look forward to meeting you.

Wanaka
Homestay
Address: 110 Matai Road, Wanaka
Name: John & Jolene Fitzharris
Telephone & Fax: (03) 443 1162
Mobile: 025 354 846
Beds: 2 Double, 2 Single (2 bedrooms)
Bathroom: 1 Guests share
Tariff: B&B (continental) Double $70, Single $40. Vouchers accepted.

Be our guest in our modern colonial home.
We've always welcomed New Zealanders and people from other countries.
We'll provide you with your own private access, family room, swimming pool and Bar-B-Q area, added to that is an uninterrupted view of Wanaka's back drop mountains
Enjoy breakfast with an uninterrupted view of Lake Wanaka..
Relax after exploring and enjoying Wanaka National Wonders - trout fishing, National Park walks, farm visits, or just lazing around the lake.
From our home watch the sun go down behind the world renowned ski field - Treble Cone - and its snow capped 2000m companion mountains. Handy to delightful local restaurants. Tea making facilities.
Directions: *Drop us a line for information or phone or fax. (Leave a call back number on our answer phone if necessary)*

Wanaka

Homestay
Address: Redwood Lane, Wanaka
Name: Margaret and Allan Jolly
Telephone: (03) 443 7072
Beds: 1 Double, 2 Single (2 bedrooms)
Bathroom: 1 Guests share
Tariff: B&B (continental, cooked breakfast $5pp extra), Double $80, Single $40, Children half price, Dinner $25. Vouchers accepted
Nearest Town: Wanaka

We are retired High Country Sheep Farmers, with interests still in farming. Our sunny cul-de-sac situation is ten minutes walk to lake front and shops, with a panoramic view of mountains. We have an extensive garden with a spring fed stream and fruit trees.

We offer top quality foods, cooked in true Kiwi style, outside barbeques when weather permits, beef, lamb, venison, fish, tasty entrees, seasonal berries and fruits.

Comfortable warm and friendly hospitality assured. Our interests are fishing, boating, bowls, gardening and both members of Lions Club International. Wanaka offers fishing, tramping, skiing, horse trekking, boating, Warbirds Museum. The puzzling Maze, scenic flights to Milford Sound and Mt Cook and entrance to Mt Aspiring National Park.

Our home not available 1 July - 1 October.

It is advisable to make a reservation the evening before and ask directions.

Wanaka

Homestay
Address: Aspiring Images, 26 Norman Tce, Wanaka
Name: Betty and George Russell
Telephone: (03) 443 8358
Beds: 2 Double, 2 Single (3 bedrooms)
Bathroom: 1 Guests share + 1 additional toilet
Tariff: B&B (full) Double $70, Single $40, Dinner $20pp by arrangement, Children under 12 half price.
Discount 2 or more nights. Credit cards. Vouchers accepted.

Wanaka's scenic splendour and choice of activities make it a place that should not be missed. There is variety and contrast here; scenery grand or intimate, fishing in lake or river, walks easy or challenging, mountain light always changing.

Our recently completed home is adjacent to Wanaka Station Park, with views over it, the lake (less than a minute's walk away) and to the mountains. Guest bedrooms enjoy the view and a sunny sheltered patio. Top quality bedding, warm rooms and quiet location ensure a restful stay.

We enjoy skiing, sailing, golf and meeting people and sharing ideas - especially about travel, geography, photography, sport, literature and music. We like singing round the piano and have mountain bikes guests may use around Wanaka.

Much spectacular scenery is off the beaten track - try one of George's four wheel drive sightseeing / photography tours (use of top quality cameras and accessories included). Transport is also available to skiing, fishing and tramping locations. We fell in love with Wanaka years ago and enjoy showing visitors why.

Wanaka
Lodge
Address: Te Wanaka Lodge,
23 Brownston St, Wanaka
Name: Grant and Ute Smith
Telephone: (03) 443 9224
Fax: (03) 443 9246
Freephone: 0508-926252 0508-Wanaka
Beds: 6 Queen, 12 Single (12 bedrooms)
Bathrooms: 12 Ensuite
Tariff: B&B (continental) $35-45 per person. Credit Cards. Vouchers accepted
subject to prior arrangment only.

It's a dream come true - we have finally built TE WANAKA LODGE! New Zealand pine inside and out make our lodge cosy and welcoming, a place to relax in that you'll never forget. Two lounges, fully equipped kitchen and dining room are all there for you along with the added privacy of your very own ensuite. Nestled in the heart of Wanaka, we are within walking distance of the beach, restaurants and shops.

On a hot summer's day, relax under the walnut tree or enjoy the lake and mountain views from the sun decks or your private balcony. Shake off winter's chill by the fire, have a chat with your fellow travellers or write all those overdue postcards (no excuses - stamps available!).

Your outgoing hosts, Grant and Ute, are "thirty - something" and have no children. They are both world travellers and take great pleasure in sharing their extensive knowledge of the area. Whether it's ferreting out local crafts, enjoying Wanaka's unique dining or adventure kayaking, Grant and Ute have done it all and can't wait to share it with you.

Parapenting, fishing, jetboating, bushwalking, skiing, scenic flights to Mt Cook and Milford Sound - did you know that all this and more is available in Wanaka?
Directions: *Turn left at the Caltex Station, we are 150 meters down on the right.*

Please let your hosts know if you have to cancel.
They will have spent time preparing for you.

Wanaka

Bed & Breakfast
Address: 'The Cedars',
7 Riverbank Road, Wanaka
Name: Brian & Jessie Anderson
Telephone: (03) 443 7933
Beds: 2 Double, 1 Single (2 Bedrooms)
Bathroom: 1 Private, 1 Family share
Tariff: B&B (special) Double $90, Single $45, Vouchers accepted
Nearest Town: Wanaka 2 km

We would like you to come and enjoy our comfortable home with us, with breathtaking mountain views from every window. Even though we are rural, we are on the main highway only 2km from the lake and town , as well as 3 ski fields not much over 1/2 hour away. Restaurants for your evening meals are close and you can also enjoy magnificent walks, scenic flights, great golf course, fishing - plus many other ways to relax in our beautiful area.
We have laundry facilities, and tea and coffee available if you wan them. Also our friendly sheep, cattle or cat 'Edgar' will greet you warmly.
You will always remember unforgettable Wanaka.

Wanaka

B & B Lodge
Address: Corner State Highway 89
(Cardrona Road) and Orchard Rd, Wanaka
Name: Oak-Ridge Lodge
Telephone & Fax: (03) 443 8614
Beds: 4 Double (4 Bedrooms/Two bedrooms are with extra single bed)
Bathroom: 4 Ensuite
Tariff: B&B (continental) Double $80, Single $60, Extra person $20, Full breakfast optional. Credit cards.
Nearest Town: Wanaka

Oak-Ridge Lodge, Corner S/H 89 and Orchard Rd, Wanaka.
Set on a 25 acre Dear Farm, Oak-Ridge Lodge offers a purpose built accommodation lodge containing 4 double bedrooms (2 with extra single) each with own ensuite facilities. The lodge includes a large comfortable Guests' Lounge, House Bar, Snooker Table, Dining Room, Outdoor spa and BBQ area.
Front lawns sweep down to the Lawn Tennis court, 3 putting greens and 150 metre driving range over the pond.
Views are north facing, towards Mt Aspiring and surrounding snow-capped mountains and glacier.
The Lodge emphasis for guests is one of quiet, relaxed and comfortable hospitality in a farm-style environment surrounded by lawn, trees, gardens and mountains. Oak-Ridge Lodge has a peaceful, tranquil rural location only 2km from the Lake shore and town centre.
The Lodge is non-smoking indoors.
Please phone or fax Oak-Ridge Lodge on 03-443-8614 for your hosts Nigel and Bronwyn Kerr.

Wanaka
Homestay
Address: 21 Sargood Drive, Ripponlea, Wanaka, Otago Central
Name: Rosemarie & Eddy
Telephone: (03) 443 9082
Beds: 2 Double (2 Bedrooms) **Bathroom:** 1 Guests share
Tariff: B&B (special) Double $80, Single $50, Vouchers accepted
Nearest Town: Wanaka

Stonehouse in quiet cul-de-sac
Handy to Lake and vineyard
Lovely garden
Conservatory (winter garden)
Sauna
Open fireplace
Central heating
Non-smoking
Our love is travel, gardening,
*   skiing, good food and wine.*
Rosemarie is a Batik artist and
*   spinner / weaver.*
Wir sprechen auch deutsch
Se hablan español
en parle francais

Wanaka
Farmstay
Address: "Wanaka Sky Lodge"
Orchard Road
Name: Ron & Claudia McAulay
Telephone & Fax: (03) 443 9349
Beds: 2 Double, 2 Single (3 Bedrooms)
Bathroom: 3 Ensuite
Tariff: B&B (continental) Double $90, Single $50, Children under 12 half price,
Dinner $25pp by arrangement. Credit cards. Vouchers accepted
Nearest Town: Wanaka

'Welcome' to our home. Expansive view of farmland and mountains provide a
tranquil setting on 90 acres with friendly farm animals.
Guests are invited to relax in a rural environment yet to be within 3km from
Wanaka's township with many tourist and recreational activities - skiing - heli-
skiing - fishing - tramping - scenic flight, not to mention the number of cafes and
restaurants.
Accommodation for 6 guests is spacious and comfortable with own ensuites, large
living areas with open fire and Stanley cooker for a home cooked meal. Coffee and
tea always available.
Ron is an airline pilot, hobbies being light aircraft and gliding which is operated
of our property.
Claudia is a keen gardener and cook, enjoys anything creative along with looking after
or should say running after their two sons 9 and 12 years of age. Dutch is spoken.
Note: Building was not completed at time of inspection, phone to confirm.

Wanaka

Homestay
Address: "Tirohanga"
102 Lismore St, Wanaka
Name: Ken & Noeleen McDiarmid
Telephone: (03) 443 8302
Beds: 1 Double, 2 Single (2 Bedrooms)
Bathroom: 2 Ensuite
Tariff: B&B (continental) Double $80,
Single $45, Dinner $25, Full breakfast $5pp extra. Vouchers accepted.

Our modernised home overlooks the lake and boat harbour being very central, five minutes walk to post office, garages, shops and heated swimming pool.
The glorious and active view from lounge and bedrooms would equal any other spectacular scene in New Zealand.
We have one double ensuite unit with cooking facilities if you wish, and one twin bedroom with modern bathroom and separate toilet.
Ken and Noeleen are semi-retired business people who have been in the hospitality business for many years and they are only too pleased to make your stay a happy, comfortable and exciting one. Your hosts have travelled widely and enjoy golf, the outdoors, boating, music and entertaining.
It is their wish to help and provide you with any service you may require whilst in Wanaka. A courtesy vehicle is available at point of arrival of from Queenstown Airport one hour distant. We welcome your visit to Wanaka knowing that you will never forget this magnificent scenery.
Note: Building was not completed at time of inspection, phone to confirm.

Wanaka

Homestay
+Self-contained Accommodation
Address: 129 Anderson Road
Name: Diana & Dan Pinckney
Telephone: (03) 443 1253   **Mobile:** 025 354 847
Beds: 2 Double, 3 Single (3 Bedrooms) **Bathroom:** 1 Private, 1 Family share
Tariff: B&B (continental) Double $70, Single $35, Dinner $20, Children welcome.
Vouchers accepted
Nearest Town: Wanaka

Our home is situated on the outskirts of Wanaka. It has excellent rural views in all directions. Our interests and work include: Real Estate, Gardening, Home Crafts, Fly Fishing, Forestry and Farming. We look forward to your stay with us.

Wanaka
Farmstay+Self-contained
Accommodation
Address: Maxwell Road,
R.D., Wanaka
Name: Kate & Roy Summers
Telephone: (03) 443 8856
Beds: 1 Double, 2 Single (2 Bedrooms)
Bathroom: 1 Private
Tariff: B&B (full) Double $120 + $30 extra person, Single $70, Dinner $25
Nearest Town: Wanaka 6km away

Less than 5 minutes drive from Wanaka tucked away in the beautiful Southern Lakes Area is a 100 year old mud and stone cottage lovingly restored by the farm owners Kate and Roy complete with its own old-fashioned garden.

The cottage offers a cosy authentic stay of a bygone era as all furnishings and fittings are of the Colonial period.

The cottage is completely self-contained with a living area, kitchen, bathroom, 2 double bedrooms and a sunny verandah with superb panoramic views of mountains and farmlands.

Join Kate and Roy for breakfast at the main homestead or you can have a lie in and make your own breakfast later in the fully equipped kitchen.

Your hosts love travelling and have a keen interest in different foods and wines (although the cooking is left to Kate) both play golf, but Roy is mad on all sports while Kate is more interested in antiques and the Arts having been in the business for many years.

Wanaka - Cromwell
Stone Cottage
Address: "Queensberry Inn"
Wanaka Rd, No. 3 R.D., Cromwell
Name: Bev & David
Telephone: (03) 445 0599
Beds: 1 Double (1 Bedroom)
Bathroom: 1 Ensuite
Tariff: B&B (continental) Double $95
Nearest Town: Wanaka

"Queensberry Inn" is a restored stone cottage circa 1880 which was originally the grooms quarters and tack room to the Inn. It is now fully heated, old style furnished with tea and coffee making facilities.

"Queensberry Inn" was an earlier travellers rest for gold miners, and others at the turn of the century. It is situated on a 5 acre property consisting of the farm buildings and amidst trees, gardens and lawn. Previously it was part of a large farming property.

Ideal for honeymooners it is peaceful and relaxing. Also handy to Lakes Wanaka, Dunstan and Hawea which are renowned for their fishing. In addition, grass tennis court.

Bev and David come from a farming background and Bev enjoys crafts and gardening.

Directions: *Midway between Wanaka and Cromwell on State Highway 6. 15 Minutes to Wanaka.*

Arrowtown
Homestay
Address: 12 Argyle Place,
Arrowtown
Name: Joycelyn & Murray Potter
Telephone: (03) 442-1267
Beds: 4 Single (2 bedrooms)
Bathroom: 1 Private (we take 1 party only)
Tariff: B&B (full) Double $70 ($65 two or more nights)
Single $40, Children (under 12) half price, Dinner $25, Vouchers accepted
Nearest Town: Arrowtown - Queenstown 19km, Frankton Airport 12km.

Former farmers, we welcome guests to share our comfortable modern bungalow in historic Arrowtown.

Our guest rooms, including bathroom, are carpeted and have heaters. Both bedrooms have electric blankets on beds, bed lamps and easy access to guest bathroom. Laundry facilities available.

The main street, close to the Arrow River, with restaurants, bistros, Post Office, Lake's District Museum, shops etc, is just five minutes walk away.

Arrowtown is twenty minutes from Queenstown and ten minutes from Frankton Airport and under fifteen minutes driving time from activities such as bungy jumping, jet boating, white water rafting, horse-riding etc.

It has a local bowling green and 18 hole golf course (clubs can be hired). Te Anau and Milford Sound are an easy day trip from here.

In winter we are centrally placed for Coronet Peak, Remarkables and Cardrona ski-fields.

Our joint interests include sports, gardening, knitting and travelling.

Directions: *Please phone for bookings and directions.*

Please help us provide the best hospitality in the world.
Fill in a comment form for every place you stay.

Arrowtown

Homestay
Address: 20 Wiltshire St,
Arrowtown, Central Otago
Name: Mrs Cynthia Balfour
Telephone: (03) 442 1326
Beds: 1 Double, 2 Single (2 bedrooms)
Bathroom: 1 Guests share
Tariff: B&B (special) Double $85, Single $45,
Nearest Town: 19km Queenstown

I am a semi-retired businesswoman, well travelled with a variety of interests including gardening, interior design, local history, arts and crafts and skiing.

I welcome the opportunity of providing hospitality, particularly to overseas visitors.

My attractive colonial-style home is located in the historic centre of Arrowtown, an old Central Otago goldmining town. The area offers both summer and winter activities. Queenstown, an international tourist resort, is about 20 minutes away.

After sightseeing you can relax on a swing in my tranquil cottage garden. Interesting breakfasts, home made preserves a speciality. Two house cats.

I can recommend activities, trips and restaurants and book these if required.

Join my other happy and satisfied guests - comments include:

"Wonderful time, lovely garden and great food"
"Yummy breakfast and very very comfortable"
"Thank you for your generous hospitality - very relaxing stay"
"So appreciated the warm and friendly welcome"

Non-smokers preferred, reservations ahead please. Two house cats.

One of the differences between staying at a hotel and a B&B
is that you don't hug the hotel staff when you leave.

Arrowtown - Queenstown

Country Stay
Address: "Taranga",
Arrow Junction,
R.D. 1, Queenstown
Name: Mrs Suzie Wood
Telephone: (03) 442-1438
Beds: 1 Double, 2 Single (2 bedrooms)
Bathroom: 1 Guests share
Tariff: B&B (continental, full $3 extra) Double $60, Single $35, Children 1/2 price, Dinner $20. Credit Cards. Vouchers accepted.
Nearest Town: Arrowtown

"Taranga" is on 15 tranquil acres beside the Arrow River with superb views of farmland and mountains. 18 kms from Queenstown, 5 kms from Arrowtown. My large living-room has an open fire: bedrooms have heaters, duvets and electric blankets. All meals are available if required. On-farm activities include gold panning, swimming, fishing and walking. I have 2 pet sheep, 2 cats, hens and red deer. Alpacas, fascinating animals, supply me with luxury fibre for my weaving. A riding stable, golf course and excellent walks are within easy reach as are Coronet Peak and Remarkable ski-fields. Historic Arrowtown offers much of interest including two good restaurants.
Guests comments include:- "Best B&B in the South".
*   "Definitely the highlight of the trip"*
*   "We came for one night, stayed a week. At "Taranga" you feel welcome"*
Directions: *Please phone.*

Arrowtown - Queenstown

Farmstay
Address: "Junction Downs"
State Highway 6, Arrow Junction,
Queenstown
Name: Mrs Pat Sew Hoy
Telephone: (03) 442 1427
Beds: 1 Queen, 3 Single (2 bedrooms)
Bathroom: 1 Ensuite, 1 Guests share
Tariff: B&B (continental) Double $60, Ensuite $70, Single $40, Children under 12 half price, Campervans $20 (share host's bathroom). Vouchers accepted.
Nearest Town: 18 km north of Queenstown on SH 1, Arrowtown 5km.

The pace in Queenstown is hectic; travel is tiring; but here it is peaceful, beautiful with an award winning two acre garden. The two storied homestead is surrounded by an 80 acre farm in an area of spectacular sweeping mountain views.
Amidst this oasis, your large, airy, romantic bedroom with all expected comforts, guarantees you a quiet restful nights sleep. A haven for honeymooners "Junction Downs" welcomes you with free tea or coffee, laundry facilities and forward B&B bookings. I and poodle Jim are always here to welcome you, introduce other guests, arrange your local bookings and help in any way to ensure a great holiday. I am retired, enjoy travel talk, people and most especially being host to my homestays.
Directions: *From Cromwell situated on Highway 6, 200 metres past Arrowtown turnoff, signposted mailbox on left. From Te Anau reach Frankton, turn right onto S.H. 6 (10 km) look for signposted mailbox on right. Welcome!*
Closed June, July and August.

Queenstown
Homestay
Address: Bush Creek Health Retreat, Bowen Street, Queenstown
Name: Mrs Ileen Mutch
Telephone: (03) 442-7260
Beds: 1 Double, 5 Single (4 bedrooms) **Bathroom**: 2 Guests share
Tariff: B&B (special) Double $80, Single $40, Children half price, Vouchers accepted April to October
Nearest Town: Queenstown 1.5 km

I offer bed and breakfast service in a very relaxed and beautiful atmosphere set in 3 acres. Guests delight in the magical sounds of native birds, cascading waterfall and the impressive glowworms.
I assure a comfortable stay with thermostat heating, electric blankets, feather duvets, woolrest underlays - all the extra home comforts.
Bathroom, shower, toilets upstairs and down. Guest lounge and sundecks. Bedrooms open onto balcony with mountain views of Coronet Peak and skifields. Tea and coffee making facilities are provided and breakfast arrangements are flexible.
My family have all left the nest.
Such a good feeling emanates from the cascading water. Being soothed and lulled to sleep and awakening really refreshed. Lovely water - tastes as pure as it can come, straight off my mountain.
I have a natural healing practice and I am a nutritionist.
Queenstown is rich with every kind of eating to suit your taste and I can direct you right to the gem spots.
Bush Creek Health Retreat is signposted and easy to find on Gorge Road heading towards the skifields.

512

Queenstown

Homestay

Address: "The Stable", 17 Brisbane Street, Queenstown

Name: Gordon & Isobel McIntyre

Telephone: (03) 442 9251 Fax: (03) 442 8293

Beds: 1 Double, 1 Triple, 1 Single (3 bedrooms)

Bathroom: 1 Ensuite, 1 1/2 Guests share

Tariff: B&B (full) $50 per person , Dinner $30.
Credit cards: Visa/BC

Nearest Town: Queenstown (5 mins stroll through the park or along the lakeside to town centre)

A 125 year old stone stable, listed by the New Zealand Historic Places Trust, shares a private courtyard with our home, providing convenience and comfort with fantastic lake and mountain views.

Our home is in a quiet cul-de-sac and set in a garden abundant with rhododendrons and native birds. It is less than 100 metres from the beach where a small boat is available for guests' use.

The beautiful Kelvin Heights Golf Course is close and tennis courts, bowling greens and ice skating rink are in the adjacent park.

We are within easy walking distance from all tourist, dining and shopping facilities.

All rooms are well heated with views of lake or mountains. Guests share our living areas and make use of our library and laundry.

Courtesy car available to and from bus depots. We can advise about and are booking agents for all sightseeing tours.

Those who choose to dine with us will enjoy 3 course dinners served with New Zealand wines. The choice includes lamb, venison, fresh fish and chicken. Breakfast is often served in the courtyard.

Our combined interests include: local history, cooking, yachting and weaving. We have farmed in Southland, bred Welsh ponies, and have travelled extensively overseas.

Directions: *Follow State Highway 6 (Frankton Road) to where it veers right at the Quality hotel. Continue straight ahead. Brisbane Street ("no exit") is 2nd on left. Phone if necessary.*

Queenstown

Homestay,
Address: "Colston House",
2 Boyes Crescent, Frankton, Queenstown
Name: Lois and Ivan Lindsay
Telephone: (03) 442-3162
Beds: 1 Double, 4 Single (3 bedrooms all with handbasins)
Bathroom: 1 Guests share, 1 Private. Separate studio accommodation if required.
Tariff: B&B (full) Double $80, Single $50, Dinner $25; Children $25, Vouchers accepted
Nearest Town: Frankton 1 km Queenstown 6 km

Our home, which is in a sunny situation overlooking Lake Wakatipu, has guest rooms with handbasins, electric blankets, bedside lamps, and heaters. Guests have exclusive use of bathroom with seperate toilet, laundry facilities, and a sunny conservatory overlooking flower gardens. We are retired sheep and grain farmers with a family of six all married. We have been hosting tourists for a number of years and offer warm and friendly hospitality, taking a special pride in our meals which we share with our guests. (wine is served with dinners). Full cooked breakfast and tea or coffee on arrival if required.
Shopping Centre, airport, coach-stop, golf, tennis, walking tracks, jet-boating, and bungy jumping coach all within 1 km of our home. Horse riding arranged if required. Guests going to Milford Sound by coach picked up and returned to our gate at night. Personal transport provided from coaches, airport, and to and from Queenstown.
Directions: *Turn into McBride Street at Mobil service station, Frankton. Proceed to where road forks and our home "Colston House", with archway over drive will be seen.*

Queenstown

Homestay
Address: 'Remarkable View',
22 Brecon Street, Queenstown
Name: Shirley & Noel Jackson
Telephone: (03) 4429-542
Beds: 1 Double, 2 Single (2 bedrooms)
Bathroom: 1 Family share
Tariff: B&B (full) Double $70, $65 two nights or more, Single $35, Dinner $20, children half price
Nearest Town: Queenstown - 3 minute stroll to Mall

Our home overlooks the town centre and has a fantastic view of the surrounding area, especially the rugged mountain range - "The Remarkables". Although so close to the centre of a very popular tourist resort we can offer a comfortable and peaceful stay. We offer 2 guest rooms, one with 2 single beds, the other with a double bed. All have electric blankets, warm bedding and are very comfortable. Bathroom facilities shared with hosts. Smokers welcome.
Breakfast either continental or cooked - your choice. We offer a nourishing 3 course dinner with wine. Being a tourist town, Queenstown has seven day shopping and many fine restaurants catering for most tastes. Plenty to do both summer and winter.
Directions: *Look for the hill with the gondola's, find the street that takes you there. We are the black house, 2nd on the left.*

Small sketch bottom of page

Queenstown

Country Homestay & Self-contained Cottage
Address: "Trelawn Place"
Arthurs Point, Queenstown
Postal: Box 117, Queenstown
Name: Nery Howard
Telephone and Fax: (03) 4429160
Beds: 1 Twin, 1 Double, 1 Queen, 1 King (4 bedrooms)
Bathrooms: 4 Ensuite
Tariff: B&B (full) Double $110-$140, Single $100, off season rate May, July,
September, Credit cards accepted

*A warm welcome awaits you at Trelawn, from Michael and Nery, Floydie the cat
and the corgis.*
*Just 5 minutes from Queenstown on the edge of the Shotover river, you can
luxuriate in the jacuzzi/spa amongst wonderful mountain scenery, relax in a
quiet corner of the garden or enjoy the company of fellow travellers on the shady
veranda or beside the sitting room log fire.*
*Four attractively furnished comfortably appointed guest rooms have ensuite
bathrooms. Cooked breakfast is served in the cosy farmhouse style dining room.
Fly fishermen especially welcome, guided services provided. We will happily make
any other sightseeing arrangements.*
Self contained stone cottage, *complete with fireplace and roses around the
door. The two bedroomed cottage is perfect for honeymooners or that longer stay.
Breakfast ingredients provided.*
Directions: *Highway 6A into
Queenstown, turn right at roundabout.
"Trelawn Place" is signposted 4km out on
this road to Arthurs Point.*

Trelawn Place
Bed & Breakfast

Lake Hayes, Queenstown
Country Guest Lodge
Address: Michael & Raewyn Fleck,
Speargrass Flat Road, No. 1 R.D.
Queenstown, Central Otago.
Name: Speargrass Lodge
Telephone: (03) 442-1417
Beds: 1 King, 2 Double, 4 Single (4 bedrooms)
Bathroom: 4 ensuite
Tariff: B&B (full) King $130, Double $115, Single $80, Children $25, Dinner $28,
Credit cards accepted, Vouchers accepted for double room.
Nearest Town: Queenstown 15 minutes, Arrowtown 5 minutes

*Our home is known as Speargrass Lodge, set in 8 acres of landscaped gardens and
meadow amidst the beautiful mountain scenery that this area is so famous for.*

*We are a family of 5, having come from a farming background; we are able to talk
about one of New Zealand's major industrys, as well as having an assortment of
farmyard animals.*

*Guests are invited to relax in the peaceful, rural environment yet be within short
driving distance of the many tourist and recreational activities that Queenstown
has to offer.*

*Accommodation for up to 10 guests is spacious and comfortable and includes
ensuite facilities, large living / dining area with stone open fireplace, games room,
outdoor living area, underfloor heating, electric blankets, guest laundry.*

*Our home is in a central location to four major ski fields so skiing plays an
important part of our Southern winters.*

Directions: *Speargrass Lodge is easy to find. Heading north on the main
Cromwell highway from Queenstown turn left to Arrowtown after passing Lake
Hayes. Then it is first left along Speargrass Flat Road.*

*Signage at the intersection. Heading South to Queenstown from Cromwell turn
right to Arrowtown on first sight of Lake Hayes then again first left along
Speargrass Flat Road.*

Continental breakfast consist of fruit, toast, tea/coffee,
Full breakfast is the same with a cooked course,
Special breakfast has something special.

Queenstown
Guest House

Address: Melbourne Guest House,
35 Melbourne St., Queenstown
Name: Cis & Les Walker
Telephone: (03) 4428431, **Fax:** (03) 4427466
Beds: 33 Rooms **Bathroom:** Private & Guests share
Tariff: B&B (Full) Double/Twin $76.50, Single $49.50,
Private Facility $125.00

The Melbourne Guest House has long been one of Queenstown's most popular Bed
& Breakfasts. It is situated on Melbourne St in a quiet location set amongst
beautiful rose gardens and only 3 minutes walk to the town centre.

Facilities are a spa pool, continental buffet and full menu breakfast available in
the dining room. Rooms are available with basin but share bathroom or for those
who prefer a touch of luxury and elegance, their own bathroom.

Full kitchen facilities and family rooms are available for those who may wish to
cook their own meals. Telephone and in house video available in all facility rooms.
All sightseeing, ski buses or airport shuttle transport pick up at the gate.

We know your stay with us will be enjoyable so we look forward to your arrival.

Lake Hayes, Queenstown
Homestay
Address: Lake Hayes,
2 R.D., Queenstown
Name: Clarice & Bill May
Telephone: (03) 442 1430
Beds: 1 Double, 3 Single (3 bedrooms)
Bathroom: 1 Private, 1 Guests share
Tariff: B&B (special) Double $90,
Single $45, Dinner $20 per person, Children under 12 half price, Vouchers accepted
Nearest Town: Queenstown

Enjoy a relaxed, peaceful holiday in beautiful surroundings on the edge of Lake Hayes and enjoy unobstructed views of the lake and Coronet Peak skifield from all rooms. All guest bedrooms have electric blankets, bedside lamps and heaters. Clarice & Bill are located 15 minutes from Queenstown, 5 minutes from Arrowtown and 10 minutes from the airport where transport can be arranged if required. Clarice and Bill moved to this spot when they retired from farming. Bill is a member of Rotary and Clarice is a retired nurse with hobbies including patchwork, gardening and gourmet cooking. Treats such as the house speciality of bran muffins made with yoghurt and bananas, served with lots of perked coffee, have led to the guest book containing comments such as "My stomach thanks you for the wonderful food, my heart thanks you for your warm hospitality" and "They have perfected the art of making folks feel welcome".
They fly the flag of overseas visitors and go out of their way to meet any special needs. Look for the pink gates and you will know you have arrived.

Queenstown
Self-contained Accommodation
Address: "Braemar House",
56 Panorama Terrace, Queenstown
Name: Ann & Duncan Wilson
Telephone: (03) 442-7385
Beds: 1 Double, 1 Single +
2 divans in lounge (1 bedroom)
Bathroom: 1 Private
Tariff: B&B (full) Double $80, Single $45,
Children welcome, (enquire other options when booking).

The apartment on the middle floor of our home is self-contained and private if guests want it that way, but our personal hospitality is always available.
"Braemar House", is situated on a steep hill section but with easy access from roadways, provides magnificent panoramic views of lake and mountains, and as guests will realise, our interest include gardening with many varieties of native trees and plants. Other activities which could interest visitors are tramping (hill walking), ski-ing, golf, photography and local history.
For travellers with their own transport, we have off-street parking, but a courtesy car is available for others. Transport and Guiding services are also available to out-of-town locations.
We have travelled extensively at home and overseas, and believe we fully understand the requirements of visitors to Queenstown.
Directions: *Turn up Suburb Street off Frankton Road, then first right into Panorama Terrace.*

Queenstown
Historic Home/Bed & Breakfast
Address: The Stone House,
47 Hallenstein Street, Queenstown
Name: Deborah & Grant Alley
Telephone & Fax: (03) 442 9812
Beds: 2 Double, 2 Single (3 bedrooms) Bathroom: 2 Ensuite, 1 Private
Tariff: B&B (special) Double $154, Single $102, Credit cards accepted
Nearest Town: Queenstown - 4 minute walk

THE HISTORIC STONE HOUSE

QUEENSTOWN • BUILT 1874

HERITAGE INNS of New Zealand

Imagine....crisp white cotton sheets, sumptuous feather pillows and duvets, a roaring open fire in winter and glorious sunsets over Lake Wakatipu on a balmy summer evening. Delight your senses at Queenstown's historic Stone House.

Our home was built in 1874 and is classified by the New Zealand Historic Places Trust. We occupy a superb location within Queenstown, being only a five minute stroll to town, and affording spectacular views of Lake Wakatipu and its surrounding mountains.

The Stone House features three well appointed guest rooms offering the ultimate away from home stay. Warmed fluffy towels, beautiful linens, fresh flowers, stylishly decorated and furnished rooms await you. The choice is yours - a room with a view or with a private garden to relax in.

Our stately lounge is the perfect place to relax at the days end. Join us for a glass of sherry in the evening to recount the days events. The pleasures of the breakfast table at the Stone House will be a highlight of your stay. The tantalising aroma of fresh coffee, home baked muffins and croissants, and a beautifully set breakfast table laden with seasonal fruits, yoghurts, homemade cereals and preserves completes a memorable meal. If a cooked breakfast is your desire, then you'll delight in the choices we offer.

We, Deborah and Grant, are well versed in the art of hospitality. We offer guests a gracious and relaxing atmosphere, with the utmost attention to detail, and the very best in personal and friendly, yet unobtrusive service.

We promise you will remember the Stone House long after you return home.

Queenstown
Bed & Breakfast
Address: 8 Sunset Lane,
Larchwood Heights, Queenstown
Name: Robin & Alwyn Rice
Telephone: (03) 442-6567
Beds: 1 Double, 2 Single (2 bedrooms)
Bathroom: 1 Guests share
Tariff: B&B (full) Double $80, Single $40

After spending 30 years in business in Invercargill, we moved to Queenstown 6 years ago and built our home in a quiet area overlooking Frankton Arm.

We have panoramic views of Lake Wakatipu and the surrounding mountains, and our guest rooms are private and spacious.

We have travelled widely both in New Zealand and overseas, and our interests include gardening, yachting, skiing and golf.

Directions: *Travelling along Frankton Rd towards Queenstown, turn right into Hensman Rd. 2nd road on left is Sunset Lane, we are last house on left, or phone if necessary.*

Queenstown

Homestay/Self contained accommodation
Address: 'Larch Hill', 16 Panners Way, Goldfields, Queenstown
Name: Elaine & Richard Bryant
Telephone: (03) 442-7126, **Fax:** (03) 442-7128
Beds: Home - 1 Double (Kingsize), 4 Single (3 bedrooms)
Bathroom: 2 Guests share
Self-contained Apartment - 1 Kingsize or twin (1 bedroom), Private bathroom
Tariff: B&B (full) Double $90, Single $65, Apartment $110, Dinner $30 (3-course with N.Z wine by prior arrangment. Free laundry available. Airport & Coach Terminal transfers - no charge. Credit cards accepted.
Nearest Town: Queenstown 3km

"Larch Hill" overlooks the shimmering clear blue of Lake Wakatipu, encircled by spectacular snow-capped mountains.

Built by Richard this unique home provides a feeling of warmth and relaxation. A restful green theme spills through the bedrooms into the dining room and sitting room with its library, both opening to a sunny courtyard surrounded by cottage gardens. On arrival you will be greeted with fresh coffee and homemade muffins. Once you have settled in, relax in the courtyard garden, or take in the lake and mountain views from the sundeck. In winter there is a roaring log fire awaiting your return from a days skiing or sightseeing tour.

Richard is a naturalist, operating walking tours exploring the local river valleys, forests and mountains. Specialising in flora and fauna, his enthusiasm for nature is contagious. In winter Richard is a ski guide and will happily help you co-ordinate your day's skiing or sightseeing.

Elaine (yes that's me!) is a nurse, and a keen gardner with a love of the outdoors. Elaine is the chef of the house and is also great at helping people plan their Queenstown experience.

At one time we ran a small lakeside sheep station, and later the famed Routeburn and Greenstone Guided Walks. So we have a mountain of experience that you can call upon during your stay with us.

Directions: 3km from Frankton Township on Highway 6A to Queenstown.
• Turn right at Goldfields (Sherwood Manor) turn off.
• Second turn to left is Panners Way.
• Phone us on (03) 442 7126

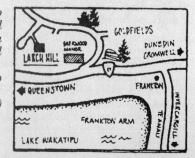

Queenstown

Homestay
Address: 12 Man St., Queenstown
Name: La Maison Te Awatea
Telephone: (03) 442-8162
Beds: 1 Queen, 1 Double, 2 Single (3 bedrooms)
Bathroom: 1 guests share. (Maximum of 4 guests).
Tariff: B&B (special) Queen $85, Double $75, Single $50, Dinner $30. Credit cards: Visa/BC.
Nearest Town: Queenstown (one street away from the main shopping area)

Keri and Roland and their son Marc, bought their spacious Art-deco home with the view to restore it to its original condition and to open it up as a Homestay.
La Maison Te Awatea is the combination of French and New Zealand hospitality. A genuine love of people and a belief that each guest who comes to stay becomes part of their family, has made this a very popular Homestay.
They are centrally located for all tourist, dining and shopping facilities, with breathtaking views of Lake Wakatipu and the Remarkables. Their kitchen and family room are the centre point of their home, where you will always find a hot drink and a warm smile to welcome you back from your days outing.
A combination of French cuisine (as Roland is French) and good old fashioned Kiwi cooking is available for those who want to dine in. For those guests who need assistance in planning their trip around the South Island (and hence utilising their time more effectively) Roland will be only too pleased to share his experience and knowledge of the area with you. As Roland and Keri are non-smokers they ask that you don't smoke in their home. They look forward to meeting you and ensure you a memorable stay.
Directions: *We would request that visitors ring early evenings for reservations.*

Queenstown

Homestay /Self-contained Accommodation
Address: 9 Panorama Tec., Queenstown
Name: Margaret McHugh
Telephone: (03) 442 8847 or 442 8512 **Mobile:** 025 347 199
Fax: (03) 442 8773
Beds: 1 Double, 2 Single (2 bedrooms) **Bathroom:** 1 Guests share
Tariff: B&B (full) Double $90, Single $45, Dinner $25, Children $12.50, Vouchers accepted April, May and June
Nearest Town: Queenstown 5min walk

My home in Queenstown's Panorama Terrace is in the frontline of the resort's dress circle with superb views across Lake Wakatipu to the aptly named Remarkables Mountains.
As your host I can offer you complete privacy and independence with a full bed and breakfast service. I live just three doors along the Terrace, which is the ideal combination for guests who want to "do their own thing". On the other hand I am available to spend time with guests who like the company.
The fully self contained home includes a double bedroom with king size water bed and a double bedroom with twin beds. Electric blankets, televisions and an ensuite bathroom.
Trained as a professional chef I will prepare evening meals on demand and promise traditional New Zealand food with a flair.
Number 9 Panorama is just five minutes walk from the centre of Queenstown but we'll provide a courtesy service. It's wise to book but not essential!

Queenstown

Homestay /Self-contained Accom.
Address: 118 Panorama Terrace
Name: Joan & John Blomfield
Telephone (03) 442 9985
Beds: 1 Double, 2 Single + 1 divan (2 bedrooms)
Bathroom: 1 Private
Tariff: B&B (full) Double $80, Single $45 (other options available)
Nearest Town: Queenstown. 1.6 km Town Centre

We welcome you to our new home in Queenstown and as the address suggests we enjoy panoramic views of Lake Wakatipu and the Remarkables.

Our guest accommodation, which is completely self-contained, has the same views, separate entrance, is private, spacious and centrally heated, electric blankets on all beds.

A continental or full breakfast is available and guests are very welcome to share our table.

Before moving to Queenstown, we farmed sheep, cattle and deer in Western Southland where we were also active members of the Western Southland Farm Hosting Group. On a recent visit to U.K. and Europe we enjoyed the B&B experience immensely and feel confident we can make your stay a pleasant one.

Our interests include most sports but golf in particular, together with gardening and handcrafts (embroidery, patchwork etc.).

Off-street parking is available and courtesy transport provided.

Directions: *from Frankton Road, turn up Suburb Street, then first right into Panorama Terrace. Access via Sunset Lane.*

Queenstown

Homestay
Address: Grants Road,
1 R.D., Queenstown
Name: Pat & Ron Collins
Telephone: (03) 442 3801
Beds: 1 Queen, 2 Single (2 bedrooms)
Bathroom: 1 Guests share
Tariff: B&B (full) Double $70 ($65 2 nights or more), Single $40, Dinner $25, Children under 12 half price, Vouchers accepted.

Pat & Ron welcome you to our new sunny warm home in a rural setting 10 mins to Queenstown. Private guest wing with electric blankets, heaters, laundry facilities. We have both worked in the tourist business in Queenstown. Ron still employed driving coaches to Milford Sound.

Our main interests are developing our garden, golf, walking and family. We have an outside Golden Labrador (Sam), and a cat (B.J)

We have a wide knowledge of our area and will endeavour to help our guests in everyway possible. Allow plenty of time. Handy to 3 skifields.

Numerous restaurants in Queenstown or dinner by arrangement. Local wine served.

Directions: *1 km from Frankton on SH 6. Name on mailbox. Go down Grants Road, house on left.*

Queenstown

Homestay
Address: 8B Birse Street,
Frankton, Queenstown
Name: Shirley and Pat Paulin
Telephone: (03) 442 3387
Beds: 1 Double, 2 Singles (2 bedrooms)
Bathroom: 1 guests share
Tariff: B&B (full) Double $90, Single $45, Dinner $20 per person, Vouchers accepted

Welcome to "Paulin Place" where you are assured of warm, friendly hospitality. Our home is situated in sunny Frankton, in a picturesque garden, with views of Lake Wakatipu and the Remarkable Mountains.
Pat, a retired school teacher, grew up in the district, so is very conversant with the history of the Wakatipu Basin. Our interests are landscape gardening, walking, fishing, mining, reading, cooking, entertaining and meeting new people. Our home is situated close to Airport, shopping centre and coach pick-ups.
Directions: *Frankton 6km from Queenstown. At Mobil Service Station turn into McBride Street. 300m south turn right into Birse Street. "Paulin Place" 5th on left.*

Queenstown

Self-contained Accommodation
Address: Moonlight Rd
Arthurs Point Queenstown
Name: Diane Barron
Telephone: (03) 442 7363
Beds: 1 Double, 6 Single (3 Bedrooms)
Bathroom: 1 Private + 1 separate toilet and handbasin.
Tariff: B&B (full) Double $70, Single $40,
Children neg., Dinner $25. Credit cards accepted.
Nearest Town: Queenstown

A unique opportunity exists in Arthurs Point Queenstown for a B&B and an extra option of superior stay on a very special NZ timber home.
Should visitors desire your host will be happy to share in your Queenstown stay, providing meals and hospitality, breakfast continental and cooked. Dinner by arrangement.
For a completely secluded and independent stay the house is yours to live in for the required period serviced, meals are optional. The house is furnished in country style with many interesting features. Ample space and all facilities available.
It has excellent indoor and outdoor living arrangements. To cater for all seasons this home can provide sheltered sundecks for summer and warm inviting log fires for winter nights. This house overlooks the Shotover Valley and is on the route to Coronet Peak skifield and Arrowtown.
All the Queenstown activities are within 5km easy access, transport available.
Every effort will be made to ensure your stay is both memorable and enjoyable.
Directions: *Turn left on Arthurs Point Hotel up the hill to Moonlight Rd 'Norrab" is 5th on the right.*

Queenstown

Guest House
Address: Spence Road,
Lower Shotover
Name: Ferry Hotel
Telephone & Fax: (03) 442 2194
Beds: 1 Double, 3 Single (3 Bedrooms)
Bathroom: 1 Guests share + extra toilet
Tariff: B&B (full) Double $88, Single $50,
Vouchers accepted except Dec/Jan/Feb & Easter
Nearest Town: 11km from Queenstown and Arrowtown on the A6

This well-known landmark, which operated as a hotel for over 100 years from gold-mining times until 1972, is once again offering warm hospitality to visitors. Situated above the Shotover River, it is just 5 minutes from the airport, Frankton and beautiful Lake Hayes, and 15 minutes from Arrowtown, Queenstown and the Coronet Peak ski fields.

Charmingly decorated bedrooms with individual heating and electric blankets, home-made jams and preserves, lavender among the linen, the wonderfully efficient wood-burner in the winter and 60 year old roses framing the long verandah, all add to the quiet cottage atmosphere of this lovely old place that I so enjoy sharing with guests.

My two small dogs and I have a separate apartment, so that visitors are assured of their peace and privacy. As the property is unfenced it is unsuitable for young children. Phone or fax Lizzie Bedwell for directions.

Queenstown

Homestay
Address: BJ's Place, 36 Lochy Rd,
Fernhill Queenstown
Name: Berit & John Brown
Telephone & Fax: (03) 442 8348
Beds: 1 Double, 3 Single (2 Bedrooms)
Bathroom: 1 Guests share
Tariff: B&B (continental) Double $90, Single $45, Children under 12 half price, Dinner $25. Credit cards accepted.
Nearest Town: Queenstown 5 min

Welcome to BJ's Place where you are assured of warm and friendly hospitality - A home away from home - with peaceful and relaxed atmosphere in our new modern and spacious home overlooking Lake Wakatipu - Cecil Peak and the Remarkables.

We are an informal semi-retired couple of English/Norwegian origin with 3 children spread around the country and we love meeting people from all walks of life. Our 2 guestrooms on the lower floor are warm, private and spacious 1 room with a double and a single bed the other with 2 single beds and guests share bathroom facilities. Continental breakfast with fresh fruit, homemade muesli, yoghurt etc or cooked if you prefer with plenty of brewed coffee or tea.

Make Queenstown your destination which offers a wealth of activities for all ages all the year round. We are "smokefree".
Directions: *Please phone for direction or pick up.*

Queenstown
Homestay
Address: 'Highgate',
8 Bolton Lane, Queenstown
Name: Diana & Murray Brown
Telephone & Fax: (03) 442 8435
Beds: 1 Queen, 2 Single (2 Bedrooms)
Bathroom: 2 Ensuite
Tariff: B&B (continental) Double $75, Single $45, Vouchers accepted

We consider ourselves very lucky to own one of the best locations in Queenstown, enjoying spectacular mountain and lake views.

Being 1km from the village centre our home provides peace and tranquillity.

The two guest rooms (one with queen-size bed, the other with two single beds) have a heater electric blanket, feather duvet etc and each has its own private ensuite.

Your hosts have recently sold their motel/guest house business in Queenstown and with family grown up and left home now look forward to providing friendly and personal service to guests.

Murray and Diana come from farming and business backgrounds and together have gained a wide experience of various business of their own. Currently we are establishing a vineyard in the Queenstown area.

Continental or cooked breakfast (you chose) but no smoking in house please.

All activities and sightseeing easily arranged by experienced hosts.

Washing machine and dryer available.

Directions: *Please phone. We recommend booking in advance either by fax or phone.*

Private bathroom is for your use exclusively,
Guests share means you may be sharing with other guests,
Family share means you will be sharing with the family.

Queenstown
Guest House
Address: Adelaide St, Guest House,
15 Adelaide St., Queenstown
Name: Noela and Ray Jenkins
Telephone: (03) 442-6207
Beds: 4 Double, 8 Single (6 bedrooms)
Bathrooms: 1 Ensuite, 3 guests share
Tariff: B&B (continental) Double $75, Single $50, Dinner $25, Children negotiable, Private facilities $95 Double, Visa/MC accepted, Vouchers accepted
Nearest Town: Queenstown 5 minute walk.

Adelaide Street Guest House is perfectly situated in a quiet peaceful neighbourhood 50 metres from the shores of beautiful Lake Wakatipu, and yet a short scenic walk from central Queenstown. The sundecks and spacious lounge, and most of our rooms, enjoy breathtaking views of the 'Remarkables Mountain Range', Cecil and Walter Peaks and the expansive Lake Wakatipu.

Our rooms are heated, and beds have duvets, electric blankets and reading lights. We enjoy hosting and ensure your stay in Queenstown will be a memorable one. Dinner is available by arrangement and Queenstown boasts a smorgasbord of Ethnic and Traditional restaurants. A guide containing current menus and price lists is placed in each room. In summer relax on the sundecks and enjoy the long twilight evenings and colourful sunsets.

In winter an open fire or wood burner warm the lounge. We are central to skifields - Coronet Peak 1/2 hour drive, Remarkables 1 hour drive. Sightseeing Information and Bookings our pleasure. Laundry facilities available, mountain bikes available for hire. Smoking permitted on sun decks. Bookings advised. Enjoy NZ.

New Zealand's Federation of Bed & Breakfast Hotels

Queenstown
Bed & Breakfast, Self-contained Accommodation
Address: 12 Brisbane St, Queenstown
Name: Barbara & Murray Hercus
Telephone & Fax: (03) 442 9511
Beds: 2 Single (1 Bedroom + ensuite downstairs) or 2 Single (1 Bedroom + private bathroom) **Bathroom:** 1 Ensuite, 1 Private
Tariff: B&B (continental) Double $85, Single $45, Vouchers accepted, Full breakfast $5 extra per person, Studio apartment (self-contained) with longer stay option available
Nearest Town: Queenstown

We will be pleased to share our recently redecorated warm / centrally heated home - parking, easy walking to all facilities, excellent mountain and lake views, solar heated swimming pool (November - March) private outdoor living area, peaceful and sunny. Laundry available.

Murray, a just retired charted accountant, former partner in an international firm, Barbara had a nursing and social work career. Our adult family are scattered so we and our Burmese cat will welcome you. We have travelled extensively in New Zealand and overseas. Our interests include music - classical / choral, our district, current affairs. Murrays background includes banking, tourism, primary industry. To assist your enjoyment of our beautiful area we can advise on local activities and assist you with bookings - bowling green, tennis courts and Queenstown gardens easy strolling distance.

Directions: *Come in on Main Road into Queenstown to Quality Hotel - continue straight ahead (do not veer right) Brisbane Street first on left. Phone or fax ahead if possible.*

Queenstown
Homestay+Guest House

Address: 27A Lomond Crescent, Queenstown
Name: "Scallywags" Guest House
Telephone: (03) 442 7083
Beds: 3 Double, 3 Twin (6 Bedrooms)
Bathroom: 2 Guests share
Tariff: B&B (Bed only-breakfast available on request) Double $50, Single $27, Children school age: half price, under 5 years free.
Nearest Town: Queenstown

You move in and live at "Scallywags", whether your stay is for 1 night or 5. Our home is your home. We are a "B&B with No B" (breakfast is available on request). Share bathrooms and kitchen facilities - bring your own food etc and use the excellent kitchen for cooking and baking. We offer free teas, coffee, milk, sugar, herbs and laundry facilities.
Comforts of home include: TV, video, stereo, microwave, large lounge and a house full of curios and original NZ art.
Linen, towels, duvets, electric blankets are on all beds.
The atmosphere is casual and relaxed and the house is situated adjacent to a bush reserve with native birds abundant - a peaceful haven just 5 minutes walk to town. The fabulous views - 180 degree captivating panorama from sunrise to sunset, lake, mountains and valleys.
Personal service, courtesy vehicle, activity booking service, local knowledge, smoke-free. Service, Ambience, Value.

Queenstown
Guest House

Address: 20 McMillan Road, Arthurs Point, Queenstown
Name: Camelot
Telephone: (03) 442 5299
Beds: 3 Double, 4 Single (5 Bedrooms)
Bathroom: 2 Ensuite, 1 Guests share
Tariff: B&B (continental) Double $85, Single $50. Credit cards: Visa/MC.
Nearest Town: Queenstown

Camelot is probably Queenstown's best kept secret. Relaxing, tranquil, unique and private with a touch of elegance.
I pride myself on giving guests a little bit of luxury and those wonderful extras I searched for during my years of travelling .
Camelot is your Castle away from home.
Situated at Arthurs Point with superb views of Coronet Peak and the Shotover River Canyon. A large sunny balcony surrounds Camelots' wooden exterior - a beautiful breakfast spot.
You are welcome to use all facilities ie. kitchen, laundry, television, video etc as they are yours during your stay.
Full house rental is also available. I am looking forward to meeting you.

Queenstown
Bed & Breakfast
Address: "Brecman Lodge" 15 Man Street
Name: Pat & Kevin MacDonell
Telephone: (03) 442 8908
Beds: 1 Double, 5 Single (3 Bedrooms)
Bathroom: 1 Guests share, 1 Family share
Tariff: B&B (continental) Double $75, Single $55. Credit Cards. Vouchers accepted 1st May - 31st October, Extras by arrangement
Nearest Town: Queenstown 2 minutes walk from the centre of town

Brecman Lodge is homestyle NZ hospitality at its best. Brecman Lodge is situated on the corner of Brecon and Man Streets, opposite the top of the Brecon Street steps, just above Queenstown's town centre.

Brecman Lodge is friendly, warm and comfortable with single, twin and family accommodation. Upstairs is a bathroom and two bedrooms; one room has a double bed and the other has two single beds. Downstairs consists of guest lounge, bedroom with two single beds and a guest share bathroom. The warm comfortable guest lounge has a television and a wonderful view of the Queenstown's township, Lake Wakatipu, Walter Peak and The Remarkables. A continental breakfast is served in the lounge.

From Brecman Lodge guests have easy walking access to the town centre, Lake Wakatipu and the Gondola. Queenstown's centre has a wide range of quality tourist shops, many restaurants and sporting and adventure opportunities all year round.

There is ample and easy off street parking.

Do come and stay - I'm sure you'll love it.

We rely on your comments about our B&Bs.
Please send us a comment form from the back of the book.

Queenstown

Homestay
Address: 17 Wakatipu Heights, Queenstown
Name: Ann & Mike Walther
Telephone: (03) 442 9414
Beds: 2 Double, 3 Single (3 Bedrooms) **Bathroom:** 3 Ensuite
Tariff: B&B (continental) Double $80, Single $45, Dinner $26
Nearest Town: Queenstown 7 minutes walk

BED &
BREAKFAST

Our home is 100 metres above Lake Wakatipu on the side of Queenstown hill. We offer breathtaking views of lake and mountains yet within walking distance to downtown Queenstown. Guests are accommodated in three new tastefully appointed garden bedrooms, each with ensuite bathrooms and deck overlooking Lake Wakatipu, Kelvin Heights Golf Course, yacht club and the Remarkable Mountains.

Wake to the sound of native birds in this quiet peaceful location. Personal attention from your hosts Ann and Mike Walther who enjoy meeting new friends sharing experiences while offering a little piece of third generation Kiwi hospitality or if preferred, your privacy will be respected.

Tea and coffee making facilities also available in rooms. As we are non smokers we ask that you don't smoke indoors. Ann and Mike look forward to welcoming guests into their new homestay accommodation. Please phone for reservations.

Directions: *Turn up Suburb Street off Frankton Road, then 1st right into Panorama Tce, second left into Wakatipu Heights.*

Cromwell - Lake Dunstan

Self-contained Cottage
Address: Brewery Creek, Cromwell Gorge, SH8
Name: Stephen & Sandra
Telephone: (03) 445 1365
Beds: 1 Double, 3 Single (2 to 3 Bedrooms)
Bathroom: 1 Private
Tariff: B&B (continental) Double $70, Single $40, Children half price, Campervans up to 4 people $30. Credit cards accepted. Vouchers accepted
Nearest Town: 5km south of Cromwell on SH8

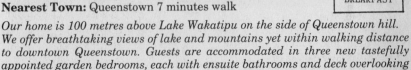

Brewery Creek cottage nestles amongst tall trees in a secluded nook on the shores of Lake Dunstan. An historic site, it was once part of Josef Kuhtze's nineteenth century brewery.

The hot summer, rocks and lakes of this starkly beautiful region attracted us to settle in Central after many years sailing the world. Guests are welcome to use our canoe kept on the beach in front of the cottage. We have a racing catamaran for more experienced sailors.

Our family enjoy exploring the spectacular countryside; tramping, horse-trekking, mountain biking, hunting, fishing and gold panning are all popular local pursuits. There are a growing number of vineyards on Central's wine-tasting trail. For the more energetic there are abseiling, rock climbing, jet boating, white water rafting and bungie jumping, and in winter, a choice of four major skifields within easy reach.

Along with the usual amenities and home comforts, including a washing machine, the cottage has wood fires and a coal range.

Note: Building was not completed at time of inspection, phone to confirm.

Clyde
Fruit Farm Stay
Address: P O Box 56, Clyde
Name: Peter and Wilma Paulin
Telephone: (03) 449 2875
Beds: 1 Double, 2 Single (2 bedrooms)
Bathroom: 1 Ensuite, 1 Family share, 1 Guests share Spa bath
Tariff: B&B (full) Double $$65-75, Single $35-$40,
Dinner $16 (by arrangement), Children half price, Vouchers accepted
Nearest Town: Alexandra 10km

*We are semi-retired orchardists, living adjacent to the family orchard on a rise
overlooking the small township of Clyde, and 1/2km from Lake Dunstan.*
*Clyde is an old goldmining town originally called Dunstan, and was the centre of
the Dunstan gold-rush in the 1860's.*
*It is now a prosperous fruit and grape growing area. Situated in the heart of
Central Otago, it is only an hours drive from Queenstown, Wanaka, and all the ski
fields in the area.*
*Come and drive or walk through the orchard, especially in the Springtime blossom
or with its spectacular Autumn colours. See the packingshed in operation (in
season).*
*Have a conducted tour of the Clyde Dam, (1km away). Go fishing from the banks
of Lake Dunstan, or climb amongst the hills.*
Use us as your base for visiting the area.
Cot and highchair available.
We look forward to your visit.

Clyde

Homestay
Address: 6 Drivers Rest, Clyde
Name: Evelyn and Hugh Smith
Telephone: (03) 449 2419
Beds: 1 Double, 2 Single (2 Bedrooms) **Bathroom:** 1 Guests share, 1 Family share
Tariff: B&B (continental) Double $55, Single $30, Children half price, Dinner $15, Campervans welcome. Vouchers accepted
Nearest Town: Clyde (Alexandra)

Your hosts Evelyn and Hugh, semi-retired, family all married. We have travelled overseas many times enjoy meeting people. Warm welcome awaits you in our spacious new home, electric blankets on all beds, laundry facilities available.
Clyde's historic gold mining town with many old stone buildings fishing in new Lake Dunstan. We're walking distance to Hydro Dam (Clyde Dam), Historic Engine Museum, Olivers Restaurant, golf club, bowling club. One hour drive to Queenstown, Wanaka, skifields in winter.
Directions: *Clydes 2nd turn of into Hazziet Street. 4th street on left Whitby Street, turn left into Drivers Rest, first on right.*

Cromwell

Homestay/
Self-contained Accommodation
Address: 3 Alpha St, Cromwell, Central Otago
Name: Cottage Gardens
Telephone: (03) 445 0628 (Phone evenings and prior to arrival)
Beds: 2 Single (1 Bedroom) **Bathroom:** 1 Ensuite
Tariff: B&B (continental) Double $65, Single $50, Dinner $15
Nearest Town: Cromwell, 1km to town centre

Cromwell is renowned for the New Lake Dunstan which our home and orchard overlooks. A 2 minute walk thru the orchard brings you to good fishing.
Central Otago is famous for summer fruits, especially apricots which we grow. We welcome you to share our lifestyle. Although our home is not big it's cosy and just right of a chat by the fire at night or on the verandah in the warmer weather. Our two sons are in their early 20's and working away.
Animals and poultry are part of our lives so fresh eggs are plentiful along with home grown vegetables. Gardening is high on our list of interests as we are developing the garden surrounding the house. Colin has been in Lions for 15 years and enjoys meeting other Lions from around the world.
Excellent recreation facilities, the golf course is within walking distance. 4 ski fields just over an hours drive. Queenstown 40 mins drive.
We prefer non-smokers and no children. Welcome to Cromwell.
Note: Building was not completed at time of inspection, phone to confirm.

Alexandra
Homestay
Address: 6 Rapuke Street, Alexandra
Name: Marion and John Clarke
Telephone: (03) 448 7885
Beds: 1 Double, 2 Single (2 bedrooms) **Bathroom:** 1 Guests share
Tariff: B&B (full) Double $55, Single $30, Dinner $15, Children half price, Vouchers accepted
Nearest Town: Alexandra 1kn

We are retired sheep and cropping farmers who are enjoying the unique beauty of Central Otago and wish to share our home with guests. Our home is sunny and warm and in a very peaceful cul-de-sac. All bedrooms have electric blankets and bedside lamps with easy access to guest bathroom. Laundry facilities available. Alexandra has the distinction of being the driest town in New Zealand and noted for its fruit growing. With its unique scenery and close proximity to newly formed Lake Dunstan it offers fine fishing as do the rivers close by. We are only 1km from town centre. We do not have pets.
Directions: *From town centre travel out Tarbert Street for approximately 1km. Turn right into Rawhiti Street then right into Rapuke Street.*

Earnscleugh - Alexandra
Orchard Stay
Address: "Iversen" 10 Blackman Road, Earnscleugh, Alexandra
Name: Robyn & Roger Marshall
Telephone: (03) 449 2520
Beds: 2 Double (2 Bedrooms)
Bathroom: 1 Guests share
Tariff: B&B (continental) Double $70, Single $40, Dinner $23, Vouchers accepted.
Nearest Town: Alexandra 6km, Clyde 8km

Located in the heart of Central Otago's orchard and vineyard district, you will find our modern home and restful detached guest accommodation. We invite you to sample the grandeur and beauty of the Central Otago landscape and share with us the peace and tranquillity of the location of our property.
For the active person there is golfing, fishing, hunting, ice-skating and more, all with in 10 minutes drive. For those with other interests the area has excellent restaurants and vineyards, craft galleries, beautiful gardens, museums and areas to visit to see gold mining history.
4 Wheel Drive trips into the hills, orchard tours, fishing trips, garden visits, and wine trails etc are available at extra cost. (Please indicate interest in these when booking.)
You can drive to Wanaka or Queenstown in less than an hour. You are welcome to enjoy our swimming pool (summer) garden setting and orchard, and if visiting early summer, you may pick your own cherries.
Directions: *From Alexandra or Clyde, travel on Earnscleugh Rd, turn into Blackman Rd. Our sign is on your left approximately 300m down the road. We would prefer advanced booking.*
Note: Building was not completed at time of inspection, phone to confirm.

532

Alexandra

Homestay
Address: Airport Road,
Alexandra, Central Otago
Name: Faye & Sam Smith
Telephone: (03) 448 7828
Beds: 2 Single (1 Bedroom)
Bathroom: 1 Private
Tariff: B&B (full) Double $65, Single $40,
Dinner $20, Campervans $20, Vouchers accepted
Nearest Town: Alexandra 5km

Our spacious home is in a tranquil setting with large gardens and swimming pool on 10 acres just five minutes from Alexandra in the heart of Central Otago. We are ideally situated to all the attractions of the area. Fishing and golf just minutes away. We have a grown up family of two, our West Highland Terrier and our cat. We graze cattle on our property.
We enjoy travel and people and offer a warm welcome to those from overseas and New Zealand and are happy to assist with information on sightseeing.
Undercover parking available and laundry fac. if required. We are non smokers. Please phone for bookings.
Airport Road is a small loop road off State Highway 8 between Alexandra and Clyde.

Becks

Farmstay
Address: Becks,
RD2, Omakau, Central Otago
Name: Earl and Pam Harrex
Telephone: (03) 447 3609
Beds: 1 Double, 2 Single (2 bedrooms)
Bathroom: 1 Family share
Tariff: B&B (full) Double $60, Single 35, Children under 12 half price, Dinner $20 p.p, Campervans $25, Vouchers accepted
Nearest Town: Alexandra 45 km

We farm sheep and deer. Guests are always welcome to assist with farming activities. We are a family of five - our three children at places of learning in Dunedin. Our older style homesteat is set in picturesque grounds. A large open fire, plus central heating provides a cosy home during the winter. Meals are served using home grown produce with local wines. All guests beds have electric blankets. Family interests include gardening, fishing, patchwork, sports including curling, a traditional winter sport. Two hours travel to four major ski fields.
We offer guests trips to historical St Bathans and other nearby goldmining ghost towns. We welcome guests to our quiet, peaceful rural setting with magnificent views of the vast openness of Central Otago.
A special extra is a choice of 4WD trips into the outback. Options to suit your watch and wallet. To make arrangements 2 days notice is preferred.
Directions: *From Alexandra take State Highway 85 to Becks Hotel. Next left turn - 2km to named motor gate on left - 163*

Oturehua

Countrystay
Address: 'Carngham' Ida Valley Rd,
Oturehua, Central Otago
Name: Annette and Neville
Telephone: (03) 444 5846
Beds: 2 Double, 3 Single (3 bedrooms)
Bathroom: 1 Family share
Tariff: B&B (full) Double $75, Single $45,
Dinner by arrangement, Vouchers accepted
Nearest Town: Ranfurly 15 minutes

You are assured of a warm welcome in our cosy home, one of the early sun-dried homesteads built in the Ida Valley, set in Central Otago's rugged landscape.

The early history is one of goldmining, an historic engineering works and ancient Maori trails and quarry sites dating from the 11th century.

This rural area with its climatic extremes in summer and winter offers typical New Zealand farming activities, with vineyards and orchards close by and an exciting landscape for walkers, photographers and painters.

Fishing and hunting trips can be arranged. Skiing, skating and the unique sport of curling are the main winter activities, with a bracing day followed by country style cuisine in a warm hospitable atmosphere.

Neville and I enjoy gardening (growing many of our own supplies), exploring our beautiful environment, and caring for our goats. I also spin goats hair and wool and enjoy pottery at nearby Ranfurly.

Otago's main city, Dunedin is 1 and 3/4 hours away.

Directions: *Please telephone or write.*

Many homes have facilities for campervans. The ideal camping spot with
electricity, bathroom, laundry and friendly hospitality.
Tell campervanners about this when you see them.

Macraes Flat

Farmstay
Address: "Red Bank" Palmerston 3RD Otago
Name: Kathleen Aitken
Telephone: (03) 465 2432
Beds: 4 Single (2 Bedrooms) **Bathroom:** 1 Ensuite, 1 Family share
Tariff: B&B (continental) Double $55, Dinner $25
Nearest Town: Palmerston, Otago

We are approximately 38km from Palmerston Otago and equal distances from Oamaru, Dunedin and Alexandra (88km). Enjoy the quietness and away from it all feeling among the tussocks and schist rocks.
You can enjoy the walks, play our versions of croquet, putting and Petanque or join in some of the farm activities. We have sheep, cattle, horses, angora goats, a donkey called Muppet, farm dogs and Tibby my Lhaso Apso, who does not go on furniture or beds.
Visit the biggest open cast gold mine in the Southern Hemisphere (so I am told). This is by appointment. We love it here and hope you will too.
We look forward to extending to you our welcome.
Further information contact Kathleen Aitken Phone & Fax 03 4652 432.

Palmerston

Country Homestay
Address: "Centrewood",
No.1 RD Palmerston, Otago
Withdrawn—Property Sold
Beds: 1 Double, 4 Single (3 bedrooms)
Bathroom: 1 Private, 1 Family share
Tariff: B&B (full) Double $70, Single $40, Children under 12 $30, Dinner $20

Hosts are retired farmers living on part of original farm. Centrewood is a large country home built by hosts Grandfather - well maintained in keeping its tradition - situated in twenty acres of native bush. The Tavora Reserve (Yellow eyed penguin) is situated next to our boundary. The penguins may be viewed coming a shore in the early evenings during the months October to March.
We welcome the opportunity to meet guests and to share our large colonial home. The guest wing is very comfortable having 1 double and 2 twin bedrooms, electric blankets, large games room with pool table, coffee and tea making facilities.
We both play golf. Wendy interested in all crafts but currently doing patchwork and quilting. We also play bridge. We have a tennis court, and spacious lawns and garden offer a quite tranquil rest area.
Dunedin is 40 minutes drive away. We suggest a two night stay to explore the local scene.
Directions: *Please phone*

Warrington
Country Home Accommodation
Address: Sunny Hill Farm,
Coast Road, Warrington, Otago
Name: Angela & Maurice Corish
Telephone: (03) 4822 631
Beds: 1 Double (1 Bedroom)
Bathroom: 1 ensuite
Tariff: B&B (full) Double $65, Dinner $25pp, Vouchers accepted
Nearest Town: 18km north of Dunedin, off SH1

Sunny Hill Farm is located outside the seaside village of Warrington, just off SH1. We offer a sunny double room upstairs, overlooking the sea and farmland, in a 100 year old home set in a secluded rambling wild garden. The 25 acres, with sheep, goats, 2 kune pigs, 3 cats and Jess the sheep dog are worth a walk around after breakfast.

Tariff includes a full farm-style breakfast; interesting home cooking for dinner, using fresh home grown and seasonal local produce. Tea and coffee making facilities available.

We are a semi-retired couple interested in country life, antiques, old houses, cookery and books.

Nearby is the newly opened Tavora Reserve (Yellow-eyed penguins) Moeraki Boulders, beaches, bush-walking, and Dunedin's numerous attractions.

No smoking and no pets please.

Directions: *Please phone.*

Dunedin
Homestay
Address: Magnolia House,
18 Grendon Street,
Maori Hill, Dunedin
Name: Joan & George Sutherland
Telephone: (03) 467 5999
Beds: 2 Double, 2 Single (3 bedrooms)
Bathroom: 1 Guests share, 1 Family share
Tariff: B&B (special) Double $70, Single $45
Nearest Town: Dunedin city centre 2 km

We live in a superior suburb on half an acre of land, one third of which is native bush with wood pigeons, tuis, bellbirds and fantails. The rest is in lawn and attractive gardens.

Our 1910 house is spacious with a large dining room and drawing room, and a more intimate sitting room.

The double room has its own large balcony looking out on lawns and bush. The guest rooms are airy and have antiques. Guests' bathroom with shower and tub. There is central heating and piano.

Two nights in Dunedin is a must. We are very close to Otago Golf Club and can supply clubs and bag. Also nearby is Olveston stately home and Moana Olympic-size swimming pool. The Otago peninsula is a wonderful day's sightseeing.

We have two cats, a courtesy car, bus nearby and no smoking.

Directions: Please phone

Dunedin

Homestay
Address: Harbourside Bed & Breakfast,
6 Kiwi Street, St Leonards, Dunedin
Name: Shirley and Don Parsons
Telephone: (03) 471 0690
Beds: 2 Double, 3 Single (2 bedrooms)
Bathroom: 1 Guests share
Tariff: B&B (full) Double $65, Single $45, Children 4-12 half price, under 4 free;
Dinner $18, Credit cards accepted, Vouchers accepted
Nearest Town: Dunedin (approx. 7 km to City Centre)

We live in a quiet suburb 10 minutes from the city centre. Our home overlooks the lovely Otago Harbour and is within easy reach of many of the local attractions _ Larnach Castle, Olveston, the Albatross colony and Disappear-ing Gun, Portobello Aquarium, Harbour Cruises and Taieri Gorge Excursion Train, also Yellow-eyed penguins.
Dunedin is a lovely city situated at the head of the Otago harbour with many interesting and historic stone buildings to view.
There are also many lovely bush walks within easy reach of the city.
We have two rooms available, one with a double and single bed and one with a double and bunks and cot available. Children very welcome and we have a generous amount of living space for you to relax..
Directions: *Driving into City on the one-way system watch for Port Chalmers Highway 88 sign, follow Anzac Avenue onto Ravensbourne Road. Continue down the Harbourside approximately 5 km to St Leonards. Turn left at the church opposite the boatshed into Pukeko Street then left into Kaka Road then straight ahead to Kiwi Street, turn left. Courtesy car available. See you soon.*

Dunedin

Homestay
Address: 24 Easther Crescent, Kew, Dunedin
Name: Mrs Betty Anderson
Telephone: (03) 4557-637
Beds: 1 King, 2 Single (2 bedrooms) **Bathrooms**: 1 Ensuite, 1 Family share
Tariff: B&B (continental) Double $70, Single $40

Our modern home is situated on a rise and offers a wonderful view of the harbour and surrounding hills. The double room has an ensuite and both bedrooms have heating and electric blankets and sun all day. The twin room shares the host's bathroom. A large lounge and living room are available to guests with washing machine and dryer also available. An excellent hotel is situated within five minutes walk and offers first class meals seven days a week and very reasonably priced. It is only four minutes away to public transport and seven minutes by car from city centre. Golf courses, bowling greens, tennis courts and most sports are nearby. I'm retired and involved with several organisations in our city.
Although a short distance from a main thoroughfare I am situated at the end of a private road.

Our B&Bs are mostly private homes.
Most do not accept credit cards.

Dunedin
Guest House
Address: 342 High Street, Dunedin
Name: Deacons Court
Telephone: (03) 477 9053
Fax: (03) 477 5350

Beds: 3 Double, 7 Single (5 bedrooms)
Bathrooms: 2 Guest share
Tariff: B&B (special) Double $90 & $70, Single $50 & $40, Children negotiable, Dinner on special request. Vouchers accepted minimum stay 2 nights.
Nearest Town: Dunedin

Our 100 year old home was the Manse for St Andrews, a prominent inner city Presbyterian Church and the home of Rutherford Waddell, a compelling preacher and noted social reformer.

The house is spacious and sunny, comfortably furnished, with a seaparate guest lounge and a conservatory. Browsing in the bookshelves is encouraged and so are laughter, music making and conversation.

Some of our general interests are New Zealand theatre, art and books. We have particular interest in organic gardening, eco-tourism, heritage buildings and environmental protection.

Deacons Court is 3 blocks (uphill) from the central business area and 10 minutes walk from the Visitor Centre in the Octagon (the city centre).

Many good restaurants are available within 5 minutes walk although light evening meals are available by specail request (24 hours notice please).

We cater for non-smokers and have a sprightly 14 year old outdoor cat.

Dunedin
Homestay
Address: Pine Heights Retreat, 431 Pine Hill Road, Dunedin
Name: Eli & Lindsay Imlay
Telephone: (03) 473-9558
Fax: (03) 477 4456
Beds: 1 Double (Queen), 2 Singles, (2 bedrooms)
Bathroom: 1 Guests share
Tariff: B&B (Full) Double $80, Single $45, children (under 12) 1/2 price, Dinner $25, Credit cards accepted, Vouchers accepted
Nearest Town: Dunedin (4.5 kms to centre)

Relax in the comfort of our cozy home with tranquil rural setting where native birds are frequent visitors. Enjoy our sheltered patio and cottage garden which we love. Absorb the peacefulness of our surroundings - views shared by all living and bedroom areas. It's like living in the country yet only a few minutes by car from the city centre. Public transport nearby, courtesy car available and ample off-street parking.

We will do our utmost to make your stay memorable. Flexible mealtimes allow time for sightseeing in our lovely city. We enjoy meeting people and welcome you to share our home and informal lifestyle. Eli, who has lived in Dunedin for over 25 years is Norwegian, and offers a unique blend of Scandinavian and New Zealand hospitality. Our dinners accompanied by complimentary wine and followed by real Norwegian style coffee are a specialty. Children of all ages most welcome.
Directions: *Please phone, preferably before 9.00am or after 5.00pm*

Dunedin

Guest house
Address: Alvand House,
3 Union Street, Dunedin
Telephone: (03) 477-7379
Fax: (03) 477 6638
Beds: Single, Double, Triple (6 bedrooms)
Bathroom: 2 Guests share
Tariff: B&B (contental, cooked by request)
Double $68, Single $48, children half price,
Credit cards accepted. Vouchers accepted
Nearest Town: Alvand House is centrally located in Dunedin.

Alvand House

Built as a "Gentleman's Residence" in 1912, Alvand House is located very centrally with off-street parking. Set back from the road behind a colourful garden it appears a sight from an earlier and more gracious era. This impression is strengthened upon entering, as a wide, pannelled, central hall gives onto spacious sunny rooms embellished with scotia and stained glass windows.
A skillful blend of contemporary furniture and modern conveniences provides present day comfort in period surroundings. The location ensures a quiet night's sleep, while it is only a five minute walk to the main shopping area, the University of Otago and the Otago Museum. An additional ten minutes will take you to the Early Settlers' Museum or to Olveston (a home of the same era on a very grand scale), all of which warrant a leisurely visit. For the convenience of our welcome guests, we have full laundry facilities. Allergy sufferers need not be concerned about pets.

Dunedin

Homestay
Address: "Castlewood"
240 York Place, Dunedin
Name: Lance & Lois Woodfield
Telephone: (03) 477 0526
Beds: 2 Double, 3 Single (4 bedrooms)
Bathroom: 1 Guests share, 1 Family share
Tariff: B&B (full) Double $80-$60, Single $40-$35. Vouchers accepted.

"Castlewood" is situated in central Dunedin, on the City Rise, just 4 blocks from the Octagon, and within easy walking distance of many restaurants and all amenities.
Besides being gracious and comfortable, our 80 year old tudor-style home has many interesting features. These include the panelled entrance hall and drawing room with beamed ceilings and leadlight windows, and a unique arched ceiling in the upstairs lounge.
The 'guest suite' consists of one queen and one double bedded room, a luxury bathroom with spa bath and sauna, a sunny sitting room , and tea-making facilities in the farm-style kitchen. The two upstairs bedrooms have a shared bathroom, and a laundry is available to guests. Light meals available on request.
Much of the furniture, including bookcases housing collections of rare books, has been restored by Lance, while his 'wood' and 'tap' sculptures provide interest and amusement.
We are a recently retired couple who have travelled overseas and enjoy meeting people.

Dunedin
Heritage Hotel
Address: 34 Alva Street, Dunedin
Name: Margi & Paul Harris
Telephone & Fax: (03) 477 9413
Cellphone: 025 320 500
Beds: 3 Double (3 bedrooms) **Bathrooms:** 3 ensuites
Tariff: B&B (continental) Double $120. Credit Cards.

Barnett Lodge will appeal to the traveller seeking accommodation at the upper end of the range.

It is a handsome heritage residence of English Tudor architecture, built of the finest materials for Arthur Barnett, Dunedin's leading retailer, in 1938.

It features an original oak panelled and beamed reception area and lounge, furnished elegantly, with accompanying sunroom and dining room on the ground floor. The lodge is centrally heated.

There are three suites upstairs, each with private fully appointed ensuite. Decor is peaceful and attractive with all facilities completely upgraded in 1993. The atmosphere is sunny and quiet. Bed and bedding are of top quality.

You are assured of a warm, friendly and informative reception and stay. Breakfasts are generous and cater for all tastes. We are strictly non smoking.

Our location is within five minutes drive from the city centre in a quiet suburb adjacent to parks and authentic bush walks.

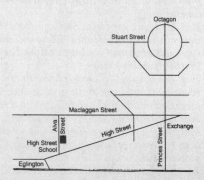

540

Dunedin

Homestay
Address: Nisbet Cottage,
6a Elliffe Place, Shiel Hill, Dunedin
Name: Kerry Kirkland
Telephone: (03) 454 5590
Beds: 3 Double, 2 Single (3 bedrooms, twin available)
Bathroom: 3 Ensuite
Tariff: B&B (special) Double $75 & $80, Single $50, Children $10, Vouchers accepted 1 May to 30 September

Kia ora! Welcome to Dunedin. We are situated 7 minutes by car from town, just off the high road to the Otago Peninsula, a perfect location to base your trips to the Albatross Colony, yellow eyed penguins and Larnachs Castle.

Nisbet Cottage was built by the Presbyterian church in 1930s and has been restored and redecorated by ourselves over the last 2 years. House has outstanding views of city, area is peaceful and quiet.

Nigel and I greatly enjoy meeting travellers and sharing a laugh. We have 2 small, sociable daughters, Zoe and Joanna.

Bedrooms have ensuite bathrooms, tea / coffee making facilities and a welcoming fruit basket. Beds are firm, comfortable, have electric blankets and warm duvets. You are welcome to relax in front of open fire in either of two adjoining lounges (one with TV).

Breakfast includes fresh fruit salad, fresh bread, home made muffins and jams, dried fruits and cereals, pure juices, freshly ground coffee and selection of teas. For those who dare. . .our cooked breakfast can include bacon, eggs, mushrooms, tomatoes and pancakes with cream and passionfruit.

We both have a wide knowledge of Dunedin's attractions and are happy to provide you with sightseeing information and book tours for you. Laundry available. We are non smoking and have no pets. Children very welcome.

Directions: *South east on Andersons Bay Road onto Musselburgh Rise. After 1.5kms Musselburgh Rise continues into Silverton St. Proceed 300m then left Highcliff Road (big blue sign). Proceed 700m, 1st left Every St, 1st right Albion St, 1st left Elliffe Place.*

Dunedin
Guest House, Self-contained Accommodation
Address: 619 George St, Dunedin
Name: Sahara Guest House
Telephone: (03) 477 6662
Fax: (03) 479 2551
Beds: 5 Double, 15 Single (10 bedrooms), 10 Self-contained units
Bathroom: 2 Ensuite, 5 Guests share
Tariff: B&B (full) Double $75-$79, Single $45-$55, Children $15, Self-contained units: Double $69, Single $59, Children $8, Credit cards accepted

New Zealand's
Federation of Bed &
Breakfast Hotels

This gabled brick guesthouse was built as a substantial family home in 1906. It now holds 10 rooms: 2 with ensuites; 8 (with handbasins in each room) share the 2 bathrooms which have a total of 5 seperate showers, 1 bath and three toilets.

The house is centrally located; just a short walk to city centre, botanic gardens, museum, Otago University and is on a major bus route. The hearty breakfast served in our bright dining room consists of a buffet style continental as well as a cooked breakfast menu. Evening dining can be enjoyed at any of the local hotels, cafes or restaurants which are within easy walking distance.

The house is kept warm and cosy with central heating as well as additional heaters in the bedrooms and electric blankets on all beds.

Laundry facilities are available for our guests and off street parking for those who require it.

The "Sahara" also has fully self contained units available for those travellers wanting accommodation with private facilities, kitchen, television and telephones in each unit.

Dunedin City

Guest House
Address: 3 Peel St, Dunedin
Name: "Glenfield" (Cal and Wendy)
Telephone: (03) 453 5923
Beds: 2 Double, 2 Single (3 bedrooms)
Bathroom: 2 Ensuite, 1 Guests share
Tariff: B&B (special) Double $135, $110, $100, Single $75, $65, Dinner $30, Children welcome, Credit cards welcome

"Glenfield" is our restored Victorian residence situated on the edge of the town belt 2 km from the centre city.
All of our rooms have heating, electric blankets, feather and down duvets, television, tea and plunger coffee. Our facilities include an original billiard room with 3/4 size table, a congenial lounge with open fire, laundry and off-street parking.
At the top of our range we offer a special double room with ensuite and adjoining sun room - a suite of rooms where you may enjoy your own open fire, dine if you prefer and have your own access to the verandah to enjoy the harbour views and Dunedin's night lights.
A sumptuous 3 course meal, prepared from Otago produce, is served in the guest dining room each night. If you are staying more than one night and have a craving for some particular food just let us know. After dinner you may wish to adjourn to the drawing room for a complimentary glass of port.

Broad Bay, Dunedin

Homestay
Address: "Chy-an-Dowr"
687 Portobello Road, Broad Bay, Dunedin
Name: Herman and Susan Van Velthoven
Telephone: (03) 478 0306
Beds: 1 Queen (1 bedroom)
Bathroom: 1 Family share
Tariff: B&B (full) Double $75, Single $50. Vouchers accepted.
Nearest Town: Dunedin 16km

Our lovely home, on scenic Otago Peninsula halfway between Dunedin and the Albatross Colony, has beautiful views, all day sun and is situated directly opposite a small beach.
The guestrooms are upstairs; a main bedroom with queensize bed, electric blanket and heating. A guest lounge, with colour TV, tea/coffee making facilities; this room can also be used as an extra bedroom. Also a sunroom, all have extensive harbour views.
The upstairs bathroom is shared and has a separate shower, bath, toilet. Downstairs is a second toilet. Our lounge is large and comfortable.
The Otago Peninsula has many walkways, beaches and is well known for its Albatross Colony, Yellow-eyed Penguins and seals. Larnach Castle and Glenfalloch Gardens are nearby, as are two good restaurants.
As a family of four we emigrated 13 years ago from Holland.
Our work is home-based making architectural models.
Please phone beforehand. No smoking. We look forward to welcoming you in our home.
Directions: *Follow signs Peninsula. We are on the corner of Portobello Road and Clearwater Street in Broad Bay.*

Dunedin

Homestay
Address: "Captains Cottage"
422 Portobello Road, 2RD, Dunedin
Name: Robert Brown & Christine Doig
Telephone: (03) 476 1431
Mobile: 025-352-734
Beds: 1 Double, 2 Single (2 Bedrooms)
Bathroom: 1 Guests share
Tariff: B&B (continental) Double $75,
Single $45, Dinner $20, Vouchers accepted
Nearest Town: Dunedin 9km

An 8km scenic drive from the city centre, the Captains Cottage is located on the waterfront in a bush setting beside the Glenfalloch Gardens, on the beautiful Otago Peninsula, enroute to the Royal Albatross, Penguin and Seal colonies.
Robert is a specialist wildlife cameraman for the BBC and TVNZ who loves to share his interest in wildlife with visitors. Christine has travelled widely and with her wealth of local knowledge and contacts can help you organise an interesting stay.
We have our own sport fishing boat and can take you fishing or explore the unique bird and marine life found in the area.
So if you enjoy great food and hospitality; BBQ's, boating, lying in the sun, relaxing beside the log fire or having a drink as the sun sets on the deck of our boat shed, then let us share our interesting home with you.

Dunedin

Homestay
Address: Harbour Lookout, 3 Taupo St, Ravensbourne, Dunedin
Name: Ron & Maire Graham
Telephone: (03) 471 0582
Beds: 2 Single (1 Bedroom) **Bathroom:** 1 Family share
Tariff: B&B (full) Double $55, Single $30, Children half price, Dinner $18,
Campervans welcome. Vouchers accepted
Nearest Town: Dunedin

Welcome to Dunedin, Edinburgh of the South.
We are a retired couple who can assure you of a warm welcome to our comfortable new home in Ravensbourne, only 3km from Dunedin's Railway Station and therefore close to all wonderful attractions Dunedin has to offer.
To find us follow Port Chalmers Highway 88, along Anzac Ave, continue into Ravensbourne Road, along the harbour side until you reach Adderley Terrace which turns uphill behind Harbour View Hotel. On entering first bend be alert for signpost on your right for Taupo St and Lane, drive in turn right downhill and into our drive with ample off street parking. Your twin bedroom with private toilet adjacent is on this level. No carrying luggage upstairs, however our bathroom and living areas are upstairs and here you can relax with a cuppa and enjoy the wonderful view. Our interests are golf, bowls and gardening. We look forward to meeting you.

Tell other travellers about your favourite B&Bs

Albatross
Guest House

Dunedin
Guest House
Address: "Albatross Guesthouse" 770 George St, Dunedin
Name: Coralie Jackson & daughter Kerry
Telephone: (03) 477 2727
Beds: 8 Double, 5 Single (8 Bedrooms/Twin available)
Bathroom: 6 Ensuite, 2 Private
Tariff: B&B (special) Double $80-95, Single $50-65, Children $15, Credit cards accepted. Vouchers accepted from 1st May to 30 Sept.
Nearest Town: Dunedin City

Kia ora! Welcome to Dunedin and Albatross Guesthouse. We are a mother/ daughter team who look forward to meeting you and making your stay extra special.

Our character Edwardian residence, located on George St, lies on a main bus route and is near the exit from the northern motorway, short walk to city centre, museum, botanical gardens, university and hospital.

All rooms have ensuite/private bathrooms, large comfortable beds with electric blankets, warm duvets and tea/coffee making facilities. Downstairs bedroom has wheelchair access and own fire.

We take pride in our warm, friendly atmosphere and are pleased to offer you rooms whose 'themes' are based upon Otago's famous wildlife.

Advance bookings strongly recommended for Albatross and Hoiho (Yellow-eyed penguin) rooms. Several rooms have own kitchenette, microwave and TV, ideal longer stays. Discounts available, please enquire.

Our sumptuous breakfasts prove too much for even the hungriest albatrosses. Choose from selection of fresh breads, fruit salad, homemade muffins and jams, dried fruits and cereals. Pure juice, freshly ground coffee, selection of teas.

Cooked breakfasts include bacon, eggs, tomatoes, mushrooms, pancakes with cream and fresh fruit toppings.

We both have wide knowledge of Dunedin's attractions and are happy to provide you with sightseeing information and book tours for you. See you soon!

Guest laundry, non-smoking. Major credit cards accepted.

When you stay at B&Bs you are staying with "dinkum Kiwis"

Portobello, Dunedin

Homestay
Address: 3 Landreth Street,
Portobello, Dunedin
Name: "The Ferry House"
Telephone: (03) 478 0497
Beds: 1 Double, 2 Single (2 bedrooms)
Bathrooms: 2 Private
Tariff: B&B (special) Double $85, Single $60,
Nearest Town: Dunedin 20 mins

*Our historic harbourside home on the Otago Peninsula, is set in three quarters of
an acre of gardens. The two warm, comfortable upstairs bedrooms have glorious
views of the harbour while both guest bathrooms, complete with deep cast-iron
bath, overlook the garden.*
*Your hosts, Nicola and Doug, serve a three course breakfast in the dining room
beside an open fire - or with the doors open to the verandah and sun. Our garden
is yours to explore and our charming downstairs sitting room somewhere to enjoy
a complementary early evening drink or a quiet read. We are a well travelled
couple with a young daughter whose interests range from geology and anthropology
to vintage radios! And we hope to make your stay on the Peninsula memorable.
We are a short drive from the Royal Albatross colony and penguin beaches, twenty
minutes from Dunedin and five minutes walk from Portobello village with it's
renowned 1908 Cafe.*
For further directions please telephone.

Waihola

Homestay/
Self-contained Accommodation
Address: Sandown Street,
Waihola, South Otago
Name: Lillian and Trevor Robinson
Telephone: (03) 417-8218
Beds: 1 Double, 2 Single (2 bedrooms) **Bathroom:** 1 Ensuite, 1 Family share
Tariff: B&B (full) Double $55, Single $35, Dinner $18, Vouchers accepted
Nearest Town: 40 km south of Dunedin

*We have a very comfortable home which is situated in a quiet street with views of
mountains, Lake and township.*
*Our double bedroom has ensuite, tea making facilities, TV and heater. All beds
have electric blankets. Dinner by arrangement.*
*Lake Waihola is very popular for boating, fishing and swimming. There is a
bowling green and a golf course within 10 minutes drive. We are only 15 minutes
from Dunedin Airport.*
We enjoy meeting people and ensure you a very pleasant stay.
Directions: *Please phone night before where possible.*

546

Waihola

Lakeside Cottage Homestay
Address: "Ivy Cottage", SH 1,
Waihola, Otago 9055
Name: Bryan & Robin Leckie
Telephone: (03) 417-8946
Beds: 1 Double, 2 Single (2 bedrooms)
Bathroom: 1 Private, 1 Family share
Tariff: B&B (full) Double $65, Single $40,
Children under 12 $20, Dinner $20 per person, Vouchers accepted.
Nearest Town: 40 km South of Dunedin on SH 1,
15km from Dunedin Airport.

*"Ivy Cottage" is only 30 minutes drive south of Dunedin on State Highway 1.
Our double guest accommodation is detached from "Ivy Cottage" in an eye-catching building affectionately known as "The Shed". In "Ivy Cottage" we offer
2 single beds with share facilities. All beds have electric blankets.*
*We are retired Restaurateurs, and continue our interests in food and wines. Other
interest include, power boating, sailing, fishing, bird watching, golf, bowls, travelling,
gardening, crafts, bridge, and keeping in touch with our extended family.*
*Lake Waihola and the waterways are well known for their birdlife and fishing.
The waterways extend to the Sinclair Wetlands, a wildlife reserve, Waipori Lake
and the Taieri River down to the sea at Taieri Mouth.*
*We enjoy hosting people and look forward to sharing the warmth of "Ivy Cottage"
with future travellers.*
Directions: *Please phone. Transport can be arranged from the Airport or Bus /
Train terminals.*

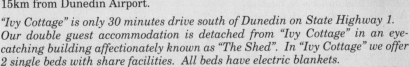

Lawrence

Homestay+Self-contained
Accommodation
Address: "Marama Lodge"
State Highway 8, Lawrence
Name: Dawn & Wayne Bosley
Telephone: (03) 4859 139
Beds: 1 Double, 2 Single (2 Bedrooms) ,
Self-contained: Sleeps 5, 2 Bedrooms **Bathroom:** 1 Guests share
Tariff: B&B (full) Double $65, Single $35, Dinner only by arrangement, Children
welcome. Vouchers accepted
Nearest Town: Lawrence 1km

*Century old Marama Lodge is set amongst majestic trees with a veranda
overlooking gardens, trees and the tennis court. It is a great place to spend a quiet
hour or to eat in summer.*
*We are a family of four and our well behaved friendly children are aged 6 and 8
years. We have an assortment of pets ranging from hens to two affectionate donkeys.
The Lodge is a spacious home with two bedrooms used for homestay within it, and
a large self-contained unit outside. The two large lounges give guests staying in
the Lodge the choice of spending time alone, or joining our family.*
*Lawrence is on the main road between Dunedin and Queenstown and we find
many of our guests are travelling between the two. We are widely travelled and
enjoy welcoming people from New Zealand and overseas.*

Milton
Farmstay
Address: Coal Gully Road RD Glenledi Milton
Name: Alan & Glenise Weir
Telephone: (03) 417 4031
Beds: 1 Double, 4 Single (3 Bedrooms) **Bathroom:** 1 Guests share
Tariff: B&B (full) Double $60, Single $35, Children half price, Dinner $20, Campervans $25, Vouchers accepted
Nearest Town: Milton 10 minutes

We live on a large sheep and cattle farm in the Glenledi district 12km east of Milton. Our modern home overlooks the Pacific Ocean, Tokomairiro River Estuary and holiday settlement.
Well situated 1 hour drive from Dunedin, and on the main route to Southland, Catlins or Fiordland and Lakes District.
Ideal stopover when travailing from Christchurch to Milford, Queenstown etc.
Our family are all married so we enjoy entertaining guests from all over the world.
Dinner by arrangement and 'spa' on request.
Close to fishing and golf.
No smoking in the house please.
For guest arriving by train or bus we are happy to meet you in Milton.
Directions: *Please phone.*

Balclutha
Farmstay/
Self-contained Accommodation
Address: "Balcairn", Blackburn Rd., Hillend, No 2RD, Balclutha, South Otago
Name: John & Karen Hallum
Telephone & Fax: (03) 418 1385
Beds: 1 Double, 3 Single (2 bedrooms) **Bathroom:** 1 Guest share
Tariff: B&B (Continental) Double $70, Single $35, Dinner $20, Children half price, Campervans $5pp, Vouchers accepted.
Nearest Town: Balclutha 22km, Milton 25km

Welcome to "Balcairn", your home away from home. 500 acres of green rolling countryside handy to State Highways 1 and 8, one hour south of Dunedin.
We are a family of four and can offer you a friendly and relaxing stay on a NZ sheep, deer and beef working farm. Guests are welcome to join in on any farm activities, including horseriding and rabbit shooting.
Our home is a modern spacious double storey house with guest bedrooms and facilities all downstairs. Cooking facilities if required. You are welcome to use the laundry.
Fishing, golf, hunting (deer) can be arranged with prior notice. The beautiful Catlins (bush walks), Kaka Point (Lighthouse, seals and penguins) just 45 minutes away. An ideal stopover for guests travelling to or from Te Anau 2 1/2 hours, Queenstown 3 hours.
Can meet bus or train at Balclutha or Milton or Dunedin airport 60km.
Children welcome.
Directions: *Please phone.*

Milton - Balclutha

Guest House, Country Inn
Address: State Highway 1,
Lovells Flat RD 2, Milton
Name: "Garvan Homestead"
Telephone / Fax: (03) 417-8407
Beds: 2 Double, 2 Single (3 bedrooms)
Bathroom: 1 Ensuite, 1 Guest share
Tariff: B&B (full) Double $100-130, Single $65-$90, Dinner a la carte, Credit cards accepted, Vouchers accepted Monday - Thursday, May - October.
Nearest Town: 10km between Milton / Balclutha on SH 1.

"Garvan Homestead" is a large historic Tudor style home set amid 16 acres of gardens and parkland, and a most restful stop-over for travellers.

The Homestead has been completely refurbished and decorated with period furniture - a step back in time for your indulgence.

We operate a small licensed restaurant and also serve Devonshire Teas and lunches. Our meals are fresh and tasty using local produce where possible.

Summer travellers can enjoy outdoor BBQ, or a game of tennis, or just laze about on any one of our balconies of patios.

Tea making facilities are in guest rooms for your convenience, and a elegant lounge with TV for your use.

Garvan is an experience you will long remember and as a family run business we look forward to being your hosts.

Keen fishermen are only 12km from the Clutha River and only 1 hour drive to the beautiful Catlins and Southern scenic coast and 2 hours drive to Te Anau.

Directions: *We are situated on SH1 approximately 13km south of Milton and opposite the historic "Old Sod Cottage". Please phone ahead for reservations if possible. Non smoking.*

Tariffs are constant for this year. However some
may have had to change slightly. Always check.

Stirling-Balclutha

Farmstay
Address: "Rotoiti" Farm,
Main Road, Stirling, South Otago
Name: Crawford & Janet Anderson
Telephone: (03) 418-0588
Beds: 4 Single (2 bedrooms)
Bathroom: 1 Family share
Tariff: B&B (special) Double $70, Single $35,
Dinner $20, Vouchers accepted
Nearest Town: Balclutha - 3 minutes

We welcome you to our comfortable 90 year old farm house with modern facilities. (Our adult family have all left.) It is surrounded by a woodland garden.

We have two guest bedrooms. Two single beds in each with innersprung mattresses on firm bases, electric blankets, heaters. Guests share bathroom and laundry facilities.

We provide 3 course dinner with N.Z. wine or fruit juice.

The Clutha River providing good fishing bounds the farm on three sides. Our son sharemilks on the farm which has been farmed by the Anderson family for over 100 years.

It is a modern dairy farm with rotary milking shed for 260 Friesian cows, supplying nearby Otago Cheese Company. We have 230 Drysdale sheep which graze floodbanks and pond paddock which is a refuge for ducks and a variety of wading birds.

The farm is one hours drive from Dunedin, 30 minutes from Nugget Point Lighthouse where there are yellow eyed penguins and a colony of fur seals. The farm is a comfortable stopover for travellers to Stewart Island or the Lakes District. A good road follows the Clutha River - an attractive route to Central Otago.
Directions: *Please phone ahead for booking.*

Clinton
Farmstay
Address: "Garton Downs" Kuriwao R D Clinton South Otago
Name: Morgan & Barbara Williams
Telephone: (03) 415 7363
Beds: 2 Single (1 Bedroom) **Bathroom:** 1 Private
Tariff: B&B (full) Double $65, Single $40, Dinner $20pp, Vouchers accepted
Nearest Town: Clinton 10km

"Garton Downs" is an 1800 acre sheep and cattle farm on hilly country, and is ideally located for an overnight stay between the Queenstown / Te Anau areas and Dunedin. It is also a convenient starting point for the scenic Catlins Coast. Fishing rivers are nearby. There are several specialist garden nurseries within easy driving distance.
The farmhouse is set in a developing garden with views to the surrounding hills. The guestroom has 2 comfortable, warm single beds, and includes a tea and coffee tray. The laundry is available.
Our home is smoke, and cat free. ("Puss" lives outside.)
We aim to make your stay a happy, comfortable, and memorable experience.
Directions: *"Garton Downs" is on the Clinton-Mataura Road. Leave State Highway 1 at the Oak Tree Inn, Clinton, and take the Gorge Road. Stay on this road for 10km. We are the first farm on the right after the turn-off to Owaka / Wyndham. Our name is on the mail box.*

Clinton
Farmstay
Address: "Wairuna Bush" Clinton
RD South Otago on Main South Highway 1
Name: Roy & Kathleen Carruthers
Telephone: (03) 415 7222
Beds: 2 Double, 2 Single (3 Bedrooms)
Bathroom: 1 Guests share
Tariff: B&B (full) Double $60, Single $40, Dinner $20, Vouchers accepted
Nearest Town: 32km south of Balclutha on SH1

KATHLEEN and ROY CARRUTHERS welcome you to their warm spacious home, set on 60 acres of farmland surrounded by native Podocarp Bush.
Unwind from your travel in peace and tranquillity.
Listen to Bellbirds, fantails and wood pigeons.
Follow newly formed walkways through 5 acres of native flora.
See Kahikatea, Matai, Miro and Totara trees (some being over 500 years old).
If you wish, Roy will be happy to introduce you to their farm dogs and thoroughbred horses, sheep, cows and calves.
Or take you for a game of bowls. There is a very challenging 9 hole golf course in Clinton and some extremely good fishing spots close by, or you can just laze around. Please phone or book in advance.

Kaka Point, Balclutha

Homestay +
Self-contained Accommodation
Address: Nuggets Road, Kaka Point,
Balclutha. (P O Box 47, Balclutha).
Name: Noel & Kath Widdowson
Telephone: (03) 412 8783
Beds: 1 Double, 2 Single (2 bedrooms) **Bathroom:** 1 Family share.
Tariff: B&B (continental) Double $55, Single $30, Dinner $15. Self-contained
flat sleeps four - Double $35, $10 extra person. Linen provided for $5pp.
Nearest Town: Balclutha 24kms.

*Our home is on the edge of the Nugget wildlife reserve, located on the Catlins
Southern Scenic route. Situated on a headland with spectacular views of the
Southern Ocean coastline and historic lighthouse.*

*We have a large comfortable home and separate self-contained flat. A large garden
provides vegetables and fresh herbs for the table with local shellfish whenever possible.*

*My interests include photography especially the wildlife, fur seals, Hooker
sealions, blue and yellow-eyed penguins. Our garden extends on to the beach
where you can fish, walk and swim.*

*We both enjoy tramping and can provide details of the many walks in the Catlins.
My husband is a farm valuer, our children all live away from home.*

We have a cat and friendly dog. We are the only accommodation at the Nuggets.

Directions: *3rd house on left, 6kms from Kaka Point store on Nugget Road.*

The standard of accommodation in *The New Zealand Bed and Breakfast Book*
ranges from homely to luxurious,
but you can always be sure of superior hospitality.

Owaka - (The Catlins)

Farmstay
Address: "Tarara Downs", RD2 Owaka, South Otago
Name: Ida and John Burgess
Telephone: (03) 415 8293
Beds: 1 Double, 2 Single (2 bedrooms) + Sleepout for 3;
Bathroom: 1 Family share
Tariff: B&B (full) Double $55, Single $35, Children half price;
Dinner $15 (3-course), $10 (2-course), Sleepout $10 per person, Campervans welcome, Vouchers accepted
Nearest Town: Owaka 16 km

Our 1661-acre farm is situated in an area renowned for its bush and coastal scenery, within walking distance of the beautiful Purakaunui Falls. Our farm runs sheep, cattle and deer.
As well as seeing normal farm activities, horse riding, bush walks and fishing trips are available in the district.
We live in a comfortable New Zealand farmhouse with two cats, as our family have all left home, and enjoy eating our own produce and local delicacies.
Children very welcome.
Directions: *Follow State Highway 92 to Owaka from Balclutha or Invercargill. Approximately 1 3/4 hours drive from Dunedin or Invercargill on a scenic road, follow signposts to Purakaunui Falls - we are the closest house to them.*

Owaka (The Catlins)

Farmstay + Self-Contained Cottage
Address: "Greenwood", Tarara, RD2 Owaka, South Otago
Name: Alan and Helen-May Burgess
Telephone: (03) 4158-259 (if no reply, phone after 6 pm)
Beds: 5 Single (3 bedrooms) **Bathroom:** 2 Family share
Tariff: B&B (full) Double $60, Single $45; Dinner $20, Children half price, Lunch if required; Campervans $25; Self contained house at Papatowai beach (sleeps 8) $50 per night (4 persons), $10 each extra person, Vouchers accepted
Nearest Town: Owaka 14 km

We farm in the Catlins district our homestead situated within walking distance from the beautiful Purakaunui Falls (features on the front cover of Wild New Zealand book).
Our home which is set in a large garden offers warm, comfortable accommodation for up to five persons. The main guest bedroom walks through to a furnished day-room with vanity unit (hand basin), giving you private living facilities and this opens to the outdoors. The bathroom, toilets and shower room are shared.
A three-course dinner may be provided.
Our 1900 acre farm is hilly to rolling country, farming sheep, cattle and deer. Alan enjoys taking people around the farm.
Our district features many beautiful scenic drives and walks through native forest and beaches. Trout, salmon or rock fishing may be enjoyed.
Directions: *Take Highway 92 to Owaka from Balclutha or Invercargill. From Owaka follow the signposts to Purakaunui Falls for 14 km. Our name and farm name is on the gate entrance (just before you reach the falls).*

Some hosts are away from home during the day.

Owaka (The Catlins)
Farmstay
Address: Glenomaru, No1 RD, Balclutha
Name: Bruce and Kathryn Wilson
Telephone: (03) 4158-282
Beds: 4 Single (2 bedrooms) **Bathroom:** 1 Family share
Tariff: B&B (full) Double $50, Single $30, Children half price; Dinner $15; Campervans $25. Vouchers accepted.
Nearest Town: Balclutha 22 km, Owaka 11 km

We farm a 1500 acre property carrying sheep, cattle and deer.
Guests may be taken on a farm tour, which includes an inspection of a 130 year old home presently being preserved and water wheel. We have a friendly fox terrier called "Boon".
Fishing trips may be arranged. Golf equipment available, 9 hole golf course only ten minutes drive.
We are near Kaka Point, renowned for beach, lighthouse and viewing the yellow-eyed penguins and seals.
You may have family dinner with us or if preferred bed and breakfast.
Guests can be collected off public transport from Balclutha free of charge.
Directions: *Take Highway 92 from Balclutha towards Owaka, first turn right past sawmill. From Owaka turn left beside sawmill up gravel road.*

Owaka (The Catlins)
Farmstay
Address: "Tocal" Highway 92 Owaka South Otago
Name: Betty Gorman
Telephone: (03) 4158 218
Beds: 1 Double, 1 Single (2 Bedrooms)
Bathroom: 1 Guests share
Tariff: B&B (full) Double $55, Single $35, Dinner $15. Vouchers accepted.
Nearest Town: Owaka 4km

"Tocal" is a 1050 acre sheep farm situated on the southern scenic route. It is 4 kilometres north of Owaka and is an ideal base from which to discover the Catlins. The farmhouse is set back from the road amongst trees.
The farm is managed by my eldest son who lives on the property.
You may share an evening meal with us or if you wish, just Bed and Breakfast. Home grown fruit and vegetables are served in season.
Coming from Balclutha Road access is 250m south of Cannibal Bay Road. The entrance is on the right.
We look forward to meeting you.

Owaka - The Catlins
Homestay
Address: 'Kepplestone Park' Surat Bay Road Newhaven Owaka
Name: Gay & Arch Maley
Telephone: (03) 415 8134
Beds: 2 Double, 2 Single (3 Bedrooms)
Bathroom: 1 Guests share, 1 Family share
Tariff: B&B (continental) Double $55, Single $35, Dinner $15, Campervans $20, Vouchers accepted
Nearest Town: Owaka 6km

Having taken early retirement we welcome guests to our home, situated one minute from a beautiful unspoiled sandy beach, at the confluence of the Catlins and Owaka rivers. For the enthusiasts, miles of unpolluted golden beach, deep sea and river fishing, golf links, swimming and seals basking on the beach, all within five minutes.

Having travelled extensively we understand the needs of fellow travellers and wish to share with you our homely atmosphere and hospitality. We have for many years hosted fellow amateur radio operators from throughout the world. (Gay ZL4JO)

We are both keen gardeners of our two acre property and organically grow our own vegetables. Share an evening meal with us, served with a glass of wine. Choice of menu with prior notice.

Directions: *At north end of Owaka follow signs to Pounawea, at golf course, go across bridge, follow signs to Newhaven and Surat Bay. First house on left on Surat Bay Road (3km from bridge).*

Owaka - The Catlins
Farmstay+Self-contained Accommodation
Address: "Hillview" Hunt Rd, Box 26 Owaka South Otago
Name: Kate & Bruce McLachlan
Telephone & Fax: (03) 415 8457
Beds: 1 Double, 4 Single (3 Bedrooms) **Bathroom:** 1 Guests share
Tariff: B&B (continental) Double $55, Single $40, Children under 12 half price, Dinner $15, Vouchers accepted
Nearest Town: Owaka (6km to the south)

Our cosy farmstay cottage is adjacent to our homestead. It is full self-contained with all modern appliances including microwave, TV, video and telephone.

Breakfast is provided in the privacy of the cottage and you are invited to dine with us in the evening by arrangement.

Our 450 acre sheep and cattle farm is also a haven for numerous unusual animals and pets.

Bruce enjoys breeding and training working farm dogs and Kate's interests are gardening, handcrafts and children. She breeds black sheep and spins their natural wool. We both enjoy meeting people.

The Catlins District features spectacular beaches, native bush walks, scenic drives, river lake or rock fishing and hunting in season.

We are 5 mins from the golf course and 15 mins from Nugget Point where you may visit the lighthouse or view the yellow-eyed penguins and seals.

Directions: *27km from Balclutha, 5km north of Owaka. 1.5km from the main highway. Please phone ahead.*

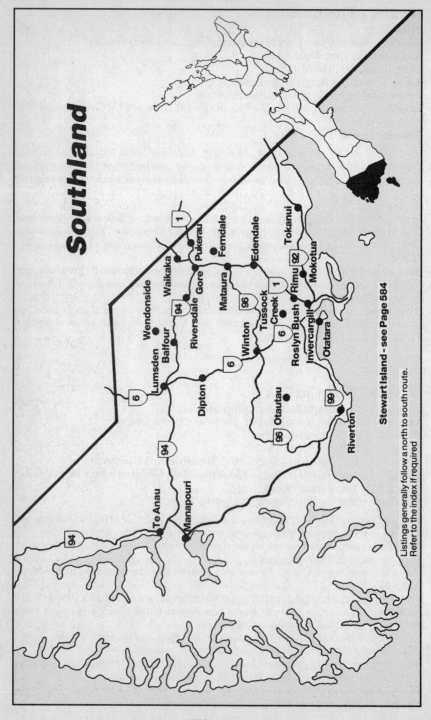

Southland

Te Anau
Manapouri
Lumsden
Balfour
Wendonside
Waikaka
Riversdale
Gore
Pukerau
Ferndale
Mataura
Edendale
Tokanui
Mokotua
Rimu
Tussock Creek
Roslyn Bush
Invercargill
Otatara
Winton
Dipton
Otautau
Riverton

Stewart Island - see Page 584

Listings generally follow a north to south route.
Refer to the index if required

Te Anau
Farmstay
Address: Sinclair Road, RD1, Te Anau
Name: Dave & Teresa Hughes
Telephone: (03) 249-7581
Beds: 2 Single (1 bedroom) **Bathroom:** ensuite
Tariff: B&B (continental) Double $60, Single $45
Nearest Town: Te Anau 5 km

A warm welcome to travellers visiting Fiordland. We live on a deer farm, 5 minutes drive from Te Anau township, just 1 kilometre off the Milford Highway.
David, besides farming, works in the Deer Industry, while I teach at the local Primary School. Our three children are away during term time - Shelley and Hayden are at boarding school, and Shanon is at University. Our pets, 2 dogs and a cat, enjoy meeting our visitors as well.
Your accommodation, which has magnificent views of Lake Te Anau and the Kepler and Murchison mountains, is a self-contained bed-sittingroom with ensuite, TV, tea / coffee making facilities and private entrance. We can assist with information and reservations to ensure your stay in Fiordland is memorable.
We request guests do not smoke in our home.
 Directions: *Continue through Te Anau on road to Milford Sound for 5 km to Sinclair Road, turn right. We are the second house on the left - our name is on the letterbox.*

Te Anau
Rural Homestay
Address: "Hillend", Kakapo Rd,
Te Anau (P.O. Box 69, Te Anau)
Name: Naomi & David Hughes
Telephone & Fax: (03) 249-7081
Beds: 2 Single (1 bedroom)
Bathroom: Family share
Tariff: B&B (continental, cooked breakfast $5 extra pp)
Double $70, Single $55, Dinner $20 by arrangment
Nearest Town: Te Anau, 9km (10 mins)

Welcome to our home "Hillend". Our small farm overlooks Lake Te Anau and has magnificent views of the lake and Fiordlands Mountains, with some beautiful sunrises, sunsets and clear starry nights.
We raise deer, sheep and angora goat. Our developing garden is interesting and colourful.
At home is Freda our youngest daughter (16). Abbey our West Highland Terrier and the cats DJ and Jaws are our spoilt family pets.
We have developed Trips 'n' Tramps over the last few years which offers an interesting and personal mini coach (9 passengers) day tours to Milford Sound. These include a cruise, walks (optional), photo stops, birds and alpine flowers in season.
Due to the nature of our business please arrive after 4.30. Please phone / fax or write for the necessary information and reservations.
Directions: *Kakapo Rd is 4km Mossburn side of Te Anau SH94. Our place is on left 4km from Turn-off (name on letterbox).*

Te Anau

Self-Contained B&B Inn
Address: 10 Dusky Street, Te Anau
Name: Shakespeare Bed & Breakfast Inn
Telephone: (03) 249-7349, **Fax:** (03) 249-7629
Beds: 2 King, 3 Double, 4 Single (5 bedrooms) **Bathroom:** 5 Ensuite
Self-Contained: 2 bedrooms 1 Double, 1 Twin, TV Lounge, Galley Kitchen, own bathroom. 2 nights minimum stay (Bookings recommended)
Tariff: B&B (Special) Double $112.50, Single $85, Dinner $28. Credit cards.

Your hosts Mike and Rosina Shakespeare (yes they are related) have owned and operated a Bed & Breakfast for many years. We are well travelled and are well aware of the service and comfort that travellers need. To this end all our rooms are ground floor with choice of single / twin / double or king size bed. Each room has private facilities also TV and tea / coffee making. Also available is a two bedroom self-contained unit with a separate lounge and kitchen (2 night min. stay). At Shakespeare House we keep a home atmosphere with personal service and hospitality. We are in a quiet residential area within walking distance to the shops and 1 min to the lake. Both the Milford Sound and Doubtful sound tours pick up at the gate. Our tariff includes breakfast, a choice of cereal, fruit, toast, jams / marmalade followed by a choice of bacon / sausages / scrambled / poached / fried eggs all with tea or several herbal teas or freshly brewed coffee. We also serve an evening meal on request.

Te Anau

Farmstay
Address: "Anak Downs", Takitimu R.D. 1, Te Anau
Name: Noeline & Ken Adam
Telephone: (03) 249-8573
Beds: 1 Double 3 Single (2 bedrooms) **Bathroom:** 1 Family share
Tariff: B&B (full) Double $60, Single $40, Children 1/2 Price, Dinner $20, Vouchers accepted
Nearest Town: Te Anau 40 km, Manapouri 20 km

Our farm is at the foot of the Takitimu mountains situated in the Te Anau Basin, with our comfortable farmhouse in a garden setting. Bathroom to be shared. We offer friendly rural hospitality which includes a tour of our sheep and beef property, and a working dog demonstration.
The Fiordland area offers much to the traveller. Milford Sound, Doubtful Sound, Milford, Kepler and Routeburn walking tracks plus many shorter bush and lakeside walks. For the fisherman there are Lakes Te Anau and Manapouri and excellent rivers. The Mararoa River forms part of our boundary. There is a beautiful 18 hole golf course in Te Anau.
Directions: *Coming from either Queenstown or Gore, highway 94, 32 km from Mossburn, lefthand turn off signposted Clifden, drive in 14 km. Our house on lefthand side of road, name on mailbox.*

Te Anau
Farmstay
Address: "Tapua" 2 R.D. Te Anau
Name: Dorothy & Donald Cromb
Telephone: (03) 249-5805
Beds: 4 Single (2 bedrooms) **Bathroom:** 1 Guests share
Tariff: B&B (full) Double $80, Single $40, Children under 12 half price, Dinner $20pp, Credit cards accepted, Vouchers accepted
Nearest Town: Te Anau, 20 km

You are surrounded by "million dollar" views while enjoying the luxury of our large family home. We are situated in a very handy position close to the main road, 40 km after Mossburn, 20 km before Te Anau making an excellent base for your sightseeing trips to magnificent Milford and Doubtful Sounds. We recommend you spend two nights so that you can enjoy a relaxing trip to the Sounds, as well as a look over our 279 Hectare (700 acres) farm which carries 3000 sheep and 100 cattle. Guests are welcome to join in farming activities that are in progress at the time of your visit. Some of New Zealand's best fishing rivers within a few minutes drive as are the finest walking tracks in the world, golf courses etc. Personal attention and service assured.
Directions: *Please phone.*

Te Anau
Homestay and Self-contained Accommodation
Address: 13 Fergus Square, Te Anau
Name: Rob & Nancy Marshall
Telephone or Fax: (03) 249 8241
Beds: 6 Single (3 bedrooms)
Bathroom: 1 Private, 2 Guests share
Tariff: B&B (full) Double $70-$80, Single $35-$40, Dinner $20-$25, Children $17.50,
Credit cards accepted, Vouchers accepted
Nearest Town: Te Anau 5 minutes walk

If you enjoy a quiet tranquil park like setting with a chance to sleep on beds with electric blankets, quality bedspreads, fresh flowers, then stay with us.
Tea and coffee making facilities in rooms that can be enjoyed in your own courtyard. Breakfast includes a full breakfast with home made bread and jams. Dinner includes fresh vegetables from our garden and NZ wine.
We are a couple retired from farming and are grandparents who enjoy meeting people.
Travellers leaving to enjoy Milford and Doubtful Sounds are picked up at the door. Most excursion trips can be booked from our home and we offer off street parking and baggage storage.
Fergus Square is adjacent to a park enjoyable for a walk to soak up the atmosphere.
Directions: *From Lakefront Drive turn into Town Centre, turn left into Mokonui Street, turn right into Matai Street,, turn left into Fergus Square.*
Reservations: *Please ring before 10am or after 4pm. Kiwi hosts - Kiwi Style!*

Tell other travellers about your favourite B&Bs

559

Te Anau
Farmstay
Address: Kakapo Raod, R.D. 2, Te Anau,
Name: Brian and Joy Pinnell
Telephone: (03) 249-7897
Beds: 1 Double, 2 Single (2 bedrooms)
Bathroom: 1 Guest share
Tariff: B&B (continental) Double $65, Single $40, Dinner by arrangement $17.50, Vouchers accepted June to September
Nearest Town: Te Anau 9 km (10 mins drive)

Our farm is set in rolling country. From it there are beautiful views of Lake Te Anau and the surrounding mountains. We farm approximately 350 deer and are happy to take you among them at most times of the year, or watch them from the comfort of our lounge.

From Te Anau you can drive or bus to Milford Sound. We can help you arrange trips to many attractions in the area. There are walks close to the town, good fishing within easy distance, and an 18 hole golf course. Brian plays golf and enjoys fishing and hunting. Joy spins and likes gardening. We enjoy our lifestyle and would like to share it with you.

Directions: *Turn off SH94 onto Kakapo Road on Mossburn side of Te Anau. Our farm is on the left, just over the top of the hill, 4 1/2 km from the turnoff.*

Te Anau
Farmstay
Address: Sinclair Road, R.D. 1, Te Anau
Name: Alan & Gayle Todd
Telephone: (03) 249-7195
Beds: 1 Double, 2 Single (2 bedrooms)
Bathroom: 1 Private (only one party at a time).
Tariff: B&B (continental) Double $60, Single $50, Children negotiable.
Nearest Town: Te Anau

We are a young family with four children aged from 7 to 13 years old, a dog and two cats. We live on a 60 acre deer farm with a lovely view of Lake Te Anau and the surrounding mountains. We are ideally situated to all the tourist attractions of the Fiordland National Park.

Our guest rooms are very comfortable and have a private bathroom beside. Phone us anytime for a reservation.

Directions: *Carry on through Te Anau towards Milford Sound for about 5km, turn right at Sinclair Road. We are the first house on the left with our name on the letterbox.*

Te Anau

Rural Homestay/Self-contained Accommodation
Address: 'Eatons',
11 Charles Nairn Road, Te Anau,
Name: Pam & Barry Eaton
Telephone & fax: (03) 249 7078
Beds: 1 Double, 3 Single (2 bedrooms) **Bathroom:** 1 Guests share
Cottage: 2 Single **Bathroom:** 1 Private
Tariff: B&B (full) Double $70, Single $50, Children under 14 half price, Credit cards accepted
Nearest Town: 2km south of Te Anau on the Te Anau/Manapouri Highway (at the end of second road on the right out of town)

Our 15 acre farmlet is situated with breathtaking mountain views and a scenic 18 hole golf course as a neighbour. Horses, sheep, hens, ducks and Bob the cat share our life here with us. As we are situated at the end of a road peace and quiet abound, yet Te Anau can be seen across the lake. We have travelled extensively around the world and love to greet fellow travellers into our home. Barry has an intimate knowledge of Fiordland, having spent much of his life hunting and tramping within this unique area. Why not join him on one of his guided walks / tramps from 3 hours to 3 days or more; small groups, away from the crowds, a real wilderness experience. All levels of fitness catered for, lake fishing available on most trips.
Pam is a horse riding instructress and lessons can be arranged. Safe storage for gear / cars available and transport to / from tracks.
Te Anau, gateway to Fiordland, has much to offer; tramping, fishing, boating, scenic flights, golf, wildlife park and a lot more. Please feel free to discuss your plans with us, as we can provide extensive and impartial information on the area and the various trips / activities available. Bookings can be made on your behalf. We look forward to meeting you and know you will enjoy the wonders of Fiordland, The Real New Zealand.

Te Anau

Farmstay
Address: Please phone
Name: John & Florence Pine
Telephone: (03) 249-8598
Beds: 7 Single (3 bedrooms - 1 triple, 2 twin) **Bathrooms**: 2 Guests share
Tariff: B&B (continental) Double $70, Single $45, Dinner $20, Children half price. Vouchers accepted.
Nearest Town: Te Anau 30 minutes, Manapouri 20 minutes

Our 586 acre sheep, cattle and deer farm offers you an opportunity to be part of the everyday workings of a New Zealand farm. On a farm tour wonderful views of the whole Te Anau Basin, the beautiful Fiordland mountains, and Lake Manapouri can be seen, and views from our home receive exceptional comments from guests Two nights is more restful and we are an ideal base for day trips to Milford and Doubtful Sounds, Te Anau Glow-worm Caves or hikes on the many walking tracks in "The Walking Capital of the World".
Our family of 3 are usually away at University, but their pets - sheep, deer and cat are always pleased to welcome you.
We have enjoyed hosting and meeting overseas guests and have travelled ourselves to England, Wales, Scotland Ireland, Europe and Canada. We look forward to meeting with you in our home.
Directions: *Please phone*

Te Anau
Farmstay
Address: Perenuka Farm, R.D. 1, Te Anau
Name: Les & Margaret Simpson
Telephone: (03) 249-7841
Beds: 1 Double, 1 Single (1 bedroom)
Bathroom: 1 Ensuite
Tariff: B&B (continental) Double/Twin $70, Single $50, (cooked breakfast available $5 extra pp)
Nearest Town: Te Anau 5km

Our 800 acre sheep and cattle farm is 5 km North of Te Anau on the Milford Sound Highway. Our home is situated well back from the road, on a terrace, with panoramic views of the lake and mountains.

Guest accommodation, with it's own private verandah, is semi-detached from the house by a courtyard. It is spacious and warm, with ensuite bathroom. Beds have electric blankets.

There is tea / coffee making facilities should you wish to be private, but we do enjoy meeting and chatting with guests in our non-smoking dining / living area.

Our adult family are now married. Les enjoys tramping and our participation in a Four Wheel Drive Club.

Margaret paints, dabbles in most crafts and enjoys gardening.

We appreciate living in this beautiful area and will be happy to help with local knowledge to make your stay as you want it.

We have a small flock of very friendly pet sheep.

Directions: *Follow Milford Sound Highway 5km north of Te Anau. Our sign is just before our driveway on Sinclair Road corner.*

The standard of accommodation in *The New Zealand Bed and Breakfast Book*
ranges from homely to luxurious,
but you can always be sure of superior hospitality.

Te Anau
Farmstay / Self-contained Accommodation
Address: "Tutoko", 2 R.D., Te Anau
Name: Ken & Jackie Wright
Telephone: (03) 249 7685
Beds: 1 Double divan, 2 Single (2 bedrooms)
Bathroom: 1 Private
Tariff: B&B (full) Double $80, Single $40, Dinner $20. Vouchers accepted Winter season only.
Nearest Town: Te Anau 4km

Our sheep and cattle farm is situated on SH 94, 4km from Te Anau. Besides being able to experience a 'working farm' environment we offer a good base from which to visit and explore the numerous attractions that Fiordland offers, such as Milford Sound, Doubtful Sound, Te Ana-Au Caves, and fishing in rivers and lakes. Also it is a good 'stepping off' point for the many walking tracks available, ranging from 10 mins to 10 days.
Our accommodation is a "Granny Crib" in the garden with your own bathroom and tea making facilities.
We have a family cat.
Please phone for reservations. Dinner by arrangement.

Te Anau
Guest House
Address: Matai Lodge, 42 Mokonui Street, Te Anau
Name: Richard Bevan
Telephone & Fax: (03) 249 7360
Beds: 3 Double, 9 Single (3 Twin, 1 Triple) (7 bedrooms)
Bathroom: 2 Guests share
Tariff: B&B (full) Double/Twin $72, Single $54, Triple $99, Credit cards accepted

The Matai Lodge is ideally located in a quiet residential area just 2 minutes walk from the lake and 5 minutes walk from the town centre. It offers clean, friendly, "homestyle" accommodation in a smoke-free environment. Full (and substantial) breakfasts are served in the dining/lounge area with tea and coffee always available, whilst there is also a separate TV lounge. All rooms are on the ground floor, have hot and cold vanity units, electric blankets and heaters.
Te Anau is the hub of Fiordland, a World Heritage National Park. Among the main attractions of the area are Milford Sound, Doubtful Sound and Te Ana-au glow-worm caves. World famous walking tracks including the Milford, Kepler, Routeburn and Hollyford all start close to the town. All excursion trips can be booked at the lodge, with bus pick-up at the gate. Off-street parking is available, with vehicles and baggage stored for guests walking the tracks.

Guests share means you may be sharing the bathroom with other guests, especially at peak season.

Te Anau
Farmstay
Address: "Boundary", Wilderness Rd No 2 R.D. Te Anau
Name: Kaye and Lyall Gray
Telephone: (03) 249 8551
Beds: 2 Single (1 bedroom)
Bathroom: 1 Ensuite
Tariff: B&B (full) Double $70, Single $45, Dinner $20, Children half price, Vouchers accepted
Nearest Town: Te Anau 19km west

"Boundary" is a 680 acre sheep and deer farm and is home for our family of four (two young children). We would like to share with you our lifestyle of peaceful and attractive surroundings, viewing any working activities on the farm including sheep dog demonstrations and joining us for meals and our family life. Our farm is nearby to the most attractive township of Te Anau, and we would be pleased to help arrange any of the many activities available there. We are both interested in sport and enjoy a game of squash and golf. Our guest room is very comfortable and has a private ensuite.
Directions: *Please telephone.*

Te Anau
B & B Guest House
Address: 2 Lake Front Drive Te Anau
Name: "The Cats Whiskers"
Telephone & Fax: (03) 249 8112
Beds: 2 Double, 6 Single (3 Bedrooms) **Bathroom:** 3 Ensuite
Tariff: B&B (full) Double $95, Single $55, Children half price. Credit cards.
Nearest Town: 9 mins walk from the Te Anau town centre

Our home is situated on Te Anau lake front overlooking lake and the Dept of Conservation Park and Headquarters. We provide guests with comfort and outside access to all 3 rooms. 2 bedrooms have 1 double, 1 single, 1 large bedroom has 4 single, a 5th bed can be added if required, ie families. All have TV and tea making facilities.
We are happy to provide a courtesy car to any of the great variety of restaurants for dinner or as some of these are close by enjoy a walk along the lovely lakefront. We have a good car park and lock up room for luggage.
By arrangement we can pack a homemade picnic lunch for your daily excursions.
Your holiday with us will be "Just the Cat's Whiskers"
Directions: *To Lakefront Drive turn left off Highway 94 where signposted on edge of town. 1st house on right.*

Te Anau
Homestay
Address: "House of Wood"
44 Moana Crescent Te Anau
Name: Elaine & Trevor Lett
Telephone: (03) 249 8404
Beds: 2 Double, 2 Single (3 Bedrooms)
Bathroom: 1 Guests share
Tariff: B&B (continental) Double $80-90, Single $50-60
Nearest Town: Te Anau

Welcome to Te Anau. "House of Wood" is an architecturally designed two storey wooden house with outside balconies and beautiful views. Town centre is just a short walk away. We are close to all tourist facilities and the lake.

Up until last year we owned an orchard in Roxburgh Central Otago for 13 years. We know the Otago / Southland area extremely well and can help you make the most of your time spent in this part of the country.

Trevor is a builder his spare time is taken up with golf, woodturning, tramping. Now that our three daughters have left home I have more time to spend in the garden, tramping and mountain biking.

We have no animals and offer smokefree friendly Kiwi accommodation. We welcome you to our home and advise early bookings for our peak period November-March. Please phone for directions.

Te Anau
Farmstay +
Self-contained Accommodation
Address: 'The Farmyard',
Charles Nairn Rd, RD1, Te Anau
Name: Ray and Helen Willett
Telephone: (03) 249 7833
Beds: 1 Double, 3 Single (2 bedrooms)
Bathroom: 2 Private
Tariff: B&B (continental) Self-cont. $80, Twin $70, Single $40
Nearest Town: Te Anau 3km.

Our home, 3km from Te Anau township, is situated on a 'hobby' farm with a spectacular outlook to mountains and bush. We have lived in Te Anau for many years and we invite you to share our knowledge and enthusiasm of the region with us.

We are ideally situated for excursions into the rugged, majestic splendour of Fiordland National Park. Milford Sound, Doubtful Sound, Te Anau Caves and the numerous walking tracks are readily accessible, as are the golf course and fishing spots.

Our pets, many and varied, include a donkey, Kune Kune pigs, goats, pony and very tame sheep! All of whom will be delighted to meet you.

Our accommodation is a detached self-contained unit, and a guest bedroom in our house with own bathroom.

It is best to phone before 8am or after 5.30pm if possible, but we are also often available during the day.

Welcome to Fiordland!

Te Anau

Homestay
Address: 57 Mokunui St Te Anau
Name: Jean & Bill Scott
Telephone: (03) 249 7875
Beds: 1 Double, 2 Single (2 Bedrooms)
Bathroom: 1 Guests share
Tariff: B&B (full) Double $70, Single $40, Children half price, Dinner $20, Vouchers accepted
Nearest Town: Te Anau

Our modern home is situated right in the town of Te Anau with just 5 mins walk to the town centre, where there is a very good shopping area and an excellent range of good restaurants. The lake front is just around the corner 3 mins, where there is a magnificent view of some of Fiordland's beauty. Te Anau is famous for its world-wide walks, the Milford Track, Routeburn and Kepler etc.

We are happy to help you organise day trips of your choice. We are retireed farmers and have been hosting overseas tourists for several years and enjoy meeting people from all over the world.

Our home is comfortable with central heating, and electric blankets on beds - guests own bathroom. We offer a choice of continental or cooked breakfast, and do our best to make your stay a happy one.

Our main interests are lawn bowls and gardening. A homely welcome awaits you.

Te Anau - Manapouri

Farmstay
Address: "Elmwood Station",
No 1 R.D., Te Anau
Name: Ron & Marie Galland
Telephone: (03) 249 5832
Beds: 4 Single (2 bedrooms, additional twin room available if requested)
Bathroom: 1 Private, 1 Family share
Tariff: B&B (full) Double $70, Single $45, Dinner $20, Children half price, Campervans $30, Vouchers accepted
Nearest Town: Te Anau / Manapouri

We are a family who enjoy entertaining and meeting people. We live on a hill country property situated on the foothills of the Takitimu Mountains, 5km off State Highway 94 and 20 minutes from Lakes Te Anau and Manapouri.

We farm sheep, cattle and deer and you are welcome to watch seasonal work in progress or walk over the farm enjoying mountain and native bush walks and views of the lakes. Horse riding is also available.

Our large family homestead is an ideal base for exploring Fiordland; Milford, Doubtful Sound, fishing, hunting, tramping, golf, rafting and many other outdoor activities. We would be happy to help you plan and make reservations.

We have large spacious lawns and landscaped gardens. We offer a three course meal with wine and a packed lunch if required.

Bathroom (bath & shower) for guests use only.

Please ring before 8am or after 4pm on weekdays.

We look forward to welcoming you.

Directions: *Please phone.*

Always have a phone card with you. Most public phones do not take coins

Te Anau - Manapouri
Farmstay+Self-contained Accommodation
Address: Hillside / Manapouri Road Te Anau
Name: Murray & Marie Christie
Telephone: (03) 249 6695
Beds: 2 Double, 2 Single (1&1/2 Bedrooms) **Bathroom:** 1 Private
Tariff: B&B (continental) Double $65, Single $40, Children under 12 half price.
Reduced rates for stays over 2 nights
Nearest Town: Manapouri 8km, Te Anau 17km

*We invite you to spend time in beautiful Fiordland. Murray and I with our two
children live on a 530 acre sheep / cattle farm situated 8km from Lake Manapouri
and 17km from Lake Te Anau. We have a delightful, warm self-contained cottage
with all facilities. Your private courtyard garden overlooks the Mararoa River and
the rugged Takitimu Mountains. This gives you full privacy but you are welcome
to join our family at your leisure.*
*Within walking distance the Mararoa River provides superb trout fishing.
Murray, who knows the Southland and Stewart Island areas well is willing to
share his experience and knowledge of hunting, fishing and tramping. Fishing
tackle is available for hire also a safe sturdy craft for use on rivers or lakes. I enjoy
gardening and have a wide selection of native plants and trees. As a young mother
I especially welcome travelling families.*
We offer you a relaxed family home where even your pets are welcome.

Manapouri
Self-Contained Accommodation
Address: 1 Home Street, Manapouri
Name: Ruth and Lance Shaw
Telephone & Fax: (03) 249 6600
Beds: 1 Double, 4 Single (2 1/2 bedrooms) **Bathroom:** 2 Ensuite
Tariff: B&B (continental) Double $60, Single $40, Children under 12 half price,
Dinner $20. Reduced rates for stays over 2 nights. Credit cards.

FIORDLAND
ECOLOGY HOLIDAYS
YOU
& ME & NATURE

*Lance and I live in a small town on the perimeter of Fiordland National Park, only
3 minutes walk from Lake Manapouri and 15 minutes drive from Te Anau We are
the gateway to Doubtful Sound.*
*Our home is a popular Bed & Breakfast stopover for birds as we are surrounded
with mature trees. A warm, homely self-contained flat with an open fire will help
make your stay comfortable. You have the option of total privacy or joining us.
I am in my 40's and Lance is in his early 50's. We both have a keen interest in
underwater and natural history photography, sailing, diving and conservation.
Lance worked with the Department of Conservation for 12 years as skipper of a
research vessel. He now skippers our 82ft charter / research yacht, which works
out of Doubtful Sound. He works with scientists from all over the world who are
studying Fiordland above and below the waterline.*
*We also run 3, 5 and 10 day tourist charters in Fiordland and by request go to more
remote locations such as the sub antarctic. We feel it is a privilege to be able to
share our knowledge and love of this part of the world.*
*I was a Social Worker for 15 years, working mainly with teenagers and drug
addicts. I now help Lance run our own business, Fiordland Ecology Holidays.
Having both travelled widely, we know how important it is to have somewhere that
feels like home. We suggest at least a 3 to 4 day stay as there is so much to do off
the beaten track, especially if you join us on one of our trips. If we can help plan
your holiday, please write to us. We really look forward to meeting you and hope
that where ever you come from your travels are safe and happy.*

Manapouri
Superior Homestay + Self-Contained Accommodation

Address: C/- N.Z. Post,
Private Bag, Manapouri
Name: Phyllis MacGibbon
Telephone: (03) 2496-873
Beds: 1 Double, 2 Single (one bedroom)
Bathroom: 1 Private
Tariff: B&B (full) Double $60, Single $35, Dinner by arrangement $20,
Children half price, Vouchers accepted
Nearest Town: 21 km south of Te Anau

Being retired and non-smoking, we enjoy meeting people, our family having grown up and left home. Interests include organic gardening both glasshouse and outside. Allowing the serving of fresh high quality fruit and vegetables in home cooked meals.

Available solely for guests is a fully serviced all electric flat to sleep up to four people. This flat of 1,000 square feet is on the upper floor of our home which is situated on the highway between Te Anau and Manapouri, overlooking Lake Manapouri, with its clean safe sandy beaches and the beautiful mountains of Fiordland National Park, with approximately two hours driving time to Milford Sound.

There are boat trips, walking tracks, fishing trips and farm tours by arrangement. Altogether an ideal relaxed holiday situation for all visitors.

Manapouri
Bed and Breakfast

Address: The Cottage,
Waiau St, Manapouri
Name: Don and Joy
Telephone: (03) 249 6838
Beds: 2 Double, 2 Single (2 bedrooms)
Bathroom: 1 Private, 1 Family share
Tariff: B&B (continental, full $3 extra pp)
Double $65-$70, Single $40-$45, Dinner $20
Nearest Town: Te Anau

"The Cottage"

Our cottage offers a relaxed stay in a tranquil and peaceful setting surrounded by bush with lovely views of river, lake and mountains.

Situated beside the lower Waiau river we are only a few minutes walk to where the Doubtful Sound launches depart. There are some lovely walking tracks beginning from here.

Row boats and canoes are available (small charge). If you are interested fishing, diving, and kayaking trips can be arranged.

We are a middle aged couple who enjoy gardening. Guests are invited to wander around our cottage garden. Our Labrador Tam and Kittie the cat will not annoy you unless you want their attention.

Dinner is by prior arrangement only. Freshly grown vegetables.

Look forward to meeting you.   Don and Joy

Manapouri

Historic Inn
Address: Grand View House, 7 Murrell Ave, Manapouri
Name: Jack and Klaske Murrell
Telephone & Fax: (03) 249 6642
Beds: 4 Double, 4 Single (4 bedrooms)
Bathroom: 4 Ensuite
Tariff: B&B (full) Double $135, Single $105, Dinner $35, Credit cards accepted
Nearest Town: Te Anau

Murrells in their historic Grandview House, through three generations have provided over 100 years of hospitality to visitors.

The house is set in its own extensive grounds which slope down to Lake Manapouri on one side, and the Waiau River on the other. Pet deer roam in half the grounds.

The grounds set behind tall hedges consist of spacious lawns and old fashioned cottage gardens offering peace and seclusion.

Built in 1889, this large rambling house features wide verandahs, spacious picture lined passages and a cosy sitting room complete with open fireplace and overflowing bookshelves.

Guest rooms are furnished with comfortable colonial antique furniture, cosy quilts, fresh flowers and a welcoming bowl of fruit. Meals are served in the Victorian Dining room, Grandma's menu is the speciality of the house.

This is a perfect base for any day excursions to Milford sound, Doubtful Sound, or any of the adventure treks available through Fiordland National Park. Dinghies and canoes are available and a number of half or whole day walks begin right here.

Directions: *Situated off Main Road, take Murrell Ave opposite store and garage, behind hedges. Bookings advisable, please phone ahead.*

Continental breakfast consist of fruit, toast, tea/coffee,
Full breakfast is the same with a cooked course,
Special breakfast has something special.

Lumsden - Dipton

Farmstay
Address: "Bilberry Oak", Dipton R.D.
Name: John and Judy Buchanan
Telephone: (03) 248 5228 (booking essential please)
Beds: 1 Double, 2 Single (2 bedrooms) **Bathroom:** 1 Family share
Tariff: B&B (full) Double $55, Single $30, Dinner $20 per person, Lunch $10 per person, Campervans welcome. Vouchers accepted
Nearest Town: 24km south of Lumsden, Invercargill 65 km Dipton 6 km.

Our farm is situated on one of the main roads from Invercargill through to the attractions of Te Anau, Milford Sound and Queenstown so is a convenient stopover point during your travels.
Our comfortable farmhouse is set in a large garden which includes a covered swimming pool.
We welcome you to have dinner with us or just bed and breakfast, the choice is yours. We also offer the use of our laundry facilities.
John is always very willing to take folk about the property, explain about the New Zealand way of farming and if possible, let you see at close hand such activities as shearing. Ours is a sheep farm with cropping and a few cattle. We also have a Hampshire Sheep Stud.
We are interested in most sports and if you feel like a day's break from sightseeing, a game of squash or golf or a few hours fishing on the Oreti River could be easily arranged.
Directions: *Take the Dipton_Castlerock road (west side of Oreti river), turn on to Boundary Road, second house on right. Please telephone first.*

Lumsden

Farmstay
Address: Caroline Valley Road, Dipton, Southland
Name: Mern & Nathlie McLean
Telephone: (03) 248-5268
Beds: 5 Single (3 bedrooms)
Bathroom: 2 Family share
Tariff: B&B (continental) Double $60, Single $35, Dinner $20, Children $20, Vouchers accepted
Nearest Town: 13km south of Lumsden, Invercargill 67km

Our home is 13km south of Lumsden on State Highway 6, the second house on Caroline Valley Road.
Our central location means travellers have just over an hours drive to Te Anau and Queenstown, with only 50 mins to Gore and Invercargill.
We farm sheep and stud beef cattle, giving you an opportunity to experience a typical working New Zealand farm.
Our area provides good bush walking, trout fishing and golf.
We offer friendly hospitality and enjoy meeting people.
If previously arranged an evening dinner will be available.
We look forward to your visit. Please phone first.

Lumsden

Farmstay
Address: State Highway 6, Josephville, Lumsden
Name: Annette and Bob Menlove
Telephone: (03) 248-7114
Beds: 4 Single (2 bedrooms) **Bathroom**: 1 Private, 1 Family share.
Sleepout: 1 Double, 1 Single **Bathroom**: Ensuite
Tariff: B&B (full) Double $55, Single 30; Dinner $20, Campervans welcome,
Vouchers accepted
Nearest Town: 9 km south of Lumsden, Invercargill 80 km

*We live on a 480 hectare farm on State Highway 6 'to the lakes'. Our home is warm and
of modern design. We enjoy meeting people and would like to have you to stay with us.
We have a large garden and lawn tennis court which you are welcome to enjoy. also
we enjoy hiking in the mountains.*
*We live beside the Oreti River well-known for its trout fishing. Our farm has got
sheep, cattle, and deer.*
Included in your visit is a four-wheel-drive trip around the farm.
*You would be welcome to have the family meal with us or if you prefer bed and
breakfast.*
Our house is on the right at the foot of the hill 9 km south of Lumsden.

Lumsden

Farmstay+Self-contained
Accommodation
Address: The Pines, RD2, Lumsden
Name: Alison and Ross Ruddenklau
Telephone: (03) 248-7395
          Lunchtime or after 6pm

Beds: 1 Double, 2 Single (2 bedrooms)
Bathroom: 1 Private
Tariff: B&B (full) Double $100, $10 for 3rd or 4th guest, Single $80, Dinner
$25pp, Children meals half price. Self-catering: Double $80 for 'cottage', 1 - 4
persons. Vouchers accepted for Doubles only.
Nearest Town: Lumsden 10 minutes west - just off Highway 94.

Try life on a progressive New Zealand farm.
*Looking to the Eyre Mountains, your own guest cottage awaits. Comfortable beds,
private bathroom and kitchen, beside the homestead.*
*Working dogs, sheep and cattle - See the farm with Ross. Our young children
Richard and Claire add their own happy perspective.*
*Self-cater or join us for tasty home cooked meals. Dinner is served once the
children are in bed - uninterrupted conversation and hospitality.*
*Excellent trout fishing in the local Oreti and Mataura Rivers, or try our own
Murray Creek.*
*Sight seeing. Milford Sound is a day trip. Queenstown - 1 1/2 hours away. Te
Anau, Invercargill and Gore are within one hour.*
*For golf, winter skiing, water sports, walking or relaxing amongst pretty gardens,
beautiful scenery and fresh air - The Pines is a great stop-over.*
*From Lumsden, take Highway 94 west. Over river, after approximately 3km turn
left, (at Northern Southland Selling Centre). Approximately 4km on left.*
Look forward to meeting you, Alison R.

Balfour
Farmstay
Address: "Hillcrest", No. 1 R.D., Balfour
Name: Ritchie and Liz Clark
Telephone: (03) 201-6165

Beds: 1 Double, 2 Single (2 bedrooms) (Fold-up bed + cot available for children)
Bathroom: 1 Private, 1 Family share
Tariff: B&B (full) Double $60, Single $40, Children under 12 half price;
Dinner $20; wine included. Campervans $20. Vouchers accepted.
Nearest Town: Balfour 3 km, Lumsden 16 km, Gore 40 km

We welcome you to join us on our farm. We are a family with three young boys and
enjoy working together and meeting people . Our interests include tennis, squash,
gardening, photography and fishing. I am fond of cooking and welcome you to
share our family dinner or if you prefer only bed and breakfast.
On our 900-acre farm we run 3,500 ewes, a few cattle and some cropping. From
our guest rooms you can enjoy views of surrounding farm lands and mountains.
A complimentary farm tour is included.
Our farm is situated 3 km from Balfour which is a popular stopover, being on the
main tourist route from the lakes to Dunedin via Gore. We are only minutes from
some of the top trout fishing rivers.
A fishing guide arranged on request.
Directions: *When arriving at Balfour crossroads, take the road to Waikaia, then*
the first turn to the left before transport depot and travel 2.5 km, we are on the
right. Please phone.

Balfour
Farmstay
Address: Longridge North, No. 6 R.D., Gore
Name: Ivor and Margaret Black
Telephone: (03) 201-6090
Beds: 4 Single (2 bedrooms)
Bathroom: Guests share shower
Tariff: B&B (full) Double $60, Single $35, Dinner $20.
Vouchers accepted
Nearest Town: Balfour 5 minutes, Lumsden 15 minutes,
Gore 30 minutes north-east

We live in a beautiful farmland valley surrounded by majestic mountains. We are
on the main tourist route to Milford Sound, Lakes Te Anau and Manapouri and
Queenstown.
We farm sheep, deer and cattle and are very fortunate to be only ten minutes from
one of the most famous trout fishing rivers in the world, the Mataura River, with
two others close by. So, if it is fishing, farming or just relaxing in our tranquil
surroundings, we will enjoy sharing it with you.
Lake Te Anau, Milford Track, Lake Manapouri and Doubtful Sound 1 hour,
Queenstown and Invercargill 1hour 15 mins.
Directions: *From Gore (30 mins) you turn right at Balfour crossroads then*
second turn left (signpost) follow tarseal, we are fifth house on left hand side (5
min). Lumsden take road to Gore, just out of Lumsden at signpost you keep left and
follow tarseal over hill. We are fourth house on right hand side (15 min) Please
phone early.

Wendonside

Farmstay

Address: "Ardlamont Farm", Church Road,
Wendonside, No 7RD, Gore
Name: Lindsay and Dale Wright
Telephone: (03) 202-7774
Beds: 1 Double, 2 Single (2 bedrooms)
Bathroom: 1 Private
Tariff: B&B (special) Double $60, Single $40, Dinner $25, Children half price
Nearest Town: Riversdale 15 km, Balfour 12 km

Come & experience 'Ardlamont', a 4th generation 1200 acre sheep and beef farm which offers panoramic views of Northern Southland.

Gourmet meals are a speciality and will be served with fine New Zealand wines. Our farmstyle breakfasts are another treat - the aroma of freshly baked bread to greet you in the morning.

Take a tour of the farm, then return to the comforts of our large recently renovated 80 year old homestead.

Having travelled widely and experienced this kind of hospitality in other countries we enjoy welcoming visitors into our home. We have 3 school-age children and welcome family groups.

We have a wide range of interests including sport, the arts, Toastmasters, music and restoring our house to its former glory.

Two of New Zealands best trout fishing rivers only five minutes away.

We are 15 minutes off S.H.94 - (Queenstown - Dunedin route) and well worth the detour.

Directions: *Please phone or write.*

Many homes have facilities for campervans. The ideal camping spot with
electricity, bathroom, laundry and friendly hospitality.
Tell campervanners about this when you see them.

Waikaka

Farmstay
Address: Blackhills, RD3 Gore, Southland
Name: Dorothy and Tom Affleck
Telephone: (03) 207 2865
Beds: 2 Single (1 bedroom) **Bathroom:** 1 Family share
Tariff: B&B (full) Double $60, Single $35, Children under 13 half price; Dinner $15. Vouchers accepted.
Nearest Town: Waikaka township, Gore 30km.

Our sixty-year-old home, renovated to give generous comfortable living area, is situated on our 360 ha intensive sheep farm on a ridge above Waikaka River. The guest room has two single beds (other single beds may be available).
You may have dinner with us or if you prefer only bed and breakfast.
A farm tour is available and as our family becomes more independent we like to share time with guests. Venture off the main road and enjoy warm hospitality, superb views and the refreshment of a quiet rural visit.
Directions: *Turn off State Highway 1 just north of Gore, onto State Highway 90. Turn left at Waikaka Valley corner, marked by church and windmill, follow signposts to Waikaka until T corner (approx 10 km). At T corner turn left, then first right onto gravel Nicolson Road. Proceed 4 km veering right at each intersection. We live on Robertson Road, the last kilometre a steep hill - 20 minutes from State Highway 1.*

Waikaka Valley, Gore

Farmstay
Address: "Glenellen",
Waikaka Valley,
No 5 R.D., Gore
Name: Brigette and Donald Morrison
Telephone: (03) 207 1857
Beds: 1 Double, 2 Single (2 bedrooms)
Bathroom: 1 Private, 1 Family share
Tariff: B&B (full) Double $70, Single $40, Dinner $25. Vouchers accepted.
Nearest Town: 10 km northeast of Gore on SH90

Welcome to "Glenellen" and to Waikaka Valley, a small traditional rural community, 10 km from Gore.
We are a young family on a 1,000 acre mixed farm of sheep, arable and beef with our first child representing the sixth generation on the property. We also maintain a Romney Stud amidst this setting of beautiful green rolling countryside. We are both well travelled and enjoy our sport and outdoor activities. There is fishing on the farm and most other amenities are available locally.
Our spacious home secluded by mature gardens offers a warm and relaxed stay and our labrador and spaniel provide a hearty welcome.. Verandahs and sunny lounge and open fires accommodate all seasons.
You may have dinner with us and enjoy a home grown, country-style meal, or if you prefer just bed and breakfast. There is a good range of restaurants in Gore. We prefer no smoking in the dining room and bedrooms.
Directions: *Please phone*

Pukerau, Gore
Homestay
Address: State Highway 1, Pukerau
Name: Dawn and David Connor
Telephone: (03) 205 3896 (home) (03) 208 5085 (business)
Beds: 1 Double, 2 Single (2 bedrooms)
Bathroom: 1 Guests share
Tariff: B&B (full) Double $60, Single $35, Dinner $20, Vouchers accepted
Nearest Town: Gore 12km

We welcome you to our warm and comfortable home.
We have a small private garden with mature trees and shrubs and have a lovely rural outlook. We have two acres where we run a few pet South Suffolk sheep. Growing a variety of Orchids is our main interest and we enjoy sharing these beautiful flowers with others. We have a daughter and son-in-law farming nearby and visits could be arranged.
We are just minutes away from several rivers including the Mataura which is well known for brown trout fishing.
All beds have electric blankets. Laundry facilities available.
We welcome you to have an evening meal with us, or if you prefer, only Bed and Breakfast, cooked or continental.
We are 12km east of Gore on State Highway 1. Please phone for directions and bookings.

Ferndale, Gore
Farmstay
Address: Ferndale, RD2, Gore
Name: Lorna and Colin Dickie
Telephone: (03) 203-8335
Beds: 1 Double, 2 Single (twin) (2 Bedrooms)
Bathroom: 1 Family share
Tariff: B&B (full) Double $55, Single $35;
Children half price, Dinner $15, Vouchers accepted
Nearest Town: Mataura 7 km

Our home is 2,000 square feet has large lounge-dining room and a pool room. We are a middle-aged, semi-retired couple living on a 100-acre farmlet. We have sheep and thoroughbred horses.
We have a motorboat and are keen on camping and fishing. We are only about 4 km from Mataura river, one of the world's greatest fishing rivers.
Our house is situated in a very quiet and peaceful area.
Directions: *Coming south, turn off State Highway 1 at Clinton Hotel, proceed south 37 km towards Mataura. Going north, turn through Mataura, past paper mills, 7 km up Ferndale Road.*

Wyndham

Farmstay
Address: Mimihau,
No 2 RD, Wyndham, Southland
Name: Beverly & Doug Smith
Telephone: (03) 206 4840
Beds: 6 Single (3 Bedrooms) **Bathroom:** 1 Family share, two separate toilets
Tariff: B&B (full) Double $60, Single $35, Children half price, Dinner $20,
Vouchers accepted
Nearest Town: Wyndham 5km, Edendale 10km

*You are assured of a warm welcome to our 40 year old home and 172 hectare farm.
We are situated on the hills 5km from Wyndham giving a panoramic view of the
Southland Plains and the mountains beyond.*
*The Mataura, Mimihau and Wyndham Rivers, renowned for brown trout, are just
a short 5km drive away. Doug being a keen and experienced fisherman will only
be too happy to share his knowledge of these rivers with you.*
*Beverly, a qualified nurse, enjoys cooking, floral art, gardening and knitting. You
will enjoy comfortable and homely surroundings with genuine home cooking
including preserved fruits, jams, home grown meat and vegetables. Special diets
available. Your are welcome to join us for an evening meal. Coffee and tea making
facilities. Cot and high-chair on request.*
*We enjoy meeting people and believe we both are of friendly disposition with a
sense of humour. We enjoy travel and have three adult sons.*
Tours of other local farms and lovely gardens are offered.
Long stayers most welcome - please book in advance.
Directions: *5km from Wyndham on the Redan-Mokoreta Road. Sign at gate.*

Tokanui, South East Catlins

Farmstay + Bush Cabin
Address: Progress Valley, R.D. 1,
Tokanui, Southland
Name: June & Murray Stratford
Telephone: (03) 246-8843
Beds: 2 Double, 2 Single (3 bedrooms) **Bathroom:** 1 Guests share, 1 Family share
Tariff: B&B (special) Double $60, Single $30, Dinner $20, Children
half price, Campervans welcome. Credit Cards. Vouchers accepted.
Nearest Town: Invercargill 80 km, Dunedin 170 km

*Welcome to our place in the Catlins, just off the Southern Scenic Route
of State Highway 92, 10 minutes drive from the Petrified Forest at Curio Bay and
the Hectors Dolphins. Our home is centrally heated, plus open fire in lounge and
is set in large garden with tennis court. The farm is 1000 acres and runs 3000
sheep, 50 cattle and 500 deer along with one eye dog and two huntaways.*
*Our family is grown up and interests include meeting people, music, cooking,
gardening and most sports including rugby. Guests are most welcome to join in farm
or community activities. Our favourite menus consists of local seafood for entree,
followed by home grown meat and fresh veges from the organic garden, followed by
homemade desserts. Breakfasts are according to your needs and range from light to
hearty with my bottled fruit and homemade jams and jellies hard to resist.*
(The Bush Cabin sleeps four and overlooks 35 acres of native bush. $15 each)
Directions: *From Invercargill follow SH92 (scenic route) and 20 km past
Tokanui take right turn to Progress Valley. We are first house on right. From
Dunedin go to Balclutha on to SH92 (scenic route) through Owaka and Catlins
Forest until sign post to Progress Valley. Turn left, we are first house on right.*

576

Tokanui
Farmstay
Address: 'Egilshay', RD1, Tokanui
Name: Jean and John McWilliam
Telephone: (03) 246 8703
Beds: 4 Single (2 bedrooms)
Bathroom: 1 guests share
Tariff: B&B (full) Double $55, Single $35, Dinner $20,
Children half price, Campervans welcome. Vouchers accepted.
Nearest Town: Invercargill, 60 km, Dunedin 165 km

Welcome to our home, which is a 640 acre sheep and cattle property on the "Southern Scenic Route" - the Gateway to the Catlins. We are a family of five, our three children having grown and usually away from home. We have a modern home in attractive surroundings with sunny bedrooms, comfortable beds and electric blankets. Guests have own bathroom and toilet.

Come and see our unique Porpoise Bay with its friendly Hectors' dolphins, and Curio Bay on the rugged south coast of New Zealand. Trout fishing, golf course, bowling green and tennis courts are all nearby. Deep sea trips available. You are welcome to inspect the many seasonal activities on the farm.

Sample a three course dinner with us which features our own homegrown produce. Continental or cooked breakfast available.

Our interests include cooking, gardening, woolcrafts and service clubs. Come and enjoy our warm Southern Southland hospitality in a relaxed, rural setting. Our home is a smokefree zone.

Directions: *Please phone or write.*

Mokotua, Invercargill
Farmhouse/Self-contained Cottage
Address: "Fernlea", Mokotua, No 1 R.D., Invercargill
Name: Anne & Brian Perkins
Telephone: (03) 239 5432 or (03) 239 5412
Fax: (03) 206 6230
Beds: Self-contained Cottage - 1 Double & Double
divan in lounge (1 bedroom) **Bathroom:** 1 Private
Tariff: B&B (special) Double $65, Extra persons $20,
Dinner $20 Breakfast foods provided - self-catering. Vouchers accepted
Nearest Town: Invercargill 15km

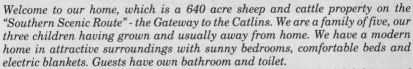

Anne's cottage nestles tranquilly in its own old world garden, lovingly restored as a romantic hideaway, it holds particular attraction for those wishing to get away from it all. Look up from breakfast on your verandah, see the cows wandering home from milking or join the fun of seasonal duckshooting on our private pond. The cottage is completely self contained with colour TV, electric blankets, microwave in fully equipped kitchen, shower, toilet, and cosy pot belly stove. Our family farm milks 160 pedigree Holstein Friesian cows and we are happy to take folk around the farm. Our extensive gardens surround a large in-ground swimming pool and barbecue area which guests are welcome to use.

Dinner with us including home grown produce is available by prior arrangement. We are close to the beautiful unspoilt area of the Catlins & Mataua fishing river.

Directions: *From Invercargill follow SH92 to Mokotua Garage (15km) turn left, 4th house on right is Fernlea. On SH1 - 17km from Invercargill - turn left at WOODLANDS BP garage, over railway line turn sharp right to Rimu Church (6km), veer left for 2.4k and at Mokotua sign turn right and Fernlea is on left.*

Winton

Farmstay
Address: 'Armagh Park',
No 1 RD, Winton
Name: John & Joyce Robins
Telephone: (03) 2217150
Beds: 1 Double, 2 Single (2 bedrooms) **Bathroom:** 1 Guests share
Tariff: B&B (continental) Double $60, Single $30, Dinner $20, Vouchers accepted.
Nearest Town: Invercargill 20km south, Winton 8km north

*Our Simmental Beef Cattle Stud and lamb fattening property
comprises of 250 acres of fertile Southland Plains situated on
the Main Invercargill-Queenstown Highway, SH 6.
Our home is spacious, modernised, warm and comfortable but
retaining character of by gone years, nestled in an extensive
garden featuring Rhododendrons, Irises and Heritage Roses.
We would enjoy to share our home garden, farming and other interests with you.
A home cooked meal featuring local produce is available if you wish or just B&B.
Visits to other places of interest in the area can be arranged.*
Directions: *Please phone after 5pm is best or before 8am.*

Winton

Homestay
Address: 28 Great North Rd Winton
Name: Margot & Jim Gratton
Telephone: (03) 236 7496
Beds: 2 Single (1 Bedroom) **Bathroom:** 1 Family share
Tariff: B&B (continental) Double $60, Single $30, Dinner $20, Vouchers accepted
Nearest Town: Winton

*In January 1971 we moved to Winton for a four year stay. We are still here and
invite you to share our home and see some of the beauty of this neglected corner of
NZ. Winton is the heart of Central Southland, a prosperous farming area, and is
conveniently situated for travellers - 30 minutes to Invercargill, 1 hour to Bluff and
the Stewart Island ferry, less than 2 hours to Queenstown, Te Anau and Manapouri.
We enjoy outdoor recreation (tramping, fishing, skiing, gardening) as well as
indoor pursuits (ballroom dancing, reading, flytying, spinning) and would be
delighted to help you participate in these while with us.
I am a teacher and Margot worked in receptionist positions before starting her own
free-lance typing business. These occupations have been successful because we
enjoy meeting and helping people. We share our home with Chi, a Burmese cat,
and she also enjoys meeting people.
Please phone or write for bookings and directions.*

578

Rimu, Invercargill

Homestay/Farmstay
Address: Rimu, No. 1 R.D., Invercargill
Name: Margaret and Alan Thomson
Telephone: (03) 230-4798
Beds: 4 Single (2 bedrooms)
Bathroom: 1 Guests share
Tariff: B&B (full) Double $55, Single $35, Children $12,
Dinner $20, Campervans welcome. Vouchers accepted.
Nearest Town: Invercargill 13 km including 4 km from SH 1.

Our home is approximately 30 years old, warm and comfortable with a sunny aspect, all rooms overlooking a colourful garden, with the farm beyond.
We run breeding ewes and also have a licensed meat processing factory on our property. The beautiful city of Invercargill is only 13 km away and the choice of trips by sea or air easily arranged to wonderful Stewart Island. Te Anau, Queenstown and Dunedin only 2 hours' travel away.
You may have dinner with us and share an evening of relaxation and friendship or if you prefer only bed and breakfast. We can provide the breakfast of your choice with all home grown products. Stay as many nights as you wish, a 'welcome' is always assured.
Directions: *Take State Highway 1, travel approximately 8 km from Invercargill (towards Dunedin), turn right (towards large green building with red roof), turn left, then right over railway line. Travel straight ahead for 4 km, we are on your left, A. J. Thomson on the mail box. Travelling from Dunedin on State Highway 1 take Rimu turnoff on left, turn right at crossroads, we are 1 km from there, on your right.*

Roslyn Bush, Invercargill

Farmstay
Address: Leyava Lodge,
Roslyn Bush R D 6 Invercargill
Name: Shirley & Andrew Sellars
Telephone: (03) 230 4714
Beds: 2 Double or 1 Double 2 Twin (2 Bedrooms)
Bathroom: 1 Ensuite, 1 Private
Tariff: B&B (full) $35 per person
Nearest Town: Invercargill, 7 mins by car to city boundary and nearest restaurants

Come and enjoy a country lifestyle. Guests are invited to relax in delightful mature gardens, and area presently being established includes stream and ponds. Wonderful views of mountains and lush fertile land which supports dairy, sheep and deer farms. A good stopping place to relax or as a base for day trips.
Fishing rivers within minutes including Mataura River. We feel Invercargill and districts have a lot to offer, wonderful gardens to visit, Aluminium Smelter, Bluff - oyster country, and Stewart Island by sea or air.
Tea and coffee facilities provided, continental or cooked breakfast. We bred and race harness horses, besides horses we have cats and a dog. Also enjoy gardens, photography and paintings. I paint mainly Southland and Otago landscapes, some can be purchased.
Andrew and I enjoy company and look forward to meeting you.
Directions: *SH 1 from Dunedin. Turn right at Mill Road North, 4km to Roslyn Road, 2km to our house.*

Tussock Creek, Invercargill

Farmstay
Address: Sherwood Farm, Channel Road,
Tussock Creek, No. 1 R.D., Winton (near Invercargill)
Name: Pat and Derek Turnbull
Telephone & Fax: (03) 221-7270
Beds: 4 Single (2 bedrooms) **Bathroom:** 1 Guests share
Tariff: B&B (full) Double $60, Single $30, Dinner $20; Campervans $25.
Vouchers accepted.
Nearest Town: Invercargill

*If you are looking for an interesting stay in a spacious residence, in a peaceful
setting – if you want to hear the bellbirds sing, hear the frogs croak and watch the
wood pigeons feed – or take a walk in our native reserve – then this is it.*

*We have a grown up family of 6 (including triplets) and farm 600 acres of river flat
with sheep and cattle. Our interests include veteran athletics, tramping, gardening,
C.W.I., and genealogy. We have travelled extensively. Derek is a current world
record holder in running.*

*We are suitable for a base as all southern tourist attractions are within easy daily
reach. Having another 400-acres at Stewart Island enables us to arrange connections
and accommodation there if required.*

Directions: *Coming from either Invercargill or Queenstown / Te Anau, turn into
Tussock Creek Road from Wilsons Crossing corner (midway between Invercargill
& Winton) and proceed east for 11.5 km on bitumen and gravel., past the radio
mast, cross the Makarewa River and our gateway is by the bridge.*

*Coming from Gore, travel on highway 96 to beyond Hedgehope and turn left into
Channel Road towards Tussock Creek. Please phone first.*

Invercargill

Farmstay +
Self-Contained Accommodation
Address: "Lorneville Lodge",
Lorne - Dacre Road, 6 R.D., Lorneville, Invercargill
Name: Bill and Pauline Schuck
Telephone: (03) 2358-031, after 6pm
Beds: 2 Double, 3 Single, 1 child's cot (3 bedrooms) **Bathroom:** 1 Guests share
Tariff: B&B (full) Double $70, Single $35; Dinner $25; Children
under 13 half price; Campervans $8.50 per person. Self-contained
tourist flat + cabins, from $15 per person. Vouchers accepted.
Nearest Town: Invercargill 14 km

*We are situated 3 km from the main highway which takes you to
Queenstown and Te Anau. We are a family who have moved out of town to enjoy
the "good life" on a 17-acre farmlet. We have sheep, hens, cat, dog.*

*Our home has had extensive renovations so that we can provide the most
comfortable accommodation possible. All beds have Sleep Well matresses, electric
blankets and sheepskin overlays. You have a private bathroom if requested.*

*You may wish to spend time with us helping with chores or perhaps you want to
sit and relax to take time out from your busy itinerary.*

*You may have a family dinner with us or if you prefer only bed and breakfast. All
meals are prepared from farm fresh produce and our vegetables come from our
own organic garden. I enjoy cooking and can promise you a delightful meal.*

If you are travelling by bus or plane we are happy to meet you.

Directions: *Travel north on State Highway 6 from Invercargill for 10 km. Turn
right at Lorneville garage on to Lorne–Dacre highway, proceed for 3.5 km.*

Invercargill
Private Hotel
Address: 240 Spey Street,
Invercargill
Name: Montecillo Lodge
Telephone: (03) 2182-503, Fax (03) 2182-506
Beds: 4 Double, 4 Single (6 bedrooms)
Bathroom: All with ensuite
Tariff: B&B (full) Double $87, Single $69; Dinner $25, All credit cards accepted, Vouchers accepted Friday, Saturday and Sunday, December and January everyday

Our Bed and Breakfast Hotel is in a quiet street and close to the centre of Invercargill.

The main building is some 100 years old and we have returned it to its original state of large rooms and ensuite facilities. Central heating throughout.

We provide a full cooked breakfast-up to 9 am. Marian cooks a 3 course dinner for our guests; fresh vegetables in season, and meat of the day; - served at 6pm in the Dining Room (Please request).

You can walk to the park and museum in five minutes.

A golf course is ten minutes walk, as well as a number of historic buildings.

We can arrange trips to Stewart Island and ensure that your next stop is booked and suitable. Free call to next B&B

Our guests recommend a two-night stay to at least find out about Invercargill, Bluff and Stewart Island. F

our nights to see it all well, and have a well-deserved rest.

Your hosts: - Marian & Harry Keil.

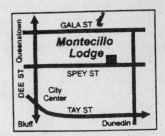

Otatara, Invercargill
Bed & Breakfast
Address: 22 Taiepa Road Otatara No 9 RD Invercargill
Name: "The Oak Door"
Telephone & Fax: (03) 213 0633
Beds: 1 Double, 2 Single (2 Bedrooms)
Bathroom: 1 Guests share
Tariff: B&B (full) Double $60, Single $45, Children $30, Vouchers accepted
Nearest Town: Invercargill

THE OAK DOOR takes its name from the front door, which welcomes our guests. A two storey home, built by the present owner, is situated in the scenic native bush and country setting of Otatara, just three minutes from downtown Invercargill, and two minutes from the airport.

Our location offers guests the opportunity to visit Invercargill, the world's most southern city, population 57,000, and the gateway to New Zealand's Fiordland, the Catlins and Stewart Island.

The tranquil homestyle atmosphere is the courtesy of your hosts, Bill and Lisa. Both have travelled throughout New Zealand and overseas. Lisa a Canadian, has also lived in Holland and the USA as well as Canada.

Note: No smoking No pets Thank you

Directions: *At Clyde and Tweed St, Take Tweed West at the roundabout, pass the airport, take the first left (Marama Ave South) take the first right (Taiepa Road) enter at the second driveway on the right "The Oak Door" Please call ahead to avoid disappointment.*

We rely on your comments about our B&Bs.
Please send us a comment form from the back of the book.

Otautau

Farmstay
Address: No 1 RD Otautau
Name: Joyce & Murray Turner
Telephone & Fax: (03) 225 7602
Beds: 4 Single (2 Bedrooms) **Bathroom:** 1 Guests share
Tariff: B&B (full) Double $70, Single $40, Children under 12 half price, Dinner $20, Vouchers accepted March to October
Nearest Town: Mossburn

Our modern home is on 301 hectares situated approximately halfway between Invercargill and Te Anau which can be reached in an hour.
We enjoy meeting people and will provide good quality accommodation and farm fresh food in a welcoming and friendly atmosphere.
We winter 3000 sheep and 200 beef cattle.
You are welcome to join in on farm activities if you wish, come for a tour of the farm or just relax. Swimming pool is available in summer.
Murray is a keen fly fisherman and will enjoy taking you to the Aparima River which is adjacent to the property.
Joyce is a keen gardener and is currently Area Representative for the International Agriculture Exchange Association.
You are welcome to join us for an evening meals or bed and breakfast at your discretion. (No pets please)
Directions: *Please write, phone or fax. At least 24 hours notice is advised to avoid possible disappointment.*

Riverton

Farmstay
Address: Otaitai Bush, No.3 RD, Riverton
Name: Ian and Elaine Stuart
Telephone: (03) 234-8460
Beds: 2 Single (1 bedroom) **Bathroom:** 1 Private
Tariff: B&B (full) Double $60, Single $35, Dinner $15; Campervans $10 (2 person). Vouchers accepted.
Nearest Town: 5 km from Riverton on Southern Scenic Route, 40 km from Invercargill

We are a family of five, our three sons all in the work force.
Our sunny and well heated house is surrounded by flower and vegetable gardens. The guest room has twin beds with electric blankets. Guest bathroom facilities. View of Foveaux Strait and Stewart Island from lounge window. You may share dinner with us or if you prefer just bed and breakfast.
Our sheep farm is situated on the Southern Scenic Route 5 km from Riverton. Riverton is one of the oldest settlements in NZ, a fishing port with safe swimming beaches. A game of golf or squash can be arranged.
We enjoy sharing our home and farm with visitors and a friendly stay assured.
Directions: *please phone.*

Halfmoon Bay, Stewart Island

Homestay
Address: "The Nest",
Halfmoon Bay, Box 88, Stewart Island
Name: Lorraine Squires
Telephone: (03) 219-1310
Beds: 2 Double (2 bedrooms)
Bathroom: 1 Ensuite, 1 Family share
Tariff: B&B (continental) Double $160,
Single $80, D.B.B.
Nearest town: Invercargill

We are a commercial fishing family and we invite you to share our home as you explore "Rakiura", Isle of the Glowing Skies.

Lindsay and Lorraine Squires
"The Nest'
Half Moon Bay
Stewart Island
(03) 2191310

Beautiful island, we know so well
Where freedom, love and peace do dwell
Haven of refuge in time of strife
Heavenly place to enjoy sweet life
A. von Tunzelman

We are a non-smoking household.

Stewart Island

Homestay
Address: "Thorfinn Charters"
PO Box 43 Halfmoon Bay
Stewart Island
Name: Bruce Story
Telephone & Fax: (03) 219 1210
Beds: 2 Double, 2 Single (2 Bedrooms)
Bathroom: 1 Ensuite, 1 Family share
Tariff: B&B (full) Double $65, Single $45, Children 2/3,
Dinner $20. Credit cards: Visa/MC/BC. Vouchers accepted
except for Dec, Jan and Holiday Weekends

Thorfinn Charters

Situated on a sheltered peninsula my home commands a magnificent panoramic sea view. A sheltered beach is only 50 metres away.
Formerly an extensive hill country farmer, now as charter boat operator, I enjoy meeting people from all walks of life, with especially a love of the outdoors.
My business specialises in viewing sea and land birds, marine wildlife, bushwalks, fishing and scenic cruises. Good discounts available to house guests on launch trips.
My home is modern, comfortable and centrally heated. It has two double guest rooms (One also has 2 bunks). Both have attached bathroom and toilet, one shared and one private.
A courtesy vehicle is available on arrival and departure on Southern Air or Foveaux Express Catamaran.
Other meals or your own use of the facilities are available by prior arrangement.

If you love touring New Zealand B&B style...

...check out what is available in Australia

The Australian Bed & Breakfast Book is the perfect accommodation guide for those who want to see the real Australia.

For ordering details, turn to the next page of this book

ORDER FORM

The New Zealand Bed & Breakfast Book
The Australian Bed & Breakfast Book

The Australian Bed and Breakfast Book and *The New Zealand Bed and Breakfast Book* are comprehensive guides to B&B those countries. They describe homes, farms and guest houses offering warm, friendly hospitality. The charges are modest and the hospitality is genuine.

Price List
In New Zealand
The books are available from bookstores andVisitor Information offices for NZ$16.95. Or post your cheque using the form below. We will pay delivery costs.

In Australia
The books are available from bookstores and information offices for A$12.95. Or post your cheque using the form below. We will pay delivery costs.

Overseas Orders
You may order by simply sending your personal cheque in your own currency. Payment includes airmail postage:

Either Book:	US $16.95	**Both Books:**	US $28.95
	CAN $19.95		CAN $34.95
	GB £9.95		GB £16.95
	JP ¥1700		JP ¥2900
	GER 24.30 Dm		GER 39.95 Dm

- ✂ - - -

Please send me by airmail

The New Zealand Bed and Breakfast Book   _____

The Australian Bed and Breakfast Book   _____

Enclosed is my cheque for   _____

Name   _____

Address   _____

_____

_____

Post to: Moonshine Press
PO Box 41022
Eastbourne, New Zealand

Index

Comment Form, Voucher, Weeks Free B&B

To help maintain the high reputation of *The NZ B&B Book* we ask for your comments about your stay. Please post the form in the envelope provided. Every comment form you return will go in the draw for **A weeks free B&B**. It will help us if you save your comment forms and return them in one envelope.

Name of Host...

Address...

It was (please circle one):
Absolutely Perfect, Excellent, Good, Adequate, Not Satisfactory.

Do you have any comments which could help your host, on such things as breakfast, meals, beds, cleanliness, hospitality, value for money.

Complete this section. It will be detached and will not be sent to the host

YOUR NAME...

YOUR ADDRESS...

✂ --

Discount Voucher

We appreciate your help, and offer this voucher in return. Tear off this discount voucher before you return the comment form. Keep it and send it to us at any time to receive your New Zealand B&B Book. Attach your personal cheque in your own currency for the equivalent of NZ$.

In New Zealand $8; to Australia NZ$12; to the rest of the world NZ$17.

Write your name and address on the reverse of this voucher and post it to The New Zealand B&B Book, PO Box 41022, Eastbourne, New Zealand

Comment Form, Voucher, Weeks Free B&B

To help maintain the high reputation of *The NZ B&B Book* we ask for your comments about your stay. Please post the form in the envelope provided. Every comment form you return will go in the draw for **A weeks free B&B.** It will help us if you save your comment forms and return them in one envelope.

Name of Host..

Address...

It was (please circle one):
Absolutely Perfect, Excellent, Good, Adequate, Not Satisfactory.

Do you have any comments which could help your host, on such things as breakfast, meals, beds, cleanliness, hospitality, value for money.

Complete this section. It will be detached and will not be sent to the host

YOUR NAME...

YOUR ADDRESS...

✂ ---

Discount Voucher

We appreciate your help, and offer this voucher in return. Tear off this discount voucher before you return the comment form. Keep it and send it to us at any time to receive your New Zealand B&B Book. Attach your personal cheque in your own currency for the equivalent of NZ$.

In New Zealand $8; to Australia NZ$12; to the rest of the world NZ$17.

Write your name and address on the reverse of this voucher and post it to The New Zealand B&B Book, PO Box 41022, Eastbourne, New Zealand